Genetic
Basis of Society

By the Origin
of Human Inequalities

by
Fred Winner, M.S., M.D.

Shakespeare Publishing Co.
Dunedin, Fla.

Dedicated to
my constant and supportive
companion — my wife,
Mary

cjs
9-24-86

PREFACE
—To the Year 5000

You may wonder that if, like Lucretius, I prophesized, died, and had not the satisfaction of knowing that the propositions herein presented were correct.

If, in one's ideas, faith exists, there is little doubt concerning veracity. Thus, approval of the future may be savored within the present. Yet, if approval never sets seal — what matters it? Deed is done — resurrection impossible — the ancient mind slumbers unperturbedly. All that I write may be wrong. Or all may be perfectly correct. I would strongly protest the former. Only an idiot would champion the latter.

If the text appears unwieldly, do not condemn the author. It is radical departure from traditional thought. Consequently, it is for successors to bring organization to the neo-science of genetic sociology.

Fred Winner, M.S., M.D.
Completed May 30, 1982

Table of Contents

Introduction

THERE IS a form of evolution which has merited little consideration. It has been buried under a convenient catch-all term named "culture." This is something peripheral to the human organism — namely, the non-organic transferral of learning.

Man teaches his children how to shoot a bow and arrow, how to till and sow a field, how to enter into contracts or wedlock, how to save, build, and hundreds of other intricacies that are passed from father to son non-biologically.

What has been left out of the evolutionary and cultural formulae is the *organic genetic basis of society.*

All of us are aware of instincts. The breasts, face, buttocks, or legs of an attractive girl arouse men. Powerful men, wealthy, handsome, reliable and marriageable attract attention of females. We enjoy sports, companionship, gregariousness and, universally, the same classes of foods.

Beneath our gray matter is a raging sea of instinctive desires, dreams, powers, reactions, reflexes and codes. We like to feel we are a taught species. It grains against us to regard ourselves as an automated form. Yet beneath our pomp and human dignity, our prestige and status, there prowls the animal past. Most of our behavior is predicated upon programmed codes. They are prefixed throughout our neurological DNA genetic system.

Because of high regard for our human selves, we have short-changed the organic basis of society. Society is the noblest of human achievement — cooperation of individuals for the benefit of the group.

Once the tallest, strongest or wisest, of those scavaging in the African valley, designated others to chip flint arrowheads, cut firewood and erect shelters. Women gathered fruits, sewed skins, and cooked. Some men accompanied the leader on the hunt. A stratification of command and obligatory functions were meted out by evolution.

In the same fashion as insects, bees, hornets, and ants or wolves or chickens erect primitive hierarchical societies, without the benefits of learning by parental teaching (culture), so did man fall into the extremely advantageous evolutionary force known as society.

Human society didn't originate overnight. It took millions of years of weeding and culling out the uncooperative. There were strong survival rewards for those pre-humans who grouped to ward off predators, hunt game, and work in groups. (Two can perform better than one.)

Under selection pressures, there came into being social formulae. It is obvious the group, able to repel predatory enemies such as tigers, lions and snakes, hunt down hither-to unavailable food sources of larger game, construct shelters from inclement weather, would further their evolutionary ascent and survive, to the extinction of more individual groups.

Because man's upper limbs were freed from locomotion and hands were able to sensitively manipulate objects, provided a giant step forward. It remains for him to pick up stones and sharp bones to act as missiles or stilettos to take a leap in evolutionary armament. Biology did not need to screw to his body a horn, claws, or saber teeth. The artful hands of man leap-frogged an evolutionary tedium in providing him with disposable weapons — rocks, bones and sticks.

Mobilization of offensive and defensive weaponry became secondary to a greater thrust in adapting to environment. It was a subtle and gradual formation of society. High impetus was given to protection of the group and value of numerical superiority.

Ability to kill, strongly nurtured in present-day man, was the launching pad for our species' supremacy. Not only did the killing act provide necessary foodstuffs, but it provided straight directional evolution to the group most war-like.

Survival of the fittest, as it applies to evolution, is represented on an individual basis. This is not true with humans. Survival is based upon group action — upon society. It was human groups that cooperated and conquered that survived and forwarded their gened progeny.

An old cliché in evolutionary study is the key to promotion of a species, is having surviving offspring. Those gene patterns that do not survive to produce offspring become forgotten tombstones.

It is not necessarily so. Society has a life of its own. It is a separate entity — it is like a corporation which, although not human, possesses human attributes, survivorship, and individuality.

Human society formulated and moved forward not only on an individual basis, but on a group basis. It required the establishment of hierarchy, caste stratification. This evidenced in every army from before the beginning of historic time.

Battles in rare instances may be won by individuals, but they are fought by echelons of unequally authorized soldiers. Armies composed of equals without leadership would be chaotic rabble.

It is an amusing paradox that democracies regard their armies as representing equality and liberty. This is a farcical concept. The ugly face of tyranny, authoritarianism, privilege, dictatorship and hierarchy pervade each army. We speak of armies because they are a clear-cut example of man's continuing biologic inequalities represented by hierarchy.

Fundamental basis of society is inequality. Otherwise, there would be no society. Each individual takes his position upon the rung of a ladder. Each, by instinctive prompting, steps aside for the common good. And much more, *each is born according to the position he is predestined to take.* Some are born to be non-competitive subservient, some to be workers, some to be leaders, and some to sacrifice.

Society is an evolutionary force in its own right. The basis of its ability to function is through human stratification, genetic variances with conse-quent inequalities.

According to Nikolass Linbergen, "Comparison of individual and com-munity leading to the idea of the community as a "Super-organism" is of great use to the sociologist. The main difference between individual and community is one of level integration; in a community integration has been carried one step beyond the individual."

Indeed, society is a super organism. Animal studies have shown when one member of the social order is laid low, another capably takes over, a new leader emerges. Talk to any corporate executive, army general, professional or shop foreman, and they will detail unashamedly the irreplaceability of prize men. Carried to the furthest extreme, no one replaces Da Vinci, Ein-stein, Michelangelo, Darwin or Beethoven. Unique genius combinations of genes are rare.

But that does not mean replacements cannot be found. It simply means occupational units, evolutionarily evolved in human society, are hard to come by. Although there is spillage from one level to the other, evolution has taken into account individual disruptions. Society as a whole is con-ceived as to buffer irregularities in individual categorized units.

Diversity is the secret to all evolutionary adaptation. To the frustration of parents, they must one day assess their offspring. The uncontestable fact is that regardless of upbringing, children are unequal in emotion, intelligence and behavior. It is with reluctance they must face reality that no amount of schooling, education or tutoring, will raise the genetically programmed commonplace to heights of erudition or high profession.

Toward the end of the 1700's, the rallying cry of revolutionists, philo-sophers, sociologists, and idealists was equality, fraternity, liberty, and freedom. It toppled kingdoms and established plebian forms of government. It substituted democracies, communistic and socialistic forms of government for autocratical and dictatorial forms.

This was window dressing. Hidden dictatorial forms of government were the communist party or elected parliaments. "Elected" is the sooth-saying password that hides the absoluteness of delegated dictatorial power. Nothing has, in effect, changed the normal societal hierarchy in man except the various modes of achieving it.

Democracies have been ruled by sovereign, omnipotent dictators as Roosevelt or Churchill — powerful as any kings of ages past. This is excused under duress and decisive requirements of war; yet, in substance, it is the same strong leadership that advanced societies in the past.

One thing is inescapable. Humans are born variant, excepting monozygo-tic twins. Whereas, variances are primary to evolutionary adaptation, advancement and survival of a species, these variants are also an indispensible part in formulation of societies.

Laboratory a society. From all ages and physical abilities, from both genders of wide sexual range, including homosexuals, from all mental capabilities and traits, from the feeble-minded to genius, we mix together in a culturally inherited pattern and geography. There is tissue diversity in its finest hour which encapsulate appalling biological inequities.

This the phenotype, the outer appearance — the manifestation of the genes. Beneath is genetic coding, the soul of the individual — the geno-type.

Some years ago, the world was impressed with Watsonian psychological school of behaviorism. They cried, "Give us a normal, healthy child and we'll make anything of him you wish — president, beggar or banker." This was utter rubbish. But it describes a time when genetics and the science of instincts were not fully appreciated.

Mutations and forces of evolution, in their search for adaptation, produce a wide range of human variance. The more capable reproduce and pass their differences into the stream of future gene pools. Yet there is something revolutionary in imposed biological inequality. The very nature of inequality immediately slots the individual into his position within society. An individual with an I.Q. of 95 may get through college or discover an oil field. He may go forth to wealth and honorary doctor's degree. This is the exception.

From the beginning, society has erected its hierarchial escape hatches. Public schools and universities, as they increase the difficulties of their privileged chambers, place orifices through which only the biologically intellectually programmed can pass. Military establishments are past masters with the art of caste system and chain of command.

Churches admit not only the theologically faithful, religious genotypes. We see pristine, aristocratic socially-oriented churches and churches which satisfy needs of the most confessionary of common men. Government is privileged, dictatorial, omnipotent and stratified, opening its doors to the clever and ruseful, faithful, obedient, and its benefactors.

Educational and religious, military and governmental institutions are large segments of structured society. Hierarchy can go on endlessly as one delves into corporations, the professions, labor organizations, and the like. What is evident is not only communist society, but all societies, follow instinctive pattern of caste, privilege, and hierarchy. Societies are stratified; never are they classless. *The thrust of biologically determined human inequality has not only made hierarchical and stratified human levels easy, it has made them mandatory.*

Human inequality is factual, not because of society's institutions, nor because of the lack of education or opportunity, but because the great God of Genes Past has ordained biological variance for survivorship — a continuous struggle to adapt to changing environments and challenges — be it tigers, malaria, ice ages or intra-species rivals.

Society is a Gestalt, the whole being greater than the sum of its parts. It is greater than any individual. Omnipotently it may purge any of its members. It is a biologically conjoined super-organism — a web of symbiotics accommodating one another. Although other forms of life have erected crude societies, human society is distinctly unique because of its complexity.

Society must be reckoned as a forceful evolutionary tool. Strong selection pressures rewarded the perpetuation of individuals who banded into union. Foremost among prompting devices were essentials of life — freedom from predators, acquirement of foodstuffs, and the repelling of competitors. Nature is oftentimes regarded as a sort of dumb ox in which extremely clever forces are ignored. Imagine millions of years, thousands of generations, this most valuable of tools, society, working its way up intellectual rungs through communication and cooperation. Then try to defend the premise that the selection sieve was sifting out everything on an individual basis. If that had succeeded, society would have perished.

A smooth-running society does not occur because people are educated to it; rather, it occurs because the genetic pool is in undisturbed traditional balance. Recent incursions of foreign genes can throw society as much out of alignment as blood invasions dispelled the ancient Romans. To further and perpetuate society, this gem of evolutionary engineering, it became imperative through selection that the variant genotypes — those chemical codes within each individual — be selected according to fitness as they operate within this super-organism.

It does not mean that some were superior than members of other societies they were competing with and whom they managed to send to extinction. It simply means that proportions and the types were more important than individuals. Subservient people were needed, muscular, sweaty, and brave, with little forward vision, who were obedient and cooperative. These are the cherished proletariat of the Soviets. The working classes — the working masses — that even though forced into education, may never read a book once their education is finished. This is not to disparage the working classes or the poor — and the terms are usually synonymous — but rather to recognize there are a lot of subservient people in the world. And, even though equal educational opportunities exist, only a limited number of the citizenry will become educated.

From recent animal studies, hierarchy is an important component to species that function in groups. From pecking order in chickens to rigidly disciplined ranks in ants, establishment of dominants to submissives is achieved. Without hierarchy, societies would be meaningless. They would amount to little more than aggregations of members, each running his own way, doing his own thing. Instinctive grouping is common. But there needs to be leadership. The fundamental element of society is its strata — its chain of command and its caste system. This requires a small percentage of leaders and a large percentage of followers which we view in human society.

We recognize that not only are hierarchical forms of individuals produced, but individuals are born with programs fitting them to certain occupational needs of the super-organism. Consider the first societies which had within their ranks artful and innovative flint tool chippers. Their society did survive over others because of bountiful and expert weaponry. Evolutionary programming didn't subtly make the decision and say if three talented flint tool chippers make a fitter society, then a society of expert tool chippers will succeed above others. Rather, three expert flint tool chippers provided the tribe with superior survival fitness, a disproportionate number would have caused chaos and innefficiency.

So it went — each man being chosen to the fashion of the societal task before him: leader, pack-bearer, digger, fighter, gatherer, pioneer, tree-climber, swimmer, painter, witch doctor, educator, tracker, mechanic, etc.

Evolutionists explain with precise formulae how, over generations, an eyelid can be folded, a nose lengthened because of blowing desert sand, skin darkened by sun, cells sickled because of malaria, hair frizzled for prespiratory cooling racks, teeth altered in the most miniscule stages because of dietary changes — hundreds of petite variances in nervous tissue brought about by evolutionary selective pressures. Then somebody is going to say this greatest selective force of all time, society, which brought man to modernity, is incapable of programming itself — that society is what passes by word of mouth and is not passed on biologically.

We are witnessing every day genotypic fulfillment of social order; a few good brains, a bevy of leaders, a goodly number of killers, and a lot of common men — each fulfilling his predestined chemicalized role. It is why there are few geniuses spewed into the mix. If genius were a quality for survival, then it would be found in abundance. Society is like a good paella, many discreet elements leading to the flavorfulness of the whole.

The mechanism of society is innately conceived and forged within the crucible of evolutionary adaptation. Thus is explained killers, thieves, and rapists. They were valuable assets in furtherance of the gene pool. Indeed, we are deeply indebted to homosexuality. Its noncompetitiveness in sexual sweepstakes is an important factor in general harmony.

Homosexuality was one of societal evolution's genius strokes. Repulsive as the practice may appear to those born "straight," it must be envisioned in the larger context of social order, tranquility and advancement. Reflect, momentarily, on those inept psychoanalysts who tried to equate homosexuality with some stage of behavioral development in arrest or with some mentally attached quirk arising out of their mumbo-jumbo. Homosexuals pervading all societies did not originate by educational or traditional error. They are within society because evolution demanded their advantage in survival of the human species. The time is long overdue that homosexuals be given their rightful, just, and respected places within society.

Never look to racism or racial superiority when comparing human biologicals. View two aspects: one being the racial unit in its own geography and environment, the other being the strata of individuals within races, which are comparable. One of the purposes of this work, *Genetic Basis of Society*, is to place a common denominator to the entirety of human endeavor. As all humans have four-chambered hearts in their anatomical schema, so they have underlying instinctive neurogenetic programming relating to their behavior.

We are confronted by actions of society. Here, millions of people gathered in primitive emotions pay tribute to some muscleman whose only deed is an ability to beat a ball with a stick — or drive a ball with a longer stick, or volley a ball with hands or a catgutted stick. Consider professions of the religious, witch-doctory, and solemn worship. Recall religious persecutions, the burning of thousands of martyrs, intersect religious conflicts. Try to explain revolutions, national wars, religious wars, wars from petty skirmishes to holocausts. Run through the gamut of society's problems: slums, poverty, homosexuality, human differences, crime, castes, and massacres. Can you explain the foregoing rationally?

In consistency of human incomprehensibility throughout races and sub-races, there is a common denominator — the genetic programming of the human. It is when we understand instinctive drives and compulsions that we will be able to cope with problems of society. Culture as hithertofore inter-preted is only in small degree relayed over the generations. Society and its concomitant culture is based almost exclusively upon genetic programming that has evolved in the evolution of the highest primate.

Our social and cultural environment is a mass of contradictions and un-explainable phenomena. As dutiful propagators we are to choose one mate unto death. We are to worship a supernatural being. Defend and die for our land. Champion democracy and capitalism. Obey a thousand odd orders.

Formerly we have explained culture, its institutions and social classes, as an invention of man, representing skills and techniques. They are for-warded generation by generation. Usage of fire, bow and arrow, wheel and axle are mere transmissions by teaching. Soldiery, religion, and marriage customs are handed down components from our ancestors' experiences.

Yet, in this cultural maelstrom veiling us, there is no solutionizing for-mulae, no basic principles upon which laws of human conduct may be erected. There is but conflict, diverging opinion, and shrugging shoulders when we mention but mere nouns representing colossal entities as war. Homosexuality. Politicians. Communism. Laboring class. Religion. Marriage. Race. Theft. Drug addiction. Women's role.

From darkness, science of biochemistry, genetics, and anthropology have flamed to reveal the mechanical man. This highest species of protein-coded cells is dissected into a biological robot. So many fingers, a choice of skin colors, a four-chambered heart, a disposition for anger and love, a myriad of traits and characteristics set down in the parental egg cells according to Men-delian laws. We possess knowledge of fantastic chemical intricacies concern-ing giant protein molecules, DNA (deoxyribonucleic acid) and RNA (ribo-nucleic acid) that code and generate our being. Physical programming and gross instinctive traits are incorporated within.

What we have not before accepted is that within the protein coding of our cells there is blueprinted the rules, regulations and compulsions for war, religion, homosexuality, social classes, and society in general, even for politi-cians. We have rejected the teachings of the early evolutionist, Lamarck, that acquired characteristics may be inherited, that the giraffe, by stretching its neck by some method, influences its offspring, through germinal transmis-sion, to develop longer necks. This contradicts the generally accepted Dar-winian/Mendel theories that natural selection permits the long-necked descendents survival over their shorter-necked brothers because long necks are advantageous in obtaining higher leaves and, therefore, apt to leave descendents to their own type.

Generally accepted variations or embryological anomalies result from food or vitamin deficiencies, drug usage, or radiation. But what has never been ventured is that our mother, during our womb sojourn, influences, alters, recodes genetically, and programs our tissues. Long before the romantic gleams in our parents' eyes contractually focused, the most cosmic compositional selection of our individual being was determined. To manufacture our egg or sperm it is necessary to play a multiple genetic choice game. Chromosomes of mother and father dutifully line up and cross over in an exchange of genes.

It is in this reduction division that every offspring is fabricated in diversity. Among billions of humans no two are similar, excepting identical twins resulting from the split of a single egg. What genes we pick from each of our parent's chromosomes to package into unique missiles or targets appears none of our conscious business.

The great Charles Darwin was confused by this, so he originated a pangenesis theory by which, somehow, the body itself influenced the germ cells and permits evolution. It was one of his few theories which was immediately discredited by his scientific successors who presently arrange elaborate geometric formulae to explain the precise mathematical nature of genetic probability and evolution.

Today there is no room for anyone who would alter the inviolability of biochemical mathematics and chance in the formulation of beings human. Genes simply cross over in chance exchange so that the Indian mother who was frightened by a black bear, and believed it to influence little Red Cloud, should simply be locked up as an unscientific clout.

We spend nine months in a womb — bound laboratory, nurtured by myriads of chemicals, buffeted by mechanisms of motion, and impaled by radiation. Are we to believe that the environment of our incarceration, the elements in the conduits supplying us, are of no special influence in our genetic composition, that mother simply attends to our wants, yet does not mold our disposition? Of course, no one disagrees that when we emerge from the womb, the environment that is about us is of prime importance in our makeup. Then why should our tenancy womb-wise be a denial of experience, learning, and alteration?

Selection for discussion in this book was made because the issues are unresolved and fit themselves to genetic formulae which we have devised. Modern sciences have not caught up. New behavioral studies have added to the lustre of instinct that for many years was in disrepute. From many scientific aspects we have been able to see the innate causation for man's actions — his erection of society upon the basis of neurogenic codes which he has inherited.

Evolutionists will not appreciate our continuing tolerance of Lamarkianism. We have been to Jews rather complimentary. Their experience with racial theory under the Nazis is still memorably horrifying, even to the point where some Judaic writers deny existence of race. Yet this wicked experience cannot still anthropological science. We must try to find out what did happen between two great subracial groups — Germans and Jews, both originating out of Caucasoid, white race.

No one has, with effectiveness, repelled the poisonous literature of communism, its tyranny and untruths. We have endeavored to reveal the biology of politics. In the chapter on homosexuality we feel we have done a service for these socially persecuted and scientifically misunderstood people.

1 Evolution: Survival Not Only of the Fittest Individuals, But the Fittest Groups

WILLIAMS, a 20th-century sociologist, writes that scholars in the field of evolution postulate selection of alternative populations is a source of adaptation. Working on a group theory rather than the individual, Darlington, Williams' contemporary, also came up with the thought that genes have evolutionary spontaneity that can prepare for future population needs, beyond ordinary chance mutation.

With introduction of selective breeding we have the opposite of natural selection. The fittest in the wild state is not always the choice of the breeder. Because of man's intelligence, a new game came into being. Because of his ability to select, he can negate traditional forces of evolution.

Anthropologists such as Montagu, Leuontin, and Medawar, state that: "Fitness is the function of the group as a whole rather than separate individuals. . . . Fitness is a system of pricing the endowments of organisms in the currency of offspring." Which leads us to believe that there is more to evolution than the fitness adaptational sieve. Leuontin concluded there is some force in opposition to genetic selection, and that group selection is the likely force. Because of the work of these excellent scientists, we take support for *Genetic Basis of Society* by carrying it a step further and stating that if groups are selected, then so must units within the groups, that is, occupations of men.

Most anthropologists attribute great evolutionary velocity to man when he descended from trees to take up socially-structured livelihood of hunting. "Big-game hunting represented a challenge more than any other single factor in accounting for man's uniqueness."

Yet there is more. The big carnivores, lions and tigers, were great hunters even before the idea occurred to man. In fact, man was one of their prey. They acted in social cooperation, the same as wolf packs, to acquire meat. If hunting was such a stimulus, they should have out-paced us in evolutionary development and we should be the object of interest within steel cages.

However, man possessed one exceptional item — the hand, an instrument of skill and exploration. In reality, the apes possess a structure of great similarity, but in addition to the hand, man's brain was the added key to our destiny. Its development came after communication.

Man is unique because of genes of speech. Its development necessitated expanding circuits — a switchboard with an ever-increasing demand, on all tissues, and on social obligations. Those who uttered first sounds of speech, who conveyed meaning and ideas, were those we may truly call the first humans.

Our genes of communication are far advanced. There is doubt a hundred newborn babies, abandoned on an island, nurtured by remote means, never hearing speech of any type, should evolve as deaf-mutes. Within fifteen years there would be a chatter which would astound you in similarity to your own. Speech was the God that blessed man. Linguists make a fuss about design features which comprise speech and variance from animals. What is paramount, it was man's first invention, his monopoly, which led to our human status. Exactly how this patent came into being lies on shelves of libraries. One of the first pages of the old Berlitz pamphlet, *Language for Travelers*, details the beginning fundamentals for Americans who wish to travel or apes that wish to become men.

They begin with greetings and recognitional signals common to most animals of the same species — *Buenos dias*. There is no need to remind either modern apes or ancient man that four words are of utmost priority: "Go" - "Stop" - "Yes" - "No." The expression of these words is so common they may be "speechless," being communicated by bodily attitude, a turn of the head, an intensity of vision, a freezing of posture that signifies "Stop," "No." In animal society there is consensus concerning "Yes" and "No." "Yes" or "No" permissiveness is operating most of the time. Concept of numbers is indigenous to higher animals. A cat has a pretty good idea when one of her kittens is missing. A baboon female certainly knows the dominants of the group.

For language to commence was to relate specific sound to action. Children learn in similar fashion. One who studies foreign language naturally, not by artificiality of grammar, develops speech patterns in the same fashion ape-man originated speech.

Imagine millions of years ago the first hairy brute who grunted "Stop" when the troupe stopped, and "Go" when it went into action. He was probably so amazed over his discovery that he must have kept himself, and less intelligent followers, entertained for months practicing commands.

On the plains were grazing beasts. They possessed what man lacked — ability to advantage themselves of coarse grasses and leaves, highly abundant complex carbohydrates and proteins which man could not physiologically break down. It became imperative that man seek their stomach, and man did by hunting their flesh. He moved out of the trees in search of a stomach that could digest the lush plant world. Flesh was substitute for gastric inadequacy and it gave great impetus to hunting.

If Darwin/Wallace and modern evolutionists' genetic theories of selection are correct, man should have by formulae of mathematics, spewed out some-one who could eat grass. Man should have selected toward a herbivorous stomach where lush energy of fields could be readily utilized. That did not occur because the characteristics man acquired and passed forward in the process of natural and sexual selection, would have it otherwise. Our role was not to direct our progeny to a mutational offspring which would con-sume grass. It was toward better merchandiseable features of men and women — sexual selection and killing.

Still further, speech and brain development would never have occurred had man not lacked a capable stomach. Man would never have gotten into a complex social hunting stimulus had digestive apparatus been adequate. It was the stomach's failure that drove man to exploration, conflict, and demand. Trees had become scarce, fruit less productive, leaves less tasty. Trees also were selecting away from ape-man parasites, residing in their branches consuming fruit, blossoms, and bark. More resistant vegetation was supplementing susceptible food man was commanding. In trees, men narrowly ranged as fruit, nut, blossom, and insect eaters. So man moved out.

Two basic mechanisms control life in higher animals. These are predation and progeny. To survive man must predate upon other forms of animal life. Even the strictest vegetarian will infuse into diet animal products, i.e., eggs, cheese, butter, milk.

Predation is a two-way street. Man predates upon every living thing he can digest. He is prey to thousands of species, from jungle cats, sharks, lice, pneumococci and treponema, to single moleculed virus. Man is fair game. In open season, from time of conception, dormant viri may be transmitted to man that bring on his demise. A majority of medicine is concerned with nothing more than a "who's who" roster of microbes, viri, parasites, and in-fective agencies that find the human logical and necessary target in the food chain. To survive, man seeks vital chemicals of other living forms. Since we have no chlorophyl to convert solar energy to combustionable foods, we reap from those who do. It is not Darwinian "survival of the fittest." It is trial-and-error genetics. A species survives if it can more successfully prey than be preyed upon.

A super-animal has never been fabricated — one with a stomach that can digest resistant wood fiber, leaves — a beast that can process all forms of plant and animal life for its own sustenance.

Such a creature has many times been attempted, but its victims were unwilling to remain permanent. The ideal monster beast has never been able to establish footing because its victims were constantly evolving, evading, and road-blocking new threats by varieties of protective armor, poisons, teeth, claws, and foul-tasting tissues.

Evolution is trial-and-error life forms, groping for supremacy, in search of master chemicals. When an ecological niche is vacant and the proper trial form is inserted, success will result. Contrarily, the fittest of dinosaur forms succumbed to predation or conditions in which they were unable to rapidly market a new product to meet evolving competition of other forms. They had gone all out for a carriage when the auto was present. Their biological engineering could not reverse in sufficient time to meet challenge, be it a mole that devoured their eggs, a diminishing food supply, predation, or colder temperatures. Predation is a living chemical that survives upon its ability to consume other chemicals. The secret of life is the secret of being greater predator than prey. It is ability to have the latest digestive apparatus in conformity with available material.

Evolution is stomach ability. Armies not only travel on their stomachs, they have evolved through them. Other physiological features are so much garnishing to further the goal. Process the chemical, predation and process, and in ever-changing flora and fauna, the stomach is the primary evolvement. So simple a formula. A brain only serves the stomach's end.

Darwin's theory is under attack. Darwin proposed living forms change gradually, *gradualism* over long periods of time. Animal variation was the response to environmental changes. The new demands forwarded the fittest, "survival of the fittest" by process of selection, *natural selection.*

Darwin's theory for the past 120 years has been refurbished by incorporating the hereditary studies of Gregor Mendel in 1866 and modern genetic research. Named "Modern Synthesis" or "neo-Darwinism," it too is challenged from facts that fossil records are incomplete. After centuries of search, transitional fossil material is missing. Links between major groups of animals are absent. And it isn't because they haven't yet been found.

Stephen Jay Gould and Miles Eldridge, 1972, proposed *punctuated equilibria* to replace Darwin's gradualism — "homeostatic equilibria, disturbed only rarely by rapid and episodic events of speciation." *Punctuationalism* is espoused by Steven Stanley, where new forms abruptly burst away from mainstream species, states, "Instead, to find rapid evolution we must look to very small, well-mixed, in-breeding populations — ones that occupy restricted, homogeneous and often novel habitats where severe selection pressure can work quickly and effectively."

There is evidence evolution of living forms takes place in spurts — a leaping, as if it were almost overnight, from one type animal to another.

There are vacancies in the progression of various types of life which can be supported by lack of fossil evidence.

Early 20th-century furor in the popular press that there was a missing link between ape and man was far-fetched. There wasn't one missing link, but dozens of stages. Various forms of men did not evolve smoothly, but rather developed startling divergence from ancestors within a short period.

Darwin expected that some day innumerable transitional fossilized forms of life would be found within the crust of the earth to complete the evolutionary picture. This is not the case. There is a consistency in fossilized gaps. Fossils do not blend gently from one form to another. It is as if natural selection is not taking place, but rather a genetic anomaly, a monster is spewed out which fits new environmental conditions. New traits are obtained — a leap-frogging has occurred and usually old form relatives are left in the wake of the new creature to perish. These are beneficial mutations. As mutations are constantly occurring and variation is the substance of normal reproduction, it is not improbable living forms under environmental duress can change direction so rapidly there is no long-term intermediary. One scientist, Richard Goldschmidt, spoke of a hopeful monster; that is, monstrous mutation occurring by which a new species may be formed.

Single mutations, as proposed in Darwinian gradualism, are not fast enough to produce rapidly-changing forms of life. Goldschmidt favored genetic changes at the embryonic level to produce major changes in adulthood. Realigning bits and pieces of chromosomes in the embryo does produce monsters and new forms of life, as witness mongolism, a chromosomal abnormality.

But changes in the embryo are worthless in creating continuing new forms. This can only be achieved by changes within germinal cells — sperm or ova. It is here inheritance by acquired characteristics may act. *And if this be fact, it is solution to the theory of punctuationalism or evolution in rapid spurts. Because acquired characteristics is a mechanism by which rapid genetic and chromosomal alternation may be achieved in response to environmental demand.*

Recently the discovery of an ancient ape-man from Afar which is 400,000 years older than Lucy, man's oldest direct kin, is supportive evidence that species change by bursts rather than gradually. Half a million years is considerable time for stability of the species found.

Punctuationalism is a new ball game in evolutionary theory. It means, some day we could wake up to news that in Kamyshlov, Russian engineering geneticists had developed a colony of future men with triple brain capacity. Acrimonious debate raged within the Kremlin whether to permit the experimental futurists to survive. Some conservatives contended the new breed would not only usurp communism, but would displace the human race. What is regrettable is that the new species, Homo futuris, is incapable of reproducing with present-day humans.

In the major trisomies of autosomal chromosomes 13, 18.21, partial deletion of the short arm of 5, and short and long of 18, produce severe mental and physical defects. One is privileged to speculate the leap-frogging of evolution via mechanical faults and not via minor mutations. It is possible that if disease and grotesqueness may result by these errors, so could double intelligence or increase in brain size, due to mechanism structure and so by-pass evolutionary selection. It could produce a super-race.

Also, we may rapidly change evolutionary course if we adapt practices similar to fellow primates as permitting dominants greater participation in sexual matters. In baboons, younger males are permitted by older dominant males to copulate with females when they first come into estrus. However, when the egg is ripe, the dominant male takes over and will father the young. This makes bachelors expendable. In polygamous people, it is the young men who must wait years to take a wife, while the older men are copulating with their third and fourth. We mirror this in our social structure today by per-mitting the young the luxury of war and death — they are still expendables.

Accelerated physiology has been occurring. The menarche, or when the woman has completely developed her sex organs and secondary character-istics, has decreased in the past century from 16 and 17-year-olds to 14-year-olds without explanation. Because we may be educationally stimulating the minds of the young, this is the signal that sufficient time has elapsed for them to program the germinal tissue for the production of offspring.

That which nature does is a chemical thrust of elements and compounds into retorts and flasks of earth's environmental laboratory. What emerges is a form of organic continuity that seeks every recess and crevis of the labora-tory in whatever form necessary to continue the master reaction known as life. Whereas, a specific compound, such as dinosaurs, dominating the earth for over a hundred million years, did become extinct, as the end of Creta-ceous times. It was no more than a shift in favor of competitive genes which adapted superiorily to available resources under the environmental condi-tions. Professor Lull, a dinosaur scholar, made the statement: "They do not represent a futile attempt on the part of nature to people the world with creatures of insignificant moment. But are comparable in majestic rise, slow culmination, and dramatic fall to the greatest nations of antiquity."

It was mammals that appeared on the scene following the dinosaur era. We conclude their adaptational competition was superior and edged out the land and sea giants in a burst of innovativeness.

As Professor Lull's "dinosauric fall of the nations of antiquity," there is new genetic perspective since 1933. It was not nations that rose and fell — for they are a cultural veneer of human genes. By absorption, rejection or hybridization of genes within their pool, they enhanced adaptational abilities. Consequently, nations disappeared or slunk off to a retreat such as to the protective low seas of Venice after the fall of Rome, to reemerge and rejoin adjacent genetic groups. Majesty in nations arose from purity of adap-tational genes. Their fall is attributable to the absorption and alteration of a successful pattern, by the injection of unadaptable and, consequently, un-assimilable foreign genes, of other subracial groups.

The wooden horse of Troy that ruefully infiltrated the besieged city to bring about its demise is not a physical weapon filled with men armed with swords, but rather men armed with phalluses filled with foreign racial and subracial genes, which are non-adaptable and incongruous to the situation.

Persia, Egypt, Greece, Rome, and others fell when Congoid genes were transported north from Africa by trade to infiltrate codes, strong and dominant, they were superiorly adaptable to intense heat of the tropics, but were so foreign to recipients that it weakened them irreparably. Faced with this breach, not in the Roman walls but in hearts and souls of cohesively long perioded gened men, it was no wonder powerful Germanic migrations of conquest took place. Caucasoid in nature, they swept down in successive invasions from their robust northlands into southern lands of Caucasoid brothers who were dociled by their admixture with races of Africa and Mongoloids from the east.

Colbert explains that dinosaurs disappeared completely about 70,000,000 years ago. Examining reasons, he suggests it is unanswerable at present. Forces that give rise to great chains of mountains at the end of the Cretaceous, the Laramide Revolution, does not explain why some dinosaurs did not live on. Climatic changes lowering worldwide average temperatures do not appear as the culprit, even though reptiles are cold-blooded animals, nor do increased temperatures which are unsupported by evidence, seem the agent. Another suggestion is that it was not competition with mammals, since it was not until after the dinosaurs had become extinct that mammals evolved to become lords of the land.

On this we disagree. Competitive chemistry is the game of life. And, although the mammals may have been small and insignificant and few of their fossils found, they undoubtedly had some evolutionary development that burst explosively into a species lush for picking. It is why a herbivore, such as zebras or wildebeast or brontosaurs whose stomachs convert plants, provides the opportunity for carnivors to evolve as lions, tigers, and tyrannosauri. It is an extension of the stomach chain, the imperative deal of evolutionary being.

When we visualize massive species roaming the earth for a hundred million years, we also visualize millions of attempts of other life-forms to get to their fleshed wealth and the treasured territories. It is like trying to get at a rich man's wealth. Someday, sometime, someone invariably will. Dinosaurs' flesh and eggs were covetable, as well as food sources they monopolized. As night was to follow day, some clever new evolutionary rascal was bound to bring them down. They had evidently passed too far in their evolutionary morphology to retreat rapidly enough to meet the new challenges which could have been as simple as a mole, whose piece de resistance was the egg of the mighty dinosaur.

It took hunters on horses armed with rifles to practically extinctualize the vast buffalo herds of the west. So all that was needed was a bacteria of virus and a carrier, such as a small mammal, whose target could have been the eggs or the reproductive ducts. Make little doubt about the villain in dinosaur extinction. It was a competitor or predator which had gain in its soul. Solidly capitalistic, it set out in a profitable market only to extinctualize its source material, as human whalers on high seas today are attempting to do.

Cooperative behavior has survival value, but the main force of natural selection favors self-seeking, anti-social actions by the individual. This is because competition between members of the same species operates by natural selection. We term this the "genie drive." It is responsible for petty animosities, tribal wars, and civil wars. Antagonisms are directed against those which are closest, contrary to anthropological thought.

Care of old folks was a burden for ancient man. However, there was excellent compensation. Wisdom of the aged was not to be lightly dismissed. Their memory storage was of value as living record of floods, invasions, poisonous plants, droughts, water holes, hemorrhages and rudiments of medical care. As today, they were excellent baby-sitters, sentinels, and the first to expend themselves in the protection of their offspring. Their knowledge of the areas of food supply and shelter was invaluable. Societies who utilized talents of the aged were forwarded.

New York State has a higher ratio of doctors than the State of Nebraska. The life expectancy of the population is significantly shorter by two and one-half years. There are racial differences and subracial differences between the two states, as well as pollution, environmental factors, and dietary differences. Nonetheless, such wide variance in life span and medical physician support demonstrates greater genetic excellence. Such a society in the past ages as the Nebraskians would have superseded the New Yorkians much in the fashion as Cro-Magnon followed the Neanderthals.

Man's life span is evolutionarily chained by adaptation to specific environment. It is because of this that no matter how excellently humans commence breeding toward longevity, we shall possibly not accomplish much more than living to the age of two hundred. Neurons are not replaceable. We cannot throw the intellectual complex away and search out a new model. We are stuck with the nervous tissue we have, unless, of course, we do nervous tissue farming and become capable of transferring the ego factor, the "me" factor, the "I am I" factor to new substrata with a reasonable amount of memoried experience.

There has been some questioning concerning the evolutionary disappearance of a type of pre-man called Paranthropus. He was five feet tall, weighed between 130 and 150 pounds, had grinding molars which were large in proportion to his front teeth. His skull gave evidence of strong jaw muscles and gorilla-like muscular attachments. It is generally agreed that he was vegetarian. Living several million years ago, it is suspected that because of his competition with the more advanced Australo-pithecus he became extinct.

The name of the game in evolution is availability of food source. Once food sources run out, it is necessary to adapt to newer ecological conditions. We could have come out of the trees because trees were becoming scarce during eras of drought. It is likely we left the trees because of a development whose potential went long unnoticed. One of the most lethal weapons is the same today as it was five million years ago. It lies with the grasping hand. Propelled by ingenious joints, directed by strong muscles and tendons and swift coordination, the pre-hominid arm, once it grasped a stick, was capable of apoplexying the skulls of predatory opponents.

This new weaponry, defensive and offensive, entailed a second equally important factor. The hand had in reality grown a tusk, a horn, a saber tooth, or what have you. The grasped stick became an inert, insensitive and dispensable prolongation of the body. Not only was this extended stick, or bone, a clubbing item, it was also a first line of defense against teeth and claws of predation. The sword-like thrusting of a sharp point into an opponent was later development. A stick or thigh bone within primitive hand had released pre-man from predators in a giant leap of evolutionary history.

At the time fear of open land was dissipating, when pre-hominid was living off roots, tubers, nuts, and that which he could find on the savanna floors, there was a marginal source of food to which the hand made him privy: skulls of animals killed by big cats. Although he could scavage some of the remains, a rock within his hand permitted access to the cranial cavity and brains, a high source of quality protein.

That was the age of atomic destiny for the pre-hominids. With but one cultural adaptation, he relieved himself of his predators and, at the same time, opened his world to the lush activity of the savannas. Man had come out of the tree with a stick in his hand. The club is with us today in our police forces. A blow in the proper area can kill as rapidly as any other weapon the modern armamentarium.

Paranthropus was specializing toward vegetarianism. There are no soft organs to tell us what else may have been happening at that period. He could actually have been selecting toward a grass digesting stomach — a ruminant — developing a cud like a cow. This would have enabled bacteria to break down the complex carbohydrate chains in the grasses, to be then digested.

This evolutionary attempt was running into intense competition from other grass-eating and vegetarian animals. There was not enough leeway for furtherance in this direction. On the other hand, Australo-pithecus, by concentrating on a predatory career, had a capable killer tool that propulsed him forward out of proportion to normal evolutionary adaptation. This momentum has never relinquished the lead in becoming top dominant animal of the biological sphere.

Individuals are born differently. Let us say, to go through the obstacle course of life one must climb a difficult mountain to be able to reproduce. Further specify that only 80% of the individuals will be capable of making the climb until they can reach their beloved. Quite obviously, those that survive the climb — survivorship of the fittest — will mate and their particular type of (fitness) genes will be passed on to the next generation.

What has happened to weed out one group and pass the other? The gate at the top, through which the fittest pass, is known as the selector gate. If all individuals were born equal, with the same genetic makeup, the selector gate would no longer exist and all would pass enmasse into the promised land. This is not so. Humans vary, and that variation is the basis of evolutionary process. Variation comes through mutations or deformations of the cells by such physical processes as radiation, chemicals, and environmental agents.

There are types of variations, a jackpot of combinations, we come up with at reduction division in the germ cells, female and male, as well as at the time when the one lucky germ cell out of millions is chosen to mate a solitary female egg. You have a gate of selection which permits the fittest to pass. You have two processes whereby human differences occur, the one being from environment without and the other from DNA gambling within. Thus, we blithely move forward through ages, the fittest being jerked through the gate and others precipitating to genetic doom. Prolific breeders who have capable fitness genes will pass greater numbers through the gate.

The gene-shuffling process is called Mendelian inheritance, and is arranging variants in endless combinations to be issued according to certain laws. What has not been mentioned is the Lamarckian hypothesis of evolution which is discredited. Yet it is the only rational thought that can explain certain unanswered problems; namely, the extreme number of straight-line progressive genes which evolutionarily pass through the gate, with a very small number of reproductive opportunities. That is, in the very few number of generations, let us say 5,000, in which the white man was able to split off from the black man, which may represent a difference in 5,000 genes.

And with genes going in various directions, that from erectus to sapiens, pre-man to man, thousands of genes had to be altered and selected for as they pass through the gate. In a period of 200,000 years, or 10,000 generations, the skull capacity increased from 1000 cubic centimeters to a capacity of 1450 cubic centimeters, or an increase of brain capacity of 30%. This is a very rapid direct selection and is too rapid to be based upon numerical chance, mutation or natural selection.

Evolution in the highest primate would conceivably develop mechanisms which are more sophisticated than that of lower animals or the ridiculous comparison with fruit flies. There had to be feedback mechanisms to germinal cells in which physiological use is able to influence heredity. In other words, environmental and ecological challenges alter physiology to produce alterations in germinal coding at the most propitious time, being cross-over. Darwin prophesized in his Pangenesis hypothesis that circulating hemotological elements will influence selection of certain genes.

The experiment of supreme value in the study of culture and its relationship to innate genes could be conducted easily and humanitarily if humans were not so sentimental. Since the northern lands have a prohibitive temperature for such experimentation, the ideal testing place would be on some isolated island off the Canal, Caracus, or Trinidad. From time of birth, 25 females and 25 males would be placed in an isolated area, fed remotely, and observed from hidden TV cameras and periscopes with tunnels leading into the area. They would never hear human speech, never see any facets of culture. Their mothers would have been brought near the area for delivery and the child immediately transferred to this isolated environment. Feeding and tending mechanisms would be operated by remote control.

What we would expect to emerge would be development of rudimentary society complete with language, laws, codes, ethics, hunting and gathering techniques, after the food supply was purposely restricted for increasingly longer periods of time. There should be props in the beginning of the experiment, such as shallow inlets harboring fish, stones, logs, and bones so that tools could be manufactured. There should be a compliment of edible animal species that the instinctable hunting traits could be observed.

Billions of dollars are spent for outlandish experimentation. This experiment, "The Birthing of Innate Culture," would for the first time explain long sought after answers in understanding the behavior of man. Such an experiment might lead to solution of war and nationalism. Mothers so honored to contribute offspring should be selected widely from all class types. Danger of solar radiation to the skin should be avoided. One would immediately look for emergence of stratified society which, in essence, would be a death blow to communism. The implications for political science would be huge.

We should expect innate forces operating against incest. What we should not expect to find is an incoherent, non-speaking, non-organized mass of seeming lunatics without social discipline, entirely dependent upon the food supply offered by the observers. And we would lay to rest once and for all the notion that humans, like chimpanzees, must observe or be instructed in the art of sexual act to be able to copulate.

This idea is not new, the idea of rearing children excommunicado. Herodotus, historian of the 5th century B.C., related in an account of Egypt that Psammetichos gave two newborn children to a shepherd to rear, "charging him namely that no man should utter any word in their presence." The king desired to know what men had come into being first. After two years, the children uttered the word *bekos*, meaning bread in Phrygian language, and so it was concluded that Phrygians were a more ancient people than the Egyptians.

One reason there is controversy whether capital punishment should exist is the changing base of political power. With dictatorships, communists, tribal and strong leadership governments, there is no question as to the advantage of capital punishment to control anything from dissidents to murderers.

Once the proletariat, the common man, has an influence in the political processes, he is extremely reluctant to sanction such method of social control. Subconsciously within his lower class genetic makeup, he is aware of his inferiority, his inability to cope with problems, and his serf-like fear of punishment. Therefore, capital punishment is violently resisted by proletariat and laboring classes, even though vicious murders and terroristic attacks have been promulgated within his society.

On the other hand, bourgeois, or dominants, know that for society to be viable, fear of heavy punishment for horrendous wrong-doings must be present. They understand genetically from society's history that serious offenders must be done away with, giving a sub rosa boost to eugenics through the natural selection of a guillotine. Higher stratas of society do not oppose capital punishment. They are the dominant genes responsible for the coordination of the social group. We find false studies by criminologists contending capital punishment has no value. They manipulate statistics from their proletariat direction. With old fashioned lamp-post hangings crime will plummet. The proletariat criminals will realize they are under traditional disciplinary control and not molly-coddled. Arabic practices of cutting off the hand of a thief is genetically rooted. You can't cure a thief because he's biologically programmed. But you can remove one of the tools he operates with.

Proletariat laborers, to the disadvantage of some nations, have escaped proper punishment by ruse of democracy — one body, one vote, no matter how sick, inferior, or depraved. It is what is happening to the free world today, in which laborers are permitted governmental roles for which they have never been biologically intended. They are to be led and obey — not in communistic tyrannical system, but in benignity of recognition of biological inequality and proper humanitarian adjustment and compensation.

Journal of the History of Medicine, 1974, Peter J. Bowler — "Darwin on Variation," "Natural selection is composed of three factors: struggle for survival — variability of those struggling — and a tendency for offspring to resemble parents."

We vary, but resemble parents and struggle to propagate. The foregoing is innate gened expression.

In *Methods and Goals in Human Behavior Genetics*, Vandenberg, Academic Press, 1965, David Freedman did studies on fraternal and identical twins in infancy concerning smiling and fear of strangers. As usual, if for no other reason than the similar genetic underlayment, there was greater concordance in the identical twins.

One would expect in fraternal twins, at the second month, Arturo to be a smile-prone sleepyhead, and his brother, Felix, wide-eyed, unsmiling and unremittingly sober. Genetic differences become apparent at birth — phenotypes emerge — behavioral variations go into action, not from environment or learning, but because we are born to a class or social caste.

Richard C., ten months, cried when the investigator donned a Halloween mask. Yet his fraternal brother, Robert C., only inspected the investigator, showing interest.

We mention early behavioral differences to illustrate, not what everyone knows, that everyone is genetically different, but that extremely early behavioral patterns are present which will relegate us to our place within society.

"Heredity plays a role in the development of positive social orientation (including smiling) and the fear of strangers. Our evidence for this is that identical twins show greater concordance than fraternal twins in these areas of behavior over the first year of life."

Obviously, you can tell a laborer by his hands. Not just from callouses or the muscular development, but from bone structure indigent to mesomorphs. Much easier to look at a man's face or hear him speak, you will immediately be aware of genetic class differences. If you look in the eye with an opthalmoscope to discover myopia, you may also conclude that the bearer of this shortsighted deformity was so picked to achieve a result within the social grouping. Its wide spreadness indicates it was a cohesive force to pay more attention to the group, local matters and local discovery and negate distant exploration.

There are many forms by which evolution takes place. One form that we have not seen described is immunological selection. That is, individuals possessing certain immunological genes survived over those of lesser enrichment. The unexplained disappearance of the Cro-Magnan man could have been due to environmental changes such as weather, in which he did not have proper immunological adaptation. Or his disappearance could have been triggered by viral or bacterial immunological suppressants. He could have been carried away by virulent plagues to which no one developed sufficient immunity.

Immunology to disease is a facet of "survival of the fittest." Mechanisms producing immunology are challenges received by antigens. Anti-bodies are formed in all of us daily as combatives. Some of our defense mechanism in early years came through breast milk, some came through by transference into our bloodstream across the placenta. But majorily, our apparatus to resist bacteria, viri, and cancer, come by way of genetic inheritance.

Challenges were fantastic in man's evolution as he grouped into larger tribes. This permitted rapid dissemination of contagion with only the very strong surviving, eliminating those of lesser gened ability. Only a small fraction in American Indian genocide resulted from flint locks. What carried the native Indian population away by entire settlements was smallpox to which they had practically no immunity. On occasion, the process was accelerated by whites donating infected smallpox bedding to their red-skinned acquaintances.

A professor of mine once stated that syphilis, when it was carried to the old world by Columbus' sailors, was extremely virulent and dangerous. But, in 400 years, it had become docile by comparison, many individuals having an inherited immunology to its ravages. If we deduct that immunological genes in four centuries spread throughout the white population, then we should consider that they did so not by mutations or survival of the fittest, but by inheritance of acquired characteristics. A syphilitic who fathered non-syphilitic children transferred his new immunological armament directly to loci for coding within his sperm cells. Our present resistance could not have come through a totality of syphilitic mothers passing it through the placenta into the embryo. It was of immense selective value in the development of society that basic immunological properties be transferred to off-spring as rapidly as possible. Natural selection is not rapid enough to accomplish this transferral. Within the gamut of immunology there could never have been natural selection from disease processes because there were too many, too varied, to permit a weeding out of those that were resistantly blessed and those that succumbed. There are, however, gross immunologic patterns which are genetically programmed by selective factors.

That the mother passes to her offspring permanently immunological equipment is spurious, because by cell division and replacement we could not carry it throughout our lifetime. This massive immunological system necessitates frequent genetic honing within the body of man, that is, apart from other evolving biological considerations, for it is continually being faced with new and evolving microbial species.

Sickle cell anemia comes to mind as a selectively chosen mechanism in the Negro for survival in malarial districts. Those knighted with the infirmity in heavy infestation areas were capable of becoming islands of genetic survival in the continuance of progeny. So pathologic and prevalent a parasite as malaria within Africa was a factor in selection toward the sickle-celled hemoglobin.

With tens of thousands of bacterial and viral challenges to evolving man, old-time evolution and the genetic inviolability of the germ plasma is no way to explain the immunological abilities of man. Only the inheritance of acquired immunology, or the inheritance of an acquired disease characteristic, suffice.

"Herpes virus saimiri has been isolated from healthy squirrel monkeys, and herpes virus ateles from healthy spider monkeys. These viruses, which do not cause cancer in the natural hosts, induce malignant lymphomas when innoculated into other monkey species, particularly marmoset monkeys." Deinhardt, F. W., Falk, L. A., and Wolf, L. G., Simian herpes viruses and neoplasis.

Those closely related animals have differential immunity. It is insufficient to say that natural selection permitted survival of the one because of its immunity. The non-resistant species is still surviving even though it is exposed to these malignant viri.

What this means is that parental forces altered the genetic immunological structure in one while the other remained untouched. If natural selection were a factor, the latter group of monkeys would be non-existent. What selection is operating is that the one group suffered continuous challenging episodes to respond through germ cell alteration.

From *The Ecology and Evolution of Animal Behavior*, Robert A. Wallace, 1973, Goodyear Publishing Inc. — ". . . Darwin treated behavioral patterns like morphological characters." He assumed that behavior, like morphology, is variable and that natural selection operates on both. Since it is not difficult for anyone to observe, even as remotely as Darwin, that behavior is innate and subject to evolution or, in fact, is a part of evolution, we would all be emotionless globs of protoplasm with no imagination. One must concede that society is nothing more or less than individually grouped behavior functioning for certain mutual benefit.

"Society evolved for many reasons: to facilitate the division of labor, to prevent intraspecies competition, to obtain protective mechanisms, to proportion offspring according to environmental receptiveness, to enjoy a bit of frivolous play, sensuosity and happiness, and finally, in the casting of one's lot with others to further the inherent, compulsed geneticism."

An individual amoeba could not care less if the amoeba beside him perished. The genetic mechanisms residing in human society care about future survival. After having been forged millions of years, they selfishly propulse their own system forward to the exclusion of other related beings. This accounts for horrendous wars, massacres, and genocides.

In structuring society many forces are at work. It is necessary for changes to take place in DNA coding, which produce wide variation. Where a particularly different human resulted, his genes were incorporated into the pool. Conscience thievery and political chicanery are gene traits of survival, as well as rapists who, in prehistoric cultures, passed on more than their share. Matings produce wide variation by chance in physical and intellectual attributes by which directions of society flow. Mutagenesis by physical agents, physiological and neural forces act upon society by altering egg cell codes. Survival of the "fittest society," that is, the society which conquered, eliminated or out-competitized its neighbors to the increase of its own seedings.

Members of a species, once they have passed reproductive age, are worthless. There is no need for evolutionary forces to continue their earthly sojourn, utilizing vital supplies within the environmental niche unless the oldsters contribute to education, welfare, and leadership of the society. In that event, the aged are of value and become a factor in evolutionary selection so that they are retained in the post-reproductive years.

Thus, the old men who bait traps, the aged technician who flakes points, the cagey warrior, or the white-haired mother who practices mid-wifing, weaves or gathers profusely, are desirable in social evolution long after reproductive years. It is why human society is age-structured — because of the cultural wealth transported in the neurogenes of the aged, which are symbiotic with genes of the reproducing. In short, the aged earn their keep.

Increase in life span is not only from conquest of disease, but from cultural genes, acquired, which permit the organization of society to be selected toward. Society is a unit rather than the individual being selected on a fitness basis.

A high incidence of red-green color blindness occurs in long civilized peoples. In primitives, the defect is rare. It is not selection pressures that have caused this, i.e., survival gear. Rather, it is modern man who has negated to utilize his color ability in hunting and has, by disuse, abandoned the function.

Single genes may cause upward to 1545 syndromes, diseases or anomalies — 1% of dominant and 15% of the recessive and sex-linked genes. Here we speak of undesirable traits, yet what of the desirable single genes or the reverse side of the coin — those components that make up skills and talents? In these one finds the basis of human differences and the logical need to permit discrimination, racially, sexually, and socially.

Morton concludes that recessive loci contributes to severe mental defect, which are maintained by mutation rather than heterzygote advantage. Yet this cannot be totally true, for the mentally defective has an excellent priority of being in a primitive society. He is obedient, hard-working, and patient. So as a dog to his master, a comfort or pawn, a sentinel or hunter, so are the defectives, the lowest of village clowns, the most servile of laborers, and the most expendable.

We sacrifice the cream codes in war. In the past, it was defective codes that were prompted to test mire or reveal presence of man-eating predators. It was their unquestioning lot to carry the burden of the higher class. Feebleminded innocence made them prime scapegoats. If selection were the only value, we would be rid of disease, especially deadly infectious ones. Tuberculosis and pneumonia are much more important than white skin or the shape of a nose. Why didn't we select away from pathogenic?

Why didn't we select toward genes that manufacture vitamin C as we moved north? Mutations could have produced it — but we didn't select toward it because evolution is not directed from without, majorily, but from within. Thus, appendicitis and scurvy were relatively unimportant.

Constellations of rare genes, as in Newton, Leonardo, Bach, or Shakespeare will out in whatever social strata. We have a limited number of loci. Either they must be acquired at the expense of other genes or they are triplications of the talented areas. Einstein was no Cassanova and Shakespeare was no Mozart. There is only room enough for the special trait talent. We have yet to come up with the jack-of-all genius.

All forms of behavior that are critical for survival are under genetic control. Mating, territoriality aggression, socialization, restraint, speech, are but a few.

Hybrid vigor or heterosis occur when two inbred individuals, such as a cousin who mates a cousin, then offspring, F_1, brother and sister are mated, they exceed the mid-parental values.

The opposite of hybrid vigor is inbreeding depression in which there is a negative association with genetic variation. In inbreeding, more deleterious recessive genes are expressed, as in incestuous matings. Whereas, in the beginning of inbreeding to produce hybrid vigor, recessive genes become heterozygous and are covered up. Further inbreeding results in homozygous recessives with malevolent character.

In royalty, heterosis ensued to be followed by inbreeding depression and consequent political fall from power. In animals, by this same phenomena, we can control longevity, body size, production, and disease resistance.

In a concise text, *Micro-Evolution of Human Populations,* Francis E. Johnson focuses into the basic reality of the science. Those who have studied evolution years back, came away with the impression of Darwinian fitness, adaption and the forces of selection weaving in and out. Rarely did we glimpse that evolution is not so much what we are seeing, the phenotypes, as it is the small changes in the nucleic acid codes, the genotypes.

These minute genetic changes at which evolution works is all the more reason to consider that extraneous forces act directly upon the germinal cells and it isn't necessary to kill off an entire human before reproduction so that adaptation may take place.

Johnson's definition of alleles is, "These various *forms* of the same gene found at the same locus are called alleles." This important word to genetics is a particularly bad one and one with which students have difficulty, even more so because various authors interpret it differently. Webster defines allele as allemorph — either of a pair of alternative contrasting Mendelian characters. But there is a lot more to be said about this nasty word, and it would be better to understand it simply as gene varieties. Johnson notes there are at least eighteen transferring alleles. "Each individual, of course, possesses only two allele, one on each chromosome of the appropriate pair." There are too many pair references in genetics that serve as a stumbling block mentally to be misinterpreted. Try this translation: Each individual possesses only one form of gene on each mated chromosome. The gene forms may be identical, that is, in the same location of the mated chromosomes, in which case they are spoken of as homozygotes. In case the forms are different, they are spoken of as heterozygous.

It has been attempted to make genetics into a mathematical science. It becomes too sticky in this pristine overweight — there are too many exceptions, too many cunning little words, and too many inventions to bend a biological science into a set of formulae. Even a recessive gene is a goof-off. When it is recessive, it cannot act when it is coupled with a dominant gene in a heterozygote. But if it is coupled with another recessive gene as a homozygote, it emerges into power. Then there are co-dominant genes. Suppose we would consider albinism, hemophilia or phenylketonuria. These recessive genes are not homozygous.

Johnson gives the standard explanation of the Rh incompatible mating. When a Rh positive father and a Rh negative mother breed, the fetus carries a Rh plus, which disturbs the mother's immunology to fight it with an anti-Rh antibody, which can cause a death in the newborn known as erythroblastosis fetalis.

This mechanism is no freak. Somewhere along the line it emerged as a birth control measure, or better still, an instrument of war. That is, war at the individual genetic level; the message is quite clear, the Rh positive father is out to destroy, in effect, those rivals of the Rh minus nation. Although it is not 100% effective in each pregnancy, it must be regarded as a weapon.

In man, a minimum of 123 loci in the sex chromosome and more than 1400 in the non-sex chromosome have been identified. *Behavioral Genetics*, Garner Lindzey, 1971, Review of Psychology.

DNA and its coded genes determine human behavior and instinct. Not more than 20% of its genes are active at any one time. Drugs that interfere with DNA transcription and RNA translation disrupt memory, learning, and reproduction functions. Behavioral performance may be interpreted not in simplistic Mendelian method referring to dominant or recessive genes, but rather in a more complex form which is dependent upon structure of many interrelated genes, in quantity, quality, and classical dominant-recessive traits, coupled with neurogenic codings.

A Beethoven is composed because he has a multiple share of mathematical and symbol genes, a large grouping of tonal memory genes with drive and creative genes all favoring the goal of musical composition.

Viral infection may not be all bad. In fact, it is suggested that it may be a "key mechanism for transporting segments of DNA across species and phylum barriers" — a process on which evolution depends.

This is the view of physiologist Norman G. Anderson, of the Molecular Anatomy Program at Oak Ridge National Laboratory in Tennessee, who points out that viruses are so ubiquitous that it seems likely they perform some useful task for the many organisms they affect. Indeed, if viral infection existed solely to confer illness, the "evolution of effectiveness means for its elimination might be expected."

Lastly, women contribute heavily to evolutionary direction. "Students of animal courtship have substantiated Darwin's assertion of the existence of 'female choice' as a factor of sexual selection and evolution. Males easily engage in courtship and promiscuous sex, while females retain a coyness. A Cassanova may spread his seed freely with great consequences, yet a female who chooses improperly may be a victim of reproductive failure and a loss of her gene stream." — *Sexual Selecting*, Bernard Campbell.

Why do we lose some areas of body hair and retain others? Smooth skin may be a subject of sexual selection on women. We lose facial hair to have a more important means of visual communication and as a seat of beauty. One of the keys to sexual selection is that those who do not possess, for example, rounded buttocks and breasts, facial and leg beauty, or virile male qualities will not find mates and, therefore, will not breed, so that our direction is toward what we regard as beauty.

We are taught that evolution takes place because of necessity; conditions are altered in climate, competition or ecology. Either we adapt or we perish. But we also evolve out of maliciousness and caprice. Sexual selection can be a game of "Guess who I'd like to bed with," having no relation to evolution's dictates.

In non-human primates little can be found to reflect the impositions imposed on sex by man. Howler male monkeys feed close together without fighting and share receptive females in rotation. A male baboon may persistently possess half a dozen females, but will tolerate bachelors within the harem, while other baboons may dominate an entire group of a dozen females. Gibbons are patterned more as a monogamous human family. Whereas, rhesus female monkeys during estres may copulate repeatedly with different males, which is often termed "rotating" mateship. In sexual behavior in humans with increasing incidence of divorce, breakdown of marriage and free love, we can conclude that religious and legislative attempts to regulate human sexual behavior will forever be fraught with failure.

Besides sexual selection, as homosexuals are doled out in purposeful numbers, so are hypochondriacs. Here one has to differentiate between what man requires for society and what is the result of genetic chemical errors which cause hundreds of diseases.

Hypochondriasis may be considered a paradox. In this instance, as in those possessed with thieving genes, survival takes place because of a trait, in this case feigned illness. You can tell a hypochondriac they are not ill and they will not believe you. That is because it is on a subconscious genetic basis. One who inherits these genes, Hy Hy, travels life with never ending series of illnesses, most of which are false, from body location to location. The holder of these society parasitical genes, no matter how intelligent, can never be convinced out of their phantom symptoms.

In the development of social order, compassion and medicine were necessary to salvage injured members. Hypochondriacs soon developed, were selected toward, knowing they could ride this phase throughout life. Who gets the grease? The squeaking wheel. They perform no useful function to the social group. They enter by way of the back door, known as parasitism. One might mention that it is a very dangerous diagnosis for any doctor to make, because if he is wrong, it could be a fatal error. Yet over the years, if one carefully observes these people, he becomes deaf-eared. One should remember that besides the host of imaginary disease they conjure up, they do run risk of diseases to which the rest of us are subject.

11 Inheritance of Acquired Characteristics: Slot-machined Children or Intelligent Direction?

S YNONYMOUS for the inheritance of acquired characteristics: parental modification of germinal cells and zygote; parental germ cell alteration, parental modification of offspring inheritance. Parental alteration of inheritance.

Darwin's theory of "Pangenesis" was an attempt to explain the inheritance of acquired characteristics as an evolutionary force — "parental alteration of germinal cells."

Back in the '50s there was a considerable controversy over reincarnation. A housewife, Ruth Simmons, described her life as a young Irish girl named Birdie Murphy in the early 1800s. A book was written concerning it. In

1975, a preacher's wife at Elkton, Virginia, in a hypnotic trance, recalls her early life and death in Germany a century before, speaking German, a language to which she had never been exposed.

It is always worthy to investigate the mystic. If the inheritance of acquired characteristics is a fact, upon which we believe — if human parents can alter and transmit information from their somatic cells to their germinal cells, then in the great subconscious world of billions of interlocked neurons, it should not be surprising to find permanently inscribed events. As a far-out one, there could conceivably be some pious and devout man of religion who was a direct descendant from one of those who witnessed the crucifixion of Christ and who could, under hypnosis or other form of neural recall, redescribe the scene as his ancestor witnessed it.

An extremely strong and emotional "record now" event within the nervous tissue of a parent may, at a susceptible time, be imprinted into the neurogene template of the sperm or ova. We possibly have hundreds of thousands of imprintations in our subconscious. We do not need to be specifically instructed as to avoid eating the major types of poisonous plants and flowers, or to avoid snakes or automatically seek shelter from ancient predators. A starving dog with an unfamiliar food supply will not partake of it. Within his neurogenes are perceptional patterns he must obey, even though it would mean his death.

How Inheritance of Acquired Characteristics Operates:
Continuously changing human genetics, from pressures below —

FITTEST BY
- Social Cooperation
- Adaptability
- Strength
- Reproductive Ability
- Greater Competitiveness
- Food Gathering
- Killing Ability
- Disease Resistance
- Sex Attractivness

SIEVE OF NATURAL SELECTION

```
                    Lean              Muscular
                 Long-lived   White   Dominant
           Fat     Thief    Combinations   Black
        Short    Tall     Intelligent   Slant-eyed
           Bourgeois        Resistant     Callus's
             Feebleminded                  Curly
                       Broad-nosed
        Homosexual          oab        Yellow
                       Casanova
                       Genius
```

GENETIC VARIATION AND HUMAN VARIABILITY —
NEW FORMS AND TISSUES

Some from acquired
characteristics of parents.

By Choice	By Mutations	By Chance	By Accident
RAYS	*HUMAN GENETIC CODES (DNA)*		*CHEMICALS*
X	*IN GERMINAL CELLS*		Ingested
Micro			Inhaled
Ultra			Contacted
Cosmic			

Blood Circulating Elements	*Natural*	*Environment*
Chemicals	Crossover	Climate
Rays	Reduction Division	Altitude
Hormones	Chance	Disease Prevalence
Excesses		Demand
Minimals		Motion
DNA codes) Broken and		Food
RNA codes) Whole		
Immune Bodies		
Acids - Bases		
Adhesives		

Subject to Parental Influence.

One of the leading exponents of Lamarckism, T. D. Lysenko, reigned over two decades as the USSR's leading geneticist. He was decorated, proclaimed a national hero, and highly admired. After Khrushchev's fall from power, Lysenko was exposed as false. Yet what is interesting is that he could maintain the Lamarckian theory for such a long period of time in a modern nation as Russia.

Even Lerner, who was by no means a Lamarckian, admits that, "There are some experiments on record with such plants as flax and eggplant that appear to show environmentally induced transformation." It is unfortunate that Lerner's experiments were not better structured and directed toward the higher animals or even Darwin's proposal with its theory of pan genes whereby blood substances would modify the germinal cells' heredity code.

From *Social Behavior and Organization Among Vertebrates*, by William Elin, University of Chicago Press, we learn: Even Darwin fell back upon the inheritance of acquired characteristic for an explanation of specific instances of evolutionary change — Lamarckism.

In Elin's book there is a statement that says the Lamarckian concept is described because it does not provide any way in which environmentally induced modifications in the body could influence the genes. This is folly. Drugs can be regarded as environmental. Many primitives subjected themselves to hallucinogenic drugs. Consider thalidomide which produced in mothers an alteration of the fetus' genetic coding. This resulted in severe anomalies. The absence of arms, fingers, or legs resulted. The modern diet is loaded with drugs, and so were primitive diets, causing direct genetic abberations to the offspring. That they affected the ova before fertilization, during fertilization or after, is inconsequential. The genetic code was modified by maternal environment. We would expect in future generations of the offspring of these unfortunates to carry abnormal coding in the same way that dozens of genetically inheritable diseases are passed downward through defective genes. The idea that the germinal cell is a *sanctum sanctorium* free from other than random mutational evolvements and genetic mixings is based upon the very crudest of experimentation.

When Lamarckism is disregarded, one is saying that we have germinal cells that cannot be influenced within the human body. When you come to tissue this complex, it is influenced within the human body. It would be a physiological miracle, an organism as man, contained tissue that was not subject to change. We can alter every part of our body under environmental stress pressures, including diet, and especially nervous tissue under duress. Why should germinal cells be set apart? If they are inviolate to physiological responses, we carry them around in a knapsack and dole them out as we see fit.

George C. Williams, in *Adaptation and Natural Selection*, a critique of some current evolutionary thought, 1974, R. C. Lowontin stated on the back cover, "Excellently reasoned essay in defense of Darwinian selection as sufficient theory to explain evolution without the necessity of group selection, population adaptation or progress."

However, the author concludes on an upbeat, "Perhaps today's theory of natural selection, which is essentially that provided more than thirty years ago . . . may not, in an absolute or permament sense, represent the truth, but I am convinced that it is the light and the way."

Waddington, 1956, is cited for his conviction that natural selection is not enough and that a theory of genetic assimilation aids filling the major gap in Darwin's presentations. Note: "It is easy to overestimate Waddington's departure from tradition and regard it as Lamarckian."

It appears Waddington performed the greatest evolutionary experiment to date. He exposed fruit fly eggs to ether vapor. Most of the offspring were normal, but some developed a condition called bi-thorax. These were then bred and their eggs exposed to ether. For many generations, the same procedure was used.

Then, what appeared should have been headline news in every scientific journal on earth — for, from eggs that were not now exposed to the trauma of ether, the new line of bi-thorax fruit flies were continuing.

Within thirty generations of the beginning of experimental breeding under a newly controlled environment, a stock was produced which contained large numbers of bi-thorax flies every generation and which did not need the ether stimulus prod.

In other words, a new creature had been produced solely by environmental forces within thirty generations, the gene coding had been altered and *fixed* permanently to give it hereditary character.

"The explanation is not in any way Lamarckian. Selection of chance differences between individuals was the evolutionary force that produced the bi-thorax stock from the normal stock. The ether did not, in the Lamarckian sense, produce the genetic variation that was selected by the experimenter, but it certainly did produce the expression of that variation." For some reason, scientists discredit Lamarck. Even when he is right, they go out of their way to repudiate him.

Let's look at fact. Although bi-thorax occasionally appeared in the past, the ether jolt to the eggs made it a permament fixture after selection, and a new "subrace" was born. What did the ether do? It can alter tissues. And in so doing, it went into the germinal cells and re-altered specific amino acid sequence codes. I am satisfied that if ether were used on human spermatozoa before artificial insemination, we would come up with some weirdos, and if we selectively bred them, we would establish a hereditarily fixed heaven-knows-what.

It is the thalidomide story over again. In poisoning the embryo, the DNA codes produce appendage-deformed offspring. Waddington's experiment is a higher run on this in that morphologic changes become fixed.

Weissman, who cut off mice tails for thirty generations, bred them and expected to develop a tail-less lineage. Where the experiment failed, in this particular instance, there was no feedback to the germinal codes.

That Waddington experiment, one of the first, has proven Lamarckism — the inheritance of acquired characteristics. Forceably, it demonstates that a hostile or abnormal environment acting upon germinal tissue can produce its alteration and, if continued over many generations, can permanently and hereditarily alter human stock. It makes one think of the days of the violent anesthetics over many hours' duration and the damage that was done to human germinal cells — in the same manner as X-rays produce serious germinal mutations.

If ether can alter germinal tissue and produce a unique hereditary lineage, then so can any of the strong hormones in the human body in excess, any of the byproducts of excessive useage of tissue, to the myriads of active chemicals found in foods, from flowers and roots to tainted flesh. If germinal tissue is inviolate, a new bi-thorax subrace would not have evolved — it would have perished. It is marvelous that we have a chemical that can give selective alteration in the DNA code.

With a vast armanitarium of drugs we shall be opening the production of new lineages of humans. No longer will we have to select genotypes already in place. We shall be able to alter the genotype and produce future races.

A mutation is so minuscule that it could never serve in natural selection totally. An enlargement of a third metacarpal gives no one advantage in survival. How bones do change gradually is by alterations from pressures required previous to parenthood — namely, a form of Darwin's paragenes.

The giraffe stretches his neck and feeds back to germinal genes the need for greater cervical length. The cat grows whiskers, feelers. It cannot radio. I need feelers like the stretching of the neck, which is a positive act. But it can respond to facial bruises due to smacking into branches in the dark. Natural selection is never going to grant survival on a few upper lip stiff hairs. But facial bruising is going to demand hair, as on the head and the pubis. Pubic hair does not guarantee selection — it is non-abrasive utility.

James V. Neal and Arthur D. Bloom, in *The Detection of Environmental Mutigens*, in a sentence summed up the presently accepted concept of the evolutionary factor: "It is the cornerstone of genetic theory that the spontaneous mutation rate of any species has through selection reached a near optimum, serving to introduce mutations at a rate sufficient to permit ongoing evolution but not so rapidly as to exceed the ability of selective factors to eliminate deleterious mutations."

This, in essence, is saying that radiation, chemicals, biological errors, etc., cause changes in the germinal cells. These changes produce some highly variable offspring. The rate of this production is not sufficient to swamp the organism's ability to rid itself of the badly programmed seeds. Rather, the changes appear with sufficiently good timing that adaptation may be smoothly accomplished.

These authors cite that drugs may act on chromosomes when they are in a single-stranded GI stage of inner phase; when actively synthesizing DNA or when the DNA is already duplicated. And carrying the argument further, even caffein or aspirin is capable of causing structural chromosome changes in test-tubed somatic cells. Neal and Bloom also caution that somatic damages cannot lead to the influence that mutigens would similarly carry over to the germ cells.

In effect, evolutionary variability occurs routinely due to a number of factors which affect the cells. The only thing left in these non-sweeping, clear-cut and proven concepts is that one of the factors can certainly be the organism itself, the human organism reacting directly to challenges of environment and codes variance into germinal plasm, which is deemed advisable. In short, the human organism has the ability to slant its germinal tissue product in an adaptational direction favorable to it and not simply be the product of unintelligent pot-luck muted genesis. Nature is far too clever, too supremely astute over the eons, not to advantage itself of riding herd on its germinal charges.

Nature and Man's Fate, by Garrett Hardin, is explicatory, lucid, and brilliant. It shows command and knowledge of genetics and, further, Hardin is a courageous sociological writer. Oftentimes the values of a science can be learned from psychoanalytical study of the minds of acknowledged authorities. It is not only the presentation but also the thought process in back of the presentation which has significance.

In the preface to this book, the author relates how, after a lecture, he asks questions. A member of his audience asked, and I would like to ask the same, "You say that X-rays and atomic radiations cause mutations and almost all mutations are bad." Professor Hardin affirmed that was so. The questioner then asked, "But isn't it true that all evolutionary progress was made possible by new mutations?" The answer was again in the affirmative. Hardin pointed out that there were no contradistinctions in the statements and that possibly only a 20-hour lecture could resolve this paradox.

It does seem odd that the weakest part of evolutionary argument should be presented first. Yet, in the material that follows, this simple quandry is not fully solved, speaking in the security of the Mendelian school.

Mutations, chemical code changes of hereditary elements, may not only derive from ionizing radiations or chemicals, but may derive from environmental demands which program the organism to alter its hereditary germinal codes. In other words, they are the inheritance of environmentally produced and demanded traits and characteristics outside of natural selection, genetic drift, or isolation. We are referring to the Lamarckian and neo-Lamarckian inheritance of acquired characteristics, but in a modified form in which the characteristics may not be acquired by the parent but rather, the parent produces through environmental demands chemicals which alter the germ plasm, a code which he passes to his progeny. This is a force of evolution. It can be likened to Darwin's paragenes in which he returns to Lamarckian concept to explain the mechanisms of heredity.

Most know that at the same time Darwin was writing, George Mendel had discovered laws of heredity. Here we were dealing primarily with sweet peas and plants, and in later experiments with Drosophila (fruit flies). It was assumed that these laws hold for much of the evolutionary development in higher primates.

There are great differences between species, their modes of action, and their ability to develop in diverse fashion. As Theodious Dobzhansky pointed out, evolution is opportunistic. Therefore, one cannot sit back and say with satisfaction that life and heredity are but a lottery, and in billions of years it was not smart enough to avail itself of directionally advantageous principles. Are we to believe that life is one big roulette wheel in the casino of Monte Carlo? Here the ball rolls in meiosis, providing the physical mechanism for the segregation of alleles, and one comes up with gene combinations, unique, rare, and delightful to behold — all by chance, all by lottery?

Life is a gambling house which extracts no commission. There is no croupier to aid us. There are no shills at the table. Neither is management guilty of having inserted electronic devices beneath the velvet. It is one happy process uninfluenced by environment — spin of the honest wheel of chance.

If this game is true, that modern genetics professes, then you can say nature was asleep, eminently inopportunistic. That nature in its billions of attempts in billions of years, and in its production of the highest primate, could neglect to avail itself of directionally guided, self-hereditary modifications, by environmental demands, is a fantasy. We are told that higher life is a stupid clod that evolves by the production of variated forms through chance. That through lottery, the supreme force becomes selection.

The majority of mutations are bad. Evolutionary progress is made possible by new mutations. One could with logic ask, "If you have more bad than good, why didn't human development go backward instead of forward?" We kept the best mutations — culled out the bad — adapted and evolved.

We are to believe that good genes always win when it comes to evolutionary sweepstakes, even though we have lethal genes and genes that destroy their own propagation. We have genes like hemophilia that ride along in some families, and innumerable bad genes. Bad genes are produced in a terrifically high ratio in comparison to good genes. The good succeed in spite of odds against them.

About anything can produce a mutation — dozens of rays or thousands of chemicals in the germinal cells, excepting their host and their host's body. In this inviolate Goddom of the germinal plasm, the Weismann theory, the independence of the germinal cells from the somatic cells, it is sacrilege to suggest that in the multitudinous opportunities available to genetic code, transformation by the host bearers cannot exist.

Primarily, we are concerned that the greater portion of culture, not its specific details, has been inherited and is transmitted within germinal plasm. Culture is antiquity transmitted and modified by changing environment (in which the forces of Darwinian and Mendelian evolution may act in natural selection and drift). Culture is acting directly through the human body, influencing the germinal codes.

We do not negate the forces of natural selection, drift, isolation or mutation, or the forces of chance. We do say, however, that in man there is a form of evolutionary evolvement which is directed by environmental demands acting upon the host to modify the progeny codes.

E. J. Klegg, in *The Study of Man*, with fairness states, "[The Lamarckian argument] . . . still has its adherents, although most would discount it as being probably untrue and certainly unprovable. This is the theory of the inheritance of acquired characteristics, first propounded by Lamarck (1746-1829)."

Klegg further points out that the idea of acquired characteristics being inherited is attractive and that it would explain, for example, the squatting facets on the ankle bones of human groups who habitually rest in a squatting position. And that the Lamarck argument is weak because it remains an unproven hypothesis.

In the *Descent of Man*, Darwin states the following, "According to the hypothesis of pangenesis, every unit or cell of the body throws off gemmules or undeveloped atoms, which are transmitted to the offspring of both sexes, and are multiplied by self-division. They may remain undeveloped during the early years of life or during successive generations, and their development into units or cells, like those from which they were derived, depends on their affinity for and union with other units or cells previously developed in the due order of growth." Under the laws of inheritance Darwin was speaking of transmission of character (traits).

Not knowing Gregory Mendel, Darwin had difficulty perceiving laws of heredity. Mendel was dealing with rudimentary trait characteristics in peas. Humans will not follow these rules because of their advanced complex structure.

Cells of the body secrete and excrete products of metabolism. There is demand of substances within the bloodstream directed by central intelligence. This commands and senses neural impulses, their needs and conditions. For example, the cells of the upper eyelid both ingress and egress materials and report their status to headquarters, subjecting themselves to orders by many commanders, the autonomic system, as well as the central nervous system.

If we name these forces, demand materials, waste materials, and intelligent assessment, "gemmules," we are on solid physiological tierra. If we say that waste materials of the upper lid, coded secretion, portions of DNA or RNA pass into the bloodstream and influence the developing germinal cells, or that reception by nervous centers create directives passing chemical messages via the plasma which influence the germinal cells, we are facing the problem, namely, that we as individuals do, by our actions, desires, needs and wants, influence the heredity of offspring. We are not simply a blot of tissue transporting germinal cells which vary in characteristics and which produce offspring according to chance.

As early man emigrated to the frozen north and formed the Mongoloid race, it became apparent that he needed extra eye protection from severe northern winters. According to current theories, we could achieve this Mongoloid fold of upper eyelid, increasing the fatty tissue and air space within, by the process of natural selection. That is, a variation, a mutation took place, his offspring were better adapted for survival and, consequently, those of the Caucasoid type eye in the yellow genetic pool perished and the slant-eyed group, proving themselves the fittest, survived.

This is contrary to all those magnificent formulae being exhibited in evolutionary texts today. So flimsy a selection as a fat upper lid could hardly have conferred the right to survival to its bearers. We were selecting hundreds of other traits at the same time — body builds, color of skin, intelligence, hair, fingerprints, etc. Half a million years ago, the Mongoloids had, for example, traits A to Y which they were selecting toward. Now along comes slant eyes, a mutant Z and "demands" he be selected toward. Since all is supposedly a Monte Carlo "spin of the wheel," we have the whole alphabet to juggle with — and, in picking Z for racial permanency, can we negate the others?

The Mongoloid eye is attractive. "Suzie Slanteyes" overwhelmed her male companions who selected toward her. Her more numerous offspring forever after carried her characteristics. This explanation is more plausible than Gregory Mendel's application to humans or Drosophila, the fruit fly's relation to man.

There are too many traits in the few years of recent human evolution to select toward for the game to be a lottery of the sperm. Animals do not survive because of an eye fold, greater body surface, yellow skin, straight hair, variations of intelligence, or of callouses on the buttocks. There is subtle programming of the germinal cells before the reproductive act and during the uterine tenancy. Somatic tissues, the parents before reproduction, and the mother housing the child, can influence DNA and RNA codes of the germinal cells through many mechanisms, from the levels of chemicals within the plasma, their demand or depletion, from the coded direction secreted by neurons.

Cutting the tails off mice in succeeding generations or observing the arm muscles in generation series of blacksmiths for permanent inherited characteristics are faulty experiments. There is insufficient time for observance of the extreme subtleness of evolutionary change. However, many generations of heavy-muscled mesomorphic workers should produce mesomorphs of greater muscular degree in genetic permanency. The continual lactic acid secretion from muscular usage should, by its bloodstream excess, influence the skeletal muscular code of DNA, granting increased numbers of cells to meet future demand.

When one appraises the mutational theory of variation, one asks, "How much?" Did Suzie Slanteyes mutate or complete her Mongoloid eye in one setting from her forebearers? Or perhaps her chain of offspring added a few thousand fat cells each generation? In other words, a fortunate and highly improbable series of mutations down the Mongoloid eye path?

Were Suzie's slant eyes born over hundreds of thousands of years gradually, that is, her eye trait? The cells for a fat eyelid are not the same as for a red or wild eye in Drosophila bombarded by X-rays to alter chromosomes. There was a simple directive being issued to *all* Mongoloids residing in frigid lands, "Hey, fellows, it's cold. Put some fat on that upper lid and don't forget to remind those guys in the basement to pass it on to junior!"

In *Darwin For Today*, by Vicking Compass and Stanley Human, Donald Michie, 1958, described this hypothesis, "It fits some present evidence as germ line heredity does not." And concluded, "I estimate that genetics has about ten years to go before it can claim fully to have caught up with Darwin." "Pangenesis," Darwin's last ambition theory, was published when he was 59 years old. However, he did not visualize sociobiology and culture as a force of natural selection. Some of his interpretations clearly distinguished racial differences of great amount when he noted, "The Fuegians were subhuman and childlike."

Darwin's theory of Pangenesis, however, does visualize a mechanism whereby the organism may modify its germinal cells. From *Variation of Animals and Plants Under Domestication*, 1883, — "Every separate part of the whole organization reproduces itself," and "Units throw off minute granules which are dispersed throughout the whole system . . . like those from which they were originally derived . . . called gemmules. They collect from all parts of the system to constitute the sexual elements."

We had better believe Darwin. Not only does culture and society originate from group Mendelian genetic selective forces, but directly from neurogenic activity and tissue demand altering germinal cells to incorporate codes of social behavior, presaging competition and surviving through cultural fitness. Our culture is regularily registered to our germinal genes. Adverse possession in law derives from our territorial instincts. Wars are men's art by genetic tradition. Animal society is based upon dominance and rank — an innate instinct.

"Hens set up a pecking order in which the dominant animal assumes control of food, roosting places, water and choice of mate. It is clear-cut linear hierarchy in which the alpha animal dominates all — the beta below it, and so on down the line." To scientize the preceding quote, it would read: "Hens have innate codings which prompt them to set up a dictatorial form of government. As with humans, there is only one king, one dictator, one president. Rule by democracy, communism or oligarchy is biologically abnormal."

African Genesis put it, "Man is a predator with an *instinct* to kill, and a greater cultural affinity for the weapon." If wars are learned behavior, hostilities and hatred of nations can be irradicated by the sagacity of education and benign world organization.

On the other hand, if men war because they are basically killers, it is genetically programmed, our parents and their parents before them have been selected in the process of evolution because they killed their brothers, like Caan killed Abel, and because they enjoyed the fruits of death and intraspecial conflict, then the force of this powerful bellicose coding must be reckoned with.

Aggressiveness is one of the cultural characteristics of man. There are hundreds of others. Our approach toward understanding these characteristics is dependent upon our understanding of that which is inheritable, instinctive behavior, and that which is learned and cultural. A genetic determination does not need to exhibit itself in specific patterns. Nervous tissue is so complicated that coded chromosomal directives will produce tendencies toward gross action patterns rather than laying down specific blueprints. We speak of these as instincts, the genetic basis whereupon culture originates.

Coon, a noted sociologist, comes close to supporting the Lamarckian theory. "Rabbits under intolerable social pressure stimulate their hypothalmus to affect the pituitary which reduces gonadotropins. That diminishes the production of eggs, sperm and sex steroids, and even produces deformed sperm. Adrenals as well are overstimulated, and the end result is stunting, altered sex ratio at birth and increased susceptibility to disease."

Crowding produces stunting. If, in the development of the somatic cells there is alteration by the aforementioned mechanisms, then in the developing sperm or egg there are the same forces at action in the building of master code element. How can there be amino acid code changes acting through hormones in the DNA development of somatic cells and not also in DNA code systems in germinal cells? Both processes are under the same laboratory conditions. In crowding experimental colonies, we shall find evolutionary change in the direction of stunting, not from selective value but from the parental direct germinal cell alteration of the master code. This is an acquired characteristic derived from environment and usage, not produced by a slot-machine choice of variables.

Dwarfing other aspects of the human body is the mind with its ten-billion-odd neurons, elaborate connecting systems, perceptional fields, memory banks, action command headquarters, associational areas, and generator demonstrated by brainwaves. One other component, most important, is innate behavioral directives that have been laid down over millions of years of tested evolution. Begin with germinal coding by the union of egg and sperms with the cerebral blueprint residing in chromosomes (being nothing more than a sequence of four amino acids). We must pay tribute to these minisculine molecules which structure genes with directives, all in terms of mushy, watery, organic chemical process.

This minute field office, a work of fantastic complexity, contains successful instructions garnered through millions of years. For so massive a task, many centers are constructed with broad range response rather than specific effect. Within this mass resides a directive history of the evolution. These are neurogenes. They are the architects. It is the function of neurogenes to conduct the orchestra of life. Neurons are not replaceable. Once they have been riveted into their positions, they are the masters. Within their domain is an immense network of instructions. A birth is nothing more than that which has been provided by DNA blueprint. Knowledge pounded into the structure may modify it to some extent, but that is lip service to an established, well-fixed fact.

Neurogenes — we use this rather than neurons (because it denotes granted authority of culture to the genes) — have the elements of society and culture recorded within them by natural selection, social selection, sectional selection, and parents-genesis. From the instructions of evolution the individual at birth has been slotted into his occupational niche. He has been programmed a strong breeder, a homosexual, or a mesomorphic worker. Too much attention has been paid to what we should be than to what we are predestined to be. From the moment the child enters kindergarten to the day he receives his occupation, society has engaged in a winnowing process. Educational or economic sieving of the individual is slotting geneticized codes into spiraled and squared holes. Genius and success derives from codes, not coddling. Not only do individuals and races vary widely in thousands of genes and physical traits, but they vary vastly in neurogenic compositions which prompt the expression of intelligence, temperament, drive, affection, dominance, and loyalty, including substantials as pain, taste or vision.

From an article in *Clinical Pharmacology and Therapeutics*, Vol. XIV, No. 4, on drugs that may affect the fetus adversely. Those cases, such as the famous Thalidomide cases where there were limb deficiencies, were listed as "aminopterin, methotrexate, progestogens, estrogens, androgens, barbiturates, aspirin, phenytoin, dexamphetamine, antacids, nicotinamide, iron." Estrogens and androgens given to the mother early in pregnancy can cause masculinization of the female fetus, notably clitoral enlargement and labial fusion. Although this occurs in less than 1% as related in the article by John O. Forfar, et al, it has extreme significance in the field of evolution.

Estrogens are normally produced hormones in the female. They undergo varying quantitative levels. Androgens, although not typically produced by females, may be produced under certain conditions. So from the level and influence of these hormones, we can expect influence upon the offspring. One could say that the production of hormones, even though they do affect the offspring, is not a factor which was acquired by the parent, but rather was passed to the parent by the germinal code. The question is, can human beings change their hormonal structures? Yes. Stress in the thyroid and environmental adaptation with other hormones will cause them to adjust. This accommodation can be transmitted to the building embryo. From M. Seip, University of Oslo, we see that drugs given for epilepsy in pregnancy affect the fetus adversely. Malformations are registered. Drugs as barbiturates, primidone, and diphenylhydanton, seriously affect the fetus.

If drugs affect somatic tissues, we know that they affect germinal tissues. In these offspring, we should expect to see alterations and mutations in their progeny patterns. What effect repeated ingestion of hallucinatory drugs by South American Indians influenced their germinal plasm and consequent evolution is yet to be detailed. Consider the ingestion of hallucinatory agents as an acquired characteristic. The influence upon heredity is profound.

Reba M. Hill, et al, recites 20 authors reporting on 1600 infants who showed heart and skeletal anomalies and central nervous system malformations of 1.3%. Arthur Herbst related how the use of stilbesterol by the pregnant mother produced carcinoma in the genital tract of the female offspring. A study from the Free University of Berlin stated that anti-epileptic drugs taken during pregnancy have been followed by children with abnormalities.

We are speaking of drugs which influence cells during pregnancy. These will produce germinal cell mutations, as well as somatic mutations. The question at issue is not manmade drugs, but thousands of substances which occur in nature that were ingested by man in evolution. Offhand we could speak of dozens of flowers, hundreds of seeds which contain poisonous and chromosomal alterative substances. Is one to believe that the majority of women were expert toxicologists and were able to distinguish poisonous mushrooms or berries from the non-poisonous ones? Outside lethal substances which confront man, there are thousands that are merely toxic and would be sufficient to produce chromosomal abberations.

Flora and fauna abounded in highly varying amounts. Isolated races were ingesting chemicals which would produce mutations in a greater amount than known evolutionary forces, providing the choice for natural selection. Little has been done with the subtle effects of natural drug substances acting upon the mother during pregnancy to produce abnormalities observable in the F_1 generation and germinal code alterations in subsequent ones.

Pica, that unusual phenomena in pregnant women that prompts them to seek out rare, exotic and unusual foods that they ordinarily would shun, may be a factor not only in providing the elements for the healthy newborn, but may be a methodology of altering germ plasm as it develops. Once the male sperm in the female ova have united, we cannot say that all systems have been finally spoken for a blueprint. During the life of a fetus, as the germinal cells develop, there is ample opportunity for environmental forces to redraft the schema.

To a God anatomist charged with architecturalizing the body, nothing would be more absurd than to slap a sack externally to the mold and place within it treasure for progeny. It is absurd to expose unnecessarily the testicle to injury and incumberance in the male when it is not done with the female whose ovaries remain inside. One explanation given for such haphazard carpentry is that the sperm needs coolness of the outside to survive. This is false because the regulatory mechanism keeps all tissues at the approximate temperature. Further, it would be no problem for nature to adapt the male cells to the same temperature as the female cells if in reality temperature is a factor for the extraordinary situs.

If you walk into an organic chemistry laboratory, you may notice some strange contraption gently jiggling flasks of solutions to aid their reaction. From the manufacture of beer to soup, agitation is utilized in integrating elements. If you happen to walk in back of a dominant male dog, one of lustful quality, you will be amazed at the motion, orbital and otherwise, devoted to the globular custodians of the sex cells.

Being the chemical laboratory they are, the agitation of the testicles is probably an important component in the process known as reduction-division. It gives opportunity for the amino acids to change location. It may be a far more important factor in making the sperm being manufactured extremely sensitive to environmental factors and thereby aiding inheritance of acquired characteristics or direct utility into the germinal code.

Theodosius Dobzhansky, a famous geneticist, when he gets outside the realm of science, becomes prejudiced. This may be a result of his European philosophy and basic desire that he wishes humans to be regarded as equals. In his *Heredity in the Nature of Man*, he states, "In some societies with such class or caste inequalities, a belief is widely held, by the privileged as well as by the under-privileged, that the social stratification reflects biological, genetic differences in human quality. The class privilege is hereditary, so the argument goes, because human ability is also hereditary."

There is no question that class privilege is inheritable. When one mixes germinal cells of higher-bred humans who display social, economic, professional and intellectual superiority, there is a mathematical demand that such attributes will continue to their progeny more than the working class or proletariat. Class derives from ability. Ability is based upon superior genes which are inherited in proportion to the quality products entering into the germinal contract. Human inequality is in any city on the face of the earth if one is to observe the privileges, wealth and position occurring to its various members.

Galton's 1869 book entitled, *Hereditary Genius*, is cited where the eminent people of England beget eminent people in far greater proportions than in the general population. Conversely, Dugdal's study in 1875 of the Jukes showed that "no-good" families continued "no-goods," spewing out criminals, prostitutes and paupers generation after generation. In 1912, Goddard followed with the Kallikak study in which a bad citizen of the revolutionary days propagated a chain of descendants majorily loaded with feeble minds, prostitutes, illegitimates, alcoholics, and immorals. Dobzhansky derides this social Darwinism — attributing social problems such as crimes and poverty to defective and inferior genes, contending that it is not subject to verification. Perhaps eminent persons born paupers would not have become prominent?

Again and again, liberals fearing for their own skin, social position, or acting from a sense of inferiority complex, will not face the writing on the wall. It is not the truth of the proverb that "genius will out" that demonstrates the genetic nature of society. Rather, it is hundreds of studies that show indisputably that individuals, subracial groups and races, given ample and full opportunity, cannot compete with others whose genes are superiorily programmed.

Examine the admission files of those that enter the university, those happy, hopeful people all given equal educational opportunities, compared to the final graduation records to see who had done what and why, and if the major factor was opportunity or genes. Or even to carry the study further and follow the graduates for a decade or so into their life situations and assess their contributions.

There is always a hassel when one speaks of superior or inferior genes, because the bottom line is what human quality or trait is most valued. There is little question when one considers musical or artistic ability, academic or intellectual prowess, political skill and economic success, leadership and rank or even cooking. Where the problem arises is in the more obscure areas of human conduct such as morality, religion, family management, truth and honesty, loyalty, sacrifice, tolerance, samaritanism. These attributes are extremely hard to weigh in conjunction with the specific traited ones. Is it better to have an honest but poor man or a wealthy scoundrel? Is a presidential dictator who leads his nation into profitless, bloody, popular and worthless wars preferred to an honest and undeceitful president?

Many studies have been done concerning identical twins who were reared apart under different environmental opportunities. They practically all illustrate that IQ changes very little between them, or that their levels of achievement differ markedly. This indicated that environment and opportunity play small roles in achievement. Heredity is "the dice of destiny."

In the formation of the giraffe's long neck it was not stretching the muscles, as Lamarck imagined, but a call for an additional vertebrae, as six fingers in polydactyly. Once the bone blueprint is processed, all other structures, nerves, muscles and tendons must accommodate to it and rearrange their own code alteration in germinal plasm. If T_3 vertebrae genes are called upon to duplicate themselves in germinal composition, then F_1, with the new additional vertebrae, will accommodate all other tissues to its necessity. F_1 will then process these new extended tissues to additional coding in the germinal plasm of F_1, so that when F_2 is joined, not only a new vertebrae will be permanently added to the genetic code of the animal, but the tissue adjustments consequent to it will also be part of the new drafting. Dominance in the non-new vertebrate mate would sweep the new adaptation away unless the new addition was dominant.

Our sexual selection toward blondes is sexual competition. Blonde, as relief from black, could be chosen by a great number, much in the same way some prefer vanilla or chocolate. So the range in red and chestnut, curly or straight, is evolutionary bait to the mate. Green hair or skin has never succeeded, for in man's experience, the majority of that which was green was unripe.

Francis Johnston makes the point that genetic variability is modified only when there is concomitant phenotypic variability, contending that natural selection is meaningless unless one has envisioned stress interacting with different phenotypes. In other words, phenotypes of anatomy or physiology must be challenged by the environment to fit themselves in best adaptation. When they do so, they request genes through selection of progeny. If the genes give you a wide-nostriled nose, then they can only be eliminated or altered by the wide-nostriled nose being selected against under changing environmental pressures. We do not like this approach because new genes originate by mutations and pre-birth parental pressures acting on germinal cells.

One may say if alteration does take place in the genotype, evolution will not support it unless it fits into advantageous adaptation. But we do not have to always adapt advantageously. It is too mathematically correct. Sometimes we simply pick up things or retain them in way of passage, such as the appendix, tonsils and coccyx-buttock obesity. While majorily everything in the body has a specific advantageous function, there are mistakes which persist as recessive genes. These range from Meckel's diverticulum to a diabetic, to male breasts.

Besides bacterial, living predators and parasites, living forms that attack the human body, mistakes by mechanical genetic errors are due to reaction to the environment. When speaking of achondroplasia, which produces dwarfs, even though it should be heavily selected against by all genetic rules, Monach found a generally constant frequency from one generation to the other, indicating that natural selection was not operating. The steady frequency of the achondroplasia allele was being maintained by recurrent mutation. Dwarfs over the time of recorded history have, among other things, been objects of amusement, good luck, entertainment, and are still employed as clowns. Would social genes have enough pressures to keep reinstating these delightful comics into the social register for strictly theatrical purposes or did they have valued qualities in entering and exploring cave shelters and burrows?

Not only does evolution give us variability in occupational and hierarchical types, it gives us discrete forms, tall, short, fat, thin, weak, strong, as well as brilliant and stupid, to weave into the social animal.

An interesting gene is PTC - testing. Some individuals possess the ability to taste the chemical and others not. That is about as far as the science goes. Yet, at one time in our ancestry there may have been a chemical or related taste within some extinct plant that was essential to avoid.

Allen Hughton Brodrick is another author who puts down the inheritance of acquired characteristics. In his text, *Man and His Ancestry*, he states, ". . . yet if one ventures to suggest that Jews have been circumcised for thousands of years but still little Jewish boys are born with foreskin, one is met with some such indefinite remarks as that 'the time hasn't been long enough.' "

This is the standard rebuttal. There is something more to be said of the experiment. It is too shallow in depth. To remove is one thing but to order, demand, aspire to and relate to by a tissue component over a period of time is quite another. Here the force is positive; a chemical change, not an absence.

Micho Titiev, in the *Science of Man*, diagrams the short stocky type of Andean Indian who lives at very high altitudes. He relates that they have seven quarts of blood compared to the five quarts in Indians who live at low altitudes. Hemoglobin appears in the highlander to be almost double. This he attributes to biological adaptation.

Roughly speaking, let us say 10,000 years ago, the Mongoloids that came across the Bering Straits commenced to disperse themselves in this portion of South America, giving them roughly about 500 generations to change their codes in their germinal cells. By natural selection it would mean that the unadaptably-gened children should die off before reproduction was possible, and those gened for high volume of blood and hemoglobin would survive. This neat trick might be accomplished, according to the orthodox interpretation, if some fortunate mutations appeared to manufacture more blood and more hemoglobin and, of course, accepted by their hosts. The problem of not having the increased blood was a lethal thing, killing the low-blooded individuals who climbed to the highlands before they could procreate.

Mass extermination of low blood and selection toward the full-blooded type may have been out of the much-taunted classic rules as Hardy-Weinberg. What complicates and renders the whole thing miraculous, without the use of inherited characteristics, is that selection never plays one chip at a time. There are hundreds of items which are being selected toward or being rejected — all the way from diseases predispositions to sexual gimmicks, to food assimilation.

To say that merely hemoglobin and blood volume was the paramount item for adaptation states little concerning the size, muscular distribution, cardiac readjustment, respiratory expansion, and many other facets of physiology which must concomitantly adjust to the increased blood volume.

What did happen was that the body commenced calling on more blood, more hemoglobin, greater respiratory area, and a more adaptable build to house these fluid dynamic changes. Darwin's paragene is as good as any example to prompt various chemicals within the circulating media to influence the germinal cells to the higher quantities needed in the mountains. Thus we have a prime example of inheritance of acquired characteristics.

Man is one of the few mammals that cannot synthesize vitamin C. Why did we drop this excellent bit of chemical know-how? We would succumb to scurvy as we radiated out into northern climates, where the source is scarce in winter. The easiest answer is that it is simply excess baggage. What we do not use we cast off. But how does selection work when it is exactly the opposite? Those not able to obtain a sufficient external supply of vitamin C to combat a disease would be rapidly selected against and eliminated. Here we have to return to the Lamarckian theory. There is evidently within the structure automatic eliminating mechanisms which have nothing to do with selection but are related to the inheritance of acquired characteristics.

Out of millions of years of man's existence there was sufficient vitamin C in his diet. There was no conscious call for it and, therefore, there was no necessity for persistence. If vitamin C never existed at any time within the antecedents of man, that is another question. What deduces is that unless there is continuous re-enforcement to those processes we have, they are eliminated in non-selective fashion.

From the book, *Reproduction, The Family and Social Structure* — "The primate placenta promotes optimum conditions for the developing embryo. . . . Another resultant advantage is the improved transmission of antibodies in the blood, which pass from the mother to the fetus and will immunize the newborn against disease. . . . When the blood proteins of the fetus are different from those of the mother, antibodies may develop in the mother's blood, 'protecting' her from the alien blood of the fetus, but in turn passing into the fetal bloodstream to cause clotting. . . . This dangerous effect, known as isoimmunization, probably tends to reduce genetic variability in blood proteins by removing variants from the breeding population."

Supportive features of the inheritance of acquired characteristics we deduced in this statement. Antibodies from the mother do influence the child's immulogical system. Mothers are by no means equal in quality of antibodies found in her body. In the process of pre-delivery life, actions, experiences and preferences provide qualities which influence the composition of offspring. The importance of pure parental transmission of acquired characteristics is emphasized.

Thus, a pre-1492 new world Indian mother conveyed a relatively low immunity to tuberculosis and a high immunity to syphilis. It was the opposite on the other side of the Atlantic. Consequently, when the two diseases were traded by exploration, there were severe dislocations in offspring. There was no weeding out the dangerous unprotecting genes. There was an actual transferral from generation to generation of immunological genes that had become the acquired experience of the mother. Gradually, the Indian became more resistant to tuberculosis and the European more resistant to syphilis — not through the slow process of natural selection, but from activating immunological forces in the offspring to be passed on to their offspring, by innate codes.

The second significant observance is the mother protecting herself from alien blood of the fetus, to remove the offspring to decrease genetic variability. Iso-immunization, in this instance, may be thought to be related to the supposed unchangeable germ plasm chain. Yet one must remember the question of immunization, experience and challenge by the environment is the prime producer of the immunology we carry. The DNA chain is selfish, and self-preservation of the genetic pool is a strong goal. By this mechanism of fetal rejection, we see the practice of racism.

A Rutgers' scientist, George Pieczenik, detailed a new view of evolution. He suggested that natural selection could occur at molecular levels before the organism develops. "The DNA sequences exist to protect themselves and their own formation. It's not the organism that counts. DNA sequences will also resist outside attempts to recode them. . . ."

To interpret this we would refer you back to the straight line of evolution and the great difficulty in varying its course. But there is a further soundness in Pieczenik's speculation. If natural selection can occur before the organism develops in the germinal cells of the fetus, and does not occur as Darwin maintained in selecting out those that superiorily adapted and left successful offspring, then truly Pandora's box has opened.

It is as if Lamarckism and the inheritance of acquired characteristics can be substantiated. For Lamarckism is nothing more than the molecular alteration of the genetic codes carried within the parents' germinal cells during their lifetime. That DNA sequence is so resistant to change explains the great amount of species extinction occurring in the past, being unable to adapt properly to changing environment. It also explains the scientist's difficulty in proving the ever-so-subtle changes which occur under parental-germinal alteration.

During reduction-division, when a pair of chromosomes representing father and mother divide in random fashion so that they reduce from 46 chromosomes to 23 in the germinal cells, this permits the sperm and ova coming together, composed of the normal 46 chromosomes. In this selection, nothing new, changed, or selective comes to the reduced germinal cell than that which was already present in the original cell.

Suppose Lamarckism is working and it slants the favorable characteristics toward one of the reduced cells — the best taken from parental chromosomes to enhance a new evolutionary form — would leave the partner of the reduction-division weaker.

Crossing over, preliminary to reduction-division in which chromosomes exchange sections, that is, shuffling the father and mother chromosome pair parts, is a magnificent time for forces to act in Lamarckian selection to produce a weighted "good" seed. It is inconceivable with spermatozoa each is equal in potential. Produced in incredible numbers, hundreds of millions, this must be an act of ulterior motive in variance.

We have a strange notion that mutations occur at random in the germinal cells to give human variance. Most scientists are appalled at the thought that germinal cells can be altered through a mechanism related to human experiences. If so, nature has to be as cuckoo as a clock to accept chance or mechanical error as a purposive scheme for individual variance. Over hundreds of millions of years, with all the cleverness one must attribute to evolutionary development, it is hardly logical to neglect such a simple and marvelous avenue of biological change. It is merely too subtle at this period in our science to be seen clearly.

Dunn, in *Heredity and Evolution in Human Population*, states that the definition of race is clear and unambiguous to the evolutionary biologist, being namely, "A population which differs from other populations in the frequency of its genes."

In spite of the hysterical overtures, race will be more specifically defined and categorized as science progresses. We will not just note the color of the skin, texture of the hair or gross physical features. We will be able to evaluate and catalog thousands of racial differences which reside within the nervous tissue in such areas as intelligence, ability, drive, emotion, love, insensitivity, and even cunning and theft predisposition.

Dunn states, "There is some evidence that selection in the long run acts on complexes of genes, on whole genotypes, rather than on the effects of single alleles."

This is obvious, because if we desired an extra vertebra it would do little good to settle for a transverse process. Evolution must jump according to physiological and anatomical body units, other genes having the accommodation such as the spinal cord and ligamentous attachments to stretch into place.

In his book, *Nature of Man's Fate*, Garrett Hardin derides the paintpot theory of heredity. He cites a Fleming Jenkin article in the *North British*

Review (1867), which in effect stated, "Place one white man on an isolated island populated entirely by blacks. Make him king, give him a dozen wives and, in the many generations that follow, the semi-whiteness of his off-spring will be so diluted that it will be completely lost, just as a drop of white paint in a barrel of black." Hardin further states, "This theory [hereditary blending] we find embalmed in such phrases as 'quarter-breed,' 'octoroon,' etc. We know that it is false, but Jenkins and Darwin did not." But is it false? All we have to do is open our eyes. Mate a pure black with a pure white and you most certainly will get a half-breed. (Let us stick to color as the trait to consider.) Mate them in either direction; that is, the half-breeds toward the pure blacks, or toward the pure whites and, in a number of generations, black or white is again dominant. There is no law which demands when white is injected into black or black into white, that these genes should be carried forward, retained and stored in a chemical closet to be pulled out one day when they have adaptive value.

Skin color, it has been shown, requires a great many genes acting to-gether. The simplified Mendelian laws of heredity do not hold, otherwise after the first generation, any white mating to the half-colored would produce a pure white, which is definitely not the case.

If Mendel's simplified smooth or wrinkled pea experiments were applied, we would find that out of the 20,000,000 American black community, which contains 30% of white genes, would pour a torrent of pure whites. Colored inheritance, white-black, does blend. If only ten to twenty genes are acting, then we have ten to twenty units to mix. That, in all justice, is hereditary blending — and is also quantitative.

In the same chapter, Hardin relates Darwin's theory of pangenesis — "Crudely summarized, the theory asserts that all parts of the body throw off into the circulating fluids some particles called 'pangenes,' which are gathered together to form the hereditary elements of the sperm or egg. The pangenes are not necessarily constant, but can be mofidied in a directional way by environmental conditions that affect all the parts of the body."

Let us go directly to the variation of animals and plants under domesti-cation by Darwin. In Chapter 25 of *Provisional Hypothesis of Pangenesis*, he states, "I assume that the units (cells) throw off minute granules which are dispersed throughout the whole system; that these, when supplied with proper nutriment, multiply by self-division and are ultimately developed into units like those from which they were originally derived. These granules may be called gemmules. They are collected from all parts of the system to con-stitute the sexual elements, and their development in the next generation forms a new being; but they are likewise capable of transmission in a dor-mant state to future generations and may then be developed."

As presented, the theory is nonsense, as was a great many other things that Darwin wrote. He seemed to take reference with extreme naivete, such as the spur of a cock being inserted into the ear of an ox, to live eight years, grow to nine inches, and weigh almost a pound, or the tail of a pig grafted into its back to re-acquire sensibility, or the guinea pigs who gnawed off their toes and then had offspring deficient in at least thirteen instances on the corresponding feet.

There was one thing that Darwin did accomplish in the theory of Pangenesis in that he called attention to the possible transferral of somatic trait characteristics to the germinal cells. One of the difficulties in proving that transferral of traits acquired by parents to offspring is that we could never expect a totality of the influenced trait, only a small portion. Darwin cites circumcision in Jews and that the inheritance of such is not passed on.

A paleobiologist, Steven Stanley of John Hopkins, in an article in *Proceedings of the National Academy of Science*, disputed Darwin's theory. He stated, "Natural selection among individuals within species does not operate fast enough to account for the overall course of evolution. There is considerable evidence that new species arose largely through the geographical isolation of small groups of existing species."

Stanley cited Darwin's gradual evolution, countering it with the almost negative evolution of lungfish unchanged for two hundred million years. And, on the other hand, he pointed to the rapid increase in mammal species after the dinosaur extinction at the end of the Mesozoic era. One notes another mechanism of evolutionary rate change and species origin when an ecological niche becomes vacant and no change when conditions remain relatively the same. These varying speeds in evolution would tend to support parental influence upon the germinal cells.

German measles (rubella) is a disease producing birth malformations. How do we know that this disease does not produce traits? Diseases which challenge the mother to produce alterations in the fetus may be an evolutionary form for variance.

In European populations the incidence of color blindness is about 8% in males and less than ½% in females. It is an X link recessive condition.

E. J. Klegg, in *The Study of Man*, states, "It is difficult to see what selective advantage is possessed by the color-blind person." He dismissed the notion that animal camouflage would be breached to advantage. We should look for color-blind utility within the social order. It would be interesting to know what is the average social position of color-blinded individuals and how their intelligence compares with the color-sighted population.

Two great giants of evolutionary science are Lamarck, who stressed behavior to a point of considering it the sole effective cause of evolution; and Darwin, who saw no reason to question the Lamarckian belief of direct influence of behavior in evolution. We are, indeed, brave modern scientists to refute their penetrating analyses. Darwin contributed the theory of natural selection to the process, and to come later were migration, genetic drift, plus mutation. It was Gregor Mendel who discovered the modern theory of heredity.

There are many forces acting in evolution. Far too simplistic are the mathematical formulae approaches to the evolutionary process. Evolution is not amenable to statistics in higher animals where the prime consideration is how many divergent directions can be resolved under natural selection, which operates on mutational change.

With explosive force the cerebellum came into being. This remarkable neurological mass at the base of the brain that permits man to stand erect on two stilts and not fall flat on his face, to relay messages and integrate them, and to contract a muscle pulling aft, sternwise or laterally, is a great feat of physiology. There is no problem with a four-legged animal.

One of the most constant increments in evolvement has been the brain. This came about for many reasons. As man came out of the trees to become erect with bi-pedal locomotion, he needed fancy gadgetry. What is more marvelous than watching a ballet dancer pirouette, a runner sprint, a man balancing himself on one leg or even a tall, slender girl walk? Compare this with deer in an orchard which, after having eaten the lower apples, must stand awkwardly on hind legs to obtain the uppermost apples. Or consider the dog which cannot manage to sit up. Or regard the cerebellum ataxic man ravaged by syphilis in a mental institution who can only shuffle about. It is no small feat to poise gracefully 200 pounds of human body on two poded rods known as legs and feet. Try standing a post-mortem body up — even against a wall.

A fantastic amount of wiring, jerking of the lower members of a series of muscle motors and pulleys is coordinated in a computerized center of the cerebellum to see to it that an erect stance is maintained, thus accounting for man's large cerebellum.

Speech gave tremendous dimension. Now there was the ability for communication, for abstract thought, and for a more complex societal development.

From the beginning of the Pliocene, 13,000,000 million years ago, the changes from ramapithecus, our possible ancestor, to the hominidae was fantastic. Here, all that goes with running, upright stance, complete change of skeletal structuring, the development of the hands and arms, the increase in speech and brain capacity, all that is indigenous to higher thought — transpired in, say, a million generations. No one could seriously believe that all these processes of extreme genetic alteration could take place in a forward direction in adapting to the varying ecological niches by the expedient of natural "survival of the fittest" under random mutation.

A million times is not enough without a directing force. To change codes involving the lumbar vertebrae and curvature would involve tens of thousands of selections toward the upright direction. No mutation was made overnight which produced wide variation toward the desired result. It could have by present evolutionary theory never evolved at all. If we relied strictly on selective pressures, we could, in each of five thousand generations, suddenly rear up our vertebral column, the distance of one millimeter would have no selective value were it not for the fact that our ape forebearers were desperately attempting to see above the grass of the savanna and run fast enough to evade enemies or capture prey, and were transmitting continuously the master scheme necessary to their germinal codings.

It is tempting to believe sexual selection plays a large role in the evolutionary process. 90% of males covet 10% - nay 5%, of the younger, better-built, more pulcritudinous females. Covetnous is subrosa today, yet in the past it was more openly proclaimed. Here we have a paradox. The homeliest misshapen and fork-tongued women have a way of getting married, having babies and even more offspring, perhaps, than their more attractive colleagues.

The idea that trends may occur without relationship to natural selection is labeled "orthogenesis" — that is, evolution proceeding in a straight line. Some say that fossil records support this, while most paleoanthropologists reject it. Still, how can there be other than long straight lines in evolution? If so, we would have tremendous numbers of deviat species within the primates. The straight line is achieved because all are striving for the same ecological maximum opportunity.

Theodosius Dobzhansky states that, "A few years ago, one of the outstanding living mathematicians sent me a long and closely argued private letter in which he urged that a combination of many gene mutations adding up to such an organ is so absurdly improbable that we have to suppose that organic evolution is guided by a deity." Dobzhansky evades the argument, charging that to build an organ is not the same as modifying existing structure. What both neglected to see is alteration of an organ by Lamarckism.

Gaylord Simpson, in *Organisms and Molecules in Evolution*, states, "There must be some sort of feedback from the organism environment interaction into DNA and, hence, into the other molecules. There are, as is well known, innumerable feedback mechanisms at the molecule level itself, and many or most of these are responsive to interactions with the environment." This is what we have been saying, yet the author explains it away. Evolutionists have fear of being labeled "Lamarckists" or supporters of the inheritance of acquired characteristics. They negate any gem that could support it.

Genetic foundations of many types of behavior is widely recognized today. Fuller and Thompson, 1960: Hall, 1951. Propensities for certain behavior are inherited. This, in itself, is evidence of the huge mass of evolutionary traits which must be forwarded by genes. Never could this come about on a natural selection basis. Germinal behavioral genes in most all instances would originate from behavioral patterns of parents; natural selection and mutation playing a minor role. Lennenberg states, "The basis for language capacity might well be transmitted genetically." If language and behavioral traits are transmitted genetically, why would it be odd for human classes to be transmitted genetically — for dominance and subordinance to arrive by similar genetic coding?

One mechanism in support of Lamarckism is to alter the genetic code by running. To run a greater amount than one's parents, the ecology progressively demanding more running, dead cells in the process could circulate their segment coding for incorporation into developing germinal cells. These showers of DNA coding produced by use would have a tendency to evolutionary evolvement greater than those individuals in which the process was in relative disuse. This is Lamarckism and how mesomorphs may be produced.

Homo habilis, at roughly two million years ago, had a brain capacity of 680 cc. Compare him with modern man with a brain capacity of 1500 cc., containing half a billion neurons. If we assume that evolution is a continuum relatively uniform — and further, that the number of new neurons needed over this epoch would be around a quarter of a billion, then we would need to add to man's brain capacity 125 neurons per year.

Since we do not develop new neurons during our lifetime, we would have to add 2000 neurons for each generation. Tell me how 2000 neurons of an average, over the era of two million years, or one-eighth millionth change in the brain — "That nobility in reason, infinite in facilities, in form and moving, how express and admirable, in action how like an angel, in apprehension how like a god; the beauty of the world, the paragon of animals" (Shakespeare) — could even possibly from generation to generation be acted upon by natural selection or survival of the fittest? What is being said is that according to modern evolution, natural selection could not possibly operate on a person who had a one-eighth-million neuron capacity advantage over his rival clansman.

To read this book you have probably exasperationally exhausted 2,000 neurons, the quota advance for your life. This would place you in no specific evolutionary advantage over your fellows. It is estimated that in the last two million years our brain size increased by 1000 cc., or 1 cc. since the birth of Christ. Is 1 cc. within but 130 generations going to provide selective factors? Consider for a moment — if the brain itself evolves at less than a drop a century, how can it be disproven by experiments that we do not evolve through acquired traits from our parents through their germinal cell transformations? To demonstrate Lamarckism, experimentation over an enormous span of time has to be undertaken.

Hulton, in *Darwinism and Lamarckism*, 1899, makes a point concerning evolutionary progression and retrogression. We tend to view evolution as a progressive process, natural selection weeding out the unfit, as the survivors come up with newer affective physiological apparati.

Suppose we no longer need strong oppositional muscle in the hand for hanging from branches, a tail to balance, or body hair and abundant pigment. To go into reverse and delete a bodily process we already have involves adjusting through natural selection. It is too much to ask both forward and reverse evolution from selection alone. Surely we got rid of our tails, but not from a faulty ability to compete and survive. We had no use for them. Such information was referred to the germinal cells which gradually deleted the tail — not overnight, but within the span of millions of years. How could 1/8-inch of tail more or less effect survival by natural selection, especially when very important selective factors such as larger brain, upright stance and stereoscopic color vision are vying for favor? The reason is obvious — use. It is a feedback mechanism.

Before Mendel was recognized, Hulton, in 1899, said, "Physiochemical forces effect, in time, the germ cells and those changes thus produced become variations capable of being transmitted to future generations. These compete with variations acquired by the ancestors. These variations may become definite through repetition and are controlled by the principle of selection, sometimes aided by use-inheritance."

Thomas Huxley, in speeches on *Origin of Species*, circa 1880, mentions in the West Coast of Africa there is something so singularly different in the constitution of the white man and black that "the malarias which do not hurt the black at all, cut off and destroy the white, thus you see there would have been a selective operation performed." Today we know that this is due to the sickle cell genes possessed by the Negro. The white migrated from the blacks a few hundred thousand years ago. There was a rapid selection toward the sickle cell genes necessary for African survival. Or did the whites, as well, have the sickle cell genes and lose them as they went north?

This gene is clearcut in function, undoubtedly resulting from selection because of the lethalness of the disease. Use had little effect. Malaria has been around for a long time on the African continent. The blacks, radiating north, carried the sickle cell genes with them. As they developed into white Caucasoids, they lost the gene through disuse — not natural selection — because there is not that much disadvantage in the hererozygote form of the disease. How was it lost? Darwin's gemmules of the sickle cell genes were not reinforcing the germinal gene codes. Therefore, the inheritance of an acquired characteristic provided negative non-promptings to sickle cell genes resulting in its elimination in northmen.

Within woman, until her germinal cells are mature, from age 14 to 18 (the menarche) there are limitless opportunities for chemicals and physical agents to rearrange the structures of the DNA and RNA codes. Thalidomide taken during pregnancy can produce severely deformed babies. Why, then, in millions of years, did nature not evolve her subtlest form of evolution, shaping the code to the measure of the time instead of a blind, nonsensical, numerical game of chance? The germinal cells are bathed in the woman's blood which contains thousands of chemicals. Differences in demands or excesses of circulating bodies cannot but alter gene formation.

Blacksmith beget blacksmith? Of course they do if the woman is hard-laboring before her menarche and during her pregnancy, and the blacksmith, likewise, is hard at labor. But do not expect the offspring to be born with a heavily-developed right bicep. Rather, look for mesomorphic offspring much as Carrel describes the worker class.

To compare us with drosophila, we are far more complex, advanced and longer-living. For nature not to alter germinal cells in 18 years and the period of pregnancy in the female; for 15-20 years prior to sexual contact in the male; for nine months each in their own uterine sojourn, a waiting game is played, passive, inactive, unchangeable, and is contrary to the laws of life.

Imagine the presexual lifetime of the boy and girl together, 30 years in total, their maternal intrauterine time, 1½ years, and the uterine time of the offspring 9 months, 33 years more or less, the formative code being buffeted by plasma and blood, ever changing temperature, radiation and movement, and this celestial code remains pristine, unaltered — one quanine doesn't locate on the adenine position. For this to pass, isolation of the code from its plasma washings would be to admit that nature is indeed stupid and unavailing of opportunity.

Evolutionists state that cultural evolution is not genetic in nature — that ideas, inventions, traditions, laws and customs are not hereditary. Such composites of culture must derive through conditioning, training, and learning. Two evolutions — one is changing pattern of the body and mind; this is organic — gene structure changes are a part of it; it is physical, an evolvement of tissue. And the other, cultural evolution, is represented in our progress from a wilderness animal to a tool and fire-user — from hunting to agriculture — from tribes to nations.

No one disagrees that with man's organic development there developed sytems of conduct which he passed from father to son. Witness the ten commandments — Thou shalt not kill, steal, commit adultery. These are a few rules within some societies that were culturally formulated over the years — respected and honored generation after generation. However, much of cultural evolution such as belief in religion, war, promiscuity, delinquency, food habits, etc. are not merely abstractions passed by teaching and learning, but are genetically determined.

Scientists cling to the belief that acquired characteristics cannot be inherited — that we spew out a great number of codes, choosing by various methods, natural or sexual selection, those that fit the ecological niche to survive. But syphilis, instead of being the scourge of the 16th century, is a relatively mild disease 400 years later. Not because the spirochete has been attenuated or mutated, but because the gene pool of Europeans has been equipped with immunological defenses passed from diseased experience of the victims of their offspring. A professor of pathology, Sam Sappington, once remarked, "Syphilis was horrid and devastating four hundred years ago. Today?" he smiled, "it's nothing."

We did not kill off the spirochete of syphilis, alter or attenuate it. We simply received a rapid transferral of immunological genes through recent centuries parentage. Bubonic, black plague, kills so rapidly there was insuficient time for germinal cell alteration. Whereas, tuberculosis, which in the 19th century was ravaging Europe, has become relatively docile. We are very foolish if we feel public health measures are the cause. People still cough, eat from the same plates, have the same careless food handlers surrounding them and live in the same ill-vented structures. Pasteurization of milk, inspection of meat, chlorinating of water, and isolation of the diseased have not been all that important, for in countries which do not employ such measures, the disease rates are often lower. Forces besides natural selection are at work.

Bernard Campbell states, "Man has one of the most efficient types of placenta from the point of view of chemical exchange with the mother." We stress this point. Here is one of the areas where acquired human characteristics are translated into the germinal and somatic codes of the fetus. The linings of the uterus are penetrated by fetal vessels so that they are bathed in maternal blood, that chemical interchange between mother and offspring is maximal.

We have never questioned that the mother transmits antibodies so that the newborn will be immunized against disease. In case the fetus blood proteins differ radically from those of the mother's blood, the mother may develop antibodies. To protect her from such an alien being, she passes them into the fetal bloodstream to cause clotting, death, and rejection — known as iso-immunization. There is no intervening maternal tissues between the maternal blood and the fetal tissues it bathes. It poses the most intimate of contact for the rearrangement of DNA codes in the developing somatic and germinal tissues.

The very fact, in so gross a nature as iso-immunization, that the mother can reject an unwanted code, is evidence of the highest type of maternal influence upon fetal development. We hear spoken that the fetus is insulated in a water-filled uterine environment. Nothing could be further from the truth. The fetus is buffeted by the degree of activity of the mother, subject to intake of drugs, varieties of food, and even to hormonal dispositions.

If a study was made of premature infants, one should be able to find a correlation between early premature and its siblings in the degree of resemblance to the mother, the supposition being that the normal siblings will have had a longer period of time to acquire maternal characteristics.

Here is the controversies update:

June 2, 1979, *The Lancet*, Paul E. M. Fine, on the sesquicentenary of the death of Lamarck (1744-1829) — "Recent years have witnessed the discovery and serious discussion of several phenomena which, though not generally considered as Lamarckian, are nevertheless tantamount to the inheritance of acquired characteristics. . . . Bacteriology has led the way. . . . Bacteriologists have discovered an almost bewildering variety of genetical insertion mechanisms such as transformation, episome, transfer, and bacterior-phage mediated transduction . . . whereby microbes can incorporate and pass on genetic material acquired during their lifetimes. In that sense these mechanisms are Lamarckian . . . their implications for microbial evolution are accepted without question.

"Also at the subcellular level, renewed interest, that from prokargotic to eukaryotic cells, occurred not as a product of nuclear genetic evolution, but by the inheritance of acquired material. . . . Recognition that extranuclear organelles have a genetic integrity of their own and inherited in a manner different from nuclear chromosomes . . . responsibility for growth of the field of extrachromosomal or 'non-Mendelian' heredity.

"Inheritance of infectious agents . . . verticle transmission — inheritance of tumor viruses . . . the inheritance of acquired infection. Many species transmit information from generation to generation by extragenetical means. Dawkins coined the term 'memes,' heritable units of taught-learned information (e.g. ideas, fads) . . . closely analogous to evolutionary characters discussed by Lamarck.

"*Anti*-Lamarckism . . . was shattered — by the discovery of the enzyme RNA — dependent DNA polymesase, or 'reverse transcriptase,' which facilitates transcription of information from RNA 'back' into DNA." Case against Lamarck was the dogma that information proceeded unidirectionally from DNA to RNA to protein.

August 28, 1980, *Medical School University of Bristol*, R. B. Taylor, on Lamarckist Revival in Immunology — Gorezynski and Steele, Nat. Acad. Sci., 1980, made the startling claim neonatally induced immunological tolerance to MHC (major histocompatibility, or transplantation) antigens can be genetically transmitted to the offspring through at least two generations. "A possibility by which one might escape frontal challenge to Weissman's dogma, is that the information could be carried across the generations by viruses as such, without requiring violation of germline DNA."

January 21, 1982, *St. Mary's Hospital*, L. Brent, P. Chandler, et al, on further studies on supposed Lamarckian inheritance of immunological tolerance — "All examples of supposedly Lamarckian inheritance proposed so far have been mistaken . . . in respect of the systems we have been investigating, Lamarckian inheritance does not obtain."

Dobzhausky states, "No modern geneticist thinks that there existed in our ancestors or that there appeared by mutation some special genes for culture. There are no genes to make for a painter or statesman. The Negro race is not homozygous for a non-existing gene for joy of music, or the Jews merchants. Genes create the setting for cultural traits."

According to Dobzhansy, the Norwegian rat has been kept in laboratories for over 100 years. This protection afforded him differences from the wild rat, such as smaller adrenals, less active thyroids, and resistance to disease, tamer and with greater fertility but of smaller brain. It is amazing that he did not notice that it was possibly not breeding which produced these genetic changes, but could have been the transmission of acquired characteristics from environmental pressures of non-selective nature.

III Instinct

". . . We inherit broad characteristics to
which we add finer detail." — Bernard Campbell

NSTINCT is a term which has been badly abused. Early in the 20th century, during the last upsurgence of the environmental schools, it sank to its lowest level. Yet today, because of our studies of animal behavior and knowledge of genetics, it is not only alive but scientifically sound. When considering that instinct must exist, we realize that there is a coded chemical basis within the neurogens that prompts the organism to respond in a definitive fashion apart and beyond educational learning or parental tutorage.

Of necessity, these ingrained responses to situations were formulated through laws of evolution. Individuals who possessed the best code responses survived to pass these reactions onto their descendants. There is a tendency to think of the organism in terms of muscle, bone, and physiological adaptations when we consider evolution. Up to the present, scant attention has been paid to the subtle more psychological processes of neurons which direct thought processes.

Good thought processes are rare. Thought requires chained problem-solving. Most moderns are either too lazy to think or do not have the necessary neuronic cogs supplied with proper energy.

Evolutionary nature, in her wisdom, supplied the answer. She said in effect, to the great majority of the social group, "There's no need to think. I'll do it for you. I'll supply you with fixed codes as I have supplied you with reflexes."

Touch a hot stove and you'll withdraw your finger before you think about it — a reflex. But travel a cliff's edge — ford a swollen stream — wend a jungle trail at night — approach a stranger, or even fondle a beloved — and in each instance your evolutionary nature will act for you. It provides you with warning signals to either stop or go. When you act properly, you will be rewarded and it shall determine what you will enjoy. In short, you are provided with instinct, which is your second brain, above reflexes.

Pertinent notes from *Human Evolution* by Bernard Campbell states that "Innate behavior, in which learning plays no part, is seen in the visual language of the honey bee. It is also the characteristic that we term 'human instinct.' However, most commonly we inherit broad characteristics to which we add finer detail."

Jimmy Carter stated to *Playboy* magazine that he had "lusted for many women." That is a normal response. Most men have lusted for women, and their varying appreciative perceptions of breasts or buttocks, face or legs, or total figure, is evidence of the strong forces directing them from within the cerebrum. While we have literally thousands of inbuilt neurological instincts related variously to particular thought, situation, and response processes, there are broader patterns which we call group instincts.

As society organized itself, it acquired within the forge of evolutionary selection common denominator response patterns which permitted its progression against competitors that were left on dead-end branches. Societies prefer groupings of members into adjacent locales, such as cities, in spite of disadvantages. Not only this gregariousness, but the rally to war, the cohesion of the clan or family, the choice of foodstuffs, are all directed from ages past.

Society did not originate overnight. It has become fixed within neuro-codes by the mechanism of natural selection. It is not only individuals that survive by being the fittest to be able to reproduce and foster offspring, it is individuals entered into cohesive and interdependent relationships with one another; that is, society, which grants preferential posterity.

Freud recognized two fundamental instincts: sex and self-preservation. Other scientists have added fear, repulsion, pugnacity, curiosity, self-assertion, herd instinct, self-abasement, parental, reproduction, gregariousness, emulation, hunger, and acquisitiveness. The instinctible components of human and social life are so far-ranging that practically everything we do individually or grouped is prompted in one form or another by these under-lying directors.

We watch the ugly slave ideology known as communism imprison a goodly portion of the earth's peoples. Its battle cry is in the name of the masses. It does not care about the masses. It is only concerned with their submission, control, and exploitation for the benefit of party leaders. This horrendous social science differs from capitalism and the free-enterprise state in that their dominants are supreme and absolute. However, both forms of political society are based upon the submissive characteristics of individuals.

We are present today as a society solely because of this dominance cod-ing. Leaders, sovereignty and control appear universally because of innate inequalities of men and the born aggressiveness of some to control. Compon-ents of races have been unequally selected. Any system of government based on true equality is bound to ultimate failure. It does not mean that the masses, and the intelligencia, the bourgeois, cannot live at peace with one another. It simply means that the benevolence to all parties, class variances should be recognized.

Lorenz and Tinbergen listed the major criteria for innateness as follows: (1) a stereotyped behavior, (2) characteristic of a species, (3) appears spon-taneously in animals that have been raised in isolation, and lastly (4) de-velops fully-formed in animals that have been prevented in practicing it.

This interpretation is rather stilted when applied to humans. Instincts do not need to follow rigid laws. As there are wide variances in other aspects of humans so are there variances in instinctive patterns.

A given individual can be predictable in action. This same predictability does not necessarily pertain to his neighbors. Consequently, when we speak of some human instincts, they may be dominant in some individuals while in others they may be strong motivating forces. There is sufficient instinctive common denominators to make class behavior predictable.

G. H. Parker stated that human beings are about 9/10th "inborn" and 1/10th "acquired." Others have agreed with this conclusion. Consequently, culture, which we have regarded as the offspring of environment and learn-ing, should be regarded as the innate expression of ages past, formulated by natural selection and gene-directed.

This is because we can't measure it in millimeters or grams or see a defined shape. Yet here is prime of evolvement. DNA codes within neural tissue prompt our every move — as an individual, as a group, and as a nation. Society is none other than neurogenic. All human institutions are the writings on the walls of the cerebrum.

Instincts are a vital part of political science for they separate communists from capitalists, left from right, proletariat from the bourgeois. They are in-herited genetic chemistry which prompts man or beast to action independent of learning, environment or reason.

Instincts are not only common to individuals in varying degree, they are specifically representative of tribes, groups, nations, and subraces. Where genes have worked their alchemy in evolutionary isolation, no subrace or group or even groups within groups as proletariat or bourgeois, have escaped having specially fixed neurogenic dispositions to meet environmental adaptations.

Through the sieves of natural selection, instincts have been passed onto social groups and races in a similar fashion as have anatomical and physiological traits. Slant eyes in the Mongoloid, black skin of the Negro, and blonde hair in the Caucasoid are among hundreds of physical variances that have accompanying mental traits suited to and selected for human groupings. The Negro's promiscuity, the white man's wars, the Mongoloid's cruelty, can be further devised to explain the Spaniard's religion, Italian's cleverness, Frenchman's stubbornness, German's discipline, and Englishman's pomposity — all descending through selection pressures that incorporate them within genes. These traits should not be considered monopolistically assigned.

INA (Index of National Aggressiveness)

C   Nations' war costs over the last century, adjusted for inflation to 1980 American currency.

K   Number of persons killed, civilian or military, in war-related activity.

W   Number of persons at least 20% permanently disabled.

P   Average national population. Calculated total population for each year divided by 100.

W   Wars, declared or undeclared.

$$\text{Cost per person:} \frac{C}{P} \quad \text{e. a. (\$25,000)}$$

$$\text{Casualty per person:} \frac{K + W}{P} \quad (.2)$$

$$\text{Number of wars:} \quad W \quad (7)$$

$$W \times \frac{C}{P} \times \frac{K + W}{P} = INA \quad (35,000)$$

It represents innate propensity for aggressiveness and possession of killer genes. Economic cost is included in the factor in order to exhibit supportive war genes in the population generally. Differences come about by natural selection and adaptation in certain isolated environments. Killer-aggressive genes are passed from generation to generation, residing within neural complexes.

Where does a given nation stand? Nairobi? Switzerland? Egypt? India? Colombia? Try for continents. Black Africa? Yellow Asia? White Europe? Answers will be in conformity with previous evolutionary, group hunting-killing experience.

If we observe conduct, we begin to recognize instinctive patterns. Consider an innocent hobby like stamp-collecting. It surfaces in conduct from our underlying territoriality instinct. A look at the kleptomaniac who steals not for gain but out of compulsion — it is prompted by our thieving instinct — one derived out of survival mechanism. To watch acrobats can be a recapitulation of our emotions when we were in the trees. Our compulsion to witness violence originates within subconscious precautionary tutelage.

Goethe of Dostoevski stated, "There is no crime I cannot commit," meaning that we are programmed for the unrational violence we enter into. Consider lions entering the Coliseum as a replay of our African history to which we pay attention. Animals in zoos command attention not because we are going to derive our next meals from them, but because we were among the last meals of their remote ancestors.

Dogs are man's ancient hunting associates, whereas cats have come into value only recently, during the agricultural revolution when they began serving to rid the granaries of rats and mice. Our instinctive imprintation of these two servants has been directly proportional to their servitude. How much dog food is sold in America in proportion to cat food?

The value of the canine cannot be expressed better than the comments of Mrs. Elizabeth Arvin of Alvanton, Kentucky, who wrote: "The dog is a working member of human society. Some fifty ways in which they earn their living are well documented, including guiding, guarding, detecting, rescuing, protecting, defending, often spending and giving their lives in the service of mankind. And millions of families are able to sleep securely knowing that even the smallest family pet will warn of intrusion. Surely they earn their dog food."

Both dogs and ourselves have mutually instinctive programmings. A student of canineology knows that the dog holds still for the attachment of a collar. Not so the horse with its bridle. The dog has been trained, educated or selected toward this sociable submissiveness. We look to the long association with man as altering behavioral genes by the inheritance of acquired characteristics.

Man's close attachment to the dog is exemplified by the increasing number of canines, the amount of money and affection spent on them, and honoring of their sacredness. Rarely do we see dog-pelt coats or utilization of the dog as human food consumption. Admunsen, discoverer of the South Pole, ate his dogs so that his goal could be reached. Such an act repulsed the civilized world.

Various studies have shown the chimpanzee has a higher I.Q. than the dog. Why is it practically impossible to make a house pet of a chimpanzee while the dog makes one of the greatest companions? It is by no learning that on a cold winter's night about any dog, if unrestrained, will jump into a sleeping human's bed.

Possibly for a million years man selected the dog and crudely bred him. He accepted subspecies of dog which advanced his development and survival. The dog engaged in the hunt with man in a mutually beneficial effort. He provided a keener sense of smell and tracking. He was speedier and could rapidly bring his quarry to bay. He had inborn fearlessness of enemies. His sentinel value is recognized and utilized. Many facets of the dog's hunting prowess such as nipping the leg tendons of large game and distracting prey for hunters' close approach and kill were invaluable. The instinct of dog and man converges.

William Etkin, in *Social Behavior and Organization*, states, "The concept of instinct has acquired new and significant meaning in the study of animal behavior, and its elaboration has provided insights into the nature and social behavior that are indispensable for modern views." Thus, early American psychologists who were trying to sublimate instinct will have to think again. Instinct is viewed as innate, requiring no experience for effective performance.

Etkin also stated, "As evolutionists we must suppose that man at one time had a biologically determined social organization." From this one may deduct that our assertions in this work are not off-track. Let us examine a definition by Etkin. Instinct will be viewed here as complex behaviors which function as adaptive units of action in an animal's life and which appear to be largely independent of learning. In other words, when we say of a behavior pattern that it is an instinct, we assert that we believe that its fundamental elements are innately organized and require no specific type of experience as background for effective performance. Further into the concept, an instinct is generalized coded behavior that is programmed within our neurogenes. From these templates, bonded in acid, we react to practically everything we do. Learning and experience are the tip of the iceberg; beneath is instinctive bureaucracy that dictates action and decision.

Care-giving and care-soliciting. The fact that we recognize charitable qualities in animals explains to a great extent why the public is easily solicited by charitable organizations, most of whose funds go to solicitors' pockets. In spite of this knowledge, people continue to give when exposed to a picture of an emaciated, hollow-eyed child or dog.

Inborn fear of snakes in apes is an excellent illustration of instinctive inheritance. At one time, primates may have encountered snakes that were mortal enemies. Natural selection permitted the ancient primates to direct toward serpent fear imprinted in the nervous system so that it passed on from generation to generation. Was it solely natural selection? Those apes which perished by the snake did not have offspring. Those that manifested fear survived. What mutation registers so complex an aversion? This could only come through acquired characteristics that were cerebrally registered. Thence the information was passed to the germinal cells. Snake fear comes early in children — at ages 4 to 8 — and in young chimpanzees through their exposure to serpents.

Women have instinctive talent for watching men slug it out, without aiding one or the other. There is no loyalty exhibited, rather as if they are awaiting the winner. Theatre milks this theme to absurdity: the helplessness of women placed within the setting of male physical conflict. This has reference in much of the animal kingdom — for witness the challenge of the chiefs by bachelors with the spoils of a harem falling to the victor.

Robert B. Zajoric, in *Animal Social Psychology*, discusses Warren and Maroney's monkeys and summarizes, "That as a consequence of conflict and competition there emerges a stable social order whose underlying basis is a dominance hierarchy." Zajoric quotes Wynne-Edwards (1962) who suggests that the function of the hierarchy "is always to identify the surplus individuals," for if and when the population requires thinning. This circumstance would have value to the whole society for survival.

Radlow, et al, have shown that the most dominant bird in a small flock of cocks can be conditioned to become the most subordinate member of the flock. Also, it has been shown that under appropriate environmental conditions, social rank can be established through learning in contradiction to the influence of genetic and physiological factors. Yet this is artificial tampering. Punishment and reward are an intrinsic part of changing dominancy.

Throughout social animal structures, including man, there appear leaders, class and subclass. Within class there appear occupational designates such as worker bees, soldier ants, and human proletariat. When dominant meets dominant, there will be struggle for position. But, by and large, genetically, society sieves its participants into their properly determined niche. It would be a short step to species extinction if dominant characteristics were issued to all. Prevention of the continuous intraspecies conflict is avoided by the paucity of alphas. Fortunately, biology never heard of equalitarianism, and placed wide individual ranges so that conflict could be avoided and survival assured.

From "Group Social Patterns — Dominant Male Rhesus," by Irwin S. Bernstein, in *Psychological Reports*, we learn, "Leader rhesus males in response to external group challenges acts as a protector by threatening or attacking the intruder, goes to the aid of the group's distress and affords group comfort by his presence. He is not constituted solely for preferential access to incentives." Obviously, he is a leader spewed out in genetic mathematics to serve a social purpose. He is not environmentally created.

In Smith's and Hale's experiments with hens, dominance can be reversed for several weeks by the appliance of shock, thus altering the social or pecking order. Communism has admirably achieved the same results by continuous punishment to born dominants. Experiments such as these prove that abnormal force will remove the true genetic structure of society.

In the works of Wendell Smith and E. B. Hale, "Modification of Social Rank in Domestic Fowl," they concluded that: "In rhesus monkey experiments it was shown dominancy could not be reversed without artificial deconditioning."

Instincts are subtly evident elsewhere. Skiing simulates the exhilaration of flying among the branches of ancient forests. A children's merry-go-round in the park is a return to a ride in the trees. Young and old enjoy the gentle stimulation of their semi-circular canals. The success of the Wild West movie depends upon primitive programmings. Open scenery combined with horses and animals puts us back to the Pliocene. Rivalry and death within a small group awakens ancient experience.

Brain was our earliest flesh. Man had the ability to smash skulls open with rocks or obtain what was abandoned with the remains of the kills of great cats. Turtles being slow came under our rock sledge. It accounts for our remaining high taste for terrapin.

We develop arterosclerosis from an excess of cholesterol in animal fats. This is a paradox, for man survived hundreds of thousands of years on a meat diet. He did have open fires but lacked pottery. Therefore, beef braized and roasted in open flame lost considerable fat content. Modern man not only eats the fat of the meat, but the residue as well when, in his processing, he ends up combining it with flour to make a gravy. Thus, it is not the meat-eating that causes the medical infirmity, but rather it is the manner in which man cooks the meat and embellishes it with fries and bakes. Man retains a meat-eating instinct.

Man selected toward artists and appreciation of art. Why else would we pay millions of dollars for paint splotches that have been perfectly reproduced? Cave artists were a premium group, lending strength to their followers and functioning in matters of religion, solace, and invocation. Before man's ape-like ancestors had a social structure, they rallied in groups. It became apparent that marching and stomping in rhythm, beating bones and stick together and grunting in chorus, "umpa, umpa," were deterrents to carnivorous predators. That is why today, when the band marches, we are filled with emotion and comraderie. The banner man saluted in the past may have been a freshly-skinned hide of wildebeast proudly carried on a femoral mast.

Instinctive functioning is evident in homeric pronouncements over the beauty of Helen of Troy, the woman with a face that launched a thousand ships. They document genetic selection that led toward the west, away from dark-skinned and large-nosed and toward more advanced Grecian women. A force in modern evolution has been toward fair-skinned, hairless, small-nosed, erect women.

Not to be negated is woman's selection toward men. In her nudity and his, and in their sinless innocence, there was a selection toward penis size because man comes off with a disproportionally larger staff than his closest primate relations. Not only that, testicles outside the body were an added attraction in the sexual market. Why should anything so ridiculously inconvenient as testicles be appended to a hunter's body if it were not for their charm? Thrusting male gonads through the abdominal wall is with risk of herniation and does produce hernia formation in a large number of males. However, the risk of disability was evidently outweighed by the first swingers who attracted a comparatively larger share of females. Such a factor weighed evolutionarily in their progeny and continued in vogue.

Franz Boas, in his work, *The Central Eskimo*, writes, "Among all the tribes infanticide has been practiced to some extent, but probably only females of children of widows have been murdered in this way, the latter on account of the difficulty in providing for them. It is very remarkable that this practice seems to be quite allowable."

To soothe the bawling infant we resort to the tree life of the past. If not a rocking chair, then an in-arms swinging. Lullaby is a well-preserved calming instinct. Originally it had little different usage — to calm the frightened newborn to silence so that predatory detection became lessened. National anthems spring from the same archaic tranquils. Professing grandeur and love of country, beneath they are to calm the fears of large people unions, to strengthen their certainties.

Society is heavily underscored by innate emotions. We simply do not enter the world and taught so that we go forth in the same image. Strong in the social code are mechanisms programmed in neurogenes relating to emotion.

One of these inheritances is fear. We have selected toward it, and although not as frequently employed as in the past ages, it is still firmly rooted. Many animal experiments demonstrate fear, especially testing drugs as tranquilizers which have the ability to block the expression. Everyone has witnessed the cat confrontation with the dog — its raised hair, arched back, wide eyes, hiss, and bared teeth. In such instances, the emotion after the event rapidly subsides.

While not wishing to get into a study which is encyclopedic concerning human fear, ranging from battlefield to office job and its sometimes psychosomatic affect upon the body, there is a humorous type of fear which has become profitable to thespian producers. It is an excellent illustration of what resides within neurogenes. By examining society, we have detailed insight into the genes residing there.

From Frankenstein to "Jaws," King Kong to "The Strange Case of Dr. Jekyll and Mr. Hyde," to the "Masque of the Red Death," not forgetting Dracula, the human spirit is enchanted and pleased with theatrics concerning horror. Beetles destroying the earth, indestructible insects chewing our faces or blood-sucking vampires killing humans are fantastically absurd. It is incredible that such fiction could derive billions of dollars in revenue for the film industry.

There are basic scientific points — the fear is a sham fear. The individual wants to believe it, yet he knows it is untrue and more especially knows he is safe. It is as if he were back fifty million years ago in the trees and watching lions rip apart his cousin.

Second is the quality of real fear. An audience that has been laughing, joking, edging in their seats, squeezing someone's hand in ecstasy or in stunned belief, would react quite differently if someone shouted "Fire!" as the theatre filled with smoke. Yet if the scene of a panicking audience under threat of fire was being shown on the screen, there would be little more than pleasurable emotion.

Neither is sham fear a tongue-in-cheek appraisal of the presentation or a superior ego reflection of the whole thing as ridiculous. Basic to the theatre scheme and to the enjoyment of the patron is the fact that the fear is false, that the individual is safe, that the audience is witnessing something that could happen to them, but is not. It is a preview of a true fear and a profound relief that the individual viewing it is not part of it. It is a warning but not a threat. For this powerful human emotion, which is universal and which occupies a reasonable time of man's theatrical viewing, the audience is willing to pay goodly sums to participate in the thespian's art of horror.

True fear with all its accompanying bodily preparations and reactions eminating from the endocrine glands, especially the adrenal, and from many neurological centers such as the thalmus, is a mechanism of survival. It is an important biological component of most mammals. Further, we not only selected toward it in our evolution, but it accompanies us in everyday life, from crossing the street to ascending the rusty Eiffel Tower elevators.

Play fear or sham fear is also a mechanism of survival. One that has been evolutionary forged. Its seat as a neurogene complex is evidenced by its universality, demand, and acceptance. That's what spooks, goblins, and the most harmless of utterances, from grandmother's "boo" to a startled grandson is about.

Sham fear is an educational process. It is necessary that children and adults alike be fully instructed into what dangerous consequences lie with every walking foot of the daily world. In that miserable ghoulish curious characteristic inquisition into the morbid and the unfortunate that we see demonstrated so often is the expression of need for genetic imprinting.

It is distressing in a hospital to watch perfect strangers gawk at the dying, especially in the old-time wards during visiting hours — yellow-jaundiced people gasping for their last breath of life, disfigured people, or those whose skin is covered with but one of the thousand afflictions of which it is heir. Upon closer scrutiny beneath, the gawkers are sympathetic and serious. It is as if they are trying to learn something to impress it into their cerebral faculties. The same is true of a dead man lying in the street. Nothing can be done, but people group to view him. A sensitive individual covers his body with any cloth nearby, displaying the difference between the more sensitive trying to protect the dignity of the dead, against those of the more ancient, attempting to view the spectacle.

One of the strongest programmed neurogenic emotions is that concerning death. This is the sum and substance of playwrights and novelists from Shakespeare to Hemingway. This is what sells movies and theatre tickets. The proportion of cash receipts is correlated with the amount of gore presented. In the formulation of society we can see how curiosity of death was an important educational technique toward survival. Nature was quite sure that it should not be passed culturally, but made an inherent part of the neuron's genes to be passed from generation to generation to assure its vital message.

One early origin can be surmised from the mere witnessing of a leopard attack upon one of the members of the defenseless pre-hominid. It is not difficult to reconstruct the gathering of the group around the remains after the beast had quit his quarry. Much as Hamlet picked up the skull of poor Yorick, so did those individuals of ten million years ago fondle the unopened skull of their relation. As some evidence indicated, thay may have bashed it open to devour the brain. This was long before sensitivities became more elegant. Later, there was the continuing witnessing of wars and accidents, battles, falls from cliffs, or drownings. While normal natural selection operated, those that had learned and heeded the lessons of death undoubtedly inherited acquired characteristics which were passed directly through germinal cells.

Lessons of death and disaster became an important part of the neuromechanism, giving innate fear something to operate upon. If death were an unknown quantity, something taught only by one's parents vocally, it could not have much precautionary force. By instilling into the cerebral apparatus awe of human termination, inquisitiveness into the morbid, fun in watching disaster of another, it served as a reinforcement of the original complex by visual learning. Law enforcement agencies are learning the more effectual type of correction for habitual bad drivers is to expose them to the injured and dying who have crashed. Unfortunately, people sometimes must experience automobile accidents before they learn to drive properly. Sham fear? Of course, enjoy every minute of it. It's the ingredient of survival. Within those chilly nervous laughs are lessons.

We inherit basic mechanisms for language and rudiments of language history. Loud speakers are represented by the larynx and vocal cords with the lungs as bellows. Within the brain is the amplification system to produce sounds. Upon entering the world we have, as it were, an uncut platter. It merely remains for parents and those around us to impress the native language patterns upon the disc. Thus, all of us come up with the mother tongue.

By individual differences some are given an uncut record which is larger and accommodates greater vocabulary. In some the shellac is more absorbent of the environmental printings, so greater depth of understanding is achieved and a rich complex sentence structure. This characteristic is based upon genes of higher intelligence. So, upon arrival, we are equipped with technical facilities to cut a speech record from environmental inputs. Our brain is wired to reason for such input.

Yet there is innate structure within the uncut disc which represents our historic language. To create such a marvelous recording and sound delivery system, coupled with reason, it is not logical there would not remain rudiments of origin. Much as in embryology, we go through stages which recapitulate our phylogeny or grow up our family tree, so in human speech there would remain historic episodes which could lead us backwards in time to discover our geographical wanderings over time and basic languages we were exposed to.

Our genealogical geographical locations would be indicated by language employed in these areas. And, in finer scale by computerizing backgrounds, very primitive linguistic codes. To tap this wealth of information, revealing to us remote ancestry, geographical abodes, subrace and race, we can employ a psychiatrical test. We call it, "in search for the alpha language."

In the Rorschach ink-blot test, the deep mind is periscoped to bring forth associations. Mentally ill may see snakes where a normal person relates to rambling roses.

In the same fashion, especially a student of language may at will produce a series of nonsense syllables and sentences. If one analyzes these closely, not only can the mother tongue be discerned but remote tongues of ancestors. Thus, an American, from study of his nonsense codes, may have English for the mother tongue, Anglo-Saxon centuries back, and the archaic tongue could be Slavic Russian in the year 20,000 B.C.

Try it. Relax, let your hand thoughtlessly write. Write nonsense. Go outside your stream of conscious thought. Write detachedly in word bursts — spurts of mixed-up letters and syllables. That which your hand is writing should provide personal historic discovery when compared with other individuals writing similar alpha language compared with other languages of the world. In a random sampling of white English people, one may be surprised to find indications of other than an Indo-European chief language family. Some may have a Ural-Altaic, Semitic, African, Indo-Chinese, or even Austronesian. With refinement, the technique may indicate Burmese, Mongolian or Sudanic ancestry. Start writing. Here is what I just wrote: "Amisco bischot oficup omit omga canif ob zamcot dashich acherjabid." Here is what I wrote yesterday: "Tashe oc demit afig oterm schel doricas ome icad."

Even beside what is written, pronouncing the sounds therefrom could lead to historic personal language discovery. If you are illiterate, which is unlikely, practice chanting nonsense syllables and words into a recorder. Then find a linguist who may be able to detect your primitive tongues — your alpha language.

IV Race: Genetic Brotherhoods

CULTURE

HISTORICALLY we have separated culture from man's innate behavior. We see man as the highest form of life with instinctive patterns. We view culture as whims, fashions, inventions, traits, and particular social developments of one group of humans from that of another. Whereas the DNA coding is physiological, man's culture is thought to be handed down non-genetically from predecessors. Perception, custom and traits divide races. This division is attributed to extra corporal factors.

What we actually find is not what distinguishes human beings in uniqueness, contrasts, or bizarre behavior, but a fundamental chemical basis for cultural behavior passed forward by genetic inheritance. Religion, with its universality, is obviously genetic. War and aggressive behavior is likewise chemically programmed; so are institutions of government, art, and other forms of social endeavor. Warfare carries many faces within many cultures from deadly and pernicuous to comical mock warfare of certain primitives. Throughout there is basic genetic programming that makes institutions possible.

From *New Perspective in Cultural Anthropology*, by Robert Kessing, we see cautious gleanings that indicate culture may be innate. They recite (Chomsky exploded a bombshell in Social Science in arguing that man's capacity for language is genetically programmed) that at birth a child knows language but does not know *a* language.

LANGUAGE

Languages are biologically channeled. Their structure is not diverse. Communicative codes are acquired not through learning, but by biological coding. Within the neurogenes are fertile fields of basic language. The emerging infant is seeded by language of parents and those surrounding him. This produces a rich harvest of thousands of items which go into a specific language.

It is why there is great difficulty in learning a language after the age of 6. One rarely learns a second language perfectly if he has not been subjected to its teachings before ages 6 to 10. To be bilingual, the neurogenic linguistic fields must be planted as the maturing process occurs. One who becomes bilingual, for example, is one who is born to a French parent who did not speak German and a German parent who did not speak French. Once genes have locked in linguistic input, it is difficult to revise original seeding.

Most Americans of older generation were rarely exposed to a foreign language before high school years. Many students studied French for years, yet they are never capable of saying more than a few rote memorized words. There is a dismal retention rate after years of study. Quite simply, the neurogenes had been hooked up prior to French language experience and there was no place for second learning of language. One can successfully learn a second language as an adult only after study and living within territories of the language.

Billions of dollars are wasted each year trying to teach old dogs new language tricks. In spite of ingenious tapes, records, textbooks and teachers, it is an almost futile pursuit. The comedy is in grammar and its rules. Foreign languages are learned by natural method. If we were to direct language teaching to the pre-school age, we could put most language teachers out of work.

BLACK / WHITE

A race, nation or culture, after a period of isolated genetic exchange, evolves into a specifically directed biology. It is why nations of Europe shall never be united by their own volition but only by force, as Eastern European nations. Then they are united politically, not because of their biological uniqueness. The Negro has never integrated within the western societies. His cultural biology is too diverse. There are many physical differences and intellectual traits between blacks and whites. What is paramount is the underlying genetically programmed culture.

Polygamy, promiscuity, illegitimacy and a matriarchal society are cultural inlays of blacks. Monogamy, legitimacy and a patriarchal society are fetishes of whites. They are ingrained organic dispositions biologically selected as whites moved north away from their black brothers.

To bed white and black together in holy matrimony on a large scale has failed. It did not fail because of the superficial cultural rejection pressures. Rather, it failed because although the black male is desirous of selecting toward the white woman, her biological imprintation rejects this notion.

A federal study in 1966, "Equality of Educational Opportunity," showed the achievements of over ½ million students in American schools:

NEGRO: The Negro failed beyond question of doubt. It was nothing that the Southern whites had not already known. The old platitude that the Negro has been deprived of educational opportunity, subjected to poverty, discrimination and poor schools does not hold water.

Ascent of the Negro by evolutionary forces fitted him for survival in the ecological niche of Africa where he chose to remain. It gave him a certain superiority in adaptation. One is sickle-celled gene ability to withstand malaria in areas that for centuries have been known as graveyards for whites. Yet the sickle cell is just one small phase of thousands of differences between black and white. The Negro's abstract intelligence is not similar to the Orientals or to whites. The whites and yellows chose several hundred thousand years ago to migrate to cold climates of the north. Encountering multiple problems of glaciation, clothing, shelter, necessity, hunting, land technique acquisition, this icy forge of the north and its peculiarily different ecology demanded greater skills and communication abilities than did the gathering type of society of the savannas.

It is why, when it comes to abstract arts and skills such as mathematics, engineering, painting and music (what the western man regards as culture), the Negro is inept. Basic elements of these latterday highly-prized skills were selected toward by evolutionary necessity. The art of war, which the whites have perfected, led to survival of the cunning and those who possessed mechanical skills. Historically, the outstanding recitals are of powerful northern nations and their successful cultures. Except for the early Egyptian and Middle East civilizations (which were Caucasoid), there is no other explanation for northern success against the adversity of their harsh climates than their remarkably gened structure.

SPORTS: Not meant here is that whites are superior to blacks. What the furor is about is that for the niche in which the races developed, each has created his own special adaptation. Within Africa there was greater premium on speed, which the northerner, with his burden of clothing, could not hope to develop. So, in athletes we expect to see everything from runners to prize fighters, to basketball players, to be within the Negroid domain, while the heavy stationary muscular skills such as shot-putting or weight lifting would denote a white preference from the emphasis placed on brute power by the northern niche.

SLUMS: Goals, desires, initiative, ambition, love, morality, crime, and family structure are all innately programmed within the races. Sociologists are continuously braying an untrue fact that if poverty were eliminated and education equal, the minorities would have greater nuclear family structure, monogamy, and less illegitimacy. The argument does not hold because the black male is not structured for a monogomous existence in a patriarchal family. All one has to do is observe his habits in native lands. Out of the slums arises the majority of urban crime. Again, the sociologists point to deprivation as its cause. Oddly enough, white slums, oriental slums, and the northern slums of past history did not produce this anti-social outpouring that the Negro and Puerto Rican slums produce today.

RACE: Anthropologists are disposed to discard the idea of race. Jews who were horribly persecuted under false racial concepts are against the idea. Both are trying to eliminate a reality by substitution of the word "race" with "ethnic groups." This reminds one of the hubbub years back over instinct which was of disreputable being. We were supposed to use the term "innate." Yet happily, "instinct" has survived and is back in good repute. In the same manner, the word "race" has never left the conceptional vocabulary of more talented "ethnologists."

Sweep racial truth beneath the carpet? It is an old song and dance that since we differ only by color of skin, it is foolish to categorize various units of human society.

Skin coloration is very complex; under the control of at least half-a-dozen genes. It is not skin, which merely denotes the geographical locale of development. It is thousands of genes ranging from abstract intellectual abilities to physical prowess that widely separate groups of men. We should be indebted to the categorization of races and subraces and should look forward to the elaboration of such data.

It is not that people are going to be demeaned by the process of racial elaborations. This has been lamentable in the past. It is that all races and subraces have variable gene structure. Some of these genes are superior and some are inferior. That one could consider superior or inferior over the other depends upon the evolutionarily adaptability they were selected for. Certainly abstract intelligence was of greater advantage for survival in the tribes of the glacial north than was fleetness of foot for the inhabitants of African savannas.

It is well for intellectuals to rationalize away genetic normals as prejudice, discrimination, and racism. Few speak about race because they do not welcome criticism. Racism is deeply innate in the genetic structure of races and subraces, registering in the rejection of racial competitors. Pictures may be taken of a white boy and a black boy playfully embracing on a slum street. This is an exception. Beneath are incompatible genes that will produce havoc when races are biologically challenged.

As the white man is incompetent in Central Africa, so the black man is incompetent in northern city ghettoes. What should be recognized is that once you alter the setting, or once you challenge the normal ecological niche that has been adapted to, there can be none other than conflict and hatred.

Races, to a large extent, correspond to continental areas which give us the major groups such as white, black, yellow, Indian and Australian. Divisions of these into smaller subraces go into the hundreds. All have specialized genetic groupings which served the particular geological niche — not only genes representing phenotypes, but genes carrying behavioral and cultural mechanisms.

BODY: The amount of muscle in Europeans is largely governed by inheritance, just as bone or fat covering the muscle are gene determined (Hewitt, 1958; Osborne, 1959). Since we can relate muscle and racial groups to genes, it certainly should be no feat to relate occupational-muscle variable within a society to genetic development as well.

Blubtren states, "There is also a well-defined social class difference in European countries. The children of well-off parents being physically larger not only at all ages, but also as adults. The higher socioeconomic groups appear to have lower weight for the same height, more linear structure, less squat, and are generally less muscular."

Bourgeois class genes beget bourgeois class genes, while the proletariat spew out the working classes. There are exceptions. Europe has had a long time to sift out its classes. Class usually begets specific class as upper, middle and lower socioeconomic groups.

If we look at the differences between Negroes and whites, such as the Negro's longer legs and arms, narrower hips, less muscular calves and heavier bones, rate of maturing and earlier eruption of permanent teeth, among a few items, we can observe the difficulty of natural selection or sexual selection being the only factors in evolution. A few hundreds of thousands of years split off from a central racial prototype is far too short in generations to account for racial variations. The only force that can account for this rapid divergence is a continuously acting force that transmits ecological adaptation directly to the germ plasma. It is fantastic to think that slightly less muscle in the calf of the Negro was a factor in survival of the fittest, or that his more muscled colleague perished because of his stronger pedal ability.

By a study of blood genes, Glass and Li determined that the amount of white mixture of the North American Negro is approximately 30.5%. This is where the problem of racial segregation exists. There are reasons for the separation of white and colored on the African continent. Yet in America, there is a commencing amalgamation. Races cannot be docilely bedded as there is too much ingrained programming to forward their own characteristics for them to accept stranger genes. One could re-breed toward black or toward white because mixed genetic components are too antagonistic to produce cohesive society.

MIXED BREEDING: The white female is not by choice going to breed toward black. A high percentage of black females have bred toward white males, but a large percentage of that breeding may have been forced by slavery and poverty. It is not that a white Norwegian girl and a black African boy as a marriageable couple are incongruous; it is that the concept of evolution is being violated. We recognize this in perceptional neurogenes as dignity and confrontation.

RAKES: The medieval practice of the *Doit a Signor*, the castle master bedding the serf's new wife first, was on firm genetic ground. It followed through with the white slave-owner forcibly infusing his blood into his

African purchases. Throughout the east, concubines and harems were once the law of the land, in which the dominant provided the majority of breed seed. There is an illustration of this breeding theory taken from the Old Testament concerning Solomon and his seven hundred wives, princesses, and three hundred concubines (I Kings 11-3).

Law tries to legislate a one-to-one monogamous ratio. Biologically there is no such reality. Be what it may, a great many men do not particularly care to breed or to scatter their seed widely. Homosexuals have no particular interest in the breeding process. Another portion of men are relatively faithful to their spouses and rarely seek outside commitments. Yet, beneath the bed of every attractive woman there is the specter of a Don Juan who has been placed within the genetic pool for a specific purpose.

Don Juan was naturally selected, but was able to break out of the narrow-mindedness of a small tribe to invade distant tribes, thus enhancing their gene pool. More than one time his type was the savior of the subraces when, under adverse conditions, his insatiable compulsion to disperse his seed widely kept a gene pool viable and prevented isolation of speciation.

RACIAL IDENTITY: Shortly, problem of racial and subracial identity will be on firm basis, thanks to advances in medical technology. Many people think they can trace their ancestry. This may be possible for extreme isolated populations as those of Central Africa, Australian Bushmen, Eskimos, or certain Mongoloids, but for Europeans it poses a complex problem. There is considerable promiscuity in family geneologies. "It's a wise man that knows his own father." This is conceded by many blood types within races.

Anthropologists describe physical measurements, skin color, stature, eye and nasal shapes, and the like. Medical laboratories quote statistics relating to anatomy, physiology and cellular structure. Psychological laboratories devise tests other than intelligence tests, such as personality, stress, emotions, and the multiple aspects of neural behavior. All these give weight to the purity of the subrace. Thousands of such facts when fed into computers will designate a person's racial pedigree.

An error in the '60s and '70s were civil rights movements. Morally, these movements were rational. What was false is that the black cannot be placed within the white man's standards. His competitive position is failure. To break out means conflict. No one is at fault, but there are underlying genetic differences. We had better be aware of them rather than screaming equality. Solid black nations adjust to their world beautifully, as do solid white nations. Even the twain may meet as Oriental and white because there is not as much genetic separation between those groups.

Racists sometimes vocalize that blacks should be sent back to Africa. They have as much right to America as anyone else. What is not preposterous is that certain states be designated as black states or territories, in which they can develop their unique culture. Society should be shifting toward fair and equal racial segregation rather than trying to integrate that which is evolutionary not intended.

INTELLIGENCE: William Shockley, Nobel Physics prize-winner in 1956 has stated, "The real threat to the future is 'dysgenics' — retrogressive evolution through the disproportionate reproduction of the genetically disadvantaged. In other words, down-breeding. . . . " He has been vigorously attacked by blacks and sympathetic whites as a racist, because his research shows that blacks are not as intelligent as whites. However, thoughts of the man must be seriously considered. In fairness to the blacks, intelligence tests and college performances in America are based upon white values and were devised by white men within white cultures. Because evolution demands different intelligence and traits for survival, one would expect to find substandard grades in the scores of blacks.

We have explained before that the physical and mental traits which differ within races were brought about by successful adaptation and survival within their peculiarly geographic challenges. It is quite unreasonable to expect blacks to play similar roles in a white society, and vice versa — whites to enter equally and assimilate into a black society. Both races are kings in their own historic evolutionary regime. There should be no animosities in society to their needs. That which is pernicuous is the retention of equalitarianism and socialistic-communistic genetic levelization attempts.

Where the problem arises is when we go to mental traits. Here some would have us believe no divergency exists, but it has been proven in racial studies that certain subracial groups are superior. To date, the Jews are superior to all groups in intelligence. Negroes as a group are at the bottom, independent of educational opportunity.

RACE RECOGNITION: Everyone can have a little bit of everyone else. But a race has a distinctive formula for physical and mental traits. As recently as 1966, Norman Cohen, in his studious treatise, *Warrant for Genocide*, wrote, "The fact there is no such thing as a 'German race' or a 'Jewish race' was of course ignored by all these writers." Start with major races — black, white, yellow, and brown classification by skin color. Within the genetic structure there are specific codes for producing these skin characteristics. In such a genetic pool, as with skin variations, there are hundreds of other variations — bone, tissue, physical and physiological traits, which are easy to distinguish. We describe an individual as Chinese, Negroid, German, French, Jewish, etc. We have been in this game too long to deny that we cannot recognize the median and majority segments of a race or subracial group.

In any capital of Europe, citizens of the host nation immediately recognize foreigners. This is facilitated by dress, mannerisms, and finally, speech. Even though the foreigner may be a resident trying to disguise himself within the culture where there are no clues excepting biological ones, racial recognition is faultless. There go Swedish girls, Scandinavians: light hair, slinky stature, fair skin. There go Chinese: glance at the eyes. There go Germans: high cheekbones, body build, even ability to distinguish if they are Austrian or Northern German. An Italian: no problem. An Englishman: as simple. It is time-honored perception. It is part of our inquisitiveness. Where do people come from? Carlton S. Coon, in *The Living Races of Man*, makes a succinct point — "Even without reference to the brain or to intelligence, the simple statement 'that races exist' drives a small coterie of vocal critics into a predictable and well-publicized frenzy."

BEAUTY: Darwin spoke of sexual selection toward beauty, but he believed that each race had its own conception of what beauty is. Not so. Why do Arabs seek French mistresses and Negroes white girls? There is a universal concept of beauty manifest in contests in which the contenders have remarkably similar approvable points. We admire hairless, light skin, a profuse head of hair, and moderate curves. Purposefully by selecting these attributes we moved mankind in this direction.

In Spain, keeping their subrace pure was no problem. Centuries ago they expulsed Moors and Jews, killed off Protestants. Excuse for preventing immigration is a lack of job opportunity. At the time of Columbus, the entire North and South American continents were composed of only Mongoloids. The Spanish conquered and dispersed their seed with the Mongoloids of South America while the Europeans killed off and displaced the Mongols of North America, all within four centuries.

The rivers of the Rhine, Oder, and mountains of the Pyrenees Alps were as much a factor in the production of subraces as the separation of the continents in the formations of racial groups. Oftentimes the Spaniard and the Frenchman are categorized as being of similar Latin quality as the Italian and Greek. Not only are there immediate variances apparent as blending of Negro blood in the latter two, it is demonstrated by the presence in the blood of sickle cell genes in Italy and Greece.

No matter how the pie is sliced, Caucasoid Europeans, in their conquest of the Americas and displacements of the Mongoloids, or the Caucasoid invasion of North Africa in the last 15,000 years with conquest, displacement and colonizations of traditional Negro lands, both the Negroid and Mongoloid groups come our second best. This crucible was not one or two isolated battles, but encounters over thousands of years. The non-white groups were found evolutionarily lacking in the skills for survival.

Pygmies will not breed with Negroes, or vice versa. When two such subgroups of the Negro race, even in close contact, fail at assimilation, how can we expect white and black to do otherwise? There is no influx of Negro genes into the Pygmy pool. It is what North America has prevented for generations. Every civilized country has racial antagonisms. Berbers, Caucasoids of North Africa, have designated to their Negro hosts occupations of a secondary nature for thousands of years. They refuse to mate with the Negro lower class.

In India, where three races met and blended — the white, yellow, and Australoid — it is significant that it represents a low point of geneticism. No people had less respect for their colony than the English, some of whose social clubs carried the sign, "No dogs or Indians allowed." Nowhere is poverty and chaos as extensive.

The outward facial expression of the Italian would be wasted on the Negro, whose darkness renders subtle visibility useless and who, therefore, must depend on the expressive qualities of his eyeballs and teeth. Facial expression is highly developed in the Caucasoid-Mongoloid, requiring separate sets of platysmal fiber as well as facial muscle fiber. This visual communication by which races differ is present in subracial groups. It has accounted for tragic chasms between German and Jew. It is not so much the communication with a foreign subracial group as it is recognition of one's own evolutionary tribe.

Carlton S. Coon, in *Origin of Races*, carries an excellently documented argumentation that races of mankind split apart in isolated genetic units a considerable time ago, as early as Homo erectus — possibly hundreds of thousands of years ago. Within his evolutionary schema he places five categories of ascending Homo sapiens.

PSYCHIATRISTS: There are nearly 2,000 psychiatrists in Manhattan alone, about one-tenth of the U.S. total. Two adjacent buildings on East 96th Street contain more psychiatrists than there are in 27 countries of the world. This concentration comes about from two genetic sources. One is most psychiatrists are Jewish and follow the line of Sigmund Freud. They pick up this profession because there is a special facility in Jewish neurogenes enabling them to deal in mathematical and abstract concepts. That is why few Jewish men go into trades which require physically coordinated effort.

New York's population is extremely abnormal in types of geneticism its environment houses. Negroes are out of context. Puerto Ricans follow closely behind, making bad adjustment to the north. Lastly, the Jewish people fit perfectly into the financial business and cultural world. They, as a subwhite race are living in the north. Mix the foregoing three races in the same city and you have justification for psychiatric treatment.

RECOGNITION: The American geneticist, Theodosius Dobzhansky, has written, "The biological function of all reproductive isolating mechanisms is essentially the same — inhibition and eventual stoppage of the gene exchange between populations. . . ." It is for this reason man tends to speciation, forming races.

We recognize genetic enemies not only by propaganda and experience, but by underlying instinctive coding. This is inherited antagonism by which we identify ourselves with our own subracial group. This consanquineous bondage with the minimum of effort recognizes the stranger. One species does not search out another for social or sexual relationship. Documentations attest to recognitional signals such as colors, plumage, odor, sound and calls, posture and dance, which alert the intraspecial mammalians to propagate their own kind.

For example, wherever Jewish people located, there was no great desire in the past to mix their genes and lose their identity in the host's pot. They were aided in this pursuit because of biological not cultural traits. The intragroup recognition was plain and identified by facial, physical and mental traits. It is why we resented the "hippie" movement. Not because they were unclean and unsuccessful, and not because they did not conform socially, but because their habitude and hairstyles were outside our instinctive perceptional affection.

IMPRINTING: A form of friends and foe recognition is an open genetic structure which appears after birth and may persist for years. This form of geneticism is known as imprinting and is demonstrated by Konrad Y. Lorenz in his experiments with geese. Basically, he removed the newborn from the parents and substituted himself. In the first few days there was a period in which the isolated gosling fixed the human master as the parent and, by doing so, this parental recognition became fixed and irreversible. After birth, the camera clicked shut on the object that was nursing, nurturing or moving and vocalizing in the fashion of a true parent.

Obviously, this was an abnormal situation for geese to be raised by other than their own kind. Yet it demonstrated an inheritable ability for genetic affection to be photographed and fixed at a point in development. Who does the human baby see first? Who does he imprint upon beside his parental imprintations which would be the strongest? They could be relatives, friends or school chums, working partners. It is interesting to note the attitudes of white plantation owners' children who were raised by black mammys.

It does not follow that school integration of black and white will produce harmony. Rather, it may produce quite the opposite because the imprinting pattern may have already been fixed. Such integration may produce discordance and hasten racial differences because of proximity of opposite directed racial recognitional genes.

I.Q.: Individual differences in I.Q. between races and subracial groups have been well documented. If we go to Dr. Arthur Jensen, Professor of Educational Psychology, University of California, we glean facts. A Jensen paper reported that blacks as a population score significantly lower on I.Q. tests than whites. He attributed the lower I.Q.s to genetic heritage and not to discrimination, poor diet, bad living conditions or inferior schools.

Put aside for a moment the proposition of whether whites or blacks have intellectual superiority. Add the yellow race and subdivisions of all races. We know that races and subraces developed in relatively isolated geographical areas, facing the vastly different challenges for survival and competition with others. By the very force of evolutionary selection we know that, by their adaptation to environmental forces, they of necessity had to develop varied-gened structures to enter the survival stream. Each race or subrace was automatically superiorly adjusted to the problem world he faced. Therefore, on any battery of tests representing human abilities or failings we shall see wide racial and subracial differences.

Where the fervor over racial superiority and inferiority originates, in assessing many traits and characteristics, is not so much in facts that are apparent, but in stubborn philosophical dogmatism concerning human equality that has jackaled at the heels of man from the time of Christ to the French Revolution. There is one massive blind spot in human thought that is the vast inequality between individual men, as well as between nations, races, and subraces.

A fall-out from the Jensen and Shockley studies is that we must examine American educational efforts. Compensatory educational programs have flopped. Minority groups who do not have the same genetic equipment can by no matter or mean, regardless of desegration or privilege, place themselves in a competition position. There cannot be equal job opportunity. Certain jobs are best fitted for the genetic programming that the applicants possess. It should be no disgrace that a fair number of whites make excellent servants to their more proficient masters. Nor should it be belittling that blacks historically have made excellent domestics. No one is questioning that equality is a beautiful Utopia and that each person should have the opportunity to radiate his skills. But this is wishful thinking, because as the world sifts out there is less equality and greater stratification in the roles commensurate with inherent ability.

Jensen demonstrated a 15-point black-white difference in intelligence and stated that 80% of this gap was due to heredity. His data inferred that blacks are born with lower I.Q.s than whites, on the average.

I.Q. is a vastly important quality when entering college where a 115-point intelligence quotient is considered minimum. Only 16% of whites make it over that hurdle; fewer than 3% of blacks achieve adequate scores. The higher engineering schools such as M.I.T. and Cal Tech, have a 130 I.Q. cut-off and only 3% of the white population make it, says Jensen.

There is little left to do than rearrange the scales back to where they originally were and permit normal weights to be registered. America is heavily white-dominated, prestiged and privileged. Tragedy is within the genetic structure. The faster we recognize individual and racial differences and obviate equality, the faster society will settle into harmonious relationship.

Jensen made a distinction between cognitive learning or the abstract use of concepts and ideas, and associative learning or rote memorization, saying that I.Q. tests are a better gauge of cognitive learning. He also stated that intelligence between races may not be of the same caliber.

Refer to the past genetic necessities which were required by the varied local groups and challenges that were presented to the evolving races. Manners of cerebral circuitry would have variance as the particular groups passes through the screen of selection and survival. The whites developed superior abstract intelligence due to their hostile northern glacial confrontations, as well as the necessary cooperative modes of life established such as hunting parties, etc. We would expect to find not only gene differences, but rearranged neural pathway differences.

EDUCATION: Education is intimately linked to the I.Q. Measure of intellectual ability is genetically based. At the commencement of the 20th century the scientific world was hoodwinked into believing that everyone was equal and that all that was needed was proper training and environment to bring out basic talents. Such a concept is false from personal review of friends, enemies, relations, associates, and contacts. In 1848, Horace Mann declared that education was "the great equalizer of the conditions of men." It is conceivable that in the days of illiteracy, education had an advantage. Horace Mann was preceded by John Locke, who believed that all minds at birth were blank states and all children were equally and infinitely educable. Rousseau also believed education began at birth and continued until the age of 25, with little hope for learning after that age when the pinnacle was attained.

Tragedian in the drama was biology, which none understood. Ignorance was rooted in the enlightenment as well as the ignorance of the educators to follow. They thrust American society into an expensive, wasteful, and inefficient educational system that trainers of dogs would have pulled up short. Thus was born a social institution, the American educational system, based primarily on providing lucrative benefits for teachers and administrators at the expense of the taxpayers. Programs like Head Start, initiated to help poor children do as well as middle-class children, became a flop. Not because of humanitarian effort, but because poor people generally have dull and dumb children, produced as a result of the geneticism of the parents.

A Coleman study, in 1966, analyzing more than 600,000 children's academic environments, concluded that there were fewer differences in curriculums, teachers, and facilities between the white and minority schools than had previously been suspected. It was therefore suggested that youngsters' family background counted more toward their achievement than did school differences; and inferred the inability of schools to reshape society.

INEQUALITY. Sociologist Jencks, in a study of inequality, concluded that if children could be made to learn equally in equally good schools, their achievement would not erase the economic inequality. It becomes apparent that educational, equalitarian pressures to formulate equalitarian masses is a "will-of-the-wisp." The rich, prestigious, powerful and privileged shall be with us in the future, as in the past, be it under whatever system of government.

One wonders if making educational opportunity equal would not, in fact, by equality pressures, bring about inequality, because then heredity cannot play its supreme role. Genetics demonstrates we are what our chemical codes have permitted us to be. Take one look at the tremendous number of faces of people that populate the earth, and you can commence to understand huge differences which are ensconced within the calvariums of each. High time for democracy to wind its way out of the fog of equality and set people into pursuits of which they are capable.

What looms in society's horizon is the necessity to return to the normalcy of the biological and evolutionary process. Instead of wasting time, money, and energy on equality, we should be utilizing the tools we have at hand. We should spectrum individuals into fields of innate programmings — to those areas where they are not overtrained. A positive step would be killing the graduated income tax which is used as a sadistic device by socialists to level the capable to the incompetent. Although the communists are the biggest mouths when it comes to proclaiming equality, they are the most pernicuous in its violation. In the Soviet Union, only 6% of the entire population are communists — that is, belonging to the communist party representing prestige, power, plus hidden wealth.

U.S. News and World Report, on August 4, 1975, told of the inequality in classless Russia, explaining that an elite group is enjoying a way of life denied to the masses. Officials not only receive better salaries, they are able to shop in special stores reserved for foreigners. The right family background is helpful in gaining admission to the best schools. Who one knows is an important key to jobs. This elite class numbers about a quarter million out of 250-million people, roughly one in a thousand.

This may be a trifle low compared with the rest of the world, but genetically it is comparable with American life. In a small city of ten thousand people you will rarely find more than twenty persons who are top quality in professions, business or leadership roles. In Japan, there is the Eta, or untouchable class, which performs the distasteful work. It is at the lowest end of the hierarchy scale and remains intact today. Although Americans do not wish to recognize this lowest genetic group because of their strong feelings concerning democracy, it is persistent.

MINIMUM WAGE: Attempts to eliminate this lower strata by enforcing minimum wage laws only thrusts its members into unemployment and welfare dependence. Economic biology has been unsuccessfully interpreted by legislators. Wage coercion is thought to restructure inequality. This is absurd, because this great group of people must be fed, cared for, supervised and babied as children. With such responsibility they can only be employed in the free market at whatever the going rate. Further, to dignify these people, their employer cannot be burdened with the infinite range of statutes and requirements that are legislated to protect them from exploitation. For high employment the government needs to subsidize the employer not the employee. In this fashion, what skills this lower labor group possesses can be utilized.

ABILITY. Karl Marx's repetitive quote, "From each according to his abilities, to each according to his needs," comes imaginatively right out of a biological dung-heap. It fully recognizes that one will take unequally from the citizenry. A good producer will be milked in the same fashion as a scant producer. Then the product, the re-feed, will be given not according to excellence, efficiency or performance, but given back according to need.

Such a statement negates the natural process of evolution and the forwardance of the best hereditary characteristics by equalizing that which was never intended to be equal, and denying survival of the fittest. Hierarchical coding was of tremendous power in survival. Its preservation will serve the population by diversity.

Hitler stated that the man who misjudges and disregards racial laws forfeits his happiness and thwarts the triumphal march of the best race. We do know that racial progression within its environmental challenge adheres to the laws of evolutionary success and natural selection. Those individuals who have been fortunate enough to succeed and propagate offspring, do derive happiness in this most important phase of genetic purpose. What we do not know is for which race the triumphal march is being played.

We may suspect that it is the white race with its Europeans, Jews, Arabs, Nordics, and the non-Mongoloid Russians, plus their issues overseas. Now that confrontational borders are fixed nations, there is all the more drive that one race shall succeed and the other perish. Inherent racial recognitions have determined that the future of mankind will never be a uniform blend. There is the inability to settle or amalgamate with the Chinese by either blacks or whites, and there are tendencies of some nations to insure that their genetic stock remains pure against intrusions, such as the Japanese and the Spanish.

It is not political factors that determine immigration-emigration policies. It is underlying geneticism of masses which demands preservation of based geneticism. The United States has been embroiled in many conflicts as a white race, a torch-bearer of Western European civilization, with no consideration for other than Caucasoids. Successfully the Mongoloids were annihilated and Negroes removed from slavery into an isolate position outside the white genetic stream.

AMALGAMATION: It has been the professed desire of black leaders to amalgamate white blood. Stubborn resistance to this, in spite of contrary socialistic, governmental, and media propaganda, has been white women. With but a few exceptions, they innately perceive a betrayal of their genetic programming. As well, racial dishonor and social ostracism would be visited upon them and their heirs. Beautiful on paper in civil rights statutes, racial equality, integration, and assimilation is nothing more than aspirations of petty politicians gathering votes. Beneath is selected biology which has recognitional codes for propagation outweighing anything lawmakers may dictate in their eagerness for self-aggrandizement.

In *Mein Kampf*, is stated, "Blood mixture and the resultant drop in the racial level is the sole cause of the dying out of old cultures; for men do not perish as a result of lost wars, but by the loss of that force of resistance which is contained only in pure blood."

If we rid ourselves of the notion concerning pure blood, we may re-arrange the thought that only those cultures survive, progress, conquer, rule, that are possessed with genetic abilities, from loyalty and religious genes to muscular, mental, and drive abilities which fit the environmental challenges surrounding them. A nation's rise and fall is attributable to the skills and resoluteness of the genes residing within their populations. One fine example of this preserving ability (the last thing from Hitler's thought) was the Jewish people who, after thousands of years of wanderings and persecution, have maintained their cohesiveness and identity, regained their homeland, and are to be found in positions of power and wealth throughout the world. Nowhere is there a more ironic example of white subracial superiority than that of "the chosen Jewish people." In the Nazi experience, their aegis of being was impaled upon the spear of racial contention. Jewish history is power of genetic drive.

A book such as *Mein Kampf*, which was almost a Bible to tens of millions of Germans, could not be in totality filled with nonsense. There are glimpses into evolutionary racial facts, even though crudely presented. One of the most painful aspects of that work is that it sets up superiority and inferiority propositions concerning races and subraces. This is accurate if one would become specific and use measurements such as cultural advancement, standards of living, political and governmental stability, democracy, humanitarianism or institution in which man differs.

Hitler speaks that giving one's own life for others is more strongly developed in the Aryan and that, as a result, he subordinates his own ego to the life of the community. This can be fairly accurate in the northern Caucasoid, as we witness huge masses of glorious fools who slug it out on field and sea in an almost perpetual death machine. Experiences of the northern whites in the hunting, killing art has instilled in them more vicious mechanisms than their black relations. There is no monopoly in any race regarding cruelty, as we have witnessed in the conflicts of Orientals and American Mongoloids. Yet, along the line of advancing social genetics, survival depended upon these malicious traits. Within the formations of races there developed a range of terrorism and inhumanity, just as someplace along the line to all sapiens came the innate characteristics of goodness and humanitarism and the soul, as we know of it in religion.

Complaining of the Jews' thousand-year-old mercantile dexterity, Hitler admitted that a Jew was far superior to the helpless and honest Aryans, so that in a short time commerce ventures threatened to become a monopoly. He regarded this Jewish intrusion a state within a state, by one who never cultivated the soil and who, after persecution, bounded back in short time. Yet Hitler's hate was not only directed to the Jews, but also to the German "princes." And, as the Jews were persecuted, so were millions of Germans who were Hitler's political enemies. There can be little question that the Jews are capable people. With their genetic makeup they are able to control a measure of economic largess out of proportion to their numbers. The same thing happens in America. Ability, drive, perseverance, sacrifice, know-how, determination and dedication are virtues which can be operated by any man equipped with the proper genes to succeed in whatever field he chooses, as an individual and not as a member of a subracial group.

Yet never can a polyglot society hold the cohesive advantageous forces represented by minorities. Intrabusiness relationships among ethnic groups has been a high advantage, even offering members of the same sect educational opportunities which would not otherwise be available.

If we ask why this came about, we must refer to genetic coding rather than to the cohesiveness of religion. The Jews simply have a frugal and persevering temperament, a personal temperance, willingness to work and, more importantly, in more abundance than in other ethnic groups, nervous tissue capacities which propel them to the forefront.

EQUALITY: One of the paradoxes of the Jewish people is that they sponsor equality of race, color, and civil rights, when they themselves are an outstanding example of an unequal superiorly adjusted group. It is no accident in that genetic experimental city, New York, where millions of Jews confront millions of Puerto Ricans and Negroes, that standards of living between the ethnic groups are fantastically unequal. Nor is it strange that in arts, sciences and professions, where everything is culturally elevated, Jews outnumber blacks by more than one hundred to one. Success in the crucible has nothing to do with opportunity, education, deprivement, or any form of persecution. It has to do with rock-solid, programmed gened abilities which are innately registered within subracial contestants.

Unfortunately, the Negro, magnificent as he is, is out-gened in a northern complex cultural environment. His being was superbly adapted to relations in Africa and among his own kind. In forced transportation overseas into cultural-gened societies of the Caucasoid, he is thrust into an adaptational schema with which he is not fitted to cope. Adaptation and integration of the black into the society ruled and structured by white genes will take a greatly extended period of time.

Immediately one would suspect that the strong Jewish drive for freedom and equality, or the creation of communism by such Jewish leaders as Marx, Trotsky, Lenin, even Lincoln, whose name is to be noted as Abraham and whose countenance is as fine an example of Jewish nobility that can be found, was based upon cultural traits compensating for persecution. It could permit the marketplace to be open to all equally wherein talents of the Jewish people could exceed. It is the championship of equality, to free the Chosen People from the tyranny of the modern-day Pharaohs.

From out of evolutionary adaptation there was strong selection toward Jews that could peacably coexist in a strange culture and who could open the marketplace to equalitarian principles. While the pre-Hitlerian persecutions of Jews throughout Europe were notable at times, they never prevented the development of Jewish societies and the success of their individual members, excepting in rare instances when they were expulsed from Spain.

Hitler railed at the German communists, princes, and political opponents as well as Jews. Fundamentally, he was seeking something that is almost unobtainable — a homogenous, subracially unmixed and consentive society. But subracial cohesiveness innately programmed places polyglot societies in continual conflict. The seed that would outsow others is native to evolutionary advancement.

The chasm between Jewish people and Hitler and Naziism had little to do with economics or high school positioning. It was admitted genetic confrontation. Consequences were staggeringly unbelievable. Once the ornamental vestiture had been removed from the contestants, it was a struggle of raw genetic survivorship. Apalling as history relates, it is companioned with incidents throughout civilized time. How will such genetic savagry in evolutionary struggle end in the future?

NEW YORK: Most American Jews are intolerant of Negroes. They do not associate with them, neither do they intermarry. The New York Negro, on the other hand, accuses the Jew of exploiting him. This is natural, for New York is composed of Negroes and Jews; consequently, the Negro must blindly point to someone close to explain his dilemma.

To the Jewish people, the Negro represents a mirror of their past. He provides a readily available distraction, a first line of defense in the rights of minority groups. It is this Jewish jurisprudence regarding oppressed peoples that is of foremost rank. In consideration of their own chaotic history, they are virtually world leaders in humanitarian efforts, democratic principles, and the rights of law.

RACIAL GENES: Hoebel, in *Races of Mankind*, states, "A more penetrating analysis of race will seek to isolate the gene qualities that determine the form rather than the contests to consider the form itself. In other words, the question becomes, What is the genetic composition of the population?" This is what the future of racial genetics will strive for and the actual genes labeled, identified, and related to the traits and qualities they produce. Once this is done, all the emotional nonsense over race will cease. The writing will be on the coded wall exactingly who has what.

Why human races must be separated is evidenced by the separation of species. One finds that two or more similar species will not inhabit the same locality; that is, unless they differ in ecological requirements — differences in breeding habits, their predators or their food. It is that they are not identical that species mix in the same locale, for each becomes efficient in their specific adaptabilities.

NORTHERN ADAPTION: With dissimilarity of races when they are placed in the same ecological niche, for example, the American system, they cannot properly compete. Such was the case of the American Indian past and the Negro present. As we move toward the equatorial countries, the Negro has better adaptability than in the northern countries as do the Indian. Polyglots, such as the white, Negroid and Mongoloid races unite in a relatively socially harmonious southern country such as Venezuela, whereas northern cohabitation for Negroes is problematic and conflicting.

It is not the air conditioner, nor the oil furnace that makes harmony practical. There are too many other facets within genes to transport the races out of their historically tempered environments. It was no accident, when the New World was colonized, that the southern Spanish chose the warmer areas in which to settle, while the northern English chose the northern, colder climates. Subconsciously, their adaptional genes were choosing their environment; the search for gold and spices was superficial.

SKIN: Human skin gives off a reflective value that may be accurately measured with a reflectance spectrophotometer. These color differences, as for example between black and white, may involve genes of three or four chromosomes.

Cavalli, in *Polygenic Inheritance of Skin Color*, points out that the F_1 generation is near the mid-point of Caucasian and Negro value, suggesting absence of dominance. Further, the number of genes responsible for differences in skin color between black and white is small, each with equal effect. One group is considered all-white alleles and the other all-dark alleles. Because the two populations, European and African, have been geographically separated for tens of thousands of years, the genes are homozygous.

Harrison and Owen demonstrated that in a white and black mating, the skin will be colored between the two, like mixing paint. If the middle color (F_1) is mated to a white, he will now have color mid-point between the two. If he (F_1) is mated with a black, he will also mid-point. The half white and black, if he mates with a white, will become whiter. If he mates with a black, he will become blacker.

JAZZ: Racial and national origins may not only be traced by morphological and physiological differences, but indirectly by the way the individual responds to various music, inclinations or nonsense syllabling. Within the neurogene platter there are side-dish components revealing ancestry. Blacks have characteristics of beat and tonal appreciation that are particularly attractive to adult whites. It is as if the brain's geneticism prepares the newborn not only how to act, but what to expect to inbed into its woof. A separation of the races would miss the great beauty which is consequent to interracial relations.

SUPREMACY: Anyone tending to build up white supremacy may forget what utter pigs, bums, scoundrels, thieves, knaves, murderers, cut-throats, idiots, imbeciles, criminals, crooks, convicts, cheats, robbers, curs and liars are within the white race. Here is the pitfall of racial arguments. It is not that black and white should be segregated, but rather interracial marriage should be prohibited. However, there are some interracial marriages, such as between Chinese and French, which appear as genetic progress. The mixing of race should be on the advice of scientists rather than on the whims of proximity and opportunity which is afforded by integration.

Within each race is the good, pure, capable, intellectual, benign, the humanitarian and the industrious. They are not in the same proportions in any race or subrace because the evolutionary format of the evolving isolation required differing adaptation. Races may remain side by side, but segregation takes place according to abilities. Enclaves of intellectualism are found in universities, in the worker class of factory towns and in artists' villages. Within each race and subrace are dominants, aristrocrats, intellectuals, as well as criminals and *estupidos*. No race has an option on the good or the bad within it.

NORTHERN: At the beginning of the middle ages, around 800 A.D., the northmen of the Scandinavian countries, Norway, Sweden, Denmark, plundered, laid waste, and settled European civilizations. They were mighty men, greatly feared. Little could stop them. It appears as if the clock of history was turning backwards. Men that came from such harsh tempera-tured lands to suddenly flare into a continuous fighting force, needed not only geographical base of operation, but a genetic base of action.

In *The History of Medieval Europe*, by Lynn Thorndyke, we can glean the DNA eruption that sparked the uprising. The author sets forth their spirit and standards, "The grimmest of all men was in his wrath, and marvelous pains he laid on his foes. Some he burned in the fire, some he let wild hounds tear, some he gave to serpents, some he stoned, some he cast from high cliffs." Yet we are further assured that he was not only "before all men for heart in battle," he was the "gladdest and gamesomest of men, kind and lowly, exceeding eager, bountiful and glorious of attire."

This explosion of animalistic ferocity and human insensitivity in Caucasoids can be explained in gene regression. There was a considerable amount of inbreeding, for homozygotes to take over the more recessive traits of decency. The thoughtfulness of an emerging society was suddenly relegated to a primitive and predatory form.

Establishment of anti-social genes, breeding and selecting toward muscular power and ruthlessness, would be an advantage in pillage and conquest. What brought these horrid men and their depredations to a halt was not the consolidation of opposing forces, weapons, inventions, but the innocent introduction of heterozygotes, more sociably amenable over the centuries through breeding of conquerors and conquered. Northmen had a proven warrior superiority. That which eventually defeated and placated them was the Trojan horse in the form of countless Helens, whom they subjected.

Earlier, Attila's rampage across the face of Europe was in similar vein. These great armies, built into formidability, did not structure themselves overnight. They were the result of slow genetic smoldering, in an isolated populace, to achieve their rapacious and conquestadorial genetic roles. Mercenaries have always been secondary army units. It is not a question of morale, drive or exortation that makes them inferior fighting units, but rather that their gene programming is not of the quality of the initiators which hire them.

BIOTIC POTENTIAL: As animal and plant populations' growth, known as biotic potential, are checked by environmental resistance, this limit, known as the carrying capacity of the species, if increased too rapidly, will overshoot and crash. Society and social populations act similarly. Man's biological ability to expand his social unit is limited not so much by the environment, as by the rivalry of other nations and their territorial tenacity. Important in the population expansion of a society is the gene specialties and abilities of the organized pool. Nations become great and powerful societies only because dominants have forcefully willed and because of superior genetic banks. One reviews history impressed with forceful leaders who seem to guide its direction. They are little more than flag-bearers. What resides within the group's genes in the long run determines destiny of a subrace or nation. It is why the South American nations are second-raters compared with the Colossus of the North. White genes of the northern European Caucasoids brought this immense divergency about.

This does not mean that these genes have superior qualities over South American mixtures. It simply means that they have pigheaded gened absurdity to engage in four bloody years of civil war to achieve what is termed "saving a nation" to preserve the union, while southern neighbors may have considered such a crusade not worth the misery or price in blood.

The frontiers of any society are in its genes and the cleverness of its eugenic selection. Under any circumstances, no one may ever expect to see the so-called Third World countries — the underdeveloped — develop into first-rate powers with high standards of living. Environment is not the limiting factor. It is codes that are keyed within the neurogenic pool of these societies.

NICHE: By diversification, competition within the habitat can be avoided. If the Negro is permitted to do his thing in his way, and other ethnic groups their things in their special ways, if the lunk-headed socialists who want to unitize everybody into a conforming mode of obedient jelly are thrown from office, then the races and subraces may cohabit the given ecology peaceably, each seeking niches which fit their attributes, thereby eliminating competition to produce a harmonious and viable society.

Andrew Billingsley, in *Black Families in America*, relates, "In the urban area where 75% of the black population live, 10% are upper class, lawyers, doctors, athletes, 40% are middle-class, teachers, business managers, truck-drivers, clerks, and skilled blue-collar workers. The lower class of 50% is fragmented into three parts: in the lower class you have the working, which are non-poor with steady jobs; the working poor; and the underclass or non-working poor."

This is not a particularly bad showing for a genetic pool which must adapt to culture of the white-gened pool. Whatever social legislative edicts may be forthcoming, they will never level strata unless at the expense of the white majority, which will be pulled down to compensate, not for the inferiority, but for artificial adaptational patterns.

As with black society, we see communist classification, 50-60% of the people of the proletariat class, 30% of the bourgeois, and 10% brains, dominants and ruling party members. Negroes never embrace communism. It is not because of lack of indoctrination. Reds have exerted heaven and earth to bring Negroid peoples into the fold to be their prisoners without success. Nor is it because of lack of intellectual ability to grasp the principles of Marxism made extremely simple through propaganda lines.

NEGRO ASTUTENESS: We must look at a genetic quality superior than that in white societies. The Negro sees through the hoopla of communistic propaganda. One form of dictatorship is as bad as the other. In majority of nations under black control, the structure is never democratic, but autocratic and dictatorial. Negro social genetic pattern forged beneath the African sun accepts a relatively lesser degree of submission to dominants. To adapt to communism is too much extra baggage.

POLITICAL GENES: Northern Caucasoids embraced forced communism, dictatorship and democracy from the rigors of the complexity of northern evolutionary advancement which demanded greater cooperation, interdependency and specialization. The communism rooted in Russia was selective, an annihilatory process evoked by Red butchers on their white compatriots carrying the best dominant and intellectual genes, to favor proletarian masses. That France, Italy and Eastern Germany have developed a different brand of communism lies not in conditions, but in checking by their upper-class, bourgeois dominants.

By freak accident communism could take over the earth. But it could take over only so long as it could control the drift of genetic pool toward the lower-gened. China, with its vast number of peasants, has never supported an intellectualized bourgeois democracy. It shall for a long time be based on peasantry and dictatorship by the few.

Thomas O'Toole, of the *Washington Post,* reported a panel of five white scientists at the American Association for the Advancement of Science, and declared there is no relation between race and intelligence. Richard Lewontin of Harvard charged that the social Darwinists based their claims on bad data. This contradicts Dr. Shockley, Dr. Jensen, and R. J. Herrnstein, who have said that there are racial differences in intelligence, such as blacks being generally inferior as measured by test scores to whites.

A Harvard biologist said that human experiments suggest that there are no genetic differences between blacks and whites. Unfortunately, the five scientists who failed to recognize vast inequalities between races and subraces and between individuals are possibly acting out of human motivational charity and religious philosophical genes.

The very existence of races and subracial groups and our ability to recognize and classify them, as well as the historic evolutionary isolation which made such divergence possible, is positive evidence concerning human diversity. Geographical and adaptational requisites required quantitative and qualitative factors specifically aligned to evolutionary advancement. The Negro did not need the same genetic library as the northern white or Oriental. Not only are there differences in intelligence, depending on which characterization is measured, resulting from radiating isolation, but an absolutism in the nature of biology. Varied traits, mental and physical, are the result of expansion and forwardance of the species.

OCCUPATION: It is not a matter of chance that immigrants choose their occupations in lands to which they have immigrated. An example is the ability of the Jewish people to continue in trade, commerce, banking, and law, to which they are programmed by millenniums of genetic experience, selection, and talent. A number of police and a far-above-average number of our politicians are derived from Irish stock. These fields suit their characteristics. The Irish love argument, controversy, and heavy drinking. They are extroverted, communicate well, and are clever at controlling a situation. Their continual warrings in their past history, their frugalness and poverty, inbred both a strong sense of sociability and durability. All these traits combined to make them admirable politicians and policemen.

We find the Germans, because they are a prime warrior race, evolving from a hunting economy, following the same pursuits, namely the armed forces, meat-packing, road-builders, constructors and scientists. They are people of mechanical and technical traits, developed in the strategies of survival when glaciers were overflowing Europe.

You cannot characterize the pure Spanish in America because there are so few. There is a host of *Mestizos*, mixtures of Indian, Negro, and a minor amount of Spanish blood, that are heir to Spanish culture and language. We do not find these people in preponderance in the professions and intellectual arts. Rather, they are farm-workers, or in the cities, factory employees. The characteristics of the Mongoloid, Negroid and a pinch of Spanish blood suit them to these occupations. For, as Southerners, their livelihood was not derived from the hunting, intellectual and technical pursuits, but from individual food-gatherers or agriculturists who did not need strategy or the scientific arts to develop.

Individuality is explained in the Hispanic American culture because there was no great necessity for cooperation, for complex social groupings. This is to be even noted in the South American countries in which, for centuries, there has been a lack of national coordination unsimilar to the European Common Market or the Anglo-Saxon world. With their vast land and mineral resources, South America should have become the wealthiest and most powerful nation on earth. However, individual jealousies, heated emotions and pride prevented this. Large-scale cooperation has never been a genetic inheritance of this special mixture. A food-gatherer, a forest-dweller, a farmer, possesses a greater independence in his individual being. The sum influence on these people has been to calcify them into a moderate approach to life, less grandiose national schemes, and more individual family withdrawal. On the other hand, the Spanish of Spain are more European and northern, and with the French, can be compared with the Anglo-Saxon culture, for theirs too was a past of hunting and warring.

Italian immigrants became almost exclusively laboring people. It was because the higher occupational niches in the American economic structure were filled by those of more adaptable geneticism. The great art, music and literature of the Italian people was unfortunately no ticket to an occupational position. The Italian expression, "in the arts," rather than the sciences and intellectual pursuits, is again genetic. Sun and fruit, the necessity for minimum housing standards, the rich fields, and the wine, give support to the pursuit of the noble arts that flood the museums and libraries of Italy.

Rh: Lerner states, "Rh disease may provide an exception to the notion that interracial crosses can have no detrimental effects." He continues in stating that, should Europeans migrate to China and interbreed, the Chinese genetic pool would be adversely affected, because the Asian-American-Indian and native Australian populations are 100% Rh positive. Thus, by injecting Rh negative people into the Orient, you inject a child disease producing factor. A plus father and a negative mother leads to the offspring's disease. On the other hand, when the male Huns invaded Europe, they settled to interbreed with the local populations. It would have been beneficial since they had none of the negative genes for the combination to work. In Europeans, there are about 40% positive genes and in Negroes, 25%. The problem arises when a positive father gives half his positive genes to the fetus in a negative mother. The first fetus and child develops no ill effects, but because of this half-positiveness, it causes the mother to produce in her bloodstream antibodies against this invasion. By the time the next pregnancies take place, the mother's antibodies enter the fetal circulation to produce a fatal, if untreated, disease in the offspring known as hemolitic jaundice.

These facts are trying to tell us more than the mere question of an antigen-producing antibodies which agglutinates some types of human blood cells. There are racial differences, and since interbreeding produces child death which is the highest of selective evolutionary factors, we may ably conclude that it is one of the methods that leads to speciation.

ME DRIVE: One of the strong factors in evolutionary advancement is selfish drive, for the lowest number of individuals to go forward and propagate their own kind to the exclusion of others. This Adam-and-Eve effect is the substance of the competitiveness within all species, and evolution is its forge. Yet it is considerably modified in man because of the fixation of social genes, whereby society becomes a high-ranking element in survival.

In the Rh exclusionary factor, a race is saying to the stranger in his midst, "I want nothing to do with you, for we shall produce diseased offspring." This evidence of racial incompatability has a factor in time. Had we not precipitated into the new stone-tool era and discovered agriculture and horticulture, man would have speciated out. That may have taken a mere million years, because geographical gates such as the Bering Straits had closed and the Mongols of America would have arisen into a separate human line, in the same fashion as the Old World and New World monkeys are distinct.

KILLERS: Consider what has happened when the dominant Y chromo-somed KK killer genes of the whites has been injected into the relatively docile pure Negroes, where the gene is absent or in recessive homozygenous form. The old South had little problem with crime, nor did the great civilizations of antiquity under even their slave cultures, excepting a few rare uprisings that may have been caused by fractional breeding. It wasn't until the white man implanted his aggressive genes into the black female who transmitted them to her offspring, that the particular nervous, anxious, rebellious, irritated and anti-social black-part white society came into being. The heterozygotic Kk and even the transferral of the KK, the aggressive killer northern genes, could have none other than disruptive effects in non-programmed blacks.

One tends to forget that in breeding, the resultants can go in many directions. When one quality is selected for, it generally brings in its wake a host of other qualities. Martin Luther King, Jr. and his movement, the civil rights' struggle, riots in the northern cities, slum conditions, and high ghetto crime rates are not sociological or economically produced. They are human dysgenics. Had the whites not forced their genes on the blacks, had the biological differences of the races remained pure, with slavery out of the way, one might witness the finest of symbiotic relationship between races.

TRAITS: Obviously you can't yank white genes out of the mixture. We know that whites are more restless, subject to nervous breakdowns, are highly prone to duodenal ulcers, are easily societized to produce massed violence and war, are more aggressive, covetous, and monogamous. They place greater emphasis on abstract spirituality. They drive harder and are more demanding of social contribution. They are patriarchical, whereas the black society tends to favor feminine dominancy. The foregoing are rooted within the genetic structure of the whites, excepting peptic ulcer, which may be the product of nicotine, caffeine, and emotion, producing high stomach acid.

A genetic road for the blacks which are intermixed is to breed back into their original founding. This they won't do. They tend to select toward white, for it may promise in reality better jobs and economic status.

Yet, with the efforts of such slogans as "Black is beautiful," and the rediscovery of their ancestral arts and history and, especially, with the emergence of black African nations which have not sympathized with the plight of the blacks in America, they could pull off an evolutionary gambit of great success.

Advantages of the return of the pure race, to breed out white genes, would be many. Less tension, more affection and a longer lifespan, as well as a greater fulfillment in aspects of individual being, including family, would result. There would be far less crime and the further development of their innate values that have been frustrated by a white society. More importantly, even in today's climatically adjusted living, they would need to migrate to the south where their physical genetic disposition is supremely adaptable.

As every drama has a setting, so race must be set in the original mold of which it was created over hundreds of thousands of years. Rapid cultural innovations may aid in some forward evolutionary selection, but it can never displace the vast fixed adjustments that nature has welded over long periods of time. You can no more export the Negro to the Arctic than you can export the Eskimo to Africa. When the white man migrated west, he was entering new territory, but familiar, adaptable, gene-tested climate, flora and fauna.

Future for the Negro in America lies not in civil rights, but in back-crossing out his white genes, a migration south, and a handle on his own sovereignty. White supremacy is a distasteful concept. We have seen how the Anglo-Saxon whites as they took over the United States, annihilated the Mongoloid population. Coon recites another displacement being that of the

Caucasoids who moved into North Africa as ancestors of Berbers and Arabs, which ousted the Bushman as well as the Negro and Pygmy to push them southward. A similar crowd-out was performed by the Mongoloids in Asia and Indonesia.

What we may interpret from racial aggression is that the northern yellow and white races developed killer genes from the rigors of northern hunting, which were no match for the darker races to the south.

No one can quarrel with the killer ability of whites. The 20th century is the ultimate testament to this racial acquisition of war-like drive. From Russia and Spain to the United States, monuments have been erected by the thousands to the heroes of the bloody art.

A pause is in order to consider the relatively small genocidal and violent wars waged by the Negro race. They have never fielded destructive armies, nor made massive horrendous bloody deeds on their relatives. Climate, warm in nature, may have had sedative effect. The basic disproportion in this wretched display of insensitive, incessant and cruel wars with its unbelievable carnage, destruction, and misery is nowhere more than in genes and especially those of northern whites. Anthropologist Carlton S. Coon states, "If Africa was the cradle of mankind, it was only an indifferent kindergarten. Europe and Asia were our principal schools." Coon felt that three of the five human subspecies crossed the sapien's line outside of Africa.

SOCIETY: From hundreds of bone-bearing sites, Coon has catalogued diligently facts to support the five major lines of human descent. However, society, in its more primitive form, goes further back, for in many species we see preliminary forms of society — namely, the tendency to operate in groups rather than individually. "There's safety in numbers." Not only is there a protective factor in numbers, there is also a ready ability for contracting sexual partners of the gene pool rather than having to search them out. Propinquity, even in modern humans (boss and secretary, students in high school) are examples of the facility in mating provided by adjacency.

Most important early elements in the construction of society which are mutually beneficial are the variation and skills of its membership. Hierarchy and dominance give the mass leadership direction. Skills in various performances give it intelligent capability and performance greater than any individual. Ten eyes can serve sentinel duty greater than four.

RACE: Coon's thesis is that half a million years ago, the erect man, Homo erectus, was divided into five geographic races. From these territorial points at different times, he developed into the Homo sapien form, or the more intelligent form. His five races include the Eurasiatic lines of white, yellow, and Australian — *Caucasoid, Mongoloid,* and *Australoid,* the African line of *Congoids,* Negroes and Pygmies, and the *Capoids,* the Bushmen and Hottentots, who supposedly migrated from the north of Africa to its south post glacially.

We would expect from long gene isolate pool development not merely an independent and cultural development, but the development of hundreds of genes and thousands of neurogenes to originate and become fixed within the pools. These variances would be due to societies reacting under varied environmental pressures, or even produced by founder genes, isolated within the large masses. Society becomes highly differentiated for races and their subracial groups. It is asininity of equalitarians whose hearts pour out from Christian and communistic ideology that one may bed, breed and culturally assimilate major races. The white in America and the black carrying 30% of white genes have come to an unpleasant impasse.

On the other hand, where the whites and blacks in the old South were divided, outside of slavery, there was mutual respect and harmonious co-exitence. Let no one feel we are speaking in favor of white supremacy. An unfavorable percentage of every race is composed of murderers, thugs, thieves, rapists, criminals, bums, degenerates, addicts, etc. One cannot gloss the majesty of man without reasonably regarding the miserable geneticisms of a portion of his population. To white, black or yellow race, this undesirable element is no tribute and they do not derive from a lack of education, opportunity or economic insufficiency. With every population there is bound to be inferior mutational variables. Even normal variables in all populations are bound to have their dregs of the keg. Will Rogers' famed slogan, "I never met a man I didn't like," is good and profitable theatre, but it is nonsensical genetics.

An intriguing observation made by Coon is that since animal husbandry and agriculture were invented by the white and yellow races, they were privileged to out-populate the other three and pressure them into the smaller areas of the world. By 1500 A.D., the Caucasoids and Mongoloids accounted for all the territories of North Africa, Europe, Asia, the Pacific Islands excepting Australia, and both North and South America.

RACIAL MIX: Further, Coon stated, "Racial intermixture can upset the genetic as well as the social equilibrium of a group, and so newly introduced genes tend to disappear or be reduced. . . . Were it not for the mechanism cited, men would not be black, white, yellow or brown. We would all be light chalk." He contends that there has been enough gene flow in the last half-million years to have homogenized us all.

These observations we regard supportive of *Genetic Basis of Society*. We have decried racial intermixture; but more than that, we have pointed out that there is an inherent gened mechanism within races and subraces that makes them suspicious of racial strangers, that isolate often voluntarily (such as the Jews) and determine breeding patterns.

"Never the twain shall meet," is a genetic truism. It is the *raison d'etre* of the divisions of humanity. Strong interforces are continuously advising racial cohesiveness and in it the prompting nations. When we consider the United States and false theories regarding its melting pot, we are faced with the fact that it is composed of a white race which has managed to preserve many ethnical groups, as well as a minority black race. Interbreeding placed 30% white gened mixture into blacks; to remain as much outside the Caucasoid sphere as if they were not intermixed.

Heredity, Evolution and Society, by I. Michael Lerner, is marred by the equality of races — to negate the concept of race, and more, to propose racial equality. Lerner contends that it may be eventually possible in genetical engineering to change the genetic instructions of skin color. He states that it is urgent that biological truths about races be introduced into the American mores so that they may influence our views and actions on racial equality and social justice. He speaks about the absence of pure races and that there is no foundation for the belief that interracial crosses have harmful effects. He relates that as the blacks develop into a power group, they may restrain interracial mating because of the black fear of loss of identity among lighter-skinned offspring. Finally, Lerner complains about a Georgia legislature which voted to prohibit blood transfusions between different races. And asks, "What do they mean by the term 'race'?"

Skin color, even if it is changed, is not the only difference in the genes between races. Look at a photograph of a white-black — one in which the pigmentation is absent. They are a pretty horrifying sight. If skin color is the only prescription for altering blacks to white, then the sociological result would be a failure for there needs to be an alteration in which blacks could approach whites, almost a million years of evolution. Retrace black environmental adaptational and social experience of Africa in the glacerial experiences of Europe, and presto, he would be a Caucasoid.

Evolution has provided for two delightful and pleasant races, with mental and physical dissimilarities, wrought by forges of time and environmental adaptive evolvements. There is no need to bed them together or excuse one or the other. They are perfectly adapted and suited to their particular geographical locale and to the form of society for which they are innately structured.

Obsessions over racial equality is a millstone that science has had to bear. Races are not equal. Evidence is overwhelming concerning divergent abilities. Hierarchies in American education and government did not arise from any racial deprivation. They arose because of differences in I.Q., ability, psychological drives and multitudes of variances in mental faculties. America has been set up as a white man's government, a white man's culture, it being impossible to break into that pattern. On the other hand, it is certain that in black governments of Africa, where they control and where their geneticism is manifested from ages past, the white man stands equally less chance of succeeding, even beyond his inability to cope with diseases to which the black is immune. As for social justice, that is the battle cry of minority groups — communists and fascists, until they gain power. In that event, justice fountainheads from the source of authority.

Very flimsy evidence is utilized to advance the theory that there are no pure races. Tantamount to this is that races contain similar genes. Further, that it is noninjurious for the races to intermix. There is little question that races have genes in common. Yet there are stunningly catalogable characteristics. In spite of those that would seek total human mongrelization, there has been preserved classic and definable differences, so much so that the great Darwin felt that the Negro was not a part of the human race.

Evil effects from interbreeding can be attested to by animal breeding experiments. We have seen its catastrophic effects in the American black who resides bitter, ostracised, and belligerent. Random interbreeding can destroy the superbly adaptable and mentally healthful genetic programming of parents who enter into it. In experimental breeding there are brought into the genetic pool characteristics which are selected toward for a specific purpose, such as featherless chickens to produce more edible protein, feeding on the same amount of grain. What is important is that hundreds of thousands of years of evolutionary adaptability are flung away by the union of incompatible variables.

Santiago Genove's *El Hombre Entre La Guerra Y La Paz*, recites: "*La falsedad de las ideas racistas queda claramente denunciada*" in a declaration by 22 worldly-wise geneticians and anthropologists for UNESCO.

Párrafos esenciales:

1. The differences between individuals inside a population are greater than the differences between races.

Untrue. While there are great differences between a white farmer and a professor emeritus, there are startling differences between their racial counterparts.

2. No such thing as superiority or inferiority of physical traits among races.

Untrue. There are definitely superior-inferior characteristics of races. It depends in what field you are referring to. Art of war, engineering, mathematics, fine arts, companionship, lovemaking, breeding ability, literature, tropical survival, democracy or football.

3. Racial mixing is not disadvantageous.

Untrue. Racial mixing is dangerous. For hundreds of thousands of years races and subraces have isolated and developed special characteristics to advance themselves. There is no need for foreign invasion of genes. Such a process bastardizes the better qualities of each race. It's like breeding a good retriever with a fine coon hound. The half-breed now will be not a water-swimming bird retriever or a racoon and possum specialist, but a sorry mut.

4. World peoples have identical biological possibilities to reach any cultural level.

False. History repeatedly demonstrates extinction of the biologically weak or their subjugation.

5. Psychological traits are attributed to certain peoples. There is no hereditary base for this.

False. Psychological traits adapt to environment in the same manner as biological traits are required to do.

6. There is no ground to suppose intellectual traits or aptitude to develop culture or physical traits justify concepts of inferior or superior races.

False. Superiority or inferiority of traits not only of races, nations, groups or individuals is the very basis of evolution. Natural selection is nothing else than the superior overcoming the inferior. It is a continuing process.

In summary, racism is a fundamental driving force of evolutionary ascent. Whether one people are superior or inferior to the other in various component traits is not the question. Racism, discrimination, segregation, adaptation with subsequent conquest, subjugation, and radiation are but some of the tools with which privileged men and their tribe inherit large sections of the earth.

African nations are having a problem with self-government. A black-gened sense of democracy does not exist. As tribes moved to nations, the economic finesse increased beyond normal evolutionary adaption. Consequently, we find ruthlessness and dictatorship.

Very early colonialism and imperialism were misjudged. The whites brought administration and genetic *savoir faire* as well as exploitation. If given the proper chance, white-style democracy may far better the lot than the black version in South Africa. Last white-gened administration should be welcomed by the Africans. Rejoice with Apartheid and white symbiosis.

Where only small tribes practicing governmental sovereignty, the black experienced genes are preferable. But moving to complex mass nations, they have not had the northern complement of expertise. For a black nation's progression into the complex modern world, they will increasingly have to rely on white-gened administration and technical skills. Evolution had not planned for the blacks the rapid advance of statehood, as was planned with northern cooperatives.

There is no reason why whites should not be proud of their race and subracial groups; blacks should be proud of their race; and both maintain their separate identity. At Churchill Downs they have a saying, "Pedigree makes all the difference in a racehorse." As the highest planetary beast, are we any different?

Prevalence of racism in America was demonstrated in the April 1983 election for Mayor of Chicago. Harold Washington, a charismatic Negro, defeated Bernard Epton, an intelligent, Jewish-looking white, by 51.8%. Racial division was rampant throughout the campaign. In the 24th black ward, Washington tallied 24,259 votes to Epton's 129. Epton carried the Polish, Irish, Russian 13th ward, 34,856 to 1,457. 80% of those registered voted. Race was the overriding concern. A precinct captain said, "The whites should be with whites and blacks with blacks." Cicero, an adjacent city, has a population of 61,232 with but 72 blacks. It is isolated from Chicago with its 40% black population. The Justice Department is attempting to sue Cicero to end old-fashioned racism. Miami, in 1980, had a racial riot in Liberty City in which 18 people died.

The foregoing illustrates that over a hundred years after the Civil War, racism is probably more a part of the American scene than it was then. Discrimination against race? What is more discriminating than the ballot box? Chicago forces us to the inescapable conclusion that racism is genetic and cannot be eliminated by legislative edict.

In the foregoing it should not be deduced that Negroes are inferior to any race. They are unique as a subrace. If racial differences are understood, geological, environmental, sociological, and host nations considered, they will enjoy a great fruitfulness of their genetic heritage since they are a noble and charming people.

There are three genetic potentials for the Negro's future:

1. *Pure evolutionary development* as seen in native Africa with sovereignty, black domination, total black population, black culture and customs. This could be enhanced by Negro migrations homeward from western nations. Or even states of the U.S. could be ceded to the black populace for

their exclusive development and sovereignty.

2. *Laissez faire, the present situation, which is an abnormal geneticism* produced by forced migration. Black infusion into white host countries finds black to white amalgamation and cultural integration stone-walled. This results in only white to black intraracial gene flow with consequent isolation, conflict, and unemployment. History is testament this approach does not succeed.

3. *Recognized racial genetic differences.* If the intelligence studies are valid, then it is for the whites to big-brother Negroes — to care for them the same as they care for the lesser intelligenced within their own race. This means opening homes to domestics, jobs to youngsters, and a huge employment market in non-skilled labor. To be achieved it means government abandons unemployment, social security, compensation, labor laws and regulations, concerning Negroes as well as permitting tax deduction for Negro employment. It does not mean that some agency will not aid in humanitarily replacing these millstones. *Big government in its bureaucratic asininity has natural selected the Negro outside of white cultural evolution.* Muzzle big government and the black and white shall move forward together in free enterprise, free market biology adaptation. Forget civil rights, not human rights, and sponsor God-given genetic discrimination that mankind occupationally slots naturally.

 V Women

"And the rib, which the Lord God had taken from
man, made he a woman." — Gen. 2:22

DE TOCQUEVILLE wrote: "It may readily be conceived that by thus attempting to make one sex equal to the other, both are degraded; and from so preposterous a medley of the works of nature, nothing could ever result but weak men and disorderly women. Americans have applied . . . economy . . . by carefully dividing the duties of men from those of women, in order that the great work of society may be carried on. They hold that the natural head of the conjugal association is man. They do not therefore deny him the right of directing his partner. Women attach a sort of pride to a voluntary surrender of their own will."

Today, with woman's equal rights movements, Dr. De Tocqueville's observations are not holding the same force, as when he felt that American men and women do not think they have either the duty or the right to perform the same offices. When he spoke of masculine authority in the home, he was no more than reiterating instinctive biological principal. Women, in their subservient roles he gave praise and stated that they were the most singular prosperity and had strength originating from what he had written and observed, i.e., the superiority of American women.

Dr. De Tocqueville felt the driving force in a revolution was to consolidate or to destroy social inequality — the rich enslaving the poor or the poor plundering the rich, nations unable to prevent the conditions of men from becoming equal. He was inbred and obsessed with equality. One wonders how he would have written had he been a student of genetics, evolution, and anthropology.

The attempt of modern women's liberation movements to equate the sexes exposes serious genetic differences, outside of the reproductive role. A psychologist at Columbia University, Sutton Smith, found that even in children's play the action of the sexes is stereotyped, revealing male and female traits.

During childhood years, girls play house and boys play war. No matter what toys are made available, the larger number of girls play with toys concerned with domestic operations — dolls and the like — while boys tend to select other activities.

A sociologist further buttressed the finding by noting that 10 and 11-year-old girls were occupied by fashion dolls and indoor board games, while boys were roaring unto the playing fields, learning to cooperate, compete, and win. Also, it was noted that because boys engage in team sports, they may learn to resolve disputes more quickly than girls, a result of their experiences in such judicial processes. These influences are undoubtedly carried over into the adult world.

We can observe, from the genetic viewpoint, that even though women may be required to engage in armies, it is contrary to their coding. If such procedure was the case in biological history, that is, women not artificially restrained by cultural roles, they would have moved into male positions. Restrictions were never that severe. Society has always rewarded and perpetuated human efficiency despite hostile environment.

Efficient roles, according to physiology and neurogenes, were very early established in the creativity of the cooperative societies. The communists especially attempted to equalize the sexual occupations and failed. One look at a photo of the highest communist hierarchy will reveal exactingly where they feel women should be. This is equally true of Congress, the President's Cabinet, as well as their European counterparts.

Take away all reference to sexual physiology and reproduction and one still comes out with very wide genetic differences. Desires, dreams and powers are differently directed. Not only do genes dictate what roles occupationally either men or women must serve, but the greatest direction of all is in placing the sexes into properly fitting occupational roles. Nature simply doesn't issue a variety of human types and say, "Run with the ball." The ingredients of types over the long period in the formulation of society had to be specially honed to fit through the selective processes that would permit survival and advancement.

Clifford Adams, a Penn State psychologist, enumerated priorities in men and women. It is because of these differences, he stated, that 75% of American marriages fail. "When a man gazes into a woman's eyes with what they think is love and devotion, they are not seeing the same thing."

After studying 6,000 couples, he found that in males companionship was first most important factor influencing mate selection, followed by sex, love-affection, sentiment, home and family, a helpmate and, lastly, security.

Women, on the other hand, rank love-affection and sentiment as most important. She has to feel loved and wanted. Then comes security, companionship, home and family, community acceptance and, lastly, sex.

In this study, more than the surface divorce rate and preferences show. Beneath this data are revealed genotypic differences. It has always been extremely difficult for the male to accept that sex is not regarded with the same fervor by the female, as he perceives it. Although women put on great sexual shows for those they would have, it's simply not all that much a delight to them. This is recognized when there is a physiological emphasis shift during pregnancy and child-rearing. It is why women place the need to be wanted and security needs first and second. It is within the cozy bungalow, well secured, wherein happiness shall transpire. Biologically her neurogenes can demand little else.

Since the male has always provided security, and it is his biologic obligation and necessity, he can regard it with aplomb. Humorously, the cinema acts out the genetic stereotype — two brave men, the hero and the villain, slug it out. The heroine is riveted in a corner, wringing her hands and sweating it out with eye movements. Perhaps, at the end of the struggle she may bash the vanquished with her handbag. It is an exaggeration of underlying genotypic composure.

The intensity of the male sex role results because he is capable of fathering, let us say, 100 newborn, while it is exceptional for a woman to conceive 10. Therefore, specifically, the strong sexual drive is foisted on some males so that the genetic pool may rapidly swerve in the designated direction. This is not uncommon in the mammalian kingdom where the dominant males openly compete for harems.

In a long wordy article about women's liberation, a salesman who disagreed with this premise made the classic statement, a phenotypic statement which insights into some of the true geneticism separating men and women: "Women aren't discriminated against! Women aren't capable of certain types of work, just like men aren't capable of raising children. A woman will fold under pressure more easily than a man. A woman can't make decisions or quick judgments."

Andrew Sinclair, in *Emancipation of the American Woman*, pays them tribute: "By choice, most American women freely adopted or rejected whatever they pleased among the privileges of the male. They did not compete for jobs in slaughterhouses or down mines; they did not dress in boiler-suits or work boots, they did not refuse the privileges offered to them by the continuance of the tradition of male chivalry. Rather, they took equality when it suited them, and retained a feeling of some moral and social superiority. Although they could no longer blame men or lack of education for their physical inferiority, they could rail in the psychologist's ear against the discrimination of nature."

This is a sensible approach. Women do live longer than men, possibly from the fractional chromosome X they possess, greater than the male's Y. In spite of morbidity and mortality of childbirth, they are physiologically superior in longevity. No matter which direction you look regarding the sexes, there is no such thing as equality — all is inequality.

Everyone recognizes the physiological differences in the sexual organs and consequent child-bearing capabilities. But what few recognize and what few take into consideration are the vast differences in goals, emotions, mental and psychological attributes.

There is spill-over marginality of a small percentage of one sex toward the other. There are masculine women and feminine men, as we would normally expect in genetic variability. Because of these small minorities, we disregard the purity of either one of the sexes. As either minority types pursuing their odd but genetically programmed goals, may not make jackasses out of men, they certainly make fools out of women who wear pants, smoke cigars, and play a role in some typical masculine endeavor.

Men and women of the past were not preoccupied with the status arrangement of the sexes. Only recently has it become an issue, and is loaded with conjecture. A tremendous amount of study must be forthcoming on mental differences between the sexes, rather than trying to equate them simply because it is the political mode of the day.

Although there is a fadism flurry today in women's liberation, the average normal woman needs no coaching as to what her relationship is, or its obligations, duties and priorities, in relationship to the man. A man similarly understands his role, which is undifferent from any other male on earth. Societies are hard to come by where women run the government, fight the wars, and men feed the children.

Just how minute and specific in the underlying perceptional genetics are the fixity of roles and their appreciation may be surmised from the appearance of a woman's magazine, designed to be the feminine mirror image of the male magazine, *Playboy.*

Have no doubt that a great and goodly number of males of all ages and vocations enjoy, are aroused, fascinated, and fantasized with the excellently composed photos of desirable nude and semi-nude girls. However, such displays of nude males directed toward the feminine magazine market (even by admission by the publisher) garnered strong support among male homosexuals and served more or less as a sensational gimmick to entice female readers, whose lack of enchantment with male nude photos was explained away by saying that women had not been properly indoctrinated in their freedoms.

A vast majority of women interviewed simply stated that the photos left them cold, were uninteresting, in bad taste, or in fact were comical, rather than sex-stimulating. They referred to more important values such as having intimate knowledge of the male, or a personalized companionship with male qualities, other than sex. Although males would be the last to believe it and females the first to admit it, there are a great many factors outside of sex that are of extremely high value. One of the great treasures to womanhood is the securement of security, love, honesty, and loyalty. No matter how promiscuous even the modern woman may be painted, it is not her true nature. Marriage, companionship, and family take precedence over the sexual life. This has been demonstrated in numerous studies.

This is the tragedy in female-male understanding, one reflected by divorce rate. The male, from his set genetic point of view, especially if he is highly wired, has great difficulty in comprehending the lack of sexual goals corresponding in the female. Many are the wise women who comprehend this apparent biological fallacy and obligingly provide theatrical sexual productions that are not enjoyable or even pleasurable to them. It is further why X-rated movies are a complete turn-off to women, whose sexual sensitivities are on a more refined plane and to whom voyeurism means little.

Multiply just this small sexual phase alone into the inherited genetics controlling the family institution and one may be appraised of the vast innate instruction with which social institutions are involved in natural selection and survival.

Staying to this slight facet of sexual voyeurism and its difference in male and female, we can note that the drive is for the male to disperse his seed as widely as possible. Therefore, his appreciation and preoccupation with feminine sex memorabilia aids, conjures up, and abets his objective. To this must be added the Adam syndrome, that is, the geni, that every male could potentially be the primodial father of all the children on earth, which would be the number one prime-starred evolutionary great orgasmal leap forward if laboratorily divided.

But for females, they have but one fertile egg to give, and even that is knocked out a year at a time with each pregnancy and, in addition, within a limitation of the time span between menses and menopause. So there is really no evolutionary need for women to cut loose. They're simply armed with a one-shot-a-year muzzle-loader, while the male is equipped with an ever-ready super machine gun capable of firing a million projectiles per second.

Natural selection, therefore, pushed forward the ever-ready male, souped his brain up with fixed genetic feminine fantasy, covetnous and voyeurism. As far as the female was concerned, it was wasted effort and the depletion of energy, from the social group, to permit her facility to choose all the available males. Therefore, her neurogene values were spliced practically without voyeurism and promiscuity.

Summarizing in this same vein, one can easily detect how a society with a proportion of dominant ever-ready males, non-competitive homosexuals, and bachelors, could corral a goodly number of non-energy-wasting females in order to produce the largest number, the most efficiently, and thereby shoot forward in the evolutionary sweepstakes.

In the family alone, this immense divergence between the male and female can be unalterably assessed in hundreds of ways, as from observing a ladies' meeting or a gentlemen's meeting, a girlie party or a stag party, or merely watching their gardening activities and preferences. Such demonstrates not only the innate genetic fixity of the sexist individual roles, but their formation into an institutionalized character which serves as an evolutionary tool, nonculture in nature, capable of competing with other societies for survival.

A tendency is seen to equate men and women sexually. A man has certain sexual desires a certain number of times within a given period, having wide variance among individuals. A woman is supposed to stack up in the same fashion so that a relative equality is achieved, namely one man, one woman. John Maynard Smith, in *Theory of Evolution*, gives us a general observation that "In animals in which the male can mate many times but the female only once, at least in a given season, it is often found that males are promiscuous and females selective in behavior." What marriage counselors, the school system in general, the mores, the laws of monogamy and the laws of the land fail to visualize is that there is the extremely strong genetically programmed compulsion of highly varying degree between the female and the male. The sexes may mate through the same eyes of equality, but the continuation of the process over a period of time is frustrated by the intensities of the varying goals.

That is why divorce in young couples is rampant in nations such as the United States. The young bride cannot and will not forgive her spouse's infidelity. It is not so much that her security is challenged, but that she seethes under the psychological oppression that another female competitor is out-besting her. To the male, nothing is more natural than extra-marital sexuality, because he is powerfully gened to process many women. There is an unfortunate factor which enters in the display of male jealousy concerning his own mate. It is easy for him to accept the double standard, which in actuality is normal to man's evolution, whereby he is permitted to mate many while his wife is subordinated to him alone.

Were it not for dominance factors in the historical male hierarchy, this would provide a serious dilemma to social order. Fortunately, the genes decided it by permitting certain men many wives and liberal promiscuity, while they deigned to others perpetual bacherlorhood and homosexuality.

In today's society these issues are not being biologically resolved; instead, they are being agitated by false psychological schema and propaganda derived principally from precepts of equalitarianism, carrying it into the realm of sex. Polygamous societies have succeeded admirably in the past and in isolated nests within the lands of the monogamous. The soaring divorce rate may be more a resolvement of false ideology, training, and teaching than of basic biology. Jealousy in both males and females concerning sex should be regarded as mental illness. That's as far as it should go, because there are many genes that would protect the mating-marriage bond from disrupture of the household, family, companionship or economics.

Genesis 3-21: "And the Lord caused a deep sleep to fall upon Adam, and he slept; and he took one of his ribs, and closed up the flesh instead thereof."

Genesis 3-22: "And the rib, which the Lord God had taken from man, made he a woman, and brought her unto the man."

There are a great many places in the Bible that show genetic awareness.

That narrative describing how woman was made out of man demonstrates intimacy and unity. In human species' evolvement into societies, one of the most basic changes became the man-woman relationship, sometimes spoken of as the bond.

Since it is obvious that each gender by physiological necessity must journey through time hand in hand, there was great selection opportunity to not only devise the hierarchy, but also to determine who was boss. All of the nonsense regarding matriarchial societies notwithstanding, there was tremendous selective pressure in the name of efficiency to divide the occupational roles.

In other words, women were given specific abilities based on physiological differences, which everyone recognizes. It is why, throughout time and history, the social divergency has been so obvious. It is further obvious that when all the fanfare has died down concerning the new fad of women's liberation, the sexes once again will settle into their programmed occupational roles.

The extent to which equalitarianism is pushing women into active military roles, into jobs requiring masculine talents, is contrary to the biologic and psychological dispositions of the individuals.

Four young European queens in swimming suits were displayed in a small primer on genetics, with the statement, "Beauty may be genetically determined." Spanish literature abounds, as well as most other literature, to center upon this cosmically fleshed radiation that sends normal men to ecstasy, insanity, suicide, or murder.

There can be a complex of genes which directs the production of beauty. We can regard those participating in the Miss World, Miss Universe or Miss America contests as the epitome of beauty. Rather than get side-tracked on such whimsies as beauty is in the eye of the beholder, beauty does have definite universal genetic traits. We can start with examples as long, abundant, wavy, blonde hair, slightly slanted eyes with long lashes, neither too full nor too thick lips but rather arched and indented, properly proportioned jaw, perfect teeth, small-bridged upswinging nose, recessed nonprotruding ears, slightly prominent molars, smooth flawless skin, and a lack of excessive facial fat. And to all this: bountiful nonsagging breasts, nonexcessive buttocks, moderately-sized feet with thin ankles, a muscular and skeletal structure gracefully proportioned of healthy contour, and you have some of the components that go into the fabrication of a physically beautiful woman.

The problem throughout a great deal of the animal kingdom is that sexual displays are important factors to the mating process. Assuredly, a beautiful woman attracts the best and most virile male suitors. Therefore, why, over millions of years, has feminine beauty not been selected toward in profusion? Such an advantage in the beauty genotype would provide a greater number of progeny, which would be better cared for by the stronger males who won out in the competition for the hand of those deemed the most beautiful.

Most conventional evolutionary theories fall flat on their face in attempting the solution. It is true that out of a 100 women comes the gambler's chance of the right-gened combinations and, *voila*, you have produced a beauty. Yet evolution has been too shrewd over the past millions of years not to advantage itself or even be mandated in selecting toward a sexual object with so much appeal-sexual selection.

Too many beauties, cast about to seed, would result in chaotic disruptions. Club and fist fights springing out all over the place as determined and virile males vied for the ever-increasing abundance of pulchritude. Homosexuality would relieve some of the pressure, but would be self-defeating if its proportion became greater than proper for an adequate birth rate to provide the gene pool survival. Then, too, there would be too much "down time" — too much cavorting and too little attention to the details of life. Work was an important asset with evolving radiating societies.

Consequently, there could only be a few beauty queens. There had to be a goodly quantity of earthy mesomorphic clodhoppers, as one may find in present-day feminine liberation movements. Stoop labor was needed to dig up the roots and potatoes — fat, muscular legs to transport the babies and cargo in glacerial safaris — fat-bellied jollies to provide humor and out-survive the muscular ones in times of famine — queens and subranking queens with brains, as well as lower echelon peasant *estupidos.*

Feminine society needed hierarchy, rank, variation, and a wide range in physical ability and intelligence to fulfill the multiple occupational roles which were being selected toward in the evolving social complex. Gene combinations were being programmed to emit those individual units which would provide tribal cohesiveness, harmony, viable offspring, lessened morbidity and mortality in the fulfillment of superior adaptation to the elimination of social rivals.

School desegregation in America has nothing to do with equal educational opportunities. Its battle is being waged entirely genetically, in the black attempt to invade the white pool, and the white attempt to repell it. Paradoxically, there has been little antagonism to the male white invasion of the black feminine genes. The latter examples illustrate the continuous genetic pool warfare which is waged on a societal basis. To comprehend nuclear evolution we must raise our sights from the individual, as a body, and give considerations to gene-pool selections.

Discrimination is basic life. Efforts to legislate against it have failed. Man directs which species of animal and plant life shall live and that which shall perish (wheat over the weed, cattle over the buffalo). He also determines the architecture of social structure, directed by his biological adaptation. The conception process, a genetic slot machine, churns out a jackpot Einstein or run-of-the-mill lemon (genius to feebleminded) in such divergency that no two on earth are the same. It is why governments may guarantee equality for women before the law, but they can never guarantee the individual's equal biology.

Out of this intention by nature results a stratified social class. Any "ism" that practices a classless society is guilty of repression of ability and must eventually perish. You can't match humans as five-cent pieces.

Today women lay claim to equal rights in employment. Any 10th-grader knows there are huge physiological and emotional variances. Labor leaders coerce an auto company to meet their illogical demands; workers, not too bright, place a series of continuous bolts in metal and receive greater remuneration than a highly-educated news reporter. Skilled professional groups create monopolies to control price and therefore gain superior economic advantages. Across the gamut of human endeavors are basic discriminations. It is not a sinister practice to be dealt with, but is standard biology. Women contending it are rushing the windmills. Laws may be laws, but those editing them, enforcing them, and living under them, are made of a firmer variable fiber — DNA codes of ages past.

It has been classical that the primitive origin of society developed a triple occupational status. Women were concerned with childrearing and food-gathering processes. Men took off on hunting and fishing expeditions, plus were concerned with the responsibility of warfare. The elderly educated, led, and maintained stability.

As time progressed, there were hundreds of instinctive programmings inserted into the social genes. One, for instance, was the gathering of information, the memory keeping of social activity and, above all, gossip. Women are the world's "yackety-yacks, say-nothing" grapevine. It reduced boredom and elevated the role of the more vocal and imaginative. Men may keep a secret, but you'll rarely find a woman who can. There was undoubtedly selection toward human communication systems. And gossip, as one of its finer units, was developed by the female.

At one time women had a rutting season; that is, a seasonal time to go into heat and bear children. A seasonal birth-delivery plan was necessary as it related directly to food supply and climate. In Pennsylvania's deer herds, fawns are born in the very late spring. At this time there are sufficient forest buds to nourish them and, with the approach of summer and fall, comes sufficient foliage to carry them safely over the desolate winters. Ashley Montague claims that the rutting season began to disappear in women almost two million years ago in the transition of ape to man with the disappearance of the great forests and the adaptation to the plains. Most important to this birth season change was man's ability to provide abundant foodstuffs in all seasons, and society was no longer submissive to weather. This would have achieved a very fast survival value, as those with the new speeded-up genes could outproduce their rivals, and may be one of the explanations for the disappearance of contemporaneous pre-human groups such as Australopithecus paranthropus.

A quick glance at the catalogs portraying pornography for sale — movies, magazines, books, and pictures which flood the American marketplace — the perceptions possessed by males become immediately apparent. There is a great range of what is stimulating. Presentations gamut from shiny leather and scantily encased prostitutes to displays of women's rears and girls in panty-hose. There's no conformity in sexual tastes.

This in itself is a selection factor, for otherwise, try to visualize the males of a society thrusting toward the few beautiful and perfect females. The range of preference must be very wide in order to service all female types and lustily propagate the races. Even illness has sexual variance. Women's health insurance rates are double the male, based on claims. Take a look into any physician's office and you'll see one lone male among a flock of long-living distressed females — and it is not because of their anatomy.

Delivery of the human brain has placed a heavy penalty upon women. Women differ amazingly in their obstetrical needs. To some the category is little more than a bowel movement. For others it is trial by fire, which may result in death to both mother and offspring.

In the advancement of the hominids, a large brain was imperative. To meet this increasing demand, an ample pelvic outlet became a critical factor. Women born with osseous developmental genes of diminutively-scaled proportions perished in childbirth, and selection kept pace by permitting the survival of large-outlet women.

With large-brain demand, the only method the constructional osseous genes could alter was by natural selection, choosing the mutational variants from out the population. As has been pointed out, so many different factors operate in evolution that natural selection alone is insufficient.

With both pain and difficulty there was feedback to the osseous genes in the germinal cells, either in one or both of the child being born or the mother's ova. This in turn passed the message to the constructional genes to enlarge the pelvic outlet. We never give credit to the amazing sophistication that takes place in the alteration of germ plasm and evolution, instead preferring simple mathematical unreasoning solutions.

It was paramount for the birth canal to develop as the human skull developed. Such sudden eruption of brain capacity as occurred in Homo sapiens could not have been achieved by natural selection alone. We would, with the very first proliferation of brains, have lost half the female population, which was non-expendable.

In the screams of the pleisticene dawns, osseous DNA blueprints were being altered. Bone itself was receiving considerable irritation and trauma as well as the stiff cartilaginous substances. Hormonal, hematological, and neurological feeback were essential. The message: "Enlarge the pelvic outlet!"

Those mothers who died permitted the survival of the large-outleted ones, to be sure, and selection was operative. Yet the vast demands in evolution cannot be met by mere selection. If, for example, I want blue eyes, black skin, no hair, large index finger, smaller nose, etc., ad infinitum, I simply remove a human from the production line, to serve these multitudinous demands of evolvement. That would be absurdity at its height.

Demands in evolution satisfied only by death or removal from the conceptional stream are so varied and interlocked that it is mathematically impossible to resolve them by a simplistic cutting off of germinal cell alteration through inviolability of the germ plasm. Women's birth pains and consequent physiology do not go unwasted.

When we see women as the heads of nations or as governors and mayors, there are two masculine thoughts that come to mind. One is that they are compromise or puppet candidates of men who are leading from behind them. And two, the women themselves are highly masculinized.

Outside the realm of homosexuality, there are very feminine men and extremely masculine women. When you reflect on it, women have been known to grow beards, be breastless and, even in some cases, possess male genitalia in which the sex is hard to denote. One can see how sexual spread comes into being.

Masculinity, femininity curves may be genetic errors in the more extreme types. But they mostly represent requirements of a variable society.

Nonetheless, what is typically female and typically male is well cataloged. That which is not genetically normal for a woman outside of the home is authoritarian dominance politically, unless it arises under genetic freaks or male manipulations of which we have spoken.

We have made a rough sketch table of genotypes that were particularly strong in women we have known. Both the neurogenes caring for intelligence and worker groups can undergo many subdivisions. To say characteristics such as the following are learned behavior is not to know biology.

Women

Genotype		Phenotype
Ii	Ii	Intelligence
Hy	Hy	Hypochondriac
A_f	A_f	Affection
C_c	C_c	Charm
S_s	S_s	Speech Activity
Ww	Ww	Workers
Te	Te	Temper
Do	Do	Deceit
Tf	Tf	Thievry
Je	Je	Jealousy
Am	Am	Ambition
Dr	Dr	Drive

In some animal worlds hostilities are reserved for members of the same sex. Male birds will exclude other males of the species while females will only attack other females. When we apply this to modern man and his history, we find men war with other men while women are in a more reserved role, playing out their animosities on other women.

This is but another facet of the asininity of equating women with men. Men's hostilities are unto violent death under the most savage and ruthless of conditions. Compassion is forgotten in the heat of the melee and engendered hatred of the enemy. On the other hand, women, excepting in legend, have never formed armies. They have served in supportive roles, but they have never gone forth in battle array with a hierarchy of feminine leadership to destroy, maim, kill, punish, capture or torture another group of females.

Women's geneticisms have not been programmed to this most offensive of male aggressive drive. If women were to wage war, marshall it from the height of sovereignty, pass orders down in a feminine chain of command, one knows that wars could last but a short duration or, what would be even more delightful, never get started.

It certainly is not the western woman's dish, but rather, is a likely locale for comic opera. Produce 24 female divisions of Red Russian women soldiers with a support system and leadership also feminine, spearheading into 24 female Red Chinese divisions somewhere in Asia after the flower of Red manhood had been carried away in nuclear attack. Without doubt, there would be casualties, bloodshed, and savage incident. But if you believe, if for one second after the first tastes that this typically genetically programmed "male sport" would be sustained over a period of months or even years, you will need to have your head buried in anthropological and primate texts which detail the divisions of labor between man and woman in their societal evolution.

Innate to women are many appeasement gestures which would act as neurogenic releasers for non-aggressive behavior. One example that readily comes to mind is a muscular, fat Italian who, after some girlie combative hair-pulling, commenced shouting obscenities as displacement rage activity at her foe in order to taper off the action. Within an hour both were drinking chianti together. If a man is beaten or insulted, make sure he doesn't return with a firebomb!

My mother would complain about the maids. Sipping her afternoon tea in the Japanese blue and white-petalled service, she would say: "She can't boil water. I must attend to everything." The maid's quarters adjoined my sleeping porch and I knew full well she was no numbskull. Mother was a superb cook. Anything she took to hand grew in gustatory delights. Our guests exclaimed praise, as guests usually do, including ones that were excellent cooks themselves. They are the real judges; never forgetting mother's sweetbreads, rabbit, crabmeat salad or delicate sandwiches with crusts removed. Years after mother's death, they resounded what a marvelous cook she was.

As I look back, it was indeed true. The maid could not boil water. Other women of whose larder I partook could boil water, but they could not cook. Who could cook? Well, there was 240-pound Mrs. Emmeneiser who helped with holiday banquets. There was my oil and gas partner, 300-pound Murphy who, within 30 days acting as cook, shot my weight up a full 30 pounds.

Do you think anyone can cook? It is supposedly the womanly art of arts, and yet I surmise that only 5% of womanhood are genuine cooks. There are many who can produce, at best, commonplace food. You better make up your mind, superior cooks are born — and their creations are art of the ages. Assuredly they inherit this ability in Mendelian fashion.

Why should we select toward a cook? Evolutionarily, the supreme of the hierarchy of women was not the mother. Any lout can have children. It was the cook who could take scraps, some waste, locate edibles, differentiate poisonous mushrooms from savorful ones, who could, in that magnificent science, field a good meal with the least cost and effort. It is what restaurateurs seek today.

Survival to the tribe came by way of the good cook. And a good cook gave great selective advantage. Recognition of edible from non-edible and poisonous from non-poisonous was a key requirement of the first cook. Experimentation, a second virtue — doesn't lizard and seaweed combine to gourmet heights? Nourishing foods and nourishing cooking meant a health-ful tribe. Third trait, an experienced palate, one who gained weight herself to hold over in famined winter, was able to pass the ability on to associates. You can't fatten humans on bad-tasting, plain and colorless foods. Fatness occurs with fine-tasting presentations.

In social evolution selection, no woman had a greater role as gatherer and preparer of the edibles than the first cook. Other women, excepting the queen, were subservient. And to men she was the queen of the palate.

Leaf through a woman's magazine. To a man, the models and subject women are unappealing. They are flat-chested. Most are skinny, hard-faced, depicting some unnatural pose. There is an incongruous penchant to wear pants. Nothing particularly sexy is ever revealed, unless it be the clothes themselves proxying for women.

On the other hand, there are male magazines which show women not as they are, but as a man would like to find them, buxomly, chic, half-naked, and inviting. We ask, why do male magazines that are unappealing to women portray "sharp" women and correspondingly female magazines feature un-feminine models? It's because women don't care for clever women. If they do, it's for a non-rival grotesque by age.

What they care for, tolerate and praise, is a mannish woman — a no-woman — a woman who, in their subconscious perceptions, substitutes for or possesses male traits: breastless, wiry, muscular, hard-faced.

The subconscious affectional perceptional apparatus of either sex is atuned, unless otherwise homosexually determined, to the opposite sex — no sweating a statement so obvious. What lies hidden is that men, when judging their own sex's handsomeness, pick the feminine-appearing male, and women the male-appearing woman. Our choices out of our own sex are subterfuged by underlying opposite sex compulsions.

More than that, it points up that men, editors of men's magazines, choose and desire sex-women in full flower — rump, breast, leg and face — a dozen stimulation points. Women aren't so gutsy. Their magazines rarely emulate male muscle of pelvic bulge or those selective of many mates and promiscuous sex. These mental sets are innate.

A lessened sexual program saved woman labor, making her more efficient in child-raising and food preparation. To make the man the hound dog, tail-wagging at every whiff of a bitch in heat, was to insure conception. But to have males hound-dogging continuously defeated survival purpose and so only the dominant males possess this remarkable trait of "Casanova-drive."

Men and women search for widely different facial values. A man is directed toward beauty, softness, and texture of skin, profusion and light-ness of hair, upswept nose, long lashes, colored pupils, and pleasant expres-sion. The woman bypasses to large measure such luxuries. If they exist, well and good, but rather she chooses hard qualities that will provide her with security — especially loyalty and love. She is ready to accept discipline in exchange for those necessities.

It is why no normal man will marry old, homely, fat hags at any price. But a young girl will sell her soul for money to the ugliest, most disgusting of ancients. It originated in the ape tribe. What was coveted by females was to be mistress No. 1 or 2 of the dominant males from whom abundance of blessings flowed. Genes of those same desires flow today.

That monogamy and fidelity have no basic nature in man's sexuality is demonstrated in work with animals. Alinquist and Wiksell have shown in experiments with albino rats that ejaculations per hour were increased by allowing the animals to copulate in groups of three. Further efficiency of senescent rats was considerably heightened by collective copulation.

Grant and Young found the male guinea pig susceptible to a second ejaculation from the stimulus of a new female. Biologists have long noted the strengthening of sexual excitement when animals, especially birds, are copulating in groups.

Human tragedy of marital sexual adjustment arises from a conceptualized biology that has no actuality in gene programming. Legally or religiously, fanatically or in simple economics or companionship, the concept of marriage has conflicted directly with underlying biology. Ideally, monogamy with fidelity is a cherished social goal. Yet the biology cannot always be suppressed.

One reason we are reading more of group sex, wife-swapping, and the alarming increase in divorce is not because of economic or personal incompatabilities. Sociologists have verified this in slum districts where economics is not cited by women as a cause of their marital disruptions. It is because true genetic nature is surfacing as we advance culturally. As with animals, man's sexual drives are prompted and guided by promiscuity — especially those individuals who are the chosen seeders, the Casanovas and Lotharios. Women are of different mood.

Portals into neurogenic mind of women come in many sizes. Lower-class women revel in soap operas — trashy, unrealistic, daydreaming love slop. Higher-class women somehow persuade men to wear tails in their formal dress, like giant birds. (Ever wonder about the disproportionate interest shown by women in birds?) Too, they are magnificent perceivers into the character of man. They have men perfectly figured out, how they will fit into their schemes until they become ensnared in some of the more deceptive genes of males. In fainting, women excel men 50 to 1. It's their displacement activity when they cannot resolve a situation, excepting the sight of blood to which nature they are accustomed. Even blondes, aside from hair coloration, are wired differently from brunettes. Blonde-gened individuals possess characteristics denoting northern origin.

Wm. Sadler, in *Living A Sane Sex Life*, makes the point: "Wifely aggressiveness is occasionally enjoyed by the husband, but this is contrary to the accepted role of the female throughout the animal world, human beings not excepted. The wife's initiation ordinarily should be seductive, not aggressive." It's already there in the sexual genes. The roles are stacked out — there is little need to worry too much about feminine rapists.

Margaret Sanger, an early advocate of birth control, was a brilliant writer. In her book, *Women and the New Race*, 1920, she states, "The creators of over-population are the women who, while wringing their hands at each fresh horror, submit anew to their task of producing the multitudes who will bring about the next tragedy of civilization."

Further, she observes, "Woman's acceptance of her inferior status was the more real because it was unconscious. She had chained herself to her place in society and the family through the maternal function of her nature, and only chains thus strong could have bound to her lot as a brood animal for the masculine civilization of the world. In accepting her role as the 'weaker and gentler half,' she accepted that function. In turn, the acceptance of that function fixed the more firmly her as an inferior."

That the word "inferior" was used is unfortunate. What the author was not recognizing is the specific biologic roles cut out for the sexes — occupations and attitudes included — which are unalterable for a progressive society.

Havelock Ellis, in *Man and Woman,* is a little tough on the gentler sex. He writes, "Infanticide is the crime in which women stand out in the greatest contrast to men; in Italy, for example, for every 100 men guilty of infanticide, there are 477 women." And he remarks that when a man commits this crime, "he usually does it at the insistence of some woman. Infanticide tends to disappear as skill in producing abortions is developed or knowledge of contraceptives is spread."

What possibly never occurred to Ellis was that women historically have been masters of their children's anatomy and, especially, the newborn. If, in their wisdom, acting under ancient genetic edicts, they choose infanticide, it is because humanity ascended a ruthless route out of sheer survival. In famine, a few more mouths to feed could wipe out the tribe. A woman's sacrifice was great and noble to terminate the unwanted, those that would have little chance for peace or happiness. It is she that giveth and it is her right (genetically) to taketh away.

Chemical codes of human behavior may not be regarded as immutable — they are subject to the same senescence as all tissue. With age some disappear or become weakened, to be overruled by more durable combinations. To knowledge, they cannot be replaced. Like a late summer garden, some blooms fade while others survive the first frosts. Few have written as beautifully of genetic decline as Wm. Sadler: "Advancing age witnesses a gradual weakening of all physical feelings, and with them the love for companions and children gradually expands into a regard for all humanity, such feelings find expression in benevolence and philanthropy; this is the final stage of love except for a temporary rekindling of sexual interest in women at about the menopause and in men usually between 50 and 60, as though the organism, soon to be beyond the possibility of fulfilling its fundamental purpose of reproduction, is attempting to make the most of its few rapidly passing opportunities."

Outside of Lady Macbeth, Catherine de Medici, and a few other rare females, the instinct "revenge" and its execution is almost an exclusive monopoly of male genes. Men's hatreds far outlast those of women. From woman's family-determined role it was of necessity that this be the case in order to shrug off insult readily. Yet even men, after costly bitter savage war encounters, within a new generation, kiss and make up, reestablish trade and exchange pleasantries. It appears that from out of selections box the directing voice has cautioned: "Come on! There's life to be done. Forget the past. Things forward are to be won."

What has evolved as women's role in society is innate submissiveness to the male. Her emotional equipage does not permit her warlike activities or even individual physical aggressiveness. Rather, as Hamlet's mother, she mourns, not too long, before posting herself upon new sheets. Hate, vengeance, muscles and soldiery are not her lot.

Rather, she is a childishly innocent creature that has great difficulty in thinking originally. What is set down and in what order she is to perform as a collegian ranks her equally with males. But of all the great works performed by males in the arts and sciences, she contributes little. Not because of small desire, but because her social geneticism has betrayed her into male submissiveness to alleviate intragroup strife.

It would be unfair not to mention the rare and radiant gem sparkling brilliantly in the tender blue heaven that woman is. Her mercy, compassion, patience, and forgiveness far outstrip any similar-acting genes in the male. By necessity man became the killer, and was solaced by woman, his confidant and healer.

Man and woman, magnificent in union but as diverse in genetic structure as they are in that singular determinant of their variance — being genitals and sex-related organs. Both nervous tissues are surcharged by social evolutionary selection with unique behavior patterns, instincts, emotions, and desires. The very approach to love of a man and woman is so interplanetarily distant that it is great wonder it works at all.

Within social selection women are chosen to pass on their traits. Fortunate among survivors were those that possessed superior child-rearing capabilities, emotional stability, nut, fruit, root-gathering capacity, as well as love, devotion, and jealousy.

Jealousy, the ingrained obsession of every woman, esconced itself in the ritual of survival. With a good man she ate. With a strong man she was protected. With true love came a true bond of alliance. It was imperative that she protect her choice. Thus jealousy is strongly genetic. A woman without jealousy or with passing interest, could watch her hairy-skinned favorite take off with another female through the highest branches, leaving her stranded, her genes available to no pool, while her successor, jealous bitch that she was, held on to a "good meal ticket" to pass on to her descendants that most pernicious yet normal of feminine traits — jealousy genes.

Speaking of the sexes, male and female, there is such a diversity in physical makeup and mental process between the two that the tongue-in-cheek joke of the century was to legally equate them in jobs and economic responsibility. Thus, the burlesque queen ended up clothed under the name of women's lib.

Nancy Reagan, wife of President Ronald Reagan, when asked if she would define a woman's role in marriage, succinctly said, "Oh, Lord . . . somebody has to give. Sometimes one gives and sometimes the other gives. It depends. But probably the woman gives more than the man. It's her nature. In spite of more modern thinking, it's her nature to give."

What Nancy did not know was that she was expertly defining the feminine role as it has evolved in genetic anthropology. There is no question that in the past ten million years the woman's role as society organized for its perpetuation was that of submissiveness. Not to all men, note, but to the male dominants who ran the tribe. Excepted were the bachelor males, who had their swing at estrus egg-laying time.

What is fatal to women's liberation movements is the erection of society and its evolutionary selection of division of labor. This resulted in a host of irregularities running from alpha dominant strong males to zeta inability to compound wars. Although there is good pseudo-historic press on Amazon women who waged victorious combat, in mental thinking sexual divergence is gigantesque.

We have spoken of submissiveness of the female to the male dominants. As society evolved and stratified, there became a number of semi-dominants who entered into relationship. Today we witness the rarity of divorce or marital problems where women are married to dominants. Where the problem erupts is when marriage is consummated with either male homosexuals or with submissive males.

In the proletariat one finds heart-rendering aspects. It is not from oppression by bourgeois masters, it is from the lack of genetic gentility wherein issues the wife-beatings, child abuse, the callous indifference for feelings, and the screaming vicious arguments which explode so frequently, often resulting in physical violence. Proletariat women have it tough. But they are capable to withstand nobly the onslaughts.

Possibly as late as 100,000 years ago, the dominants of the social groups were siring and protecting the majority of the women. As this phased out, more women were squaring off with submissive males that were incapable of handling them or of assuming proper patriarchial control. This is the nemesis of the Negro race, with its emphasis on matriarchal society. It is the reason successful male dominants have little trouble finding whatever mate they desire. It is why women of young age, such as Jacqueline Kennedy in her second marriage, select elderly, obese, dominants to marry. Why? Never let it be said that women are gold-diggers or money-hungry. They are obeying instinctive genetics. Regardless of what the successful dominant looks like, thinks about, or smells like, women in the most preferable of ages will choose him in opposition to handsome mesomorphs.

With pupils up to the age of 14, women make marvelous gene-directed teachers. Tendency to overplay the role was traditionally held in check by the males and later by principals, superintendents and school boards which were largely male-composed. Yet, when a woman is given an administrative job, she is euphorically carried away beyond her programmed capacities and becomes tyrannical. In a position of authority to which she was evolutionarily deprived, she has none of the diplomacy, wheeling-dealing, chicanery, and subtleness of the male.

This is no speculative observation. From women in government to business, and even operating room supervisors, there is a disproportionate number of mean "bitches." An average businessman shudders if he must deal with the opposite sex in an administrative post, unless he is clever enough and willing to deal through their natural weaknesses.

Woman's suffrage was possibly a social error. Coming before sociobiology, at the height of antidiscrimination and equalization, it infused an abnormal component into government. To counter it, men gave token service to women's vote, allying them with their husbands, or catered to their whims. Women's contribution has produced little positive, unless it be a series of continuous bloody wars, which one would feel their influence would negate.

It is not that the vote should be retrieved from them, but that the entire democratic system should be reinterpreted in terms of knowledgeability and genetic capability. When we speak of government, one should not neglect the traditional innate form. Women can never get over their primary goal.

It follows them into administration or business, where they become suspicious, arrogant, unyielding, dictatorial and uncomprehending, but submissive to the first clever fop who cultures their image of a proper spouse. On the other hand, men roll with the punches and diplomatically negotiate, there being no need to be distrustful of contact. Consequently, as administrators, there's more give and take, compromise and chicanery. When a woman says, "No," she means it! When a man says, "No," he couches it, feigns it, presents an alternative or doubt.

As a summary example, consider: In June 1978, a woman psychiatrist appearing on television — the Today Show — stated that one out of two American men cheated, had adultrous or extra-companion-relation sex, and only about 30% of women. Men's behavior she attributed to something wrong in the home or marriage or to prove their masculinity. She inferred that the remedy was to rework the marriage problem. Women believe that drivel. Men cheat because their genes tell them to. It is incorporated in their blood. They can have a sexy 19-year-old, beautiful blonde, wealthy princess with magnificent personality and companionship, who loves them dearly and aims to please in their castle boudoir, and if a young robust maid properly presents herself, they'll enjoy every guilty minute of it.

It never sinks into women that promiscuity in men is gene-determined, is a programmed compulsion. It is not intended as cheating or disloyalty, but as recreation. Yet women never climb out of this childish covetness. That, too, is gene-determined from her millions of years' sojourn as a member of the harem under male dominants.

What of the 30% of women who cheat? They do it in revenge, to be accommodating, or to get out of the house. A little excitement to be sure, possibly an economic raid on another's property, but rarely does it mean the same as the guts-and-beauty theme of the male.

Time magazine, Dec. 15, 1980, in an article, "The Gender Factor in Math," details superiority of males in mathematical reasoning. Benbow and Stanley tested 9,920 students and found a large sex difference in mathematical ability in favor of males. . . . "Boys outnumbered girls more than 2 to 1 in math scores over 500."

The article concluded that many women "can't bring themselves to accept sexual difference in aptitude," says Benbow. "But the difference in math is a fact. The best way to help girls is to accept it and go from there."

A personal observation: An increasingly large number of women are being utilized as news commentators and press reporters. They fall flat because they cannot convey with believability the same force a male dominant can. We believe people in ratio to prestige and authority we place in them.

Until the age of 17, a great deal of what "Mom" said to us was believable and reliable. We can have no quarrel with the innate teaching ability of females to below college-age students. In mature years, the ear is peaked more acutely to the voice of the male when serious matters are considered. If a female details an emergency, one investigates further. If a male details an emergency, one acts. However, many women commentators are so charming, their presentations so delightful, we say, "Who cares about the news?"

Yet women have held high political office since the dawn of time. To be voted in was unnecessary. If women properly performed their familial obligations, they had a life-long, praiseful, loyal, and grateful constituency.

VI The Jews

"O ye seed of Israel his servant, ye children of
Jacob, his chosen ones." — I Cor. 16-13.

THERE HAS rarely been a people who evoked so much universal
animosity as the Jews. Seldom have descendants of a nation so
perfectly preserved heritage, culture, and religion over thousands of
years, although residing in dozens of host countries. Never has there been
such a cohesive and loyal citizenry, of a genetic-religious pool who prosper in
spite of cruel opposition.

By refusing assimilation, Jewish people are a prime example of subgroup
racial tenacity, of a white Caucasoid-gened Semitic pool, who have etched
their mark upon marbled pages of history with courageous blood to retain
their identity.

It is because of remarkable traits in these intelligent people that the *Genetic Basis of Society* examines biological motivation. Why were they persecuted? Why did they succeed? Was the Star of David the cross they bore? Or was their crown of thorns the cohesive genes forged by an isolated anthropological pool that refused assimilation even though geographical isolation had ceased?

American attitudes toward the usage of the word "race" are broadening. *Time* magazine, May 1, 1978, Lance Morrow, in reviewing the TV program "Holocaust," stated startling usages of a most sensitive concept. ". . . It did not anguish stylishly enough before the abyss, over the race that went up the chimneys in smoke. . . . To keep the victims from the oblivion that the Nazis desired for the entire Jewish race."

Time's essay is in error. In the jargon of Hitler, the Jews are a race. From *Mein Kampf*, ". . . Jews; for after all, their world existence is based on one single great lie, to wit, that they are a religious community while actually they are a race — and what a race!"

Anthropologically, the Jews are Semites the same as the Arabs. Both Jews and Arabs, as well as English and Germans, are members of the white race, the Caucasians. Yet each — Italian, Jew, or Spaniard — transport differing biologic characteristics and traits due to their historic geographical isolation during tribal evolution of their unique genetic pools.

Basques or Serbs or Ukrainians, Jews or Germans, French or Irish, are subgroupings of the white race, i.e., subraces.

In examining Jewish history to account for persecution, we must look to more basic factors than envy, cohesiveness, mutual aid, and religion. Those elements ascribed to Jewish hatred may be ascribed to any ethnic group. One facet differentiates them. Reluctance to assimilate into a parent society, and with that would come true genocide, the disappearance of their distinctiveness which they have cherished. Among some Jewish writers this is the real fear today, that except in Israel, they shall no longer exist as a group.

From Publius Cornelius Tacitus' *The Histories, II — Imperial Rome*, translated by W. Hamilton Fyfe: "They killed a ram, apparently, as an insult to Ammon, and also sacrificed a bull, because the Egyptians worship the bull Apis. Pigs are subject to leprosy, so they abstain from pork in memory of their misfortune and foul plague with which they were once infected. Their frequent fasts bear witness to the long famine they once endured; and in token of the corn they carried off, Jewish bread is to this day made without leaven.

". . . Renouncing their national cults, they were always sending money to swell the sum of offerings and tribute. This is one cause of Jewish prosperity. Another is that they are obstinately loyal to each other, and always ready to show compassion, whereas they feel nothing but hatred and enmity for the rest of the world. They eat and sleep separately. Though immoderate in sexual indulgence, they refrain from all intercourse with foreign women. Among themselves anything is allowed."

From *Paradox of Hate*: "Anti-Semitism is neither more nor less startling than other forms of religions and racial hatred and persecution. It is neither more nor less startling than, for example, the hatred or persecution of the

Catholics in 18th-century Ireland, the Protestants in 16th-century France, the Hussites in 15th-century Bohemia, the Manichaeans in 5th and 6th-century Byzantium, all Christians in 2nd-century Rome, and most recently, the Eastern European in the west and the Negro and American Indian in the United States. . . ."

When we read Jacob R. Marcus' *The Jew in the Medieval World*, on the Cremation of Strasbourg Jewry on St. Valentine's Day, February 14, 1349: "The Jews throughout the world were reviled and accused in all lands of having caused it [the plague] through the poison which they were said to have put into the water and the wells — that is what they were accused of — and for this reason the Jews were burnt all the way from the Mediterranean into Germany. . . .

"Nevertheless, they tortured a number of Jews in Berne and Zofingen when they admitted that they put poison into many wells; and they also found the poison in the wells. Thereupon they burnt the Jews in many towns and wrote of this affair to Strasbourg, Freiburg, and Basil, in order that they too should burn their Jews. On Saturday — that was St. Valentine's Day — they burnt the Jews on a wooden platform in their cemetery. There were about two thousand people of them. Those who wanted to baptize themselves were spared." Marcus suggests that *"about a thousand accepted baptism."* Imagine a thousand people today being willing for cremation as a price to the retention of their faith. Yet faith is here, a bioism, a banner, which refuses integration even at the price of death. What this cremation reveals is the powerful overriding geneticism of a chosen seed. Once they would become Christians they would intermarry — that is the fine print, so the faith renunciation they could not do.

Martin Luther, founder of the Protestant religion, provided the blueprint for Hitler. Luther shrieked, Jews would be "noble lords of the world" and "masters of the Christians." Not only was Luther unwilling to be upstaged by a rival faith, but "masters and lords" is quite specific, denoting physical ascendency, the success of an ethnic group. Luther was asked, "What then shall we Christians do with this damned, rejected race of Jews?" Even at that time racism was considered. Luther was envisioning the DNA code of the Jews, not flimsy ether of unsubstantiated spirits.

Luther was not dealing with precepts of the life hereafter. He considered the most stringent of economic strangulations and group elimination: "The Jews," he said, "are poisonous bitter worms." He insisted that only by the absolute humiliation of European Jewry could Christendom survive and prosper. "Their synagogues or churches should be set on fire . . . their homes should likewise be broken down and destroyed. . . . They should be deprived of their prayer and books and . . . their rabbis must be forbidden under threat of death to teach any more. . . . Passport and traveling privileges should be absolutely forbidden to Jews. . . . They ought to be stopped from usury. . . . Let the young and strong Jews and Jewesses be given the flail, the ax, the hoe, the spade, the distaff, and spindle, and let them earn their bread by sweat of their noses as is enjoined upon Adam's children. . . .

"Lastly, let us apply the same cleverness as the other nations, such as France, Spain and Bohemia, etc., and settle with them for that which they have extorted usuriously from us; and after having divided it up fairly, let us drive them out of the country for all time. For, as has been said, God's rage is so great against them that they only become worse and worse through mild mercy, and not much better through severe mercy. Therefore, away with them. . . ."

The Jew, in caricature, has been conceived in different periods and in different countries, and on the surface they are different from one another in tone and purpose. Some are quite funny, others are quite grim and caricatured as an enemy of the political, economic, social and moral (or sexual) life of Christendom. He is in league with the devil, he betrays Christ, he is the anti-Christ. He insanely castrates little boys. He is portrayed as clown, outcast, the despised, a sexual ogre, a war-monger in France. In Russia, in 1907, on the front page of a periodical, *Pluvium*, he was depicted as a political gangster.

Adolph Hitler, in *Mein Kampf*, had similar views: "The cleanliness of this people, moral and otherwise, I must say, is a point in itself. By their very exterior you could tell that these were no lovers of water, and to your distress, you often knew it with your eyes closed. Later I often grew sick to my stomach from the smell of these caftan-wearers. Added to this was their unclean dress and their generally unheroic appearance.

"Was there any form of filth or *profligacy*, particularly in cultural life, without at least one Jew involved in it?

"If you cut even cautiously into such an abscess, you found, like a maggot in a rotting body, often dazzled by the sudden light — a kike!"

Jews are mindful of the vicious persecution and genocidal onslaught of a rabid racist like Hitler. He commenced by removing them from prestigious offices and jobs, to replace them under the aegis of racism. It was not a question of efficiency or ability, but interpretation of race. *Yet, today in America, quota systems are being erected in universities. Minority groups are being given preference over the more capable under the guise that their educational deprivation via social factors requires it.*

This is the way it started in Germany. The racial issue was false. The Jewish people are as much a part of the white Caucasoid race as are Arabs, Russians, Swedes, and French. They are a subgroup, but are white Caucasoid. So if quotas according to race rather than ability are enforced in search of equalizing minorities, we are back at the Nazi signpost. It is the individual's genetic ability under legal equality of just democracy which seeks the proper level of attainment — not self-imposed false quotas erected upon minority groups by socialistic schemers. Discrimination is life. It is not altered by lawmakers. It is the God who composes coded biology which determines capacity and place within society.

If the animosity between the German and Jew was not strictly biological, how do you account for German aid to Israel? From 1963 to 1965, the German Federal Republic loaned Israel $560-million, more than 3% to be used for developing the Negev. Discarded tanks were sent to Naples for refitting and shipment to Israel. Ludwig Erhard (1964) agreed that arms' supplies to Israel would be German not American. Present-day Germany has no animosity toward Israel — genetic conflict arose when the two peoples were in non-isolated geography.

Cohn makes an excellent observation: "Only a third of the civilians killed by Nazis were Jews . . . whereas the Russians, Poles and Yugoslavs were decimated in the name of racist theories . . . the drive to exterminate the Jews sprang from demonological superstitions inherited from the Middle Ages." The fact was the Nazis were killing subraces — demes of Caucasoid origin whose integration posed a threat to genetic direction. Nazi vociferation of racial existence and the possible subconscious awareness of genetically-coded purity compulsion has its moments of truth, but the means whereby they executed the resolution in genocide is the most heinous chapter in history. Biological tendency and humanitarism should have been reconciled with wisdom.

From *Justice in Jerusalem,* some statements of Eichmann, the executioner of European Jews, are given by Gidem Hausner: "Personally I never had any bad experiences with a Jew. . . . The enemy was not persecuted individually. It was a matter of a political solution."

He told Sussen, "To be frank with you, had we killed all of them, the 10.3-million, I would be happy and say, all right, we managed to destroy an enemy." Time and again Eichmann stressed he had nothing to regret. To imagine the cold-blooded assassination of a people as a political solution is above belief. Yet political solutions do involve genocide. This is biological solution, and Eichmann imbued with racial fantasies was seeing just this. What he was relating to was programmed genes from the Pliocene age millions of years ago.

From Hausner we also learn that 19th-century loathing of Jews was fashionable in German intellectual quarters. With intellectuals we expect logic, deduction and humanitarianism — tolerance above all. Such sentiments as the former cannot be based on culture, they must be instinctive behavior — the very behavior neither Germans nor Jews would recognize in relation to subrace and, even that, the Jewish people are prone to explain away as non-existent.

Friedrich Hegel, philosopher — "The Jewish genius as an embodiment of 'a demon of hatred.'" Bruno Bauer — "Jewry as the expression of Asiatic lust and egoism." Political scientist Von Treitschke — "The Jews are our misfortune." Professor Fries — "The Jews should be wiped off the map"; while novelist Boetticher considered them "cancer germs in our life," and writer Marr pointed out, "Semitism is the antipathy of Germanism."

Venom such as this is representative of biological conflict in its fullest flower. Jews are attacked as a people, as a unit, possibly in the same way as Homo transvaalensis may have systematically eliminated Paranthropus robustus some 700,000 years ago. We may draw upon this example in contemporaneous evolution. Some 900,000 years ago, Paranthropus, Homo transvaalensis and Home sapiens were in competition. Any one of these three man-apelike creatures had perfect adaptability to descend to the present day. Instead, we find them radiating off to extinction 400,000 to 800,000 years ago. Our closest relatives are apes. The hominids, with their increased brain capacity, their upright stature, usage of tools and possibly speech had superior equipment to ascend the evolutionary scale to modern man than lower species relations apes, as the gorilla, chimpanzee, orangutan.

Many primate species become extinct like these near-man-apes, while the human strain straightened it to the pyramids. Why? Homo erectus was less adaptable than the chimpanzee. When demes, genetic pools formed through isolation, there erupted racial wars, racial hatreds and what we term as extinction was merely the human line practicing its age-old policy of genocide.

Few wars are as vicious or bloody as civil ones in which a subracial neighbor is involved. We must assume that modern man ascended the evolutionary ladder by his systematic elimination of his less adaptable brothers by warfare, genocide or environmental exclusions. It is why we have a species no closer to us than the anthropoid apes. Man's law of evolvement is the massacre of divergents, the survival of the fittest.

Justice in Jerusalem refers to race: "On top of all that was piled a hatred based on racial themes. The Jew was to be discriminated against and later destroyed, not for what he believed in, or for what he represented, or for crimes he had allegedly committed. He was abhorred for the fact of his birth and for his mere existence as a Jew, irrespective of what he stood for."

We have repeatedly reiterated this theme. *Religion was not important. Biology lays beneath. It is here solution must be sought to avoid horrors. The truism is that people in a nation are only secure if their racial geneticism has been sufficiently assimilated.*

It should not be overlooked that individuals of various subraces or races, when in working, playing or personal contactual relationships, diffuse the biological antagonistic stereotype to some extent — to the extent of their friends and general tolerance. Yet so long as there are demes, genetic pools, subraces, ethnic groups or races, there exists specific DNA coding demanding rivalry and elimination of the challenging foreign system.

Again and again we witness the tenacity of Jewish people to maintain evolutionary isolation. From *Antisemitism (Its History and Causes)*, we read: "Everywhere they wanted to remain Jews, and everywhere they were granted the privilege of establishing a state within a state. By virtue of these privileges and exemptions, and immunity from taxes, they would soon rise above the general conditions of the citizens of the municipalities where they resided; they had better opportunities for trade and accumulation of wealth, whereby they excited jealousy and hatred."

Thus, Israel's attachment to its law was one of the first causes of its unpopularity, whether because it derived from the law benefits and advantages which were apt to excite envy, or because it prided itself upon the excellence of its Torah and considered itself above and beyond other peoples.

Rival churches were far too clever to contest the Jews in the realm of the ethereal. Measures were instituted to make their lives on earth as miserable as possible — to set them apart, preventing their assimilation, which they also did not desire. The churches were waging their battles on earth, not in heaven above and, as such, were engaging in ethnic group discrimination and population control — the highest of biological priorities.

Because the Jews were not allowed to own property, they became merchants — from merchants to usury.

We learn in *The War Against the Jews*, by Dagobert D. Runes: "Christian names were forbidden to Jews by many Catholic bishops and nobles. In 14th century Spain, the Cortes of Toro (1369) and of Burgos (1377) made this prohibition a point of Christian law. Here, too, Hitler revived an old Christian practice."

Gelbe Fleck (or Yellow Badge): "The yellow band issued by the Hitler Germans, with or without the Star of David, has its origin in an edict of the Catholic Church. It was promulgated during the Fourth Lutheran Council convoked by Pope Innocent III in 1215. These badges of shame imposed upon Jews by the Vatican in many forms in different lands: hats, armbands, and/or circlets, made Jewish men, women, and children easy marks for attacks. Genocide was preached a thousand years before the Germans ran amuck in their Jewish hatred. Church-inspired crusaders put to death or caused the suicide of more than one-third of the Hebrew population in Central Europe in the 11th century. When Emperor Henry IV issued an edict permitting the forcibly converted to return to the faith of their fathers, Pope Clement III forbade, under dire threats, such disregard of holy baptism."

We have had a tendency to regard Germany as the arch-anti-semite. However, the Jews in Russian history fared little bitter than in other lands. Nations were unwilling to have a competing geneticism within their borders.

We read not about religious exclusion but genetic. In 1741, Elizabeth Petrovna ordered, "All Jews, male and female, of whatever occupation and standing shall, at the promulgation of this our ukase, be immediately deported, together with all their property, from our whole empire. Both from the Great Russian and Little Russian cities, villages, and hamlets. They shall henceforth not be admitted to our empire under any pretext and for any purpose unless they be willing to adopt Christianity of the Greek persuasion. Such baptized persons shall be allowed to live in our empire."

The Jew is to be eliminated or assimilated. From the German or the Russian experience we see pure biology. From *European Jewry Today*, by Selig Levenberg, "There are approximately fourteen million Jews in the world today; if not for Hitler's policy of a 'final solution,' their number would probably have reached the figure of twenty-two million. This estimate is based on the loss of natural increase which resulted from the extermination of six million Jews.

"The Jewish community in the USSR is not allowed to have any ties with other Jewish communities; there is no contact with Israel. In fact, there is no state-approved organized Jewish community in the USSR; there are just three million Jewish individuals living there.

"In addition to the general characteristics of Soviet society, that minorities must conform, is the fact that Stalin's policy regarding the Jews is not completely dead. Both he and Lenin believed that assimilation was the ultimate solution to the Jewish problem, and the continuance of this policy explains the steps taken to silence expressions of Jewish national consciousness. . . ."

Two great nations — Germany and Russia — maintain a biological imperative: the choice between assimilation or elimination.

Try this quote from *Out of the Whirlwind*, by Albert H. Friedlander, and try to imagine that such action resulted from religious differences. "Although the unfolding of evil in Germany does not mean that all Germans were evil, and yet for the first time in modern history, a condition of living was created in which the citizens of a country were encouraged to live as criminals: violence was rewarded and decency punished.

"The vast majority of Germans supported their leader. . . ."

Germany under Hitler had become a biotic state — both in actuality and proclamation. Jewish people could not suddenly understand nor believe that the forces beneath their woe were not political, not religious, but were genetic, the expulsion of a population pool, *the attempt at an eugenic evolutionary evolvement*, even though it was shouted to the rooftops by seeming madmen. For some unknown reason they refused to recognize race, sub-race or ethnic group variance, even though they had practiced the art successfully against tremendous odds over the centuries. *The tragedy was the failure to recognize ethnic genetic pools in conflict.*

Now that Israel may bear the burden, in the future we may see the total assimilation of Jews in foreign lands, as spoken of in *The Golden Tradition*, by Lucy S. Dawidowicz: "My wise mother once said, 'Few things I know for certain. I and my generation will surely live and die as Jews. Our grandchildren will surely live and die not as Jews. But what our children will be I cannot foresee."

We find hatred can go in both directions. *The Jewish Factor in My Socialism*, by Chaim Zhitlowski, states, "Towards Germans my father felt deep respect. The German type enormously impressed him and he valued the German highly for his absolute honesty, for valuing highly his own human dignity, for having a stiff backbone, and for demanding respect for himself as a human being. . . . Russians? Our whole environment was completely permeated with hate for Russian landowners and officialdom that milked us dry, conscripted our children for the army, persecuted us in every way possible, and treated us like dogs. As for the Russian masses, we regarded them as brute animals.

". . . (this period I am writing of came about ten years after the Polish uprising in 1863). My father particularly was anti-Russian. We had only fiery hate for the power wielders, ridicule and contempt for the whole people. . . . Writing my memoirs, I suddenly recalled the conversations and jokes around our dining table about the ignorance and stupidity of the Russian peasants."

Hatred forms within the biology, not the classroom!

Zhitlowski continues, "From our own way of life, I first understood the true meaning of exploitation, that it was a way of living at the expense of someone else's labor. All the merchants, storekeepers, bankers, manufacturers, landowners, both Jew and Gentile, were exploiters, living like parasites on the body of the laboring people, sucking their lifeblood, and condemning them to eternal poverty and enslavement.

"The anti-Semitic press made charges against Jews and these anti-Jewish accusations were at least partly true, though the anti-Semitic press had no right to make them.

"Yet it was true that, with few exceptions, Jews engaged in exploitation and led a parisitical existence. But the blame lay not on our lack of civil rights, but rather on the whole social order. Both anti-Semites and philo-Semites would have to disappear, because they belonged to the old world."

This may be taken to mean assimilation; genetic — not economic integration. *A World Problem*, a psychological and historical study by Stephanie Laudyn, states, "What did their religion tell them, what commands did the God of the chosen people give them? Was it the God of the universe, or was it an exclusively Semitic God? Right here is the tragedy of the Jewish soul, the kernel of its original greatness, and likewise the source of the downfall, calamity, disintegration and woe of the Jew. The Jewish religion is a religion of exclusion, hatred and detestation. The Jewish God is a cruel and revengeful God, and their law of living is based on this vindictive principle: 'An eye for an eye, and a tooth for a tooth.'

"The psalms of their sacred books teem with pride, revenge and contempt. Jehova says to the chosen people, 'I will give thee the Gentiles for thy inheritance, and the utmost parts of the earth for thy possession,' and 'Thou shalt rule them with a rod of iron, and shalt break them in pieces like a potter's vessel.' (Ps. 2-8.9) and the Jews believe today as they had done centuries ago, that these promises will be fulfilled, and that Jehova will bring their enemies under their feet.

"Immediately before the Christian era, Strabo wrote of the Jews as follows: 'The Jews penetrated into every city, and made an attempt to become leaders. Strongly united . . . '

"Juvenalis thus writes of the Jews: 'The son of the prejudiced worshiper of the Sabbath bows only before the heavens and the clouds. Following the example of his forefathers, he hates the rest of the people. He would not show the road to a man of a different sect, nor would he show the spring to the thirsting traveler.'

"Similar testimonials of the Jewish soul were given also by such recognized Roman historians as: Cicero, Horace, Martial, Seneca, and others. Several centuries before that, Hamor warned King Ahasuerus against the foreigners settling all over his land, who observed their own laws and treated lightly decrees. Such were the Jews thousands of years ago. Has their Semitic soul changed any since?

"They afford revelations which dispel all doubts as to the hidden Jewish spirit, whose centuries-old depth is being revealed by Jewish writers and poets. The poet Abrahamowicz speaks of their religious idealism as an uplift to the Jewish welfare.

"Let our enemies know that the strength of the divine nature which directs us, which will not permit us to become lost, nor suffer us to be crushed under the foot of our enemies and destroyed from the face of the earth. The biblical spirit acts within us, as an electric current, the voice of Jehova drives us onward as the motor does the wheel of the machine — our voice will not die away for ages to come!"

In summary of the Jewish past, we find it is not primarily spiritual, but of more rugged substance — an ethnic group challenging other groups — a subrace that would prosper and survive — a geneticism which wished its unique preservation. (From *The Paradox of Hate, A Different Viewpoint*).

"It is perhaps an extreme irony that in the United States, where anti-

Semitism has 'lost half its evil by losing all of its grossness,'" the Jew should himself thus become an anti-Semite: the specter of his other self. One might almost argue that, having escaped from irrational cruelty, he must perpetually remain the victim somehow of his own atavistic, irrational guilt.

"Anti-Semitism . . . is only a symptom of a much deeper problem, that of our human irrationality in all its forms: irrational fear and irrational guilt, the irrational desire of men to live at the expense of one another, and the irrational impulse to hate, to destroy, and afterwards to kill and be killed." What else is being described than generalized genetic aggressive programming?

Nathan Ausubel, in *Pictorial History of the Jewish People*, states, "Anthropologists agree that the Jews sprang from the Mediterranean subdivision of the Caucasoid race. It is assumed that they, as Hebrews, appeared some thousands of years ago, a small part of the migratory movement of the semi-nomadic Hyksos, and under the name of Israelites, settled along the coastal plains of Canaan. Where the kingdom of Judeah was established, its people were known as Jews.

"Jews reveal different physical characteristics. This, says the anthropologist, is . . . due to the fact, besides influences of climate and diet, the Jews since earliest times have been fused. Are the Jews a language culture group? The variety of languages of 'mother tongue' . . . which the Jews speak is quite staggering. What is it then they have in common? . . . They draw from a common group awareness — a consciousness of being Jews. . . . In greater or lesser measure, each of them is linked up in some way with the historic Jewish past . . . they or their ancestors, have had a common Jewish culture heritage and a religion from which to draw and together to establish a common group identity."

We need only add that with cultural heritage, a common religion, and group identity there is inevitably a pooling of human genes. The latter has undoubtedly been the most influential in Jewish achievement as a people. Intelligence and generalized success are simply not components of culture and one's faith. This is a very excellent summary of the Jews, not as a race, but as a division of a race — a subrace — an isolate geneticism with unique genotypes, phenotypes and common culture.

Without great fanfare, it is pointed out that Jewish people reveal different physical characteristics from Gentiles. "This, says the anthropologists, is . . . due to the fact, besides influences of climate and diet, the Jews since the earliest times have been fused." A non-Jew always has the impression that the Jewish people wish to deny race as well as subrace or ethnic group and never wish to concede they are physically different. *Jews have shied from biological consideration of themselves from their German nightmare.* Here Ausubel is quite frank and speaks also of common group identity.

In *American Jews in Israel*, we find, "For *Sartre*, 'it is neither their past, their religion, nor their soil that unites the sons of Israel. If they have a common bond . . . it is because they have in common the situation of the Jew,' and this situation is to be the object of hate and rejection."

Again and again, authors strive for understanding while omitting the very uniqueness of subrace. Heaven only knows the Germans recognized the Jews and the Jews recognized the Germans. They didn't recognize them by a divergent spiritualism, as their ancestors had done. They recognized them by biological differences which the Nazis went to great premature and erroneous lengths to classify. We have little difficulties recognizing a Negro or Mongoloid or Caucasoid. Why should it open the gates of Hell to consider biologically Swedes or English? If it hasn't already been done, we shall witness shortly Israeli scholars distinguishing biological differences between themselves and Arabs. Anti-Semitism is a Lutheran tenent.

"The Protestant church of Germany was Lutheran in Anti-Semitism. When the Nazis placed the Jews in ghetto camps, burned Jewish synagogues, homes and schools, robbed the Jews of their possessions, they only did Luther's bidding." We have been absorbed with the deeds of the Nazis rather than focus on historic precedence and genetic compulsion.

In *Warrant for Genocide*, the myth of the Jewish world-conspiracy and the Protocols of the Elders of Zion by Norman Cohn — "It is of course true that the French Revolution, like the American Revolution before it, really did help the Jews. Since it proclaimed 'the rights of man' and championed the principles of liberty, equality and fraternity, it was logically bound to grant civil rights to French Jews. . . . Wherever Napoleon's power extended, the Jews were emancipated; in the Simonini letter one can hear the crash of the Italian ghettoes as they fell before the French armies. This was quite enough to convince reactionaries that Napoleon was the ally of Jewry, if not a Jew himself. Those who identified themselves with the ancient regime had to account somehow for the collapse of a serial order which they regarded as ordained by God. The myth of the Judeo-Masonic Conspiracy supplied the explanation they craved."

Here again we see basis for the Jewish obsession with equality. This, in turn, leads to blind spots when one must deal with individual and group differences — intelligence and ability, genetic variances — race and subrace. While championing equality, the *Jews themselves are the prime example of inequality, with their high intelligence, dedication, drive, reserve and social cohesiveness all based upon underlying genotypes. They face a two-edged sword. Do they grant quotas in universities and jobs on a one-for-one basis or do they recognize abilities — inequality — as the factor of justice?*

Jews themselves disagree on exactly who and what they are. One thing is certain: It is that they are held together by their religion, the Torah, religious rights and customs. It has been the centrum of their loyalty. Sometimes they think of themselves as belonging to "the Jewish race."

"Race" as an idea and subdividing mankind, even in subgroups, is unappealing to anthropologists. Yet Jews did derive from a Mediterranean subdivision of the Caucasoid "race." In their exile from Palestine in many nations, they underwent biological fusion to some extent in the nation in which they settled. Thus, a stereotyped representation is by no means representative. However, one must consider here the potential genetic dominance of many characteristics from the original tribes. It is quite possible that with all the various races and peoples with which they have bred their blood to minor extents, they still preserved a Jewish identity by dominant genes.

John Dickinson, in *German and Jew*, comments on the Nuremberg Racial Laws of 1935. "Nothing is said about Jews being bad — they are simply declared to be of other 'blood' than the Germans and 'hence' excluded from German society. Not Jews but 'racial mixture' is what these laws assume to be bad; they assume it is possible and desirable to strive for a 'pure-blooded' society by the elimination of 'alien blood.'"

Contrast the foregoing with the fact that Jewish religious law forbids intermarriage. *Neither the Jew nor the German seemingly desired dilution of their parental strain seeds.*

In retrospect, concerning his interviews, Dickinson states that some Germans treated Jews with conscious malice. Some were aware they had some malice, yet not aware of how it had been energized by long-held traditional attitudes. It was easy for a German to offset his malice by resorting to rationalization provided him by the government such as "Jews are Germany's misery."

Needless to say, the Germans were brainwashed by constant propaganda of the government and were heir to traditional anti-Semitic attitudes passed from Caesar's time. The German did not see truth in the proper perspective. Possibly many of the noxious occurrences he alluded to did occur. But such noxious behavior occurs in all peoples and tribes, and when placed in perspective is merely the minority of criminal element found in all cultures — certainly no basis for generalized hate or antagonisms, *excepting the underlying subracial genetic propensity to preserve one's own.*

Ambassador to Germany in 1966, Asher Ben Natan, stated to an Israeli newspaper: "The Germans cannot free themselves from their past. They are oppressed by it and concerned with it." It is equally true of Americans of German heritage. Our ancestors' history is a psychological asset in our disposition. It gives us pause that those of the same genetic fountainhead could so wretchedly distort the name of the product.

However, to believe that in repentance is cure, is another myth. Any nation on earth may similarly be inflamed in short propagandized notice against any rival biology, within its ports or distant. Culprit is within the DNA codes we carry — that ruthless Godded structure that permitted us survival unto today. *The law of biology is not that others within a species may live, but that others will perish by the successful succession of one's own offspring. This is the essence of evolution and human conflict.*

These selfish genes we transport are modestly countered by another. Charity, aid to the underdeveloped and compassion, is a biological anachronism. Here we truly have developed a unique gene — humanitarism — of recent origin. During our evolutionary descent it became apparent that each member of a society had value and there was selection toward those groups that manifest this trait. As nations arose, such humanitarism biologically became meaningless, in fact, became anti-biologic in its presumption to encourage other peoples' proper development and fruitition which later would result in competition against the charitable group.

Nevertheless, in many individuals this strong gene group manifests itself in "aid to Biafia, to the Pakistani, to be more commonly shared in compassion to the sick and weak, the Red Cross or Community Chest." If the stronger nations had the faintest idea of their conflicting biology, they would demand limitation of population at the same time their charitable compassion was being effected. In time, massive populations existing at a subsistence level can only result in bloody orgies of war.

It is this insensibility to biological reason that prompts the Catholic Church to prohibit massive birth control. It is their humanitarian genes at work.

During the Second World War, six million European Jews were in cold blood murdered by the Nazis. It was not an act of warfare, which could historically excuse such conduct. It was a deliberately calculated and systematic slaughter of helpless innocents by rational humans aided and abetted by the populace of one of the most civilized nations on earth.

What staggers our conscience is that this is man. Unfortunately, it could occur again. It could have transpired with similar ease in France, Poland, or Russia. And it did, dark punctuation on the pages of European history, but on a lesser scale. The guilt must be shared. It cannot be shrugged off as the work of madmen to be forgotten.

This inhumane destruction was for the avowed purpose of removing a subracial group. Under the guise that they were an "inferior race"— a malevolent being, an unfair competitor, and possessed a wealthy monpolistic worldwide conspiratory network capable of destroying any existing society wherein they resided. A warrant was issued to liquidate in mass this socioreligious geneticism known as the Jewish people.

The Jews blame the Nazis — and the Germans. The Germans blame the Nazis and point to historically similar anti-Semitic actions by other peoples. Today, Russians and Arabs occupy the stage of anti-Semitism.

It's easy to say Hitler was a mad dog, and permit grass to grow over grave sites. Hitler and those about him were lucid and specific. He had written the script beforehand, clearly in *Mein Kampf*. His followers had diligently attended his words. Further, irrational men do not write consistently or speak forcibly, or convince, or control great nations over a period of years.

Why was this man obsessed with Jewish hatred? And, as one man — Herr Hitler — what was it possible to do? How could *one man* volcanize the catastrophe? Obviously, there wasn't one Hitler that accomplished this feat, but thousands, possibly millions. There needed to be allies, similar in beliefs to constitute the sepulchraled gas chambers.

However, in fairness to Germany, we should note that this peculiar brand of "racial" hatred was rampant in many nations, such as France, Poland, Russia, and to a lesser extent, also in England and America, and was made a nonproblem by the expulsion of all Jews in Spain in the 15th century. Hatred of Jews by the host country has been episodically characteristic of history.

Having been labeled an inferior race by the Nazis, one often wonders why the Jews did not counter with claims of superiority, nullifying the contentions. Of course, that would have made the pot boil, because their founder's claim as the "Chosen People" never resided well with their neighbors. Be it as it is, in spite of the past, science is taking new steps toward respectable racial study. Whoever likes or dislikes it, races and subracial groups do exist and they do possess varying talents. We should use the term "race" not in Hitlerian terms but to understand why this horrendous massacre took place. What are the opportunities to prevent its recurrence? Not the militancy of "never again," for this may breed further militancy.

In a welter of information inundating libraries we search for cause of this cosmic infamy. We find theories, beliefs, and propositions. Not one explains it. All reason in resolving the universal and repeated phenomena of one people's or nation's hatred for another flounders in wordage. We accept the concept of genocide, racial elimination, as fact of man. It is not until you apply the science of genetics, of race, that you can solutionize. It is with these infant sciences rather than distortion of them that this most sordid event in human history shall be explained.

One should read *The Paradox of Hate*, by Morton Seiden, 1967. Among the intriguing pages there are thoughts which pertain to our particular study. First, that religion and race form the base for persecution.

We accept that there may be racial hatreds and conflict, and this is unquestionably based upon biology and the specific genes of the antagonists. What is more difficult is to equate religion with biology. As we have spoken, natural selection was in favor of religious spiritualism, and in its universality it has become a fixed genetic factor of most people. Some, such as the evangelists, possess a compellingly forceful variety of these genes.

When we examine Protestants and Catholics, our only distinction is that they differ religiously and not on a biological basis. Yet, here we fail to recognize that religions in themselves are selective factors to biological isolation. The Jews themselves refuse to proselytize their religion, thus keeping it genetically exclusive. Most assuredly, the northern Protestants of Europe, England and Germany, differ in ethnic characteristics from the Catholic Latins such as the Italian, French, and Spanish.

Yet what of the French Catholics doing away with the French Protestants in an event such as the St. Bartholomew Day massacre on August 24, 1572, in which 10,000 were murdered? Did these groups differ biologically? To answer this, enter a dozen Catholic churches at random selection in the United States and a dozen Protestant. Do biological studies and ancestral notations, and you'll find genetic differences.

Seiden calls attention to Jewish hatred being expressed unequivocally in the arts and literature of not only every century, but also every nation. For example, even in the works of Chaucer, Shakespeare, Voltaire, Chekhov, and T. S. Eliot. *There can be little doubt that the Jewish people, in their history, have been the leaders in racist theory and practice.* They did not crusade their religion to others; they remained isolated and, by forbidding intermarriage with other ethnic groups, developed a unique genetic pool. Here is where the hatred arose — biological divergence and consequent antagonisms.

Yet they were faced with a dilemma. If they submerged and assimilated with the host nation into which they had transferred their talents and abilities, it would have ended Judaism and their prideful DNA code. They should have been the first to proclaim theories of racism. This was unthinkable because they were outnumbered by the Christians surrounding them. What was open was religion — it was a usually acceptable premise that man may have his own chosen rendition to the spiritual world. But proclamation of race would squarely challenge rival biologies to immediate retaliation. *Racism was subterfuged into religion.* It is here one finds most hysterical emotion with Jewish people in ethnic or subracial considerations. And it was here, unfortunately, that Hitler waged his anti-Semitism.

"Accusations," says Seiden, "were made against the Jews as a race and not the individual — through faulty logic." Yet, this is the greatest of logic. The group is challenged by a rival bioism. The individual is unimportant. This, that is forever England — France — Poland, with their battlements bristling and frontiers guarded, is what the entire human society is all about. *My land, my country,* maybe also *my God,* right or wrong, *my, my,* a biological unicism, against all others.

Immediately one points to the United States — that most successful unity of rival bioisms and divergent ethnics, cooperating and giving allegiance to a single land. First off we whacked the American Indian and terminated any rivalry of Mongolism or interracial mixing into European genes. Then we ousted the French and Spanish, fought the British and Mexicans, took on Cubans, Spanish, Germans, Austrians, Japanese, Italians, Korean, and Vietnamese, and had a big go north and south in a bloody civil conflict, to name but a few. *At no time was religion an issue in our wars or our hatreds.*

Obviously we fought many, both racial and subracial groups, under a lot of souped-up propaganda concerning economics, defense, security, and humanitarianism. These were biological enemies. When we stabbed one another, north or south, over an issue which was being peaceably resolved over the entire earth, namely slavery, we were again asserting biology. The north had become industrialized with large immigrant populations, while the southern agriculturist wished his own traditional genetic development isolate from the Negro in his midst. Cause for the Negro conflict could have mattered less.

For all of the lofty idealism and flowery rhetoric of Lincoln or John Brown, witness in the ensuing 100 years, Negro status was comparatively little better. His isolation is still definite. He is programmed by the whites who are his masters.

The southerner had 300 years to readjust and pool his genetic compulsion, exclusive of black seed. Europeans who chose the warmer climate were a selection group. There was little migrations of peoples north and south. On the other hand, the north was reservoir for adventuresome, outcast, or dissident peoples of northern Europe spirits that moved the nation west. Their geneticism was newly mixed and recklessly potentized. We were about to diverge. That DNA factor which directs the cohesiveness of family, tribe and nation was not about to permit it. So the biologies met to valiantly blood soak the farming fields of Gettysburg — that their combined genes shall endure — not that man shall be free. Did not the south have right to freedom? And what a nation it might have been. Two biological-gened forces met in one civil war. Southern cohesive societal and subracial diverging genes.

We have focused upon the Jewish people. It is too broad a scope to include other peoples who have experienced their tragedy, even those who have experienced the final event — extinction. Disinterested people give causation of anti-Semitism to a failure to assimilate. Assimilation is unacceptable to a genetic pool because it is the end of the line — a divergent geneticism which does not selfishly evolve, becomes commonplace and lost by a larger pool structure.

Yet, when Seiden analyzes anti-Semitism, he truly analyzes man. It is man — his peculiar geneticism — his compulsion, which is the culprit.

In *Warrant for Genocide*, by Norman Cohn — "Hitler would never have come to power without the world depression, which at one time brought the number of registered unemployed in Germany to six million.

"He attacked the allies — republican regime, the left, right, plutocrats — in fact, everybody. His most ferocious attacks were reserved for the Jews.

"All witnesses seem to agree that the Germany in which Hitler came to power was not in fact a country gripped in a frenzy of anti-Semitism — it played only a limited part — indifference was important in facilitating subsequent persecution."

In 1930-35, in a small German town, W. S. Allen found that for the fanatics, anti-Semitism was deadly serious, others regarded it as so much talk, quite unrelated to the Jews they knew personally. "Almost all the Jews who were prominent in the Soviet Communist Party in 1935 were just then being liquidated by Stalin."

Hitler defined his war as a war waged by "world-Jewry" against Germany. This was a constant theme propaganda, hinting that the Jews were being made to pay with their lives. Goebbel's propaganda stressed that if they lost the war, Germany would be annihilated by "world Jewry."

M. Clandin's investigations of the pogroms of 1938 by young Nazis looting shops and killing scores of Jews, conversed with 41 party members. Those who expressed indignation at the outrages amounted to 63%, while 32% were noncommital and only 2% believed it was justified because terror must be met with terror against the Jewish world-conspiracy. Four years later, only 16% of those interviewed showed concern for the Jews, 5% believing international Jewry provided the war.

"On the one hand the mass of the German population never truly fanaticized against the Jews — never obsessed by the myth of Jewish world-conspiracy — never really thought the war a struggle against 'Eternal Jewry.' Between 1938 and 1942, the population had been conditioned not so much to positive hatred as to utter indifference.

"Traditional German subservience to authority restrained them from voicing opposition to Jewish policy. Yet they protested so vigorously against the killing of lunatic inmates they reverse the practice. The former was an avowed state enemy — the latter a human.

"In the extermination camps, guards were not representative of a typical cross-section of German society. True, there were some actual sadists, hungry for the privilege of beating and torturing. In any society, what percentage are true sadists and what degree of sadism pervades all people?

"Jewish religion has encouraged a separateness and exclusiveness, notably by making it impossible for a strict Jew to marry a non-Jew and difficult for him even to eat together with non-Jews. The fantasy of Jews as a brotherhood of evil was first conceived between the second and fourth centuries, as a device for immunizing Christians against attractions of the parent religion."

Christianity developed from the parent Jewish religion and immediately commenced to consider it a rival. This, as a cause of friction, is window-dressing. Basic genetic structure of the advocates is different. Herein lies the conflict.

No matter how whites see blacks, they cannot see them as hidden mani-pulatory Jewish "elders." A world-conspiracy cannot be projected onto the Negro. This is why the Negro does not have dread of genocide. This attitude may change when white occupational security is challenged and white exclu-sive germinal plasmal integration is threatened.

From Hitler's SS to the Tsar's Black Hundreds, the Jew-killers of history operated from an idealogy to legitimize their behavior. Tales of ritual murder of Christians to Jewish world-conspiracy found the base to see themselves as angels overthrowing the powers of darkness. Beneath all was the image of rival geneticism.

Genocide is the deliberate destruction of a racial, political, or cultural group. Hitler chose to emphasize the racial aspects. The Jewish people chose to ignore race and ridiculed the professed superiority of the Aryan stock.

What lay fallow in the Jewish-German confrontation were a few simple principles from the infant science of genetics. If Hitler could contend and convince tens of millions to accept his assertions that his special group was superior, there was only one question to ask: "Very well, master race, in what aspects are you superior?"

The Jewish people chose not to fight on this battleground. Today, from their experience as territoralists in Israel, they capably parade their powers as warriors, list their contributions in science, culture, and the arts, man B'nai B'rith as bastions of counter-propaganda, open their temples and religion to view, intermarry, and enter into a less recluseful social order.

What interests us are but a few fundamentals of genetics that should have been obvious in the 1930s when the death warrants were being printed. Namely, life is a coded chemical. No two individuals are coded similarly (excepting identical twins) and, in the progressive evolution of the highest primate, tribal, national, and racial, differences emerge in marked degree. Not only in skin color, facial characteristics and intelligence, but in the most subtle psychological of variances as personality, abstract thought, ability, emotion, alcoholism, sexuality, drive, humanitarianism — the gamut, you name it.

Evolution decreed that this should occur. Once a group became isolated over a period of many centuries, they adapted to each other and to their environment. The latter required certain skills not imperative to other groups under different environmental conditions. Consequently, natural selection pruned the mass to fit the need.

Nothing in the whole of science is more ridiculous than to discredit race and say we shall all end up in one evolutionary bed — to contend we're all similar people, we humans, black, yellow, white, brown, red, etc., and that fundamentally, we only differ in a little skin coloration, a few blood grouping percentages, and that we should get together and forget the whole mess of race.

One need but to witness the vicious cockfights staged by the world's most intelligent diplomats at the United Nations to learn that mankind is not about to peaceably blend — now or ever will — with other divergent bio-mechanistic groups. The special coding we share with others is not about to relinquish its destined monopoly or its selfish self-perpetuation.

Breed the Spanish with the Arabs or Negroes? The Gibraltar Straits separates biological groups. It is not that the Spanish male did not give freely of his seed in the new world to Mongoloid groups, it is that his female counterpart had entirely different notions in which direction the geneticism of the Iberian Peninsula should move.

Man will donate his sperm to anyone, practically for the asking. However, women have a quite different approach to whom shall father the progeny. It is why we impose such ghastly penalties on so biologically natural a process as rape. Woman is the prime mover in evolutionary advancement and divergence. Beauty as a process of selection rapidly favors transition toward her particular geneticism and, as she chooses, so goes the race.

Had it been possible for Jewish people and Germans to intermate, had they been both willing to join in union, there would have been no problem. They were both of the Caucasoid race, both had the same God, with a disagreement over the existence of His son Christ. Subracial amalgamation was the answer. However, although progress in those lines was being made, both groups were bent on retaining their original identity, cultural as well as biologic.

Within you, within each of your cells is not only the formula for genocide, there is the active structure prompting you to perform it. Nuclear missiles are pointed and programmed at this very moment to wipe out hundreds of millions of people within hours — to destroy empires and republics — but more especially, their peoples and their ability to rival you, not only economically, but to outbreed and therefore out-territorialize you.

How many times did you hear, "Drop the bomb on North Vietnam and get it over with"? We have dropped a couple in the past — with justifiable and rational reasoning.

If a nonaggression pact with Russia was signed tomorrow, and the two governments wished to prevent the horrible bloodbath seen emanating eventually from Red China, within months protective annihilation of the entire billion yellows could be approved by the majority of white masses, once the two propaganda machines fed daily doses of hate into the receptive chromosomal structure.

In spite of all human goodness, one ethnic or racial group, given the proper opportunity to annihilate the other, will choose to do so. Where did the early Romans go, the original Greeks, the Assyrians, Babylonians, Celts, the Neanderthals? They assimilated — perhaps a little — look what happened to the native American Indian.

Examine the case of recent genocide. I have before me two books that I picked casually from the library shelf. For possibly the most poignant sentence written, attend William Glicksman's dedication in his book, *In the*

Mirror of Literature '66 —

> "Dedicated to the memory of my parents,
> Abraham and Miriam (nee Klazner),
> and the members of my family who perished
> in the German-Nazi gas chambers in the years
> of the Second World War, 1939-1945."

Now attend Stephanie Landyn's preface in *A World Problem* — Jews — Poland — Humanity — translated from Polish, 1920: "Poles and Jews — these two peoples have lived for centuries on a common soil, and created a serious problem for Poland — where half of the Jews of the world have lived. The Jew stands alone with his original national type and his peculiar soul. The infiltrating Jewish spirit is dangerously affecting mankind — a Jewish infection."

Before we get into Landyn, who wrote in 1917 and whose work is filled with subtle hatred, half-truths, libel, and outright fantasy, whose beliefs were one of many that bricked the ovens for the hideous final solution of the Jewish problem by the Nazis, we must search for undercurrents in physical thought that permitted this black page of civilized history. More than that, we must appraise if actual biological aggressive mechanisms were alerted and animosities developed independent of religious professment, which too often has been the focus.

We tend to forget that Hitler was not the only national leader of anti-Semitism. The Jews have a long history of persecution by almost every nation of Europe. During World War I, both Poles and Russians did everything in their power to bolster and sustain anti-Jewish sentiment. The war was followed by systematic economic strangulation resulting in heavy Jewish pauperization, 75% by 1935. Yet rooted in Polish soil, the Jewish community considered itself an integral part of Poland and clung to the hope and faith of a peaceful existence among the vast masses of Poles.

The inhumanitarianism to Polish Jewry in the first half of the 20th century may be described, revulsed at, and for retrospectionists remain a puzzle. Jewish authors excellently detail the woes and injustices, yet they have great difficulty in relating to the firmer substance of cause.

Today, fortunately, the Judeo-Christian religion is under attack by atheists. This is heartening to hear, because now at least in defense they are brothers. Now there can be no argumentation of who killed Christ. And there should be no injection that the Jewish religion is a separation, or at least a separation sufficient to bring retribution, disrespect or persecution, one to the other.

Religion is a minor factor in Jewish persecution. Most important is a rallying point of breeding strains. Attend to Landyn's venom: "The individual Jewish soul is subordinate to and cemented to the universal soul *united* by tradition, forged by hatred, it is so well-disciplined that persecution cannot crush it. One God — their own *exclusive* master — herein lies the source of their enduring separation. The religious *isolation* and their *unique* laws made them a people who saw nothing but their own commandments."

Landyn may not have sensed it, but she was not speaking about soul or religion. She was referring to ethnics. That quality of people to develop an independent culture.

A Jewish corner on the gold, financial, banking and loan market has always been an irritant. Envy is the underlying factor, because any people, including individuals, envy and will react to wealth. It denotes a homogenous group acting in association that raises biological storm warnings.

The crux to sensitivity is the supposition that criminality has an ethnic background. Here is where issue is joined. Paramount is the group whereon to attach the twisted hate — Jews are Shylocks, Italians are gangsters, Germans are mass murderers, and Russians are atheists. We need only an inbred recognizable ethnic group to meet the needs of our biological animosities. From these we appelate what we choose at the moment of conflict for effective mobilization.

Try this: Even if the Jews had controlled all the wealth, economy and political position of a nation wherein they resided, there would not have been persecution against them — providing they were indistinguishable as a group within the host territory. The one premise of rebellion is predicated upon group divergencies, customs, and uniqueness. Of course, in the hypothetical foregoing situation, we would not be dealing with Jews, for their identity would have been removed — and obviously, the most important aspect of such a premise would be anthropological identity or biological identity.

Juvenalis has written: "He does not partake of pork, subjects himself to circumcision, and brought up in contempt of Roman law, he acknowledges only Jewish law which he reveres."

So customs of a people are different. It can be passed off as merely the educational forwardings of a tradition. Yet, when even the least of these persists by not blending into a culture to which it is inserted, it cannot be seen otherwise than as a biological alert that the sect is foreign.

If, in my heart, in the quiet of the night, in locked bedroom, I profess allegiance to my God Dippy-Dumb. no one shall disturb me or note my apartness. Yet, if I sit at a table with others repeatedly demonstrating my religious allegiances, wear group apparel to set me apart, or work, pray, and act in discordance with the major population, then I shall repeatedly reinforce for all the world to see that I am not only in God and belief isolate, I am indexed as a member of a species unlike others, i.e., cultural tradition reinforces the perception of fixed heredity animosities which are innate.

The Jewish Book of Days, by Cecil Roth (1966), notes June 6 — "Massacres begin in Spain, 1391. Hitherto it had been usual for Jews to remain steadfast to the faith of their fathers at whatever cost and to go gladly to their deaths rather than be converted. At this point the morale seems to have been broken and though a large number met their fate as martyrs, the majority preferred to save their lives by submitting to baptism."

This demonstrates that faith under severe conditions can be broken and the group assimilated. The Spanish cruelty realized that once the faith was foregone, the biology of separateness was everted. It really wasn't faith that was the contention. It was that you will become one of us biologically. This is the oldest practical behavioral tenant of group existence. This applies to subraces, but not to races whose differences are too great to assimilate.

"Isolated, disdainful, proud and haughty, self-centered and hateful of everything outside of itself the first spirit lives." This can, of course, apply equally well to some Protestants and Catholics. In reality, it is a psychosomaticism, it is religious genes with their outward manifestations. If we believed in Dippy-Dumb, we certainly shouldn't be ashamed of the fact, and it would manifest itself in physical symptomotology.

"It is true, the Jews never and could never have any sincere sympathy toward the Slavs. The spirit of the two races is too antagonistic. The common Jews sided with the Germans. The Russian army was quick to perceive this and showed the Russian inborn hatred of the Jews," 1917. Isn't that a kettle. Everybody hates everybody, Germans — Jews — Russians — Poles — all distrustful. Why?

What is the perpetual rhubarb among these groups? Today, the Russians refuse to permit emigration of Jews yet still persecute them. Why the hatred? You could add Americans — Turks — Hungarians, etc. Hatred — hatred — hatred. War and preparation for war. All with varying amounts of religion, some with multiple religions. Yet religion is not entirely a sufficient reason to activate the warrior and genocidal genes. Later we shall examine chemical structure of religious genes — demonstrate them in encephalography, biochemistry, and from microscopic neural studies.

It is interesting to note that Landyn speaks of "the refined Polish Jews" or so-called "assimilators" — the most refined among them whom "are actually Polish." What Landyn is saying but doesn't quite comprehend it is that once an attempt, or the process of assimilation sets in to the parent majority culture, objection no longer occurs. And what else is assimilation than biological blending with the surrounding cultures?

International Institute of Peace — "World War I Germany is no enemy of the Jews. But their only true friend and protector. In Germany the Jews enjoy full rights and privileges. Germany is the true stronghold of Judaism, Tottendam Zionists — 80 Rabbis."

Whether the foregoing is valid or not, it was printed and represented a Polish viewpoint in 1917. Its paradox lies in the catastrophe which followed in Germany by the time of World War II. As many have signified, the entire world was unprepared and unsuspecting for that which ensued when the Nazis gained power. Within but two decades a nation had been activated anti-Semitically. However, it is doubtful that the Germans fully knew or understood the horrendous road they were undertaking. It is doubtful that a referendum of genocide to the Jewish peoples within their borders would have been acceptable.

But then again, the haranguings of a demogogue upon the tribe can spiritize action not very remote from the ancestral roots of the primates. Application of mass psychology by the most benign of leaders, when applied upon vestigal genes of our savage evolution, can lead to holocaust. Witness John Kennedy's Cuban confrontation with Khrushchev. It would have taken little for mass approval to wend nuclear death its Armageddoned way.

Once one has read the venom of many authors stating that Jews are wicked, the Germans criminal, the Russians savages, etc., never-ending, we wonder who is good. There is no problem to find points prejudicial to an ethnic group. What it all amounts to is that this is us — our normal antagonistic selves, who recognize the enemy by his uniqueness. Hatred within the same species — selfishness within the total — is the part and parcel of the DNA prescription. We fail to understand this because we fail to recognize ourselves. Everyone else is wrong — it is we, the United States, or we, the Russians, who are in the right.

"Two approaches to the German problem that offer promise. One more ruthless than even Morgenthaus. This would entail the extermination of the German people as pariahs, outcasts, human devils. It could be brought about by a slow starvation. Another possibility would be the moving of the German people as slaves into other countries of the world, hoping that the high mortality rate . . . and the settling of people from other countries in what is now Germany would eventually lead to extinction." — *American Military Government in Germany*, 1947. However, the author did point out that such a solution would be inhuman, Nazi-like, betray ideals, and could backfire.

It is not the statement that frightens us, because mankind has wasted groups and races and nations. It is that any one of us can, without too much prodding, come up with a "final solution" for a fellow nation we tend to dislike. Hitler annihilated Germany's Jews. His enemies destroyed Germany, reduced it to a second-rate power, and Israel regained the Jews' homeland at the expense of the Arabs.

So goes the biology of human genetics. The evolution of sexual selection has had to recess, to a secondary role by the racial ethnic group selection of nationalistic conquest. What was survival of the fittest humans has relinquished to survival of the species specifics. Old-time evolution is being outgunned.

Hundreds of excellent books have been written retrospecting the German-Jewish relationship. One thing always escapes the very astute authors and that is, did the Nazi really have anything to go on? Admittedly they were stupid, biased, inhuman and brutal, yet there had to be basis.

Basic foundations are either skillfully or painfully outskirted. Karl Schleunes, in *The Twisted Road to Auschwitz*, poignantly and magnificently written, derogates biology or racism. "The Jew who emerged from biological alchemy — defining the biological Jew — failure to isolate blood characteristics of Jewishness — an equally mystical process forced someone with Jewish blood to accept Judaism."

This unwillingness to face human genetics is contrary to the spirit of science. As we have said, it was tragic and unfortunate that budding science should be grotesquely distorted to a political purpose. It is great irony that with the mental genius possessed by the Jewish people, such propaganda was not countered with graphs, studies and illustrations of the benignity of their group.

In view of the racial and assimilation difficulties encountered with the American Negro, it would be welcome to see the initiative studies of genetic variance and its sociological consequences come directly from the Jewish scientists. Then no one honestly attempting to visualize the total picture could be accused of anti-Semitism — racism or the like. Jewish authors do themselves a disservice when they blindspot race. To the average American the concept of race carries not one-hundredth of the fisionable power as it does to those of Jewish descent.

We have examined hundreds of works by Jewish authors. We come away from this study saying, "Were the German people that gullible? Couldn't they tell fact from fictional propaganda? Didn't they have something biting them caused by a material substance — not anti-Christ, a ritual-murder, or well-poisoning or illicit sex?" Sane people couldn't believe that drivel. To root, there had to be a quantity of "interwoven truth."

To be sure, envy is a dastardly thing. As many writers point out, although Jewish people did not control the professions, press, finance, commerce, etc., they did have a higher share in them. This same sentiment can be elicited today in America in people who make every effort to be civil and not anti-Semitic, let alone anti-any-other-minority group. We have never been overly impressed with the attitude studies sponsored by B'nai B'rith — that the higher-educated profess smaller amounts of anti-Semitism. It's simply having more education they are more cautious to venture answers to interviewers which would reveal prejudice.

We speak of envy and anti-Semitic prejudice in America at a time when philo-Semitism is in ascendency. Envy! *Life* magazine, in an article, mentioned something about Nixon's efforts to place a non-Jew on the Supreme Court. Not in those words, but rather my interpretation. Yet, now you think, how many are there? You don't think they are all brilliant and the choice is well-made? You really say, "Well, that's out of proportion and sort of not cricket." When you think that way, you're thinking the Nazi venom. But how do you shut off "think"? All someone has to do is point out that observation and you have the makings of rationalizing disfair play.

On the other hand, a Jew for President? A great idea, and the United States will have one. Because here is the tenent of tolerance. You can have one and, like Kennedy, it's time for someone else in proportion to population. But if 40% of the medical profession become Jewish, no matter how you slice civil liberties, there will be envy and resentment among other groups. It is the very crux of the Negro's dilemma today. He wants proportional representation. The Germans also wanted that. And if they had held it there, you may have excused them, because this is the very heart of coalition government, proportional representation.

A friend of ours is bitter about the excessive number of Jewish people in theatre, movies and television. About everyone is ready to blow their lid at the old hacks and hams who are continuously being promoted, their entire lives, to face us in countless dramas. We say, if they'd only give someone new and young a chance.

The fact that one religious group, ethnic group or minority group outweighs and dominates to the exclusion of others is prime evidence for resentment and envy. There is not only feasibility that each minority group should have his representation before the screens and as editors of the documentaries and news, but that the change be paramount to give others, especially the younger, a chance, and that representation be biological in percentage. This is a sore point with Americans, but appears in no anti-defamation league studies. An ethnic group such as the Jews, instead of saturating an industry like television, newspapers, law, and giving preference to their own, should from experiences recollect that this can only lead to envy and the recognition of ethnical differences, creating the highest of prejudices.

What would be in order if an ethnic group monopolistically concentrates in a business area where other groups are captive? Such control should be voluntarily dispersed and limited to avoid what will inevitably follow. It is very easy for Catholics to give preference to Catholics, for Protestants to favor Protestants. But in a media where all must participate, it is foolhardy for one group to be in excess, no matter how concerned one can be in caring for one's own or no matter how excellent a "one's own" actress may appear in one's own eyes. In another eyes, from his special biology, she may be unappealing. One genetic subracial pool does not view with equal appraisement those of another genetic pool. Education, training, propaganda are not factors. Displeasure resides in the genes.

In the development of the biological theory of "cause," we admit envy, a psychosociological trait does influence human action. Not that envy isn't genetically based, it is. Yet it is not enough to send a million innocents to gas chambers. Envy, as a "causative" factor, can be eliminated by removing the object producing it. You can't eliminate biology.

This was done by the Nazis. Wealth was confiscated. Prestige destroyed. No need for envy. This did not stop the juggernaut of hate initiating the *Twisted Road to Auschwitz*. Envy — goofy propaganda of unrealistic fantasies — all were not enough to propel the final terror. There remains only race — blood. Discredited? Stupid? Unscientific? Yet within it had to be unperceived seeds of biological truth.

A Canadian engineer working in the United States with whom I was driving, said, "If the Niggers pull a lot more rioting, like they did, the Americans will wipe them out like Hitler!" Well. Let's look for "cause" before we have a racial repetition. Let's not be too timid to return to the laboratory of biology.

The shut-out of Polish citizens residing in Germany before the war is stark testament to the free borders of anti-Semitism. Often we condemn the Nazis, but when 12,000 Polish Jews desirous of returning were expulsed to the Polish frontier, they were met with wire fences and machine guns to prevent entry. Boatloads of immigrants could find no port willing to take them. Why?

"Marveling at the strange phenomenon of the Jewish people would imply some knowledge of their history, some general perception of the Jewish destiny. Jews in our day seem to have no true consciousness of the unique phenomenon they represent. Jews have always been felt by Gentiles to be something more and something other than the representatives of a mere creed and also as something apart from the unquestionably established nationalities."

This author did not say this, but Erich Kahler, in his *The Jews Among the Nations*, 1967, said "There is no denying the fact that everyone agrees the Jewish people are different and apart — that they have historically desired this particularity to consider themselves as a special group."

This desire has preserved the basic genetic pool which is what evolution is about. It is a corollary of the formation of species by isolation, that they shall give preference to their own kind in interbreeding. Thus, the straight line of the coded nucleic acids can succeed in its compulsed objective.

Not that Gentiles or Jews or Chinese are in danger of speciating — that is, to an extent where interbreeding among races becomes impossible. But had extensive radiation of tribes progressed, we may have had many human species. Clannishness leads to divergence, and maintained for sufficient ages, prohibits reassembly with the parent strain.

We can take a look at non-human primates and state that but for the lack of mobility, sociability, and interbreeding with human stock, we should have some prize relatives. Possibly Neanderthal man could not assimilate either. He may have become a species. Shut out by blood line and consequent rivalry, he assimilated or was hunted down by the modern human.

No one is going to contend the modern races of men were about to speciate. But no one can deny that the genetic pools of tribes or nations maintained over thousands of generations in relative exclusiveness do diverge and do contain hundreds of coded chemical structures which clearly identifies the group more so with each succeeding generation.

Kahler contends the Jews are not a race because the origins of people remain indistinct. Jews, to a higher or lesser degree, mingled with other ethnic stocks but are still originally and essentially a tribe. There exists a very real Jewish "consanquinity" not purely physical.

Kahler continues that Jews are of distinct character — a quality that distinguished "us" as a group — by our experience, by an indisputable feeling of kinship with fellow Jews. He relates a strange Berliner on a cold night whose face was wrapped in a woolen scarf so that only his eyes could be seen, being approached by an old Orthodox Jew, because "the eyes alone were enough to reveal a Jew to a Jew." Such a revelation, although not of high scientific fabric, nevertheless details what we are saying. That biological characteristics are recognizable and utilized in subracial groups.

Kahler points out that the racial anti-Semitism theory commenced as a political instrument to defeat the superiority of Germanic nobility in France. There is a bit of naivete when he analyzes his tribe. "There is *something* which distinguishes them and that is the magnitude of the demands which their *God,* or their destiny or their aspiration, whatever we may call it, has made upon them, demands that they have never relinquished."

Without being accused of blatant philo-Semitism and within all non-prejudicial science of genetics and human breeding, could he have not substituted for *something* — biology, and for *God* — genetics?

It is proposed that the vehement hostility of the Christian church was the basis of anti-Judaism and that Nazi atrocities would have been impossible without the Jewish picture painted by the church in two thousand years. Granted, this was a malevolent influence, is out of scientific perspective for animosities of such horrendous nature to be predicated upon the belief and worship of ethereal nothings such as God or Christ.

It is patently absurd to crucify a man upon his belief. His disloyalty to the state, yes, is time-honored. But his loyalty and professions to some cock-and-bull deity in outer space is fantasy of dreams. A more concrete basis must be sought for explanation. If it were a matter of Christian against Jew, by what cosmic rationalization could the Christian persecute the father of his religion, or his Christ?

Gunther Lawrence, in *Three Million More*, 1970, laments that the Russian mind is unfathomable when it comes to emigration. "There are cases on record where Russian Jews have been jailed or severely punished merely for requesting permission to leave." Aside from the Russian Jew being valuable to the state via his technical and intellectual abilities and, thus, mass emigration would constitute an economic loss, it is possible that some genius within the ruling communist hierarchy, conscious of Hitler's error, wished the Jew to assimilate his genetic pool into the polyglot Russian populace. In other words, premium upon the good biological seed possessed by the followers of Judaism. What other reason could there be for enslavement?

At the end of the 19th century, relations between Germans and Jews were good. Intermarriage was becoming so increasingly common that leaders of the Jewish community feared total assimilation and loss of identity by its end. German Jews were uninterested in Zionism because they had a homeland. They were also in a much less precarious position than their Russian counterparts. The plain fact was that Eastern Jews regarded Germany as a haven from persecution and an opportunity for higher study.

In 1873, Wilhelm Marr was the first to detail a theory of racial conflict between Germans and Jews. "If a people are racially determined then there is nothing and in no manner in which they can change. They are apart."

In this commences the "hyperissimo" sensitivity of the modern Jewish people. In spite of science and for all that, plain visual observance, people do vary. There are individual differences and who would contend there are not family differences. Animal breeding has demonstrated wide differences through selection. Then, why is it so untenable for groups of people deriving from a common ancestry intermarrying over millenniums not to have achieved genetic differences, veritably chemically tissue-coded differences?

The argument of race was viciously turned against the Jews. A rational approach to any facet of it immediately rips open old wounds in protestations of racism or Nazism. Facts of genetic variations, especially in tribes or nations, need not be derogatory, nor should they be the springboard for unfavorable comparisons. Much as a modern-day beauty contest, what we regard as the best nose, physique or talent is highly individual. Judging is not meant to be offensive, but rather a critical summation of traits preferred in the said day and date. Human genetics would have been off to a better start had not nit-wits for political purposes promulgated vicious theories of racial differences.

One of the problems of logic is part truth confounding it. Hitler's obsession that it was the aim of the Jews to infuse their parasitic blood into the veins of superior Aryans is unworthy of serious contemplation. That Aryans are superior or that Jews are parasitic are merely opinions, nothing more than evil name-calling. It is unfortunate that at the rise of the racial doctrines there was not an Einstein geneticist who could demonstrate remarkable and disadvantageous properties possessed by a subrace. Had this ensued, the course of history would have been widely different.

Alder's *The Jews in Germany, 1969*, notes that Jews have been living around Germans since the origin of the German state at the time of Charlemagne. During the first Crusade, hordes looted and killed Jews, followed by their banishment from England, 1290; France, 1306; Spain, 1492, and Portugal, 1497.

"Could a Jewish minority exist in a Christian state, given that Jews follow a despised foreign religion, distinguished from the ruling nations in languages, culture, tradition and socio-economic structure?"

No mention is here made of biological differences. What is seemingly important are those facts of culture that are added to a group. What about the underlying biology — those mental and physical abilities that may be incompatible with the host nation?

Again and again, Jewish writers return to the premise that the woes of the group were due to religion, culture, and isolation of a special and economic nature. None of these factors provide sufficient motivation for long-term or sporadic persecution. What upset the Christian nation group was that within their midst was a biologically cohesive clan, of Mediterranean origin, who were readily identifiable by a few features, emphasized by, for example, black hats and clothes, beards, and mannerisms — all pointing up the fact of their uniqueness as a subrace.

Not only was it critical that the medieval or orthodox Jew could be immediately identified, it was unfortunate that he possessed greater mental ability of abstract nature, greater industry, greater thrift and sacrifice than his non-Jewish neighbors. He was superior in certain traits. This is the *sine qua non* of persecution. Envy! No one truly envied the Jew his religion, his thrift or culture. But unconsciously they did envy a biological rival who was able to outdo them in many fields, especially economic ones.

This problem doesn't relate only to history, but returns to the millions of years of the forests. Those who commanded the banana trees in days of want were certain to have primate relations executing pogroms upon them.

Were the Jewish people a non-touchable caste of extreme poverty, there would never have been a digit raised against them. Their enemy was their tissue design which prompted them to superior economic survival.

There was always an amount of Jewish assimilation into the blood pattern of the host nation. Yet, as Adler points out, "More than assimilation was asked of Jews; they were asked to conform completely — a kind of extinction. The Jews could not assimilate quickly enough for the enemies."

Of course, if the Jews had said, "Our blood or genetic pool shall be a part of the 'host nation,' we will forego religion, language, our culture, and blend our bodies within the majority culture," such a choice would have certainly ended persecution, and it would have ended Judaism itself.

It's like telling the American Negro that if he mates only with whites or one whose skin is lighter than his own, in time his problem will be solved. Yet, the American is not willing to accept color, as the nations of the world were ready to accept Jewish genetic assimilation. Further, by the very nature of the life process, it is contrary for a race or subrace to efface itself within another rival biology.

Species originate not only from isolation, but from a willingness to be unique, separate, and give off similar progeny. Race and subrace, in their programming, are not different.

Dr. H. G. Adler laments, "Hatred of Jews had two forms — first, state accusations. The second, a new point of reference — race. The logic inherent in this position could not lead to demands for corrective reforms, but to expulsion and physical destruction — the racist postulate — everything connected with Jewish race and its 'malice' — an assertion to be taken for granted — everything created by Jews was by necessity bad."

It is stark tragedy that genetics was utilized to discredit Jews. Obviously, there is nothing you can do about your inherited chromosomes. Rather than recoil in horror at the science of human genetics — race — and attempt to debate its existence, a day may come when the Jewish people shall advocate racial concepts — when humanity accepts race and subrace as a blessing.

"In reality, the number of Jews who died in killing factories and concentration camps — collected and forwarded through Eichmann's well-staffed Berlin office — could not greatly have exceeded a single million out of four million or more who perished in all Europe." — *The Final Solution*, Gerald Reitlinger.

S. Levenberg, in *European Jewry Today*, 1967, states: "Since before the Second World War only half as many of the total Jewry lived in Europe, a third of them in communist countries. In Russia there is a policy against Jews occupying posts in leadership of the Communist Party, diplomatic service, higher army echelons. Discrimination against Jews is not discouraged. There are no Jewish schools, cultural or religious institutions, or means for the younger generation to learn Jewish history or literature. There is no organized Jewish community — only three million Jewish individuals living there."

Levenberg concludes: "European Jewry is *a part* of a larger unit, but apart from this it is engaged in a struggle of its own — *a struggle to preserve its identity*, a struggle for the right of self-expression, a struggle to continue the 'golden chain' of Jewish history."

This is exactly where the problem always has lain. Some Jewish people do not wish to give up their identity. Is the American willing to give up his identity or a Swede or a Frenchman or a Basque? Of course, and even today, more and more of the Jews and Jewish culture, according to many authors, are being assimilated, absorbed and lost into the general populace. With the huge number of non-religious in the U.S., religion is no longer a rallying standard of identity or a means in the perpetuation of culture or subrace.

Quite possibly the tenacity, in the face of rapacious persecution of the Jewish people to preserve their religion and culture was not of flimsy sociology, but rather was, like the fundamental desire of all ethnic groups, to preserve the *good blooded seed,* of which the Jews had been amply blessed on the plains of Judea.

Leo Katcher, in *Post-Mortem, The Jews in Germany Today*, speaks of philo-Semitism: "I have profited from philo-Semitism. I tell myself that if some Germans feel it necessary to be excessively good to me, let them. Their need is greater than mine. They have a guilt for the dead."

His character continues, "Why did God have to create both Jews and Germany? Didn't He know they could not exist together?" What is being said, aside from religion and culture, is that Semites and Teutons are biologically incompatible.

Ironic in prophecy, Richard Wagner, 1881, who considered the Jewish race an enemy, stated, "It is quite clear that we Germans . . . will perish through them."

Ridiculous as it was that the German wars were Jewish-promoted, there were influences in other countries that aided in the destruction. Hitler not only exterminated six million Jews, he destroyed the German nation and its ability ever to resurge upon the scene of important history. Aside from the "madman" and his cohorts, humanity faulted in that the qualities of both gene pools could not assimilate. Christ was a red-herring issue of ignorant superstition in the German-Jew conflict and was of minor importance.

In 1881, a 300,000-person petition to Bismarck, warned: "We are faced with the increasing predominance of Judaism, whose influence springs from *racial* peculiarities which the German nation neither can nor will accept without losing its own soul."

By 1930, a German parliamentary bill was proposed against "the debasement and disintegration of the German *race* by mixing with members of the Jewish blood community or with colored races." Horrid as this is in its implication, it nevertheless is a biologically accepted truism that species by definition are isolate and "near-species" prefer breeding within their genetically similar pools.

Julian Huxley states that the word "race" is a personal matter resting on subjective impressions and must be regarded as incapable of scientific determination. Ethnic group or people is a superior term possibly to race.

Modern Jewish writers are conscious of past bloodlines. Irving Agus, in a very interesting work, *The Heroic Age of Franco-German Jewry — 10th & 11th Centuries,* 1969, relates, "Practically all the Jews of Germany and France of that period were the descendants of a little more than one thousand families. In the scores of years following this date [800 C.E.], these families proceeded to interlace and intertwine, through marriage, to the effect that the members of this group became well aware of the very *close blood relationship* that existed between them. Customs — laws — conditions — played an important part in strengthening the cohesiveness of the group, thus creating the vitality and *nationalistic force* that contributed so greatly to its [Ashkenazic Jews] success in its struggle for existence."

From this we not only see that assimilation was unwanted, but blood and genetically Jewish preference was a factor in design and perpetuation. This is elaborated in Agus' preface: "What *natural* qualities did they possess, what background — forms of inner organization — special education — cultural traditions, that enabled them to successfully control their very hostile environment and emerge the most significant branch of Jewish people of the 20th century."

Jewish literature is resplendent with the apartness of the Jew — his differences — and basically these point to underlying biology and not pure tradition and culture.

Agus notes early relations between Jews and non-Jews. It seems the Christians were getting what the Jews did not desire. If meat was unacceptable by its slaughter inspection, then it was sold to Christians. Even some of inferior quality was reserved for sale. Jewish law ruled that any wine poured, touched, or shaken by a non-Jew was forbidden to Jews.

Correctly, Agus concludes such actions led to resentments and prevented the growth of friendships between Jews and their neighbors. Emotions accompanying fetishes as these prevented assimilation and fusion into the major group.

Thus, not only was restrictive biology an exclusive ethnic promotion, it was reinforced by laws and habits that narrowed cultural blending.

Robert Byrnes, in *Antisemitism in Modern France*, writes, "Recent events show profound new areas where the hatred is strong, such as the American blacks, some of whom see the Jew as the principal immediate bar to their rapid advancement. Appearance of anti-Semitism in Harlem, rural Picardy, and Brittany shows that it reflects the unsettled condition of the world."

Byrnes' observations are succinct — "The Jews proved to be unique people — convinced they were 'Chosen People' and that their God was the God of all. The natural feeling of superiority and, therefore, of aloofness, and the magnificent stubbornness of the Jews, constitute some of the principal causes for resentment directed against them. They refused to abandon themselves and their souls to another religious faith."

In one that has few "religious genes" it is incomprehensible to equate persecution of the Jews with religion. So what if Christ was a phoney and the Jews did execute the rebel? When they came up against a tight Christian culture, what harm in accepting the concept of the writings about the paranoiac?

Why didn't they profess belief and within their minds they could have their *own* reservation? Because within they had reservations or should have had reservations about their own God — Father of the Christian one, for that too was an unsubstantiated fantasy. How could so many people, both Christians and Jews, be so utterly hypnotized by a passed-down superstition?

If the Jews believed in "Destir," a God that directed the murder of all Christians, whenever feasible, maybe one could interpret the steam. But here they had a 50% option on heavenness under Christian definition. Religion had been ballooned out of proportion as a factor in human strife.

If we regard religion merely as the banner of a biologic nation, its flag, its center of identity, as a rallying point of all good and true nationals, then we are on more solid terrain. If we say Judaism is a nation independent ready to strike at all foe, a cohesive oneness, if we say Christianity is a nation, against all others, and the flag of the nation is Christ, so perish the communists — then in this text, religion is paramount because it signifies the sovereignty of a state.

If we regard religion as the insignia of the tribe, not a whim of the will, then its aegis shall foster all of the rooted aggression normal to evolutionary development. Religions as banners of groups of biological antagonists prevent the population expansion of other groups, non-integrating with them and identifying with their own.

Wars and persecutions are never religious. They are genetic and biological. It was on this horrid single thread of racial misinterpretation that Nazi venom avalanched. Yet the thread of biological causation and racism is not to be dismissed, but rather examined for the truth that was distorted.

Marie Syrkin, in *Hayim Greenberg*, calls attention to Bernard Shaw's opinion of Nazi racial theories, claiming the fault of the Jew is his "enormous arrogance" based on his claim to belong to God's chosen race, that the Nordic nonsense is only an attempt to imitate the posterity of Abraham, and that the anti-Semitic does not see "*how intensely Jewish is the Nazi thesis of race pollution.*"

"Jews display no desire to convert others to Judaism. They do not wish to defile themselves through religious union with the 'Gentiles'; they believe that members of other 'inferior' races are not worthy of becoming their co-religionists — the Jew regards his religion as a racial monopoly. Some Jewish writers have demanded that before we attack Nazi racial theories, we first renounce our own — that Hitler pursued the same line of Ezra the Scribe — regarding intermarriage as 'racial pollution who advised to cast off non-Jewish wives and purge themselves of Gentile contamination.'" — *Hayim Greenberg.*

Continue with Greenberg on biology — "Regulation for biological segregation decreed by Ezra and Nehemiah were uncompromising for eternity — were later modified making marriage conditional upon the conversion of the Gentile spouse. Such racial law passed from racial motivation to religious character. Jews discriminate in mixed marriage as do those of other faiths — Christian or Moslem. Yet, from the inception of the Christian Church as a consolidated institution, marriage with non-Christians has been frowned upon."

From this we can gather that the contention the Jewish people were given insufficient time to assimilate in Europe was simply untrue. There is a strong biological process at work within the framework of a religious culture — namely, to remain pure and identify itself with the past. Words and professions and faiths do not survive without underlying biological exclusions, although Greenberg feels it is majority religious.

Attend the bitterness of Leo Katcher (1968) in *Post-Mortem, The Jews in Germany Today*, as his character drips, "Germany is not a country for Jews. We don't belong here. Time is only widening the gulf between the Jews and the Germans. The Jews must never forget what happened here. The Germans do not want that memory. I make no judgment. We are *two different peoples*. Our experience is not part of the German experience."

Such an attitude is tragic. But if they are separate peoples, they are so biologically not by experience, for Jews lived in Germany from before the time of its Emperor Charlemagne, 500 A.D., and all of their togetherness was not unpleasant or uncalculated toward common good and humanity. If a future geneticist would correlate genes in a "group-race" according to desirability and concluded that of the world's peoples the Jews had amassed the more beneficial ones and were indeed "the chosen" of humanity, wouldn't that sweeten the forum to open discussion?

One Jewish author observes it is becoming fashionable in America to love Jewish people and their culture. To the pronouncements of race by the Nazi, many Jewish people retorted that their blood and culture were superior to that of the Aryans. Here is where the issue sticks in who is to judge which are good and bad genes. But for an example, intelligence. In many studies, the Jewish are found to be the most intelligent subrace on earth. So we can't hide our heads and say human breeding is unimportant and cannot be compared with animal breeding.

Gerald Reitlinger, in *The Final Solution*, comments on German officials. "They had to invent a mumbo-jumbo language about biological material, inferior strains of blood, asocial, and unlaborer worthy types, and so forth — to hide from themselves what they were doing." And, "It is possible that murderous racialism is something ineradicable in the nature of ants and men — but the robot state that will give it effect cannot exist."

Crux to that pronouncement, "in the nature of ants and men" is what we are contending. Evolutionary selection — selection of the white bloodline to the exclusion of the Negroes and their economic strangulation, is every bit as much genocide, but on a more humane and acceptable scale than the Nazi horror.

Biologically prejudiced, we select our mates. We are programmed with recognition guiding us to and within the closest relative line, though avoiding incest. All of the manned lecterns incessantly preaching the oneness of humanity will never succeed in gaining what has evolved in hundreds of thousands of years, not to bed with strange "ethnic" groups.

No group is possibly greater "racists" than the Jews themselves. New York City, composed principally of two racial strains — the Jewish and the Negro-Puerto Rican — have succeeded to what extent in assimilation and intermarriage? If the Jewish people, overwhelmingly opposed to the mention of racism, and from their experience they cannot be blamed, are unable to assimilate to the most minor degree with their city neighbors, why cannot they be termed "racists"?

None other than nonsense is the allegation that "racism" or "racist" is a bad word. Seventy percent of the world's people are racists and, in the past, a goodly 100%. It's time we rephrase this much-maligned word. To have pride in one's race is what harm? Is anyone ashamed of their race? Or subrace?

Stember, in *Jews in the Mind of America* (1966), in a chapter on the Decline of Anti-Semitism, comments that "The Jews' phenomenal involvement with professional work cannot be attributed exclusively to the economy's ever-growing need for educated and professionally trained personnel. It is evidently a fact special to this group that the proportion of Jews in the professions is increasing at a rapid pace. As noted, Jews are once more strongly represented in the category of 'proprietor, manager or official'; a number of executives in large national corporations."

From Stember's tables we see Jews from two to five times more prominent in occupations requiring intelligence than is the population as a whole.

We could deduct this is because now opportunities are open to them and their cultural heritage prompts them to seek other than manual labor.

Aside from the Jews' continuous history of being persecuted, they are an eminently successful people. Granting that Arabic culture had its heyday a thousand or more years ago, we must literally close our eyes because of one-sided over-intensity when today we compare the two groups. Although both Near-East residents derived from a common Semitic ancestry, the level of biological genetic advancement between the two is staggering.

A triumvirate of many powerful genes, intelligence, industry, and modesty of habit has placed the Jew in the forefront of occupational positions. None other than Semitic "blood" — Jewish type — could be responsible. Would the Negro be capable of doing likewise? We know that this cannot be because of his distribution of intelligence. It is not that the Negro is some second-rate type of human; it is by the way we measure him, for in our type of modern civilized structure, he has and will have great difficulty in competing.

Contrarily, if by some cosmic wave we had to all return to Africa to survive, the Negro's possession of genetic facets would soon render him superior to other racial groups. Evolutionary selection in case of the Negro was not directed toward abstract computerized ability. Rather, it programmed toward survival in a hostile, torrid, germ- and parasitical-infested continent.

In a prime point, Stember states, "Marriage constitutes the ultimate degree of acceptance, the lessening resistance to Jews as potential wives or husbands. *Opposition to intermarriage remains much more widespread than any other form of rejection* for which we have current data, but seems to have declined at the same rate as hostility in work, residence and education."

What peoples' attitudes toward intermarriage on a questionnaire are and what happens in actuality are separate. What is the percentage of intermarriage? Is it a biological rejection? After all, Protestants and Catholics for centuries didn't mate well. It is attributable to religious differences and, as a consequence, genetic differences.

In short, are there religious biological differences? Did Martin Luther's offshoot group attract a physically variant personality to that which remained with the founder group? Those venturesome, starving, dissatisfied hordes from hundreds of nations that immigrated to America to produce its greatness were not of the same genetic composition of the non-pioneers that remained behind. Selectively, they came from the less successful, more manual workers.

Attend what Howard Singer, in *Bring Forth the Mighty Men* (1969) says. "The point in the center of organized anti-Semitism has moved from Berlin to Cairo and Damascus now. It's sickening. To begin with, don't fall for the notion that the Arabs are not anti-Semitic because they are Semitic themselves. All the word really means is that they are anti-Jewish. It always did. Hitler — an expert anti-Semite — had no hesitation in working with Arabs."

How could it come to pass that a people joined by a common religion and blood could engender a vicious response in nearly every nation they settled in?

Protestants and Catholics have had their go at wars and massacres. Yet, in time, after the original heat had dissipated, they resolved in a stand-off respect. Today, with Jewish governors and statesmen, it is not uncommon among intellectuals to hear unpleasant references to Jews concerning their traditionally attributed malevolent traits. Yet rarely are anti-Catholic or anti-Protestant slurs involved.

It is as if the forces that have beleaguered the Jews through the centuries have convinced their neighbors that the Jew is different — a monopolist — a Shylock — an insensitive human — an anti-Christ — and made it stick. A religious basis — anti-Christ — is pure absurdity. A lot of those who are regarded Protestant are not only anti-Christ, they don't believe.

Religion was a force in motivating some wars. In most wars, however, of recent vintage, the same ethereal gods flaunt their banners in both camps. So you don't blame the Jewish plight on religion. It doesn't hold. If we go to war against the Russians or Chinese, or both in some combination, it won't be because one or the other's flag is a deity symbol. Deep animosities such as war represent are no longer stirred by heavenly hosts. Religion is out. Yet here we see continuing aggression against the Jewish people. As Singer says, the word is anti-Jewish.

Or is Jewish culture, that which has been learned and passed down, the mecca of hate generation? Hardly. All races and subraces have their own idiosyncracies. Is it because Jews isolate themselves? Again, no one pays antagonistic heed to Pennsylvania's Mennonites or Dunkars, who are an extremely unique nidus within a gross culture.

Is the world envious of the Jews? Of course it is. Of their money, success, ability, and heritage. The world is envious still, from nation to nation, tribe to tribe, individual to individual. We all possess envy. Further, the Jews are not solitary in the qualities that compound envy. Wealth, beauty, intelligence, capability cut an undistinguisable swath across the racial faces of men and, much like bacteria, respect no human origin.

The contention that during the Middle Ages Jews ritually murdered children to use their blood in the manufacture of Passover cakes persists today in Arab propaganda. Such grotesque thought should be presented humorously as "Yes, but good sacrificial subjects are so expensive these days, and with the price of flour . . ." No *sane,* intelligent individual could, and I seriously doubt ever did, take such disposition seriously.

Beneath, subconsciously, the myth is accepted because it symbolizes fear that Jewish blood will displace the blood of the non-Jew. Children of the non-Jewish sect will be eliminated by the more successful biological survival of the Jewish people. What is seen is the fear of a more dominant human strain supplanting existing strains — as the Neanderthal or Paranthropus or Dinosaurs were breached in their evolution.

Listen again to Singer: "Listen, you know Jews. To us war is not glamorous, it's stupid. It wasn't that we never had the brains for war, it's that we never had the taste. . . . We took pleasure in creating things, while so many take pleasure in destroying. We still would rather compromise than fight. . . . The Israel Defense Force . . . well-named . . . in character. That way Jews were able to overcome their deep feelings that fighting is bestial, that it is something for the stupid *muzhik*."

What is being said is that the fighting had not been with the Jewish character. Today the Israeli have demonstrated their superior fighting ability. So we must conclude that time and place forges the cultural attitude.

There is more to this, though. Suppose the German is actually chemicaled to warrior disposition — the Jew to peace and creativity — by genetic structure. How can you then account for the Israeli military success? *Bring Forth the Mighty Men* unknowingly answers that: "We haven't changed, not basically. We still would rather compromise than fight. We are still passionate only when we try to preserve — the army is simply a part of the preservation process." To wit: genes of instinctive preservation will surmount and redirect activity over any other characteristics.

In the selection of the Jewish bloodline there is no argument against the characteristics of peaceability and creativity being genetically directed and invented, possibly as components of intelligence. What interests us is that a subrace has a physical basis for traits which formerly we ascribed to cultural hand-me-downs. In short, subraces of earth differ physically, biochemically, to produce human race characteristics formerly thought to be learned. Not color, slant of eye or stature are DNA coded alone, but peace-ability, aggression or humanitarianism.

Albert Memmir, in *Liberation of the Jews*, states that "Right is won when the bed's undone." In short, mixed marriages can seem the loyal road to liberation for the oppressed. He continues, "No visible attempt at assimilation can be accepted without anger by the Jewish community. Mixed marriage means disappearance in the long run. This explains the agreement between believing Jews and atheist Zionists in condemning it."

Here once more we return to genes. Why are Jews and Germans both angered at the admixture of patently unsimilar genes? It is here you witness the full flower of anti-Semitism. It's not really the myths, the Protocols of the Elders, ritual murder, anti-Christ, monopoly and isolation, it is what the mind's eye recognizes subconsciously.

When all of the prejudicial persecutory contentions are examined closely, they are so much window-dressing. You could and can ascribe such tall tales to any culture. You can even find instances of verification. What culture is not proud? Some groups profess the intention to hoard gold, control monopolistically, or dominate. Look at how our presidents are assassinated. Does that represent American culture? Are we anarchial killers? Occasional horrors don't stigmatize a people.

The genes remain. Let us seek a mate through a young man's eyes. Many recognitional components enter the calculation — general figure, thigh, breast, nose, color of skin, age, movement, possibly speech, action, intelligence, a wide range of preferable attributes, beauty personality. Or the woman's eyes. Proximity may be a factor. Yet you may be sure that programmed within neural tissue is an outline of favorable design. Does the French nose (not DeGaulle's) usurp preference over the Semitic nose? A mechanism within us directs us toward specific sexual selection. This is a major way we evolve.

If given a choice, we would not mate with the Australian Aborigines in preference to Swedes. In the past we had no choice; we could not move out readily into other people's genes. But we did have recognitional indexes denoting what was *our* genetic pool, *our* group, and what mate was proper to union.

Race is not cultured upon us. We see it as one species of bird recognizes a small red dot on another and declares, "It's one of ours." Every subrace in history has recognitional direction, biologically asserting their own and foreign. If we're one big happy, all's-fine-with-everyone group, how come, with all of the cultural enlightenment of America, we are after centuries still divided into our hereditable divisions? Is it culture or gene recognition?

Hitler said, "Germans must realize that Jewry forms a racial entity with very strongly marked racial characteristics, of which passion for material gain is the most dominant."

Agreed, all that has been said is downright nonsense, fantasy, invention, and much for the ignorant.

The Jew has a religion that is a bit exclusive, which makes marriage and table habits impossible between strict Jews and non-Jews. That he segregated, lent money and concentrated on commerce, did not necessarily distinguish him from others. Look what modern-day Gentiles in their banks and loan companies with their credit cards are doing to an unwary public. Usury as this was never thrust with such profusion, high rates of interest and disconcern in the entire history of Judaism.

As Norman Cohn observes, these factors by themselves would never have led to attempts at genocide. He explains it, "Exterminatory anti-Semitism appears where Jews are imagined as a collective embodiment of evil, a conspiratorial body dedicated to the task of ruining and then dominating the rest of mankind."

But why? Other minorities are not so favored with aspersions of evil and conspiration. There must be something, for you can't have effect without a logical cause. You can begin with deductive reasoning.

In some manner the Jewish people are different to create such cataclysmic antagonism. You can't quarrel with the premise, because history is its witness. No people have been so persistently persecuted as the Jews.

Two, they have been viciously misrepresented to create hatred in the areas of their settlement — ergo-anti-Semitism. No debate.

Three, therefore they differ. By (a) characteristics common to them by culture. For example, aggressiveness in business, industry, thrift, which have been passed down in forms of learning; or by (b) characteristics determined by genetic structure, being physical in nature, and secondarily mental from the underlying physical basis. Said chemistry being the *raison d'etre* of the Jewish subrace to begin with — a Semite group — that by intraracial breeding — cohabiting and selecting among themselves has evolved into a purity — or structure that is unique — the same way the Swedes or Italians are unique.

As we develop the genetic or race theory, please remain calm. Hitler was not mad in the sense of known mental disease, but by every other standard he was. It is of great tragedy that such a creature latched onto the beginning science of genetics. Many geneticists regret this. The onus of Hitler, unfortunately, imprints any attempt to speak racially. Yet it is time we freed ourselves from this dead man's throttle.

"Even a blind pig will find an occasional acorn." If, in all Hitler's demagoguery, he came upon a bit of science and espoused it, we cannot blame the science. In spite of what some writers would have us believe, that there are no races but only language groups, the science of evolution and genetics portrays the contrary.

Maybe it is difficult to draw the line and say, "This race is yellow; this race is blue; this race red," because our main base is color of skin. If we include many other factors — blood types, structure, physical traits — we can component hundreds of races depending upon how finely we wish the categories. In short, a race or subrace is a group of human primates which possess certain physical and mental characteristics, enough to distinguish them from other groups, to categorize them qualitatively and quantitatively. It is dependent upon a group possessing a pool of genes having common identification.

One forgets that during the Russian Civil War between 1918-1920, over 100,000 Jews were killed. You must remember that this "Kill the Jews. Save Russia" campaign preceded the Nazis, with equal savagry, in murder, atrocity and arson of their dwellings. Why? Why Russia, Poland, Germany? Why was the Jew so hated? The answer is biology — genes of antagonism — and you can choose dozens of subraces with the same history of persecution — more than that, extinction.

Germany's Nazis made it painfully difficult for anyone to discuss race rationally and not offend some group or other. That which adds insult to their propaganda line was that they were not scientific men, nor did they base their claims upon firm anthropology. Their chatter was intended as political issue, easily translatable to ordinary people.

As we read *Mein Kampf*, Hitler's master work, it is clear that we are dealing with low-educated people. What is even worse, out of the untruth and semi-truths of its 700-odd pages, is that there are actual truths included. Anyone who writes that much about any issue is bound to stumble on some accurate facts and, because of this, when anyone ventures close to that which *der Fuhrer* has put down, he is bound to be accused of racism, Nazism or Hitlerism.

Hitler has become a very useful instrument to beat down any scientist who so much as opens his mouth concerning race and equalitarianism. He has so stigmatized the subject matter that most writers simply avoid the field. Mankind has a way of returning to fact and examination, no matter what the taboos are that surround it. So, with the foregoing apologies in mind, we shall look at this man from the viewpoint of genetics.

There is a great desire to consider Hitler as a madman. Psychoanalyists have ripped open his character and personality to expose every psychosis in the book. All for all, it is what a great many people wish to think, for they and their families and friends have suffered grievously at the hand of this ogre. So have, especially, the German people.

What Hitler possessed was a fantastically strong drive for leadership and power. He overflowed with DD genes. His entire political life is evidence for his struggle for dominancy and its maintenance. Even in the face of final adversity, another man would relinquish power. Richard Nixon had similar drive, but when the writing was on the wall, he broke down and fled precipitously to a safe California retreat rather than remain in the bunker until death would him part. Franklin Roosevelt is an excellent example with strong DD genes, even to the point of destroying tradition so that he could continue in the presidency emperor-like. It was only illness and death that removed him from his unassailable political citadel.

Winston Churchill, on the other hand, though possessing strong dominancy genes, seemed fully willing to be retired by the electorate in democratic fashion. Neither did he struggle to overturn democracy to fulfill the egoism of the dominant genes. Whether it be Mussolini, Stalin, Franco, Mao-Tse-tung — those who come to authoritarian control are ever reluctant to relinquish it. History is replete with dictators, sovereigns, strong emperors and commanders. So, in this fashion, Hitler was no different than other butchers and despots in the chronicles of time.

Where he did suffer was in an obsession that was concluded to his apparent satisfaction. It was so horrible and extraordinary that it shall never be forgotten. Yet all men possess obsessions to more or less degree. Howard Hughes was obsessed with privacy; John the Baptist with the coming of the Messiah; Einstein with physics; Beethoven with music; a fat man with food, and an alcoholic with drink.

Hitler's obsession was with the Jews. There was a strong, fixed, underlying hatred of them. Hatred again is another normal characteristic of varying degree and, under varying circumstances, in the body of man. Wounded Knee, Malmedy, Mai Lai, St. Bartholomew's Day, and murder of the Innocents, are merely a few of the long list of human massacres. Hatred is an easily activated motivational gene that is routinely alerted by propaganda in preparations for war. It is to be frowned upon but never when it is officially sanctioned by nations. Our nation, as any other nation, has had its officially blessed hatreds, as wars blossomed, so did derogatoriness: the Yankees, the Rebels, the Japs, the Huns, the Gooks, and the British. And, as the fighting waned and terminated, so the sanction for hatred diminished.

Nothing is new in man's hatred for another nation — for conquest, annexation, or even annihilation. Such racial groups and clans have been fighting one another viciously for millions of years. Their record is on the books.

Genetic supremacy for one's own is the driving force of evolutionary evolvement. When Darwin said "survival of the fittest," he should have added "survival of the socially organized fittest." Society has its own evolutionary force which is directed by selection for the benefit of members of the organization.

One recoils in disgust when one sees Hitler with obsessional hatred against the Jews, putting into effect an evolutionary selective force by their European annihilation. This is social genetics in its most murderous form. The fact was that its author, with the aid of the converted, was able to exterminate Jews and millions of other political adversaries, including Germans. This dastardly act was ruthless application of genetic social evolution. It was a calculated drive for the purpose of subracial purity in the same fashion white Americans eliminated the Indian.

This force has been employed and is routinely employed in social evolution against those outside the tribe, nation, subrace or race. It is the morally unnatural, normal mechanism for survival of the specifically related codes.

Dietreick Eckert, in *Bolschevism from Moses to Lenin*, attempted to prove that Judaism was the great destructive force which had ruined western civilization. What was said is not as important as the reality, that subracial groups existed and were identifiable. The tendency of the Jewish people to preserve their own cultural blood and heritage in other nations to set themselves apart as an isolate was countered in similar fashion by the nation in which they resided. Throughout this book we use the word "blood" in a general and literary sense, denoting a geneticism rather than the specific componency of blood groupings, which indeed do differ among subraces such as the Basques, in a province of Spain, from the other Spanish, or the Mongoloids from the whites.

The Jews exist because of the fact of their cohesive genetics, the same as the Italians or Germans. And when placed side by side or within an isolate subracial pool, there can be none other than an eventual conflict. Religion, possibly, has the least of any "factor" in the situation where there is ethnic proximity and confrontation. That which is operational has identities which are recognized within the social mixture. America's experience is new and her confrontations are only now emerging from the vastness of her space. Black assimilation has not progressed in centuries, and press propaganda toward mutual bedding has accomplished little more than firm the white resolution to unity. Forced school busing has fortified the racial cleavage rather than breach it. Politicians are not geneticists and, therefore, are not comprehending the racial codings.

Justifiably, the Nazi has been accused of hatred of freedom of speech and press, equalitarian justice and democracy. There is a reasonable basis for a shift of attitude with modern society. Under the threat of dictatorial communism, democracy, because it has not adjusted in the middle of the 20th century, is on the run. Communism has taken advantage of the freedom of the press and speech and equalitarian labor justice to make heavy inroads toward the leaderships of many nations, such as Italy, France and Portugal, that were once bastions of the free world alliance. It demonstrates that there is no such thing as a stable political science, and every nation must roll with the punch as times progress.

That which is permanent is the political science which is residual within human biologic coding. Discrimination is the tool of evolution. Without it, mankind would never have come out of the trees. So, as we look for what truths we can find in the Hitlerian philosophy, we can see that there was also a great hatred of communism, its advancement, its association with Jewish leaders, and the biologies of the masses. The rise of Hitler goes much deeper than the rise of a ruthless dictator. It was a counterforce to communism and a political thrust toward absolute dominancy and control.

Conrad Heiden said that, "By incantating the principle that men are not equal is the theoretical purpose of *Mein Kampf.*" What is tragic is that such a principle is fact. Look about you, walk down a street, go in a store, talk to people — simply talk to a hundred people in the various walks of life and you will be amazed at the incredible differences. No one knows this better than educators who chop, prune out and cut off their charges from the advancement up the educational ladder at every stage. There is no such thing as democracy in education. It is pure aristocracy in its worst form. The chosen, such as the medical and legal professions who have monopolistically gained access to the inner sanctum, slice the pie exactly as they please and nothing is going to root them out of their privileges.

On the other hand, had our evolutionary biology equipped us as social and intellectual equals, we would have never been able to erect one wooden log house in the forest to ward off the freeze. Nature was very thoughtful and astute in her creation of biological inequalities and dominancy scales. This had strong selective value in the formation of society by preventing internal conflict and delegating to some men the meanest and riskiest of tasks. To be sure, it is unfair. Yet it is the substance of society. The recognition of this fact shall be the death knell of socialism and communism one day.

We may have already put the eugenic show on the road by college people tending to intermarry and the laborers likewise, splitting not only the classes into distinct neighborhoods and cultures, but breeding the biological future.

In examining the consequences of racial crossing in Hitler's *Mein Kampf*, he cites North America as being largely composed of Germanic elements. We must remember that the English and French are Germanic in origin also, as well as the German people, northern Italians, and a great deal of Europe is mixed from the Germanic migrations at the time of and after the fall of Roman civilization. Whereas, the North American mixed but little with the colored people, the Latins of South America mixed frequently with the Aborigines.

The Americans eschewed breeding with the Indian Mongols, even with assimilating with them. Rather, they chose to isolate and annihilate them. Hitler concluded that "The Germanic inhabitants of the American continent who have remained racially pure and unmixed rose to be master of the continent. That he will remain master as long as he does not fall a victim to defilement of the blood, the result of racial crossing which will lower the level of the higher race and regress its physical and intellectual qualities, bringing about a progressing sickness, which will be nothing else but to sin against the will of the eternal creator."

Of course, most of this is nonsense. There is no such thing as one race being higher than another. For such an appraisal it would have to be from the prejudiced eyes of the beholder. But what there is is a wide range of racial differences based upon genetic coding resulting from isolated, geographical existence and adapted according to the environment. Evidently, what Hitler was trying to show and what is demonstrable is that the North Americans have a greater sense of administrative ability, loyalty and democracy, which placed them in control of their continent. While the Latins who mixed in their area with the natives may not have produced an economic and military colossus such as the north, their form of government does contrast sharply with their eternal series of revolutions, dictators, and political strife.

Some factors within the genes of this mixture do not suit them to the submission dominancy scales, loyalty or stable democracy, as is demonstrated in the North.

That the Latin or native blood, by mixing, was defiled is scientific absurdity. That which did happen, however, was that a new genetic mix of unfamiliar coded patterns was introduced into the regulatory biological government of the white Latins, the yellow Indians and a sprinkling of Negroes, to produce a couple of dozen of highly politically unstable societies.

Separately, the Spanish have had one of the highest civilizations and, as nations go, relative political calm. Mayans, Aztecs, and many cultures in South America demonstrated excellently evolving primitive civilizations. When not the blood mixed but the germinal cells carrying their respective codes of adaptability to certain traditional societies, there evolved peoples of incredible government instability. In time, evolution in its wisdom, in thousands of generations, executions, ambushings, isolations, annihilations, and population controls, will adapt the volatile product to political sensibility, whereas education and philosophy have failed.

As is being demonstrated in studies, there are racial differences both physically and intellectually. Racial mixtures will enhance some factors and lower others. This is nothing more than what has been known to mankind in animal breeding experiments since the time of the agricultural revolution. There's no need to get uptight about it, but rather face facts. Again, that which weighs heavily upon the heart of man, as in all races and subraces within the pure ethnic groups, are tremendous variability, with there being true princes within the black race as well as real gutter-scum in the white. Yet this divergence does not present the eugenic signal for interbreeding. For each isolate historic genetic pool presents its own unique diamonds and genetic thorns adapted to that traditional social group.

Hitler stated, "All great cultures of the past perished only because their original creative race died out from blood poisoning." That is stupidity. But if we were to substitute dysgenics for blood poisoning, we could be on realistic ground. Genetics is the very warp and woof of evolution. Species of men and societies rise and fall because of the slight advantages given to one over another — a more erect figure, a better stereoscopic vision, a taller structure, a more opposable thumb, a more articulate speech, and a few million more neurons to calculate by.

Whether it be the culture of the Cromagmon, the Neanderthal, a Homo erectus, that which accompanies their special codes and the social forces today are acting no differently. The future will not see the homogenized atypical human, but will bear witness to the traditional shifts in the adaptional current of evolvement of the fittest.

From *Anti-Semitism and the British Union of Fascists*, an interesting generalization is noted: "Anti-Semitism appeals to deep-rooted social forces — psychological, religious, national and economic." It is pointed out that in anti-Semitic propaganda, recurrent themes are the clanishness and self-containment of the Jews. Irish Catholics looked askance at their alien way of life. As a group they have distinguishing religious and social customs that they have adhered to over the centuries, partly from choice (their own "chosen people" attitude). Whereas, Jews mostly were not an agricultural people, but stayed in towns developing crafts or utilizing their wealth and financial skills to purchase going industrial concerns.

"The attitude of the Roman Catholic Church has been a sorry one toward Jews." Stupidities as Christ-killing and ritual murder was an additional plague to set Jews apart. Religion is without doubt a selfish instinct. Regard the Protestant and Catholic massacres and wars. Religion provides a basis for conflict. Yet one cannot eliminate underlying biology as a propagator. In reality, when people believe in their God "Dippy Dumb-Dumb," it has no serious antagonism. It is only when "Dippy Dumb-Dumb" is the banner of a divergent genetic pool that it does.

"Jews are undeniably different. They have remained stubbornly and proudly a self-conscious minority and have therefore chosen to draw fire upon themselves." Everything, all, sum in total, the hundreds of Jewish writers we have surveyed, agree enmasse that the Jew is different and set apart from others.

Golo Mann speaks of anti-Semitism with forceful clarity. "It had a long past. Was it stronger in Poland than in Germany or in Russia or in France? I do not know. I should have thought that about 1900 it was strongest in France. And the slogan, 'The Jews are our misfortune,' I would dare to state that anti-Semitic passion in Germany was never more rabid than in the years 1919 to 1923, much more so than in 1930-1933 or 1933-1945." Here again we note universality in the attitudes of host peoples. It was not only the Germans. Yet there were all types of minority peoples within these nations. Why were the "chosen" singled out for persecution? They preserved their biological coherence identity, it was not a question of patriotism — loyalty to their adopted country, religion or wealth. There was in each land an island, a true genetic pool, a selective subrace.

"German anti-Semitism was different. The obscene hatred of Jews which the young Hitler had acquired in Vienna, the only genuine deep emotion of his black heart, his peculiarity and that of his more intimate supporters. One single devil in human shape made all the overall decisions — the executioners were easy to find." Mann points out that Herman Goring's statement, "I have never been an anti-Semite — ask Bernheimer," at the Nuremberg Tribunal, was not a lie.

The degree of guilt among the German hierarchy and its citizens is of issue. The event was supported by attitudes and actions of dozens of previous generations. That a few leaders in an ape tribe can actionize the masses is within anthropology. A modern general commands any action, stupid, murderous or brilliant, with the baton he carries. For leadership of great magnitude to exist there must be basic genetic agreement in purpose and submission.

Heinrich Himmler's plan in 1943 to murder all German princes and all members of former ruling dynasties because they were just as much alien in blood, just as international and treacherous as the Jews, is noteworthy.

Here is the intra-subracial conflict. Hitler and his brood were not of aristocratic intellectual stock, but derived from the worker group. This divergent geneticism, in this respect, resembles the worker Red Russian massacring their "white" aristocratic Tzarist blood — worker versus intellectual or leftist versus rightist — founded in specially evolved genes, we, are born to — proletariat versus bourgeois.

In concluding his brilliant speech, Galo Mann assessed that "The assimilation of the German Jew was almost completed before 1914, irrespective of whether they remained faithful to their religion or not. In order to bring about the catastrophe, it required a combination of circumstances. It required this one individual [Hitler] to unite these forces and instincts, to mobilize them, to lead them to this end. Whoever has lived as a German through the '30s and '40s can never fully trust his nation — cannot trust men in general — will remain in the innermost of his soul a sad man until he dies."

To analyze this sensitive writing, look to the words "instinct" and "trust." Mann doesn't say "animosities," "religion" or "cultural" differences. What the word "instinct" denotes, whether it was meant in this sense or not or was a subconscious prompting, is that within men are coded action patterns. Since many of these patterns are self-protecting and selfish in nature, they cannot be trusted. It is why nations are rival armed camps and civilized men carry keys.

Third of the speakers being reviewed, from *The German Paths to Israel*, by Rolf Vogel, Dufour Editions, 1969, is Salo W. Baron. The shameful badge of a yellow star that Jews were forced to wear on their garments when walking a German street had a remote history. "It was imposed upon Jews by a decision of an ecumenical council of 1215 for the purpose of preventing too intimate a relationship between Jews and Gentiles — which in essence both parties desired. The Bishop of Speyer, the first recorded founder of a German-Jewish ghetto, had done it in 1094 as a favor to Jews, in order to attract them to his city and thus enhance the dignity of his bishopric."

Again and again, history and fact support the evidence that the Jews desired to be cohesive and apart and to intermarry within their own group. By so doing, they demonstrate the very process of eugenics, evolution, and a private genetic pool permitting isolation and the development of divergent characteristics. Hitler's racist rantings should have come as no surprise, because from the record the Jewish people, among all those of earth, were able to keep their individuality in any environment or nation those chose. It appears they were the first people to successfully practice isolation and human genetic pooling in whatever land they journeyed. Their isolation is rapidly being reinforced in the modern world in Israel.

Martin Luther's statement, "If the Jews could kill us all, they would gladly do so; aye, and often do it, especially those who profess to be physicians," has interest, not so much in religious competition, but the fact that Luther feared "warfare" — blood-letting. This is biological fear, not the competition of Gods. This is an ancient instinct — his DNA code recognizing the enemy.

"That the Jews had not kept their part of the bargain of becoming fully assimilated to the German people — this contract myth has been exploded by Harry Sacher." This is a point that is ridiculous to belabor. The "madness" of Hitler was impossible to foresee. Had the preview of events to come been detailed, and it should have been because of the forewarnings over the centuries, purposely planned assimilation could have been of top priority and highly effective. Yet, had the Jews assimilated, civilization would have lost one of its jeweled genetic pools for the present and a priceless multi-faceted DNA code for the future.

In *The Tenacity of Prejudice*, by Gertrude J. Selznick (from the Anti-Defamation League of B'nai B'rith) — "Uneducated people harbor a greater anti-Negro and anti-Jewish prejudice. This is not compatible with the theory that prejudice arises out of competition — because the uneducated do not compete with Jews.

"Nevertheless, competition is the basis for prejudice and whether a group cannot successfully challenge competition, such as the uneducated vs. the Jewish, this very limitation in itself is a restriction and a source of envy.

"In the study of white attitudes, 53% of the northerners and 79% of the southerners interviewed felt there should be laws against marriages between whites and Negroes, and 89-96% agreed a white owner should not have to sell to Negroes. High percentages, 47-76%, did not wish their children to school with a 'lot of Negroes.' "

Obviously, aside from manifest prejudice, the whites were asserting what their biology was directing them, in time-honored tradition. They wished their genetic pool to remain consistent by non-marriage, reinforced by geographical isolation.

This is the very basis for origin of a species — by genetic drift. We could never be so naive as to imagine that species origin resulted solely from living out of contact with fellow animals until such time as the reproductive apparatus was incapable of rebreeding.

Within every species are recognitional signals, sounds, sights, odors, feelings that prompt it to permissible and selective mating. When divergence is to take place and a new species formed, selection is instituted by, for example, the size of a feather, the length of a claw, or the color of skin, not by mutation chromosomes or genetic crossover of genes or heterozygosity alone, but majorily in sexual selection of mates.

Also, by mutation or common ordinary variation, a gene pattern decides upon a course of selective mating — it is prejudicial. White-headed birds with green tail feathers are programmed not to socialize with black birds or red.

What has happened with the human primates is that insufficient time elapsed to qualify various members as separate species. And, although there was isolation, it was not sufficiently enforced to prevent the introduction of a minute amount of one gene pool into that of another, keeping the sexual option open.

There should be no need to cry "foul," to permit the human primates to diverge, select, and evolve. And if any group in history has been sexually prejudicial, it is the Jewish people who historically have not approved of mixed marriage or the dilution of their religion or culture.

This was not a policy of selfishness, but an enlightened venture of nobility. By hoarding their germinal plasma exclusively into their group, although dispersed throughout the world, they insured their uniquely brilliant and prideful heritage to the benefit of mankind, and so disproved the power of religion and culture as large factors in prejudice.

Yet, can we say equally kind things concerning the Negroes, or anything in a comparison without being called "racist"? One has but to compare the two geneticisms himself and draw his own conclusions.

It's not that, as some anthropologists would have us do, mate equally all the earth's peoples to come up with a homogenous non-discriminatory blend, it is that all groups, all genetic pools, all tribes, call them races or sub-races, do differ and vary and have evolved in capacities, emotions, and industry. It is simply untruthful and fraudulent that all the groups of mankind are the same. Being individualistic and unique, rights, privileges, and honors are granted to their special uniqueness, including the right to racial prejudice, unfortunate as may be such a connotation. If it were otherwise, nations should not exist — there would be no frontiers, for a period at least, until divergence again emerged.

If we were to amalgamate by racial cohabitation, would we eliminate genetic claims of quality and inequality? No way! Were the earth's peoples all colored sunset orange, the very nature of biologies' coding system would set in other traits, everyone apart.

Racial homogeneity could destroy all the selective good gained by some and do nothing for the evolvement of others. Instead, being outraged at prejudice, we should be as prideful in group genes as one is of their own family. Otherwise, there would be no Spanish, French, Israelis, Congolese or Egyptians.

In 1957, Louis Schneider found that American Jews had over half their numbers working in professions or as managers or officials, or with an income of over $7500 per family. Whereas, for Protestants and Catholics, it was less than 21% — 33% of Jews attended college to 19% of Protestants and 14% of Catholics. What conclusion can be drawn from these figures? If we tried an anti-Semitic approach, we would say the Jews succeed because they have money, are clannish and conspiratorial, deal one to another to the exclusion of others, and are in the principal locals of power, being able to favor their own. For the sake of argument, don't bother to contest the foregoing, which could be applied to many ethnic groups.

Jewish people, that special subgroup of the Caucasoid race, when examined over wide terrain, gravitate to vocations which require mental ability. Competition is open in America — in its schools and factories. No special privilege is granted in universities. Ability is rewarded. It is obvious the Jewish people possess superior mental geneticism, and it is for this and this alone that they are found in the highest tribunals, laboratories, and offices.

In brief, are American Jews superior to Protestants or Catholics? A superior subrace? Here is where the racial issue runs into sticky ethnics. Unquestionably, as a group they are superior in abstract intelligence and mental ability. To achieve this may have sacrificed manual ability.

Racial superiority is fact. But one must specify in which facets of gene pools the superiority exists. The greatest champions of sport have been Negroid. You can be well assured that the physical ability that permits this was ancestry. Ancestry was of prime importance to survival of the human race. Each race or subrace, tribe or nation, which has pooled isolated genes over a period, has specific superiorities or inferiorities in traits and abilities.

There is but to list the talents being sought and credit to each ethnic group their relative prowess.

We have failed to do this for we have felt it would be offensive. On the contrary, it would not only be revealing, but may well demonstrate abilities which we had never believed existed in special national groups.

Why has the Jew been persecuted? We find many reasons. His religion has made him a cohesive unit and he is easily identified by his adopted mannerisms which are uncommon to the lands wherein he resides. For almost two thousand years he was residing as a minority group within the framework of other nationals. He has been faithful to his religion. But no more faithful than the Catholics or certain groups of Protestants. So adherence to one's religion does not necessarily set him apart. To be true, he commenced with a conflict. His was the parent religion from which derived Christianity. By not recognizing Christ, he came in severe opposition to the split-off followers of his original deity.

If one is to look in from outside, let us say a non-religious person, he is amazed over this tempest in a teacup. "Both the Jews and the Christians adhere to a non-scientific folly — a primitivism, a mysticism, a superstition — an old wives' tale — heresay, a lot of rubbish — this nonsense which is religion."

Scientific men may profess religion and be devout in their application. But they never can apply their scientific methods, laws, and truths to the foible. It is as if their minds contain one compartment for religion and another for science, with a wall dividing them that is non-perceiving and non-communicable.

This horrid persecution by Christians — by medieval superstitious killers, by the Tzars, by the Nazis, by people in almost every land in which Jews have resided — cannot be attributed to religion alone.

Catholics and Protestants persecute one another. Witness today in our great time of scientific enlightenment the savage disturbances in Northern Ireland. And there have been vicious wars and massacres over the centuries between the followers of Martin Luther and those of the parent church in Rome.

However, in the Catholic-Protestant conflagrations, and in the Moslem-Christian wars, once the disturbance was over, there was clean breakoff and normal relations established in trade, amnesty, and in respect.

Not so with the Jew. He is never free from a hidden hatred, suspicion, fear or envy. Animosities can easily be kindled by the most ignorant rabble-rouser or even among intellectuals, the snidest of anti-Semitic remarks may be passively agreed to.

What do people see in the Jew? What do they fear? Why is he different? Departing from religion, there is intense jealousy when a group becomes economically successful, when the group's success is seemingly disproportionate. Here you are on the bread-and-butter issue that is dear to the human heart and is open to persecution. Here is envy and jealousy, that to the average citizen is an injustice, who asks why are the Jews favored and not my son?

That the Jews pay the same taxes and serve their government and community loyally and beneficially does not seem to matter. That their minds, because of their genetic abilities, are more capable of interpreting law, or that their training, their culture and their industry prepares them superiorly and promotes them more effectively in finance, is not considered.

However, in envy, success and jealousy lies a great antagonism. Be it prehistorically a primate ancestor whose tribe discovered, settled, and defended a lush banana grove, or to the successful and well-adjusted Jewish community of today.

This is not learned behavior. This is not something that derives from a culture. This is a very fundamental trait of the animal world — the struggle for available food, location or position within the specific society, and is at the bottom biological genetic selfishness.

This is genetics at work in its fullest form. Those that descended out of evolution's maelstrom were the strong, the successful, and those which were capable of seizing the abundance about them.

For example, if we wonder why the Jews protect and defend the Negro community, it is because, from the years of persecution, they avidly seek democracy, liberty and freedom. Too many times they have been in the isolated ghetto themselves — economically and socially.

Now if we examine the Negro and the Jewish genes, both groups having been sufficiently isolated in their evolution to give them many characteristics and features, aside from color of skin, we see biology in full force. Studies have shown that the Negro genes do not have the same level as white genes. That is, they are not as fully capable of competing in the civilized framework in which they are placed. In Africa, in primitive societies, if an intelligence test were devised by Negroes under their conditions of livelihood, it is quite possible that white genes would prove to be inferior.

In the evolution of the white genes, natural selection acted in favor of abstract quality. It commenced with leaders of the hunt, calculating the best strategy. White genes' evolution selected toward intelligence. Industry was rewarded. Successful traders were chosen for posterity.

Thus, with Jewish people we see not a religion that benignly grants them superior position, but a biologic structure which gives them special abilities. These abilities reside in academic prowess rather than manual technical skills. Their progressive composition obviously did not select toward manual skills. Here was the real paradox in Germany. Jews as a group with the highest mental faculty and Germans as a group with the highest technical and mechanical faculty. It is indeed a shame for humanity that the two were never fully wedded. Still, evolution is never a wedding — it is a fracas.

Where do the American Jewish people stand today in attitudes and prejudices by their neighbors? Studies have been performed, most of them in the form of questionnaires and personal reportings. The questionnaire form of investigation is unreliable. It is open to capriciousness. More intelligent people, the educated, where the least of anti-Semitism is found, have the greatest ability to hide their prejudice.

The secure method of reliable statistics would derive from programmed situation monitored by spies or eavesdropping. This seems, however, a weighty procedure, when most of the facts are fairly well assessed. After the Negro riots, it was easy to elicit anti-Negro feelings. And within almost any group of Gentiles, it is not overly difficult to find acquiescence in some form of anti-Semitism if one probes the situation tactfully.

It is not that Gentiles or others wish to be anti-any-group. But the very fact that a group exists which has different customs is sufficient to provoke a comradery in those observing it. Religion is not the issue. Americans as a group couldn't care less what anyone believes. What upsets them is as we have spoken — economic rivalry and being captive to some monopoly, such as movie and television, where a recent study indicated, "Jews pretty much control movies and television; 47% indicated they thought this."

Jewish people have been brilliant in low profiling their church or waving religious banners when compared with the lavish, vulgar oratorical displays of Protestant crusaders and healers. If complete biological assimilation is not a goal of the followers of Abraham, then the Elders should attend to the danger areas, for as is pointed out in *The Tenacity of Prejudice*, "In an economic crisis of sufficient magnitude, however, Jews could well become an object of hostility and blamed for society's ills. Since the working class is apt to suffer in an economic crisis, their present acceptance of anti-Semitic beliefs takes on more than incidental significance."

And, "As the educational level in the country rises, anti-Semitic prejudice is likely to decrease; however, education is not a cure-all." It is within the fields of the educated that competition and friction arises. Jewish people have the best of intelligence and, as a Jewish author indicated, a tremendous zest for education. No one is perturbed greatly to be outclassed by one's own, but to be outrivaled by a distinct cultural group sets hurricane warnings flying. It implies inferior biology and such reception is rooted in the pyramidines and purines of the beholders.

October 10, 1980, in an article in bi-weekly, *Pyonerskaya Pravda*, read by millions of Soviet school children, the old stereotyped international complaints were charged to Jews — American newspapers, TV and radio, are in Zionist hands and orchestrate anti-Soviet campaigns; Jewish bankers established the Jewish Defense League, an organization terrorizing Soviet diplomats; weapon production monopolies are controlled by Jewish bankers whose business in blood brings them enormous profit. The author, Korneyev, explains Zionism claims lands from the Nile to the Euphrates through big Jewish bourgeois in order to become even wealthier and more influential.

November, 1981, Abdullak, Commander of the Saudi Arabian National Guard and royal family member, stated, "There is a government within the government in the United States. . . . American policy is really run from Tel Aviv. . . . Certain elected representatives want to impose policies that contradict U.S. interests." And continued that America and Israel were the greatest threat to Saudi Arabia than the Soviet Union or communism.

Israel versus the Arabs. Both are Caucasian-raced Semites. Their geneticisms are struggling in a civil war for survival. It is not that they are brothers, it is that laws of evolution demand progression of grouped social units to the elimination of others.

Any political "ism" — socialism, communism, democratism — ranks secondary to "bioism" — evolutionary rule. Their struggle is not over oil wells, fishing rights or deserts, but historic time-proven subracial clashes for dominancy. Genes, not armaments, are evolution's weapons. In short, it is the genes of the Jewish people that make them successful, resilient, and progressive — not their religion or culture.

In 1982, the Israelis had driven into Lebanon and defeated the Palestinians. The Star of David was in ascendancy. The future is propituous. The only limitation for Israel as a super-power is failure to proselytize their religion and bring forth Jewish children in unparalleled abundance — average ten per couple and marriage at age 14. Genetic evolution by population explosion is not only the road for the Jewish state, but for any state that would long survive; that is, providing foodstuffs and territory are adequate. Yet there are signs of internal dissention. In Israel, January 1983, there were 100,000 Sephardim Jews — Orientals, Asians and Negroes — who protested against state policy. They also claimed they were being discriminated against by the Ashkenaim, or European Jews, which is the minority population. Afoot is a Jewish organization sponsoring a union with the PLO for a Holy Land State for Jews, Christians, and Moslems. What torturous roads lie in front of Israel! As Meir Kahane, in *Why Be Jewish?*, 1977, puts it: "Baruch! Jewish — *real* Jewish is beautiful."

VII Homosexuality
Tribute Long Overdue

T IS estimated that from 15 to 20% of human societies are homosexual. The sexual behavior patterns of these individuals have, more often than not, been met with public antagonism and punishment. Functional, developmental, or psychoanalytical explanations have been found wanting and absurd.

Such a large section of the population displaying neuter gender consistently, historically, and universally, demonstrates that innate organic forces must be at work. So the first question we must ask is: Does the homosexual contribute to the evolutionary survival of the human species — or has he?

Unequivocally, the answer is in the affirmative. By reducing intra-group sexual competition, more cooperative societies were able to advance evolutionarily by natural selection of the fittest.

It is a striking anachronism that male homosexuals have been represented as feminine when throughout history they have been valorous warriors. It is equally mis-stereotyped to portray them as weaklings. They are as robust, muscular, and sweaty as any "straight" on the block.

Nothing shall be more difficult than for society to accept them fully on an equal basis until the geneticists of the future isolate the alleles on their x germinal chromosomes, which produce their neuter sexual behavior. A stroke of masterful societal evolution removed the homosexual from the heterosexual contention sphere. This was every bit as important in evolutionary evolvement as bipedal locomotion or the discovery of fire. Without the origin of homos, society would have had to resort to alternative methods of restricting individual sexual behavior.

Back in 1969, the magazine *Time* presented a fairly comprehensive, concise study of homosexual behavior. It is noteworthy still because gross views of interpretation can be derived from it. If we apply scientific interpretation to what the authors and the participants in the conference said, we can emerge with a totally new view concerning this sexuality which is so perturbing to heterosexuals and society as a whole.

Right off, the authors manifest their prejudice with the psychiatrical usage of the word "invert" to describe homosexuals. Invert means to change to the direct opposite. If correct, it would mean a man changed to a woman, and woman synthesized to a man, each of whom, in a relationship, would produce children that regressed to sperm and ova.

A much more fitting terminology is "neuter gender." They are really neutral if one is to find a substitute word for homosexual. They do not enter the mainstream of heterosexual reproduction. Rather, they are an important and designated part of human society in its evolutionary advancement.

Time's authors go on to state that "most experts now believe that an individual's sexual drives are firmly fixed in childhood." This is one of the most challenging statements ever penned by the hand of man. Sex drives are irrevocably fixed the minute the sperm penetrates the ova. As any high school biology student knows, if that fast-moving flagellate carries the y chromosome, one out of 46 of the body's complement, the individual produced shall be male. If the sexual chromosome is an x on the sperm, the resulting produce shall be female. Since the female carries only the x chromosomes, definitive and innate production or sexuality is determined by the x *or* the y, transported by the spermatozoa.

Let us continue with science and not the atomish chatter of the psychoanalysts. Not fixed in childhood by external actions or parents or environment, sexual drives and preferences commence to manifest themselves early in life. The homosexual gene would necessarily, and because of its relationship to sexuality, be carried on either the x or the y chromosome, or both. However, nature is usually sparing in wasted effort, so it could be transported nicely on the x chromosome without involving the y. This would tie in with the occasional femininity witnessed in male homosexuals.

The homosexual gene or genes do not necessitate an anatomical change of the genitals or their physiology. Homosexuals are perfectly normal in their corporate bodies and their functions. What the gene does determine is none other than what used to be termed a secondary sexual characteristic, as change in voice tone, breast enlargement, muscular distribution, fatty deposits, etc. This is a neurological pattern, innately cerebrally located, which complements homosexual perceptions rather than opposite sex attractions and perceptions.

This is why pornographic pictures of solitary nude males in various states of erection will fill heterosexual males — straights — with either comic interest or revulsion. Gays, of course, thrive on such "beefcake." To each his own. The very evidence of art sexuality preference has indication to the underlying neurological affectional sets — ones rooted stoutly in amino acid codes. Within the brain are the drives and directions for homosexual behavior.

Clothing plays an interesting role in homosexuality. Transvestites (trans: across + vestire: to clothe) meaning those who enjoy wearing clothes of the opposite sex, have formerly been supposed as an indication of underlying femininity or masculinity within the same sex. This may be so. But being homosexual, it is very clever adaptational ruse in attracting the preferred sex. If a man dresses as a woman, there would be an attraction to the pure gay in conforming with the wishes of society, and to the marginal gay in assuaging his societal-swayed conscience.

Time had the answer beneath its ink tip, and it is incredible that their experts were clouded to the truth. They stated, "The only thing most experts agree on is that homosexuality is not the result of any kinky gene or hormone predispositions — at least *none that can be detected by present techniques.*" (Italicizing ours.)

Then comes the deluge. They continue: "The diverse psychological components of masculinity and femininity — 'gender role identity' — are learned." And "Sex roles are most powerfully determined in the home . . . in the first years of life . . . that is set before they know it."

This is, of course, Freudian speciality nonsense. No one needs to teach, direct or misguide a human into his genetically predetermined sexual role. The Casanovas and Benvenuto Cellinis and the countless whores of history come flying out of their ringside corners to engage the opposite sex with fervor that astounds all of the commonplace. To be sure, as in every large biological group, there is variability with a few masculine females and a few feminine males which may be diverted from the chemically mechanical sex roles.

More psychoanalytical blot is attributing male homosexuality to families where the father was either hostile, aloof or ineffectual, and the mother was close-binding and intimate, and the creation of lesbians to the opposite parental condition. Argument for such a statement is that most mothers are close-binding and fathers, by their very nature of work outside the home, can be regarded as mandatorily aloof and somewhat hostile because characteristically and innately to the male has fallen the task of family discipline.

Time continues its stance in stating, "Social selection rather than anything genetic makes homosexuality somewhat more common among so-called 'pretty boys.' " This may be so, but again, the reason is genetic. The homosexual product is marketed out of deference to birth control and the reduction in societal competition in the furtherance of human evolution. It would make sense for the process to weigh toward the "pretty" or feminine characteristics in the male homosexual. Yet this only occurs in small proportion, for homosexuals, their talents and their musculature, were vitally needed in the species' survival.

It is pointed out that "only about one-third inverts can be helped to change." No greater evidence could be forthcoming than this, that homosexuality is genetically rooted and not amenable to the whims or therapies of society.

"Psychoanalysts insist that homosexuality is a form of sickness." Today, the concepts of Freudian psychoanalysts are being bombarded from all sides. It is not the homosexuals who are sick, it is the psychoanalysts who are sick in theory, judgment, and science.

An interesting revelation in statements made by Time's interview, "Four Lives in the Gay World," shows that none are particularly distressed, sick, or possessed of anxiety concerning their sexual roles. "I live in a completely gay world. Now that I no longer try to cope with the straight world, I feel much happier." And, "I couldn't erase the fact that I loved another woman, but I began thinking that as long as I was a woman, too, things couldn't be all that bad. All I know is that life ought to be loving." And Tom says, "I like men better now than I did before. I'm no longer afraid of them." And lastly, "Katie in the past three years has given up dates with men" — obviously by preference.

A conclusion of this article was a discussion by two sociologists, two homosexuals, a psychologist and a psychoanalyst, a reverend, and an anthropologist, concerning the thesis, "Are Homosexuals Sick?" Most vocal and unflattering was the psychoanalyst. "They see around them a complete disaster to their lives. They see that the most meaningful human relationship is denied them — the male-female relationship.

"Everybody is now saying that the homosexual needs compassion and understanding, the way the neurotic does or anybody else suffering from any illness. That is true. I agree with that.

"A human being is sick when he fails to function in his appropriate gender identity, which is appropriate to his anatomy.

"Some of you feel that homosexuality is not an illness, that homosexuality should be proposed as a normal form of sexuality. I think this would be a disaster. If you sell this bill of goods to the nation, you are doing irreparable harm. It must be declared that homosexuality is a form of emotional illness which can be treated that those people can be helped."

To the latter statement, the homosexual answered, "With that you will surely destroy us."

To rebutt the psychoanalyst, there is no disaster in a homosexual existence or in their denying male-female relationship. The disaster only occurs in the narrow prejudicial minds of the heterosexuals who are revulsed more by social taboos and cultural fetishes to their acts than the acts themselves. If we straights would adopt humane attitudes, acceptance of the gene drive and view their sexual act scientifically as a component of evolutionary society, both sexualities could reside peaceably and with dignity.

To compare the homosexual with neurotics, needing compassion and understanding, is exactly the same way I compare psychoanalysts, and I know I am correct. Also, in order to relate sickness to the inappropriate use of one's sexual anatomy, it must be qualified by the definition of appropriate use. Homosexual behavior is appropriately utilized according to normal genetic programming. As for homosexuality doing harm to any nation, this is a far-fetched old wives' tale. Our evolutionary and cultural indebtedness to homosexuals is tremendous and it is time we honored their physiological structure as normal behavior.

A psychologist came out with this "beauty": "I have heard psychiatrists perfectly soberly say that 95% of all the population in the United States is mentally ill." So be it. It fits our treatise perfectly because we shall show that less than 5% of the population, the higher bourgeois, the upper echelon of society, are the true dominants, the ones who rule and control all thought and intelligible planetary behavior.

Another participant in the discussion poignantly observed that instead of anxieties provoking homosexualism, it could as equally be that homosexuals in our persecutory society, in reaction, develop anxieties. Another noted that the homosexual pays a terrible price for the way society runs itself. A homo points out, "When we are told 'you are sick,' and 'you are mentally ill,' that finishes the destruction to the individual."

Delightfully, the reverend showed his humanitarianism: "An acquaintance of mine, a man who has been 'married' to another homosexual for 15 years — both of them very happy and very much in love — asked me to bless their marriage, and I'm going to do it."

ILLUSTRATION

In homosexuality, something like the following occurs genetically,
by x-linked recessive traits:

H = symbol for the gene of heterosexuality (dominant)
h = symbol for the gene of homosexuality (recessive)
xx = symbol for the female sex chromosomes
xy = symbol for the male sex chromosomes

Sperm carrying either x or y — mate with ova carrying only an x chromosome to give either xx a female or xy a male:

Heterosexual females	$x^H x^H$ or $x^H x^h$
Homosexual female	$x^h x^h$
Heterosexual male	$x^H y$
Homosexual male	$x^h y$

* * * * *

$$\text{(homo — italicized)}$$

$$_xH_xH + {_xH_y} \quad _xH_xH + {_xH_y} \text{ heterosexuals}$$

$$_xH_xH + {_x}{^h}y \quad _xH_xh + {_xH_y} \text{ heterosexuals}$$

$$_xH_xh + {_xH_y} \quad _xH_xH + {_xH_xh} + {_xH_y} + {_x}{^h}y \text{ male homosexual}$$

$$_xH_xh + {_x}{^h}y \quad _xH_xh + {_xH_y} + {_x}{^h}{_x}{^h} \text{ female } {_x}{^h}y \text{ male homosexual}$$

A study of the many diseases such as hemophilia or G6^{PD} reveals that true Mendelian proportions may not hold with recessive genes. Colors and wrinkles may come in large percentages, but if the same ratios held, hemophilia would be epidemic. Some factors operate with the rarer genes to hold down their frequency expression — possibly they carry greater germ cell mortality or lesser conceptional success.

Thus, homosexuality is inherited, by gene patterns, selected toward over millions of years by providing greater fitness for survival in human societal evolutionary advancement. Lessening intratribal male competitiveness, controlling excessive birth with limited food production, and providing human variation, were important factors in the incorporation of the gene of homosexuality.

In Kinsey's study of males, he found a continuum of behavior ranging from exclusively heterosexual to exclusively homosexual, with many beheaviors in between. He found that nearly half (46%) of the adults engage in both heterosexual and homosexual activities and react to persons of both sexes in the course of their adult lives. These males are termed bisexuals.

Far from happy and content are the lives of continuously practicing bisexuals. For some it is harmless, for others breakdowns are precipitated. A homosexual pastor advised to get married, commented, "I could have intercourse with my wife, but five minutes later I would feel something was lacking." Another homo stated he had one experience with another male six months after his marriage and felt completely satisfied. A lesbian noted her marriage wasn't hideous, it was just incomplete. "I thought I must be frigid — something was wrong with me."

To most people, bisexual play is nothing more than a remote incident in the night. Soon they discover they have no bisexual potential. To genetically calculate for this sexually wishy-washy group — on and off occasion — we can expand the formulae.

If the y chromosome carries both the (H) heterosexual gene and the homosexual (h) gene, then we have the complete wide-ranging genital dispositions of man.

Female heteros

$$_xH_xH + {_xH_y}H \quad _xH_xH + {_xH_y}H \text{ exclusive heterosexuals}$$

$$_xH_xH + {_x}{^{II}}y{^{h}} \quad _xH_xH + {_x}{^H}y{^h} \text{ male bisexual}$$

$$_xH_xH + {_xh_y}H \quad {_x}{^H}x{^h} + {_xH_y}H \text{ female bisexual}$$

$$_xH_xH + {_xh_y}h \quad {_x}{^H}x{^h} + {_x}{^H}y{^h} \text{ female and male bisexuals}$$

Female bisexuals

$_xH_xh + _xH_yh$ $_xH_xH + _xH_xh + _xH_yH + _xh_yH$ 2 hetero F&M
2 bisexual

$_xH_xh + _xH_yh$ $_xH_xH + _xH_xh + _xH_yh + _xh_yh$ 1 hetero-F
1 homo-M

$_xH_xh + _xh_yH$ $_xH_xh + _xh_xh + _xH_yH + _xh_yH$ 1 hetero-M
1 homo-F

$_xH_xh + _xh_yh$ $_xH_xh$ $_xh_xh + _xH_yh$ $_xh_yh$ 2 bisexuals
2 homos-F&M
2 bisexuals

Female homos

$_xh_xh + _xH_yH$ $_xh_xh + _xh_xH + _xh_yh$ bisexuals

$_xh_xh + _xH_yh$ $_xh_xH + _xh_xH + _xh_yh$ 2 bisexuals
1 homo-M

$_xh_xh + _xh_yH$ $_xh_xh + _xh_xh + _xh_yH$ 2 homo-F
1 bisexual

$_xh_xh + _xh_yh$ $_xh_xh + _xh_xh + _xh_yh$ 2 homo-F
1 homo-M

Male homos

$_xh_yh + _xH_xH$ $_xh_xH + _xH_yh$ bisexuals

$_xh_yh + _xH_xh$ $_xh_xH + _xh_xh + _xH_yh + _xh_yh$ 2 bisexuals
2 homos-F&M

$_xh_yh + _xh_xh$ $_xh_xh$ $_xh_yh$ 2 homos-F&M

From the above, exclusive heterosexuals beget heterosexuals. If they mate (which selection is far from intense) two homosexuals, male and female, carrying strong and exclusive genes, $_xh_xh + _xh_yh$, will produce homosexuals. Those carrying a recessive heterozygous gene for homosexuality, known as bisexuals or not strongly heterosexual, if they mate they may produce all ranges from homosexuality, to heterosexuality, to bisexuals.

In short, a comprehensive, unbiased, and thorough study of known and proven homosexuals — lesbian women and homosexual males who have produced verifiable offspring by blood tests — should indicate the transmission ability of homosexual genes.

An excellent article, "Youthful Male Homosexuality," written by Roesler and Deisher in the *Journal of the American Medical Association* (JAMA-72), comes up with some startling insights. Homosexuality represents a variety of phenomena, behavior, and psychological experience. It is found within all groups of American society. Female homosexuals have given rise to less social concern than that of male homo behavior. Also, at least 48% of the subject article population had visited psychiatrists, one solely to justify his belief that the medical profession could do little in the way of therapy.

"A few youths in the study had decided they were homosexual before they had any sexual experiences with other men. This decision was usually based on a strong sexual attraction toward men."

Ranging in age from 16 to 22, one had experienced fellatio with approximately 3000 male partners. The median age was 50. Sixty percent had had at least one orgasm with a female. Another said that when masturbating, he imagined men more often than women.

What is evident from the figures, putting aside all psychoanalytical feces concerning environment such as that found in one article that says, "Homosexual behavior being the outcome of highly pathologic parent-child relationships and early life situations," is that very early they realize their innate sexual inclinations and establish their identity in their later teens by "coming out," that is, debuting to the homosexual subculture.

Early self-recognition of the homo status is exactingly what we would expect from the genetic viewpoint. No kinky genes are involved. Rather, it is a cruel and heartless, uncomprehending society that has forced them into secrecy, and oftentimes despair and suicide, as they attempt to express their underlying genotype. There can be no doubt that to strong heterosexuals such as many of you reading this, and to myself as well, there is a very definite uneasiness and repulsion to the act. What could be more natural? Our genes don't call for it. Some people prefer scotch, some can't stomach it.

The real tragic revelation of this article is that society is to blame for the misfortune of the youthful male homosexual. Their problems range among "instability," "discovery," "lack of acceptance," "repulsion of others," "guilt," "rejection from society," "embarrassment," "marry to cover up," "desperation," and "low esteem." They certainly have humanitarian and biological rights equal to heterosexuals. Society must shift its outrage from ignorance to the understanding of genetic coding and tolerance. It must even be grateful for their evolutionary role in both the formation of society and for mankind's survival.

July, 1977, witnessed an emotion-packed debate of the United Presbyterian Church as to the ordination of "gay" ministers. The Rev. J. Harry McElroy said, "A pastor needs to be above reproach in his ministry, and homosexuality is a sin and bars a person to ordination. We should devise a ministry for the homosexuals so that they can be cleared of this sin."

Resolutions from Alabama and Pennsylvania claimed the Scriptures were clear and unequivocal in that gay behavior is just as sinful as prostitution, adultery, and fornication.

This is delightful non-physiological chatter, for prostitution, adultery and fornication are as old and as normal as man himself. Marriage was invented no more recently than possibly 50,000 years ago. As far as the Bible goes, there is a very strong suspicion that Christ and his disciples were a band of homosexuals. That they shied at and deserted their women to go on a side-show, miracle-producing, fund-raising campaign, and that they gave little indication of their desires for lusty feminine companionship as would any wandering group of salesmen — their only preference seeming to be for wine — bespeaks strongly of a gay group.

A Titusville, Florida, Boy Scout leader was convicted of sexually assaulting a 12-year-old boy. He was so distraught, he asked for the death penalty or life imprisonment rather than return to the life of a homosexual. The judge sentenced him to 15 years in prison.

Such cases represent stark human tragedy in a so-called modern society that is so blinded to one simple fact: that homosexuality is normal human behavior and it is because of such that our society exists today. This act of a Boy Scout leader was a relatively victimless crime. Heterosexuals and parents deplore such things, but there are far more important issues for justice to be concerned with than the benignness of those individuals who do not compete sexually for progeny.

The "Cleveland Street" case of the 1880s, a scandal that shocked Victorian society, revolved around a male homosexual brothel on Cleveland Street, London, England. It was staffed by Post Office messenger boys and patronized by those in the higher ranks of Victorian society. Although only two men who ran it were jailed, the Prince of Wales and the Prime Minister struggled successfully to keep the matter quiet. Police wanted to prosecute Lord Arthur, the Prince's equerry, but he exiled himself to France before action could be taken.

That homosexuality traverses all social classes is a further indication of not only its universality, but the evolutionary process necessary to insert non-competing sexuals into the social realm. There can be small doubt that one of the strongest human emotions, especially in younger individuals of society, which was also the case in man's past, is the morbidity and mortality arising out of jealousy concerning the bonded heterosexual beloved.

Fighting words right up to murder, and the most vicious of revenge were the results of male reaction to infidelity. If we take from Boccaccio's *Decameron*, we pick up such tidbits as Sir Guillaume de Roussillon giving to his wife her lover's heart, which he tore out with his own hands. First he had the heart prepared as a dainty dish and then served it in a silver porringer as a dainty ragu seasoned with spices. He ate none, but his wife, finding it good, ate it all. Upon learning of the foul deed and deceit, she rose to her feet and fell backward through a window, falling to the ground where she was "broken in pieces."

Literature, theater and the media, as well as the law courts, abound with seamy tales of sexual infidelity. So, therefore, let one try to imagine, if all males and females were programmed with equal heterosexual vigor, in the extremely fragile evolution of human society where there were many predators, diseases, and an inconstancy of food supply, plus climatic adversity, we should have perished, if only by permitting the luxury of too much jealousy, to evolve.

For millions of years in our social evolution there was only extremely minor reaction to polygamy and sexual indiscretion. As society became more complexly formed and as brain capacity increased, so did the perception of the value of bonding to a good woman, to be cherished, guarded, and protected.

Right then and there the human ball game would have been overdue to internecine tendencies. The gong that saved us was society's selection toward non-competitive homosexuals, the lesser-sex-driven individuals.

Revolting as the act may appear to present-day culturally-trained heterosexuals, homosexuality was indeed one of the greatest accomplishments of human evolution, outranking the agricultural or industrial revolutions. We would never have gotten to that point. We would have been back slugging it out with thighbone clubs, collar-bone daggers, and lower jawbone knuckles for the exclusive possession of the root-and-fruit gatherer, the bearer of the young, and the object of one of the few pleasurable accoutrements accompanying life. Homosexuality was a magnificent victory in evolving society.

In a *Time* magazine article of 1974, the American Psychiatric Association reported that the board voted to cease classifying homosexuality as a "mental disorder." The trustees declared that many homosexuals show no signs of psychopathology, are satisfied with their sexual preferences, and can function effectively in society.

Interestingly enough, there was dissention such as that expressed by New York psychiatist, Charles Socarities, who called the ruling, "The medical hoax of the century," and stated, "It is flying in the face of the one fact we know, which is that male and female are programmed to mate with the opposite sex, and this is the story of the half-billion years of evolution and any society that hopes to survive."

It is lamentable that the statement contains both truth and conjecture. Characteristically, evolution does proceed by heterogeneous mating in the majority of higher animal forms. But societies do not survive by heterosexuality alone, or even monagamy for that matter. Human society, especially, is richly indebted to the non-conflictional nature of both the male and female homosexual. To eliminate heterosexual aggressiveness, which produced inefficiency, morbidity and mortality, those societies which incorporated a goodly percentage of homosexuals were strongly selected for evolutionary furtherance.

If anyone with the least of rationality could imagine that the estimated 11,000,000 American homosexuals voluntarily chose or, by some freak in behavioral development, entered a social order heavily weighed against them (both in criminal persecution and social stigma) of their own free will and volition, he is simply not facing the basic facts.

Sappho did not suffer humiliation because of her love for women. Of the great majority of male homosexuals who are frank, and especially those who are willing to be open concerning their gened expressions, there is no sense of shame. Rather, the slogan, "Gay Pride," has gained considerable ground in the general recognition of the homosexual as a normal human being. With the underlying genes programmed to this type of sexual behavior, there is no need for treatment or for clandestine behavior. That which millions of years has wrought must be regarded as one of the key-stones of society rather than a failure in moral behavior.

The origin of homosexuality began with psychological castration. Among dogs and fowl no attempt is made to mate when in the presence of the dominant animal. In species such as those, suppression of mating even persists in the absence of the dominant. In the monkeys and some apes, mating with outsiders is only achieved when the dominant is occupied with other females or when he is satiated during the female estrus cycle.

In all cases, the dominant, by his forceful gene structure, has inhibited the sexual actions of other males within the group. Thus, selection went in two directions — one toward the dominants and their preservation, the other toward homosexuals through societal factors: in not competing or disrupting the essential hierarchy of dominants' leadership and discipline of followers. By this mechanism concerning the good of the societal whole, homosexuality established itself in the sex chromosomes as recessive genes. Later, homosexual love arose as a byproduct of male-male hunting associates.

More male babies are born than female, 105-100. This is, by old-fashioned genetics, not correct. According to the rules of chance, the mix should come out even. A sperm carrying a y chromosome rather than the x has a missing arm and, therefore, may be faster in the race to the target egg. But there is also a society factor. More males were needed because, in their occupation, there is a greater mortality and a greater need for males as breadwinners. Natural selection was sensitive to these needs of evolving society, and promoted the larger percentage of males. At the same time, nature curbed the sexual ardor of the male beast by rendering a goodly number homosexual.

French author, Roger Peyrefitte, in an article in an Italian magazine, *Tempo,* called Pope Paul VI a "homosexual." News coverage was wide, and from the *St. Petersburg Times,* Florida, Peyrefitte was quoted — "It was well known that Paul VI had as a boyfriend a movie actor whose name I'm not going to mention, but whom I recall very well." The Pope called the accusation "horrible and slanderous."

There is one thing certain, and that is that in male religious orders, in prisons, and in any area where men are confined abnormally without feminine companionship, there is a high rate of homosexuality. Even the very nature of a religious order would prone itself to this type of selection of normal human genecity. For what is not needed in the field of religion are heterosexuals, too many commanders, or dominants.

In regard to the church doctrines of celibacy, no marriage or sexual life, and in the concept of nunneries, no marriage or sexual life, aside from theological propositions and tenants, there is a very interesting biological inversion. Not to seek sexual relationship or progeny may be superb as far as population control exists, but to profess and practice asexuality while condemning homosexuality, is pulpit double-talk.

It is an amazing paradox that some religions may take for their high priests and spokesmen the sterile, the asexual and non-productive, by ecclesiastical edict and, by the same set of resolutions, rant against abortion, sterilization, and birth control, and abet in the very poorest and miserable of backward motions the prolificacy of offspring. It is Orwellian tragedy from the shrines of the sacred. We do know that some church groups renounce heterosexuality for their leaders. Unfortunately, we do not have the statistics to know if homosexuality is the replacement.

With classical Greeks there was a golden age of respect in attitudes toward homosexuals. There was tolerance and acceptance of male homosexuals — in fact, even praise was a hallmark of Grecian culture. It is said that male warriors who fought side by side with their male lovers were more valorious and dedicated in the art of battle than heterosexuals.

By the linkage of opposing sexes we evolve. We are fitted with sexual signals and rewards to make heterosexual mating imperative. Homosexuals do not fit within this pattern. We perceive by different recognitional mechanisms. The breasts and legs of a young woman have facets that will not conjure in the gay the activating forces of the face and thighs of a man. It is not based on culture, training, or teaching. It is a geneticism of physical characteristics that demands homosexual experience.

Great harm was done by Sigmund Freud and his ridiculous postulations. Primarily he was basing conclusions on mysticisms, dreams, and fabrications. He was not observing true cause, only subjective symptomatology. Gifts of hot air to a cadre of followers, the psychoanalysts erected a mumbo-jumbo of nonserveable terms setting back medicine half a century in psychological interpretations.

From these wicked scientists came all sorts of appelations portraying the illness that was supposed to reside in homosexuality. They were following in the footsteps of the ignorant who, for centuries, castigated and imposed the severest of legal penalties upon the practitioners of homosexuality.

Homosexuality is a capacity in all mammals; it is commonplace in primitive societies and it is not contrary to biological order. It is not a sickness or a disease, rather it is selective geneticism that provides species with survival, especially those species which rely on social order.

Psychoanalytical theories explaining the homosexuals are childlike and range from the belief that faulty child-rearing practices or close relationship between mother and son or a domineering or seductive mother can equally produce a homosexual solely by environmental influence.

Recently it has been discovered that homosexuals have a lower level of testosterone in their blood. We would expect to find this is one of the components of one of the multiple genetic formulae for homosexuals. However, the simple medication of testosterone will not change or realign the homo's nature. This has been tried in the past and has failed. The genetic coding for homosexuality is extremely complex and runs into many traits.

The American Psychiatric Association was locked in one of the bitterest disputes in its 129-year history over the question of homosexuality. As previously discussed, it was the year 1974 which found the association removing homosexuality, an issue concerning some 10-20-million Americans, from its official list of mental disorders.

Possibly one factor in the decision was that there was a number of psychiatrists who were professed homosexuals, who, in "doctor talk" were able to explain the dilemma far more reasonably than lay people who regard homosexuality as disgusting.

A genetic basis for so large a group of individuals within all races and subraces is clearly obvious. Homosexuals comprise 20% of the population, above the estimated 11%, and presents a large social segment.

Few evolutionists or scientists dispute natural selection as a means of evolutionary advancement and survival. Homosexuality, if it did not serve a survival purpose, a species advancement or a socially programmed adaptation, would with the greatest of rapidity forthrightly be eliminated from the genetic pool.

An avowed bisexual, fighting dismissal from the service for homosexual behavior, was reported in *Time* magazine, 1976, as " . . . 24 years old, son of a Navy chaplain, was an average student and dated girls frequently. He readily admitted homosexual acts with three civilian males during the past seven years — plus heterosexual activity. An expert witness told the board that the ensign was highly intelligent, balanced, and creative." It was his father, Commander Berg, who put in the punch-line, "Some people are born lefthanded and some righthanded. In our family we accept people as they are."

In this case, there are two important insights: Had the father been a geneticist, he might have wished to have said, "My son is genetically programmed toward homosexuality, which is a biological normalcy within the development of human society." The second point was that he had the ability to engage either heterosexually or homosexually, apparently not out of capriciousness. This would indicate not only an underlying dual ability located within the DNA amino acid alphabet code, but even a considerable anthropological advance, if one would care to regard it as such. It is stark tragedy that normal-coded behavior in sexual matters is persecuted.

Grace and Fred Heckinger, in an article in the *New York Times* magazine, March 12, 1978, entitled "Homosexuality on Campus," reviewed the usual problems of the monosexuals. Yet they noted the real issue — "Some day solutions may well become available, but not until new discoveries — physiological and psychological — unravel more of the mysteries of homosexuality. . . . And this is a fundamental lesson for American society as it awaits more scientific answers to the question of how and why homosexuals are made."

Act 3, Scene 2. [from Shakespeare's *Hamlet*]. I hope we have reformed that indifferently [tolerably] with us, sir. Hamlet: O, reform it altogether!

No selection pressure of any type can be so forceable as the voluntary castration of large numbers within a species. This is what selective breeding is all about in dog breeding, horse breeding, animal breeding — the breeder selects the desired characteristics from either sex and mates them to achieve certain results. He performs an act similar to homosexuality because he selects and permits breeding by a few, eliminating the others. In the act of homosexuality, the persons themselves voluntarily withdraw their seed from the gene pool. Therefore, long ago, we should have expected the complete elimination of these homosexual genes.

However, this does not occur for two reasons — One is that most homosexuals do at some time have heterosexual matings with consequent offspring, and secondly, the gene has been ingrained with the survival of the species.

We can no more eliminate homosexuality by selective breeding than we can eliminate one eye or the rear left molar. Too long has the advantage of homosexuality persisted in the prevention of internecine warfare. Too long has the social animal developed, through minimized group strife, to permit rapid homosexual genetic elimination. It is remarkable that so great a proportion of humanity is homo-inclined. Witness that the queen bee is the only one laying the eggs. If humans had developed this same style of social structure, a few Casanovas for all womanhood, our only warfare would have been between the rare human drones battling as to whom shall service the queen, with the workers comfortably watching the spectacle.

There is a tendency to regard the male homosexual as a weakling. It can be quite the contrary. They can be excellent mesomorphic specimens. If we turn our attention to the heterosexual "straights," we can find some glaring inconsistencies with what is considered proper and judicial behavior.

Murdock detailed some 564 marriage systems of the different peoples of the world. Among these food-producers and food-gatherers, approximately 75% are polygamous, or devoted to a system of more than one wife or companion, and the rest are monogamous. There's a sprinkling of a few percent where they are polyandrous, in which the female is related with several males.

Here we see that man's sexual disposition is toward promiscuity when viewed from a worldwide natural scene. It further indicates that monogamy may be a recent development and is tied in because of economic reasons. But, more importantly, such statistics demonstrate that it is natural for some men to have more than their share of the females. This is supportive in accordance with society as we have described it — that a large percentage of humans are relegated to homosexuality so that they shall be both non-competitive and non-progeny productive.

Being the custodian for the human genes has always resided with the Don Juans and Casanovas. Regardless of their size and shape, they have been given an overzealous urgency to disperse their seed widely. And, of course, this is the unfortunate reason for their existence. There is no force as strong in evolutionary radiation and movement as the force to propagate the most. With these compulsive DD and JJ genes, not only goes the urgency but all the other corteged genes which aid in procuring receptive subjects "by hook or by crook."

Seeing it differently, Franz Boas, in *Central Eskimo*, makes the following observations on sexual order: "Monogamy is everywhere more frequent than polygamy, only a few having more than two wives. A strange custom permits a man to lend his wife to a friend for a whole season or even longer and to exchange wives as a sign of friendship. On certain occasions this is commanded by religious law."

In monkeys we find the male as dominant, being surrounded by solicitous females of his harem. Outside his group are young males who, from time to time, challenge his leadership. Within this latter group are the homosexuals. A receptive female chooses first those subordinate males and juveniles and, later, at the height of her estrus, seeks the dominant males. In this manner it is that the dominants are selected toward while the impulses of those left out are satisfied. Copulatory efforts may be witnessed by the group, and on occasion the males line up patiently to await their turn. Jealousy does not exist in this sexual situation.

When we compare the foregoing actions of monkeys whose gene programming we stimulate, we become aware of the difficulties encountered in the modern sexual schemes of law and culture, and why divorce and unhappy marriages are frequent and sex crimes rampant. We have foisted upon a physiological mechanism codes of conduct and laws of sexuality which are contrary to basic design.

A homosexual is stimulated to action in the same manner as heterosexuals are stimulated. From a perusal of such magazines as *Playboy*, one would note that men are stimulated by young and attractive women, specific areas of reference being the face, legs, breasts, and buttocks. Not necessarily in that order, but different neurogenic structures in different individuals focus more on one component than another. Within the proper setting, internal releasing mechanisms (IRM) prepare the male for behavioral advancement of one sort or another. The male homosexual is released not by the perception of women, but by various presentational factors in the male. We would expect a graduation from heterosexuality to homosexuality, yet this is not the case. Once a homo always a homo. No amount of education or treatment will alter the fact.

Legally we speak of sexual deviation and punish those that participate in it. We have arbitrarily set up standards of sexual conduct which fit a rather stereotyped performance. Anything that differs from what, let us say, is the moral consensus of a specific population, is to be abhorred, repressed, and chastized.

In effect, what we are saying is that people who do not conform to the proper manmade guidelines are deviate by the assumption that all should fall into the central part of a normal probability curve. That is, considering the normal central portion is acceptable behavior and those at either extreme are outside of legitimacy. At the right end of this "normal" probability curve of sexual behavior we find Puritanism and Catholicism in their finest flower, with no divorce being permitted, adultery labeled a crime, abortion a high-order crime, contraception unthinkable, and the marital bed to be composed in pristine statute.

At the left end of this curve would be the rake, the prostitute, and those of the "everything-goes" school. Wife-swapping, abortion, contraception, complete sexual freedom, promiscuity, overt and frequent solicitation, "all manner of perverse sexual acts, homosexuality, transvestites, lesbianism, exhibitionists, rapists — physical and statuatory, adultery, fornicators, swingers, and all that netherland group which meets the disapproval of general society."

The middle section of the curve, the largest body group, needs small comment other than to say they get through their lives without the onus of public stigma or the lash of justice.

This concept of sexual behavior is all well and good if we regard that humans divide themselves in a quantitative bell-shaped curve of probability.

That is, 10% are saints, 80% are normal, and 10% are criminal, human beings strung out on the sex line as so much laundry, each possessing various facets of sexuality counted up as so many buttons, stitches or colors.

But this is hypothesizing. We know that humans differ in sexual behavior much as we differ in height or weight, some possessing some really rakish drives, while others fast at the foot of the cross.

There is no such thing as a bell-shaped curve of humans displaying various degrees of sexuality. You can bell-curve apples and oranges, crocodile and pansies, but to bell-curve people there must be a basic, recognizable, common denominator. Human sexuality does not have that. Humans are spread out in Mendelian fashion according to mathematical chance and the desires of social selection.

This giant gamut of sexual variances — or rather, should we say, of sexual types — should never even be included in the same framework of legal and social considerations. Manifestations of sexual selection may be gleaned from the perplexing behavioral patterns we try to explain as fads, irreverence toward social values or escapism. I refer to the recent (at this time) incidents of "streaking" in which the nuded individual runs through varying audiences. This is nothing more or less than exhibitionism, for which we have severe legal penalties. It is nothing less than nudist colonies. For the display of the naked body, especially the genitalia, to other than one's spouse, requires an audience. And here is the rub — modern societies do not take kindly to exhibitionists displaying their "privates."

A housewife wrote to a magazine — "In 1971, I married an ex-convict, an intelligent man whom I love very much. We agreed to let the past stay buried and try to build a future together. Bit by bit I learned about the boy who is now a man and came to understand the mystery called sex deviation and the hostility of society toward it. My husband is an exhibitionist. From the age of 19 (he is now 32) he has been in and out of prison repeatedly. In February, 1972, there was a recurrence of his problem. Now I am learning what it is like to be the wife of a prisoner. I hired a local attorney, not to get my husband released, but to get psychiatric treatment for him. He has not yet been tried and has been held during this time — which I am told will not count toward his sentence. The more I press for some kind of rehabilitation for him, the more rejection I run into. I've changed my job from secretary to waitress to earn more money for the fight. I have been turned away when I've tried to visit him, though exceptions are made in jail-visitation rules for other people. I've seen him only six times since last April.

"I have a psychiatric evaluation of my husband which states that with proper motivation he can become a useful and functioning member of society. I believe that. I am going to keep on fighting — I will not sit back and complacently accept more years uselessly chopped from my husband's life with no attempt made to help him."

Well, I am a physician, and I have studied psychiatry as well as humanity, and I would like to help. I see no crime or need for treatment or the necessity to punish exhibitionists, or to remove them from society. A group of us, physicians and their wives, were departing a late party, when the doctor host appeared on the balcony with his penis hanging out. We thought it uproariously funny. A medico commented, "My, Dr. xxxxx, what a big nose you have!"

Genes, sex chromosome related, responsible for this natural advertising behavior, are widespread throughout all strata of society. The go-go girl, a semi- or completely nude dancer found in bars and night clubs, is doing little else than expressing her underlying genotype, and all that I have witnessed, usually by entering the wrong bar, seemed happy, well-adjusted, glad for the extra dough, and tickled with the accolades and tributes from their audience for their very fine anatomy.

An old ham argument is put forth concerning the damage of public genital exposure upon children and old ladies. If television has the right to show, and the newspapers the right to print about horrible murders, atrocities and sadisms, then every male in America has a right to walk about with his penis hanging out if he so desires. Actually, no psychological damage is ever meted out by witnessing the human body in its natural states.

Homosexual, as well as other sexual patterns, are non-contributory to propagation. It is to be assumed that straight unadulterated sex would be the shortest route to efficient reproduction — there being little need for the by-lines. Animals tend to go in fairly direct sexual procedures, and one would think that natural selection would prefer this simplicity. Not so in man.

Playboy magazine reported on American sexual behavior in the 1970s, using over 2000 people in 24 cities for their testing. It was found that pre-marital sex is becoming more frequent. This is evolutionarily unimportant in our study, because sexual patterns were set down long before marriageable type bonds existed. What is unanswered is that such practice as heterosexual fellatio and cunnilingus, as well as masturbation, showed fairly high overall age incident in humans of around 50% and anal intercourse being as high as 25%.

Such profuse side-track detouring is certainly counter-productive to re-productivity. Yet, to be so widely documented, the practices must be considered as genetically based rather than a whim of faddism or culture. If we ask of the *Genetic Basis of Society*, we can find two plausible theories for these actions — one being a method of birth control, the other in the masturbatory group, which results in the removal of a sizeable portion of hetero-sexual competitors, aiding society's non-conflictional advance. A third potential in the widespread practice of fellatio is that it may have served as an early means of transporting to the mate high-quality protein.

Sadism and masochism are types of sexual response involving only a small percent of the population. That it is genetic and innate cannot be denied. Yet quite possibly this genetic programming could be derived from errors rather than purposive pluckings from natural selection. These forms, however, are persistent and have been recorded over the centuries. So there must have been some slight social value, though it may be difficult to ascertain.

Outside of the sexual system, sadism does have a fairly large following verifiable as we witness the sickening slop thrown out by the television media to satisfy it. Why screams of injured should elicit pleasure is certainly not for a surgeon to comment on, or even conceive. I know from experience that I have personally suffered other person's injury.

Perhaps there was an educational shift incorporated into the neurogenes. Pain in another may have warned of dangers and what they were — such as a fall from a high tree or cliff, or to be ripped by the claws of a leopard. The escapee did derive pleasure at his own safety when viewing the other's painful misfortune. That which was encoded was the lesson of averting certain dangers and by performing such averting acts, to be rewarded with pleasure.

Penis and testicles dangling outside the human male body is absurd anatomy, allowing too much danger and encumbrance for streamlined function. Humans, like birds, could have had a type of flat, sideswiped kiss and so eliminate such awkwardness. However, it must be deduced that the visual appraisal of the instrument and its sac by heterosexual females or homosexual males was the prompting force in permitting the display. Add to this the pleasures derived from such fondable toys by both sexes and it becomes apparent that the force of evolution resulted not in a streamlined anatomy, but rather, by prompting sexual selection in those individuals with adequate displays and thus achieving greater matings, progenizing in a disproportionately heavier ratio.

Peeping Toms and sexual exhibitionists we must regard not as deviates, but as normal humans processing evolution in the time-honored fashion. The increasing popularity of nude male magazines and nudist clubs emphasizes this strong genetic force.

Certainly the male with the largest or most perfectly shaped genitalia should not be the only requisite on the female prenuptial shopping list. It does demonstrate our Puritanism since that view is not made more readily available to provide multiple choice selection in one facet of the evolutionary mating game.

We derived penile magnificence by sexual choice of the more fertile women in spite of more cleverly designed retractable gear. Clothing has all but destroyed this form of natural selection and evolution. If we continue our loin-masking technique, succeeding eons may find their male apparati rudimentary in the least.

Exhibitionists and peeping Toms, although distressing procedures, we can regard as normal and due to natural selection.

In evolution we speak of selection as a direction mating chooses. If all men of all races preferred natural blondes with white skins exclusively, soon there would be a great amalgam of white blonded people. Known as sexual selection, the sales value of white blondes would have enticed the human race in that direction. Not so simple is selection by fitness, in which the individual is capable of superior adaptability, and so survives to propagate offspring with genes similar to his own. By the process he has selected toward, he has endowed his offspring with the specific virtues which provided him superiority in his setting. A man who could run faster to escape prey and gain food, would survive and pass on his superior locomotion genes.

These are conventional interpretatives of how we evolve. There is quite another — a social group whereby we, as primates, possessed additional prowess to cope with the rigors of life. It obviously had selective advantages.

Where there were but a few dominant leaders among dozens of subordinate males, conflict was avoided, kingship, or junta, formation of government was established. In so doing, stability gave the tribe fitness advantage over less cohesive groupings. This, in turn, provided survival and direction toward monarchies and oligarchies.

It is not so much innate gregariousness, compulsion for humans to cluster, that produced social advancement, but rather small societies that formed with checks and balances, aside and apart from learning or aspects of culture, were able to pass to their offspring genetic coding for social organization.

As most primitive primate social units had relative isolation from other groups, genetic drift of full throttle was possible to develop special codes. Groups that threw out homosexual genes were most capable of survival and, therefore, their geneticism of homosexuality was preserved and enhanced to point of today's population, at 10-20%.

Those unacquainted with homosexuals may have the stereotyped conception they are weaklings with high-pitched voices under hideous psychoanalytical maladjustment to parents, friends, and environment. These so-termed "fairies" are anything but woodsprites. They are intelligent, creative, resourceful, brave, loyal, and physically strong. Their hang-up is purely evolutionary biology. Their *modus operandi* of love, distasteful to the straight member of society, is none other than expression of genetic normalcy. Yet they are a non-dominating group, as they were intended to be in structurization of society. They were not created to be dominants, thereby weakening society by perpetual conflicts of challenge.

We should indeed be grateful to homosexuality as it has had a great part in our social evolution. In the same manner, the submissiveness of women eliminated conflict and tension ensuring survival. Women's liberation and equal rights, nobly conceived, is biological disaster and social failure.

Parade magazine, Nov. 8, 1980, "Ship of Shame," by Lloyd Shearer. At the Pt. Hueneme Naval Station, 50 miles north of Los Angeles, the USS *Norton Sound*, a secret missile-test ship, is currently being referred to as "The Love Boat," "The Sex Ship," and "The Ship of Queers." — "The only hope for that ship in the U.S. Navy," one officer declared, "lies in a quick name change. I can't think of any man or woman in the Navy who would pridefully want to serve on it today. The ship's been sunk by its reputation." Alleging to sexual offenses committed by lesbian crew members, of 61 women aboard after a two-month probe, the Navy cleared 16 of 24 *Norton Sound* women of alleged homosexuality. Navy regulations prohibit solicitation, attempt or engagement in homosexuality. The Defense Department said the homosexual person is unsuitable for military service, and the Air Force holds that homosexuality is not tolerated.

These archaic opinions will soon have to change because homosexuality in the general population is at 10-20%. This would carry into the military of all nations. It is time homosexuality is recognized as normal innate biological behavior, carrying great social sacrifice. The modern age has so far failed to comprehend its magnificence as a forwarding force in human evolution.

The greatest issue facing earth is over-population. Fortunately, homosexuals have done more than their share to alleviate misery resulting from population pressures upon limited world reserves of land and foodstuffs. Not only has homosexuality diffused a portion of sexual male dominancy struggle over prime females, but has been a forceful factor in birth control. Social structure in the advancement of the human species demanded:

1. *A proportion of males shall be non-competitive* with other males vying for female mates so as to reduce group tensions.

2. Certain members of society shall *perform sexual behavior in a non-propagating fashion,* insuring birth control and population limitation.

3. A proportion of *females shall be sexually oriented toward other women,* providing cohesive harmonies within female groupings.

Evolving society, creating male homosexuals and lesbians, was a magnificent genetic leap forward. It assured sexual non-aggressiveness in a portion of the population and provided a humane and efficient method of birth control. Infanticide was a common event in early civilization to limit population. High infant mortality, designed to cull human chaff and forward superior geneticisms was insufficient to offset birth productivity following the agricultural revolution.

Genes cannot be commanded to reproduce less, as this would be tinkering with the basic mechanisms of life. Any mis-step could lead to extinction — getting out of hand mechanically when seeking the antithesis of being. Instead of putting out hundreds of millions of sperm in a single ejaculation, nature via the evolution could have decreed, "Put out only a million . . ." Such a rash move, for we find today low sperm counts produce infertility, would be extremely risky.

There was available a wiser reaction to limit offspring without tampering with central direction — produce homosexuals. This would satisfy evolving society's needs. It would provide increased man and woman power by non-competition sexually. Infanticide was wasteful. Excess offspring utilized nine months of feeding by the mother and restricted her group effort. Lesbianism is comparable to bee society in limitation of female effort.

Overpopulation is a serious evolutionary goof-off. Not only are food supplies strained, but intragroup competition leads to aggression to syphon off excess. On the periphery are predators, diseases, and war — waiting to move in on this lush extravagance.

Homosexuality permitted one to have his cake and eat it too. Reproductive ability was not interfered with. Society was provided a cooperative worker unit without infanticide waste. Throughout millions of years, homosexual ratio could be adjusted to social demands. High rate of homosexuality today may well be biological adjustment to burgeoning population.

There have been reported "cheater" genes which disobey Mendel's rules. Then there is the issue, if homosexuals do not have children, why aren't they selected out of the population and disappear? The answer is their genes are passed on by heterosexuals under the direction of social pressure. Group selection determined in millions of years that tribal units passing on homosexual genes had greater survival fitness. We are blessed today with those who sacrificed reproductive drive for the good of society as a whole.

Not unlike Mr. Pangloss in Voltaire's *Candide*, "that things cannot be other than they are, for since everything was made for a purpose, it follows that everything is made for the best purpose" — biology has the most erudite of purpose. That is to probe the earth with every form and group of continuing organic chemistry to achieve perpetuation and dominance. Homosexuality aids that goal.

Masters and Johnson, April 20, 1979 — NBC-TV: "Homosexuality is a learned condition. No indication of genetic determination. Can be converted to heterosexuality by psychotherapy. Homosexuals share more and can treat their needs better." Author's comment: "!XZZ!*** !!Z**!"

Ellen Kaplan, a nuclear activist, pressed assault charges resulting from an incident in which she asked a former Secretary of State, "Do you sleep with young boys at the Carlyle Hotel?" The judge found the accused innocent. — *Time* magazine, June 21, 1982. Oscar Wilde, the famous playwright, accused of homosexuality, went to court to defend his honor only to wind up in jail. It is lamentable being accused of homosexuality should elicit reaction other than, "Unfortunately, I'm not," or "Great fun, isn't it?"

The essence of our contention in *Genetic Basis of Society* is homosexuality, being a beneficial factor in the evolution of man, is confirmed independently by the following paragraphs from the Pillard, Poumadere and Carretta. We began our studies in 1970 and their article only appeared in 1981. "That a genetic predisposition could even be considered as a casual variable in the HS orientation seems, at first, paradoxical because, as Moran (1972) points out, the HS trait should be negatively selected and should eventually disappear except for occasional mutations.

"However, Hutchinson (1959) reasoned that genes for homosexuality could persist if they conferred a special advantage for the heterozygote; that is, if HS individuals and their kin have in their genetic makeup alleles that, in the heterozygote state, confer a reproductive advantage sufficient to balance the disadvantage of the homozygous HS phenotype. This advantage could be some characteristic unrelated to sexuality, such as enhanced IQ or, as Hutchinson suggested a 'paraphilia' that might be expressed by the capacity to make closer bonds of comradeship, to establish dominance, and to secure mates.

"Alternatively, homosexuality may be an example of an 'altruistic' behavior, that is behavior which decreases the fecundity of the individual but benefits kin. This possibility was suggested by the geneticist W. D. Hamilton and expanded by Wilson, Trivers, and their students (Wilson, 1975; Kirsh and Rodman, 1977). Weinrich (1976) suggests that homosexuals in preliterate societies may have formed a 'sterile caste' that provided special benefits for the kin group. If the gene, rather than the individual, is the unit of selection, behavior that diminishes individual reproductive fitness but benefits kin may be favorably selected."

Finally, in *American Medical News*, Sept. 10, 1982, a photo of one hundred physicians marching in San Francisco's annual Gay Pride Parade was shown. Gay leaders who are MD's spoke out with some rather startling comments. Dyan Dreisback said, "Being successful, productive and happy, and being a lesbian are not mutually exclusive." Dr. Kessler believes "Gay people are satisfied with their sexual orientation and are not interested in converting." (There are dozens of gay medical groups in the country and a possibility of 25,000 gay physicians.)

It is becoming obvious that the 20th century is witnessing the liberation of homosexuality. The 21st century will find a homosexual in the White House. Once Americans understand this complex genetic process, they will redress the wrongs of ages gone by.

Recently, science is recognizing the validity of homosexuality as a factor of heredity rather than choice. Richard Pillard, M.D., et al, in an article in *Archives of Sexual Behavior*, 1981, asked, "Is homosexuality famial?" He summarizes, "Family studies report that homosexual subjects have more homosexual siblings than do heterosexual subjects and more than would be expected given population frequencies. Twin studies find in general a higher concordance in sexual orientation in monozygotic twins."

Ellis reported positive family homosexual history in 24 of 62 cases. Henry's data supported a family factor. Kenyon identified first degree relatives predominantly homosexual in 18 lesbians and only one heterosexual control. Mangolese and Janiger. Out of 24 heterosexual men, only two reported homosexual relatives. Of 28 homosexual men, 17 reported homosexual relatives. Dank cited that out of 10 children in one family, 6 were homosexual and the other 4 had homosexual experiences. Hoenig and Duggan sketched a family of 177 members in which 12% had transsexuality or transvestism. Kallman's study of identical and fraternal twins was regarded as "evidence for the presence of a genetic factor."

Pillard, Poumadere, and Carretta stated their studies add up to a persuasive conclusion, "Homosexual subjects report more homosexual children than heterosexual subjects. And more than would be expected given population frequencies. . . . And male and probably female homosexuality is a disposition which runs in families." They also concluded, "There is no proven association between homosexuality and mental disorder."

VIII Capitalism, Communism, Socialism

"The west won't contain communism; it will transcend communism.
It won't bother to denounce it; it will dismiss it as some bizarre
chapter in human history whose last pages are even now being written."
— Ronald Reagan, May 1981

C APITALISM — "A special system based on the recognition of individual rights, including property rights in which all property is privately owned."

Ayn Rand refers to the *Encyclopaedia Britannica*'s definition that it is a dominant western world economic system since the breakup of feudalism, with a relationship between private owners of means (lands, mines, plants known as capital) and free workers who sell their services.

Rarely spoken of and by far the most important ingredient is genetic capitalism. A top-flight education costs in the tens of thousands of dollars. Training of skilled and unskilled workers are also extremely expensive. The basic units of genetic capitalism are intelligence, good functioning physiology, drive, and morality.

The professional class does not carry with them any great non-personal material, except possibly a few law books or surgical tools, but represented in the neurogenes is as much wealth as there is in any warehouse or tugboat.

Capital is definitely personal. Upper classes possess it by birth. They are unsympathetic with labor because they are born capitalists or have themselves acquired capital. Unskilled and the semi-skilled classes in the lower part of the social structure have nothing. They are laborers in the system. As education and specialized training advanced so has labor's lot under capitalistic doctrine. Basically, capitalism is an economic science of free men through natural selection, recognizing hierarchy and privilege.

Capitalism had its origins millions of years ago in the free competitive marketplace where banana groves, women, water, or a favorite shade tree were sold. That is why a communistic society is absurd. It is an abnormal departure from traditional biology.

There is a tendency to bargain collectively for wages — an elaboration of egalitarianism seen in such inanities as minimum wage. Nothing is more detrimental to human welfare than trying to twist biologic abilities. Since we are all coded differently, each person has unequal value and as such should be waged accordingly.

Labor unions are especially vicious. They coerce membership, drive up prices, and support human inequality by taking from those with merit and giving to those without.

In the past few hundred years, the capitalistic system has had a tendency with the aid of the socialists to erect a number of "sacred-cow" institutions. In school systems, hospitals and the post office bureaucracy there has been a stifling of competition. The cost to the public has been tremendous. If we were to do away with the strange rules that protect such privileged bureaucrats and turn them loose into free markets, we would achieve a great social step forward. Institutions that are restrictive and non-competitive are abiotic.

Socialism is a system of economics that advocates ownership and control by government. Its avowed purpose is to incarcerate, control, restrict, and bind the biologically able, successful, and innovative within the same confines as the lower classes. With such a system it is difficult to focus on biological freedom, the ability of the allelic dominants to perform their function, and not be recessed. Shortly socialism will be displaced by forced eugenics and genetic democracy.

Genetic Fix, a text by Amitai Etzioni, states, "The taboo we now have against the deliberate breeding of certain types of people is so effective that just thinking about it made me somewhat ashamed and somewhat defensive." However, selective breeding will soon have its day in the greatest social revolution of all, which will make Christianity, communism, the agricultural revolution, look like children's toys. Genetic engineering is upon us. We quickly need to be better prepared for human breeding programs. Out there in the future some stunning nation will commence developing the world's most terrifying weapon, selective human inequality.

The very reason we don't have many Shakespeares, Leonardo da Vincis or Beethovens floating around is because, within the genetic formulation of human society, there was no particular need for the especially gifted types. On the other hand, our lower intellectualized population, and even to an extent the morons of the upper feebleminded, were incorporated as necessary units to the successful advancement of the social specie.

There is a tremendous harangue about universality of education and the equalization of all. Social genetic structure has no part of this. There are many reasons why society carries lower intellectualized individuals. Foremost is the reduction of intragroup competition. This permits a smooth-running hierarchy composed of classes from dominants to the obedients. If we hadn't had serfs working the medieval fields, accepting plagues and religious fanfare, we would have slogged slowly to modern times.

Not only was class and hierarchy important formations of human society, but the lower units were also blessed with insensitives, strong and resolute physiological muscularity, and blind courage. Insult, both physical and mental, had to drop off their backs like the bread they sweated for. If all society were intelligent, where would you find the stupid fools sallying forth to fight inane wars for the benefit of protecting their dominants? Where would be the expendibles?

Issue at stake is how will mankind use selective breeding and genetic engineering? The very nature of society will demand that he not contract into equality, but will radiate into a brilliant evolutionary future of class structures.

Don't be surprised one day with the creation of "Mapes." Those creatures, half man, half ape, will be sold as pets to be incorporated into a form of slavery — master-owner. With considerable genetic breeding, the product will fit nicely into economic schema. That fact alone will bring them into existence.

Much as the Negro was enslaved to work the Southern cotton fields, highly initiated through economic necessity, so shall the "mapes" perform within the agricultural world, in servitude, and in armies. It will mean a shifting and redesigning for the lower-skilled jobs. It will bring profuse prosperity to the nations that employ them. If communism has not already been destroyed, the "mapes" will finish it off.

For in "mapes" you will have a sub-proletariat, non-human, who will be adaptable to supersede the communistic schema. Top elements of society will be further widened, with professionals, scientists, and the highest intellectuals occupying a relatively low percentage. Almost eliminated in the new schema will be the proletariat class, whose function was important evolutionarily, but due to machines and genetic engineering, will be displaced.

There is no question that machinery has displaced the unskilled worker. The future shall find this continuing. As humanity settles into new adaptiveness, there shall be evolutionary shifts in traditional biological format. Mapes and machines will substitute for lower classes. There will be less crime and violence because crime and violence are indigenous to lower class genes. There is, however, another route which will be followed contemporaneously with the production of mapes.

Sociological engineers will classify society into more discrete units. If the government would keep stupid edicts out of the marketplace, there would be excellent opportunity for utilization of high grade feeblemindeds. They could be bred to a distinct group. They would fill the economically lower rungs of society. There is no reason that their lives should not be fulfilling and content. No matter how anyone wants to cut the human pie, so long as individuals have variant gene capacities, the slices will be unequal.

One of the sad miracles of the 20th century was the bloody authoritarian precipitous transformation of a huge land mass of backward feudally oriented peasants and workers into one of the top industrial and political powers of earth within slightly over half a century. Have no second thoughts that this miracle of national economics was due to one thing only. The forceful and revolutionary institution of communism — the ideas of Marx, Engles and Lenin, put into totalitarian practice by absolute tyranny.

Obviously, the political science promoted by them was highly successful. Yet one should note that the ideas expounded by these men of Utopia vision were perverted.

One of the appeals of communism is the father image. It becomes dominant and is the provider. To go into the world and compete for subsistence is difficult for many people. It is easier to accept some type of dictatorial direction than struggle in a world where one has small genetic advantage. Little people will always cling to the leader because by biology they are deficient in structure to experience full life. It is for this they eagerly grasp for the worst of demagogues. Strong dominants provide for lack in their thought and ability to govern themselves.

What came out of the morass of communistic propaganda was a bloody, ruthless, totalitarian dictatorship. The use of symbols, slogans, glib words, falsities and inverted reasoning, managed to convince the working classes, the massive bureaucracy and the class stratified army, that they, the leaders, were acting in the interests of the people, of humanity, of all the peoples on earth.

The historic miracle that launched Soviet Russia into the forefront of the 20th century to dominate, by 1983, one-third of the world's population, came about by the fast words of the con artist — the sleight-of-hand faker — the fraudulence of the soothsayer. Earth-shattering advances of the Soviets was the precipitous conversion of a feudal land to one of the most pristine and perfect forms of capitalism.

What had succeeded in Russia was the transformation of a politico-economic structure into one giant monopolistic corporation. The communist party, who owned all the preferred and voting stock, bilked the workers out of their right to strike, to assemble, to free speech, to freedom of movement, to expression of opinion — it bilked the workers out of every known human right, excepting the right to behave and act as prescribed by the communist party. Regardless of what is in the books or in the preambles, regardless of what rights of freedom are proclaimed, these are false rights subject to the permissiveness of the party.

Yet there was a right that was reserved to the workers, bureaucrats, armies, and peoples of Russia. They were each given a share of the non-voting, common stock of the corporation, in return for the lands and property that the Soviet leaders had expropriated. This stock paid only what dividends the directors wished. If the directors decided to concentrate on heavy industry, then the people were left with little food and drink, shabby clothes and apartments, and long working hours. Non-voting stock gave no right of protest. There was no court which could uphold justice to the stock-holders. In addition to being a monolithic, monopolistic corporation, the policies, prerogatives, directorship and law resided in the hands of the precedium party congresses, secretaries and secret alliances of the very few, which held the preferred voting stock.

Communism was the greatest stock swindle of all history, and it stuck. The corporate papers issued with the bloody ink of the 1917 October Insurrection resulted in one of the finest capitalistic corporate charters in history. A Wall Street firm so constituted would laugh itself to death in peels of hysterical joy.

Imagine a company with no labor problems. Any backtalk or sabotage, any strikes, slowdowns or set-ins, any discussion over wages, living condi-tions or grievances, that were not settled easily with the aid of lower rank committees, one merely instructs the plant supervisor to jail or liquidate dissenters.

Police complete the executive act. Is there reluctance on the part of the fellow workers to dispatch fellow workers? Have no fear. Within the charter of the Great Soviet Corporation, behind the print, is the dictator's finger preventing dissention. Rebellious workers, those that impede production, are not workers. They are enemies of the Corporation. The Corporation has the sovereign right to remove anyone from property who is committing a dis-turbance. Workers can't go outside the gate and picket peacefully. The Cor-poration owns the sidewalks outside the gate. It owns even the company row houses and the company store, a practice which caused so much anti-capitalistic furor at the end of the 19th century in America. The Corpora-tion can jail a dissident worker. He is an enemy of the Corporation, imped-ing production. He is an enemy of the state.

With the collectivism of farms, forcefully and brutally, the Corporation embarked upon what they thought would be a more productive form of agriculture. Shareholders, who were the people, who each had a share of non-voting stock, representing all the lands and property of the Soviets, were workers who had to comply with the edicts of the board of directors of the Corporation without dissent or grievances. This was accomplished by blood-letting of millions of non-cooperative little people. Finally, the Corporation got things well under control. For all Soviet labor is slave labor. They are owned by the director masters and are paid whatever they decree.

The other great capitalistic society, the United States of America, which is non-monopolistic, with millions of farms, has been able to repeatedly bail out its brother economic system, the Soviets, by the shipment of massive amounts of grain at reduced prices, when the Soviet Corporation runs into its chronic problems.

Who can argue with the merits of one of the finest capitalistic closed cor-porations on earth — the U.S.S.R.? It did a magnificent job of propagandizing its workers. Its revolutionary negotiating teams achieved a labor contract that would enthrall the heart of the staunchest reactionary. Why did communism succeed? Why does a monopolistic corporation succeed which has no labor problems?

Pay attention to the equalitarianism of Russia and China. They are peasant societies excepting for the veneer of intellectual upper strata from whence their technology derives. Their governments have set into motion premiums on conformity and submission. With emulation of lower class masses, the biologic variability will select in this direction. In centuries to come, we shall observe the retrogradeness of their societies. Free world academicians will rapidly out-balance monolithic structures which promote human equalization.

If acquired characteristics are transferrable, then this process shall be rapid, much beyond normal selective factors. Outside of this potential, political science influences sometimes severely the genetic directions of society. Nazi extermination of Jewish populations and American extermination of Indian-Mongoloid populations are classic examples. There are instances wherein a large culture has swamped a smaller population. For a short period, the slave worlds — socialistically controlled populations — may succeed. Then their political purpose will result in breeding selectivity. Finally, that alteration of character by artificial selection will lower fitness. Then will come communistic demise.

On the other hand, the open capitalistic, competitive and bourgeois society will be reflected in biological sponsorship of higher strata class, will be tuned to adaptability and fitness in splendid diversity.

In the free world, and in the slave-socialistic world, there shall appear variance in total fitness. This will permit the free world to extend itself at the expense of the disadvantaged gened socialists. That is, provided the free world selects toward freedom in all its political aspects, culling out the idiosy of human equality, and permitting the blossoming of strong elements. It means, specifically, permitting the strong to rise at the expense of the weak, in the traditional fashion of evolutionary advancement. If freedom can be correlated with birth control of lower society elements to permit the expansion and privilege of the upper classes, then free societies shall remain permanent, powerful, and well-defended.

No error in any of the societies and nations of man can be greater than to ignore the evolutionary forces which produce fitness, stability and adaptability leading to survival. To achieve this, governments must be reregulated to the minimum and the weak permitted to decrease by contraception, nonbreeding, and abortion. Libraries filled with ideological political science and human equality cannot withstand the advance of society formulated upon traditional evolution.

How did society become gened? Social genes are no different than genes that make up architectural functions of bone and muscle. They obey the same laws of mutation. Genes reproduced may be miscopied or altered by chemicals, radiation, or physical forces to form aberrations and variances. In the ascent of social man, these variances, if they proved advantageous, were seized upon and incorporated into gene pools.

Bitter philosophies of Marx, Engles and Lenin, the unholy triumvirate which resulted in the infection of communism, were the product of misconceived, misinterpreted social injustices and biological ignorance.

In *The State and Revolution,* Lenin's major work, published in the historic August of 1919 — the true restoration of Marx — he expresses through Engles: "The State — is cleft into irreconciliable antagonisms, which it is powerless to dispell. But in order that these antagonisms, classes with conflicting economic interests, might not consume themselves and society in sterile struggle, a power — standing above society became necessary — the state."

Lenin says that this fully expresses the basic idea of Marxism on the meaning of state, the state being the product and manifestation of the irreconciliability of class antagonisms. No class aggressions — no state. If you have a state, it is proof there are class antagonisms.

Marx made it clear, the state could not arise or continue to exist if it were possible to conciliate classes. The state is an organ of class rule, an organ of oppression of one class or another. It creates "order" which legalizes and perpetuates oppression by refereeing the collision between the classes.

The unscientific radicalism of the communist movement is clearly evident from these few important phrases by its confused prophets. They speak of class, but there is no definition of class other than one related to conflict or antagonism. Marx, Engles and Lenin were revolutionary criminals working from paranoic hatred. Venom was not directed so much against class as it was against the successful ruling symbols of law and order.

From the depth of hatred they were able to philosophize and revolutionize into the most hideous tyranny of all time. Totalitarian communist regimes are so oppressive in nature it is a mockery to compare them with regimes against which the ignoble trinity was revolting. In their obsession, the worker, toiler, and exploited were heroized. The enemy was identified as the wealthy, professional elite, landowners, business owners, and all government in general. Thus we have two major classes — the workers and the directors.

In their mad rush for power they did not change the order of classes. They made class distinction more acute. Persecution and exploitation became more fearsome. For today in Russia we still have the working exploited class and the class represented by the communist party. The latter is absolute and criminally oppressive. Witness free exiled writers, such as Solzhenitsyn, whose *Gulag Archipelago* is a Dantesque horror tale of the insensitivity of the Soviet state.

What the unholy three could not envision were biological discoveries of the 20th century. Marx, Engles and Lenin were revolutionary socialists, not biologists. They could never have conceived great biological laws that were commencing to formulate at the turn of the century. Biology is an exact science. Its tenants are ameniable to proof and mathematical analysis. Whereas, the ingredient of socialism is peasant urine on a hot tin roof.

One of the first social biological laws was the formulation by a Frenchman, Binet, of a simple method for determining individual differences in the quality of cerebral nervous tissue, commonly known as IQ or intelligence quotient. Thousands of tests have verified this wide range of mental variance. Yet our three revolutionaries were thinking in terms of egalitarianism in which men are equal but class struggle renders them unequal.

Here is great fallacy of the Red hammer and sickle prophets. A laboring class does not exist because of persecution or oppression or exploitation because of capitalism. It is genetically programmed to exist. It exists because half of society ranges below the IQ of 100 and because the other half ranges in higher IQ's where they rightfully fulfill their role in biological society as leaders, chiefs, politicians, poets, inventors, and entrepreneurs.

The lower IQ class is born to follow and mesomorphically to toil. Their tenure upon earth is at the benevolent mercy of intellectualized ruling, professional, and business classes. Look at organization in primates to witness determined propagation of biologically-classed society.

Socialistic dreamers do not take into account non-human animal society. Diatribes of Marx, et al, originates from paranoic delusions of persecution by ruling classes or the state. These men, by genetic inheritance, struck out against the state and dominants. Not because of sympathy for the working class, but in contestation of dominants, for their own selfish advancement. They were not born dominants, but were programmed as political challengers to the existing order. The fevertness of the revolutionary bent indicates mental disease of a paranoic order.

Nowhere is the abnormality of their thought process more strikingly demonstrated than in their repetitive assertions in various phraseology. For example, from Lenin's *The State and Revolution*, quote, "Special representative force" for the suppression of the proletariat by the bourgeois, for the suppression of the millions of workers by a handful of the rich, must be superseded by a "special repressive force" for the suppression of the bourgeois by the proletariat (the dictatorship of the proletariat).

What this double-talk is trying to say is that state bourgeois represses the worker-proletariat. They must be displaced by the state of proletariats, suppressing the bourgeois.

There is more in which the state "withers away" or "is put an end to in the course of revolution." There is still more in that "democracy is also a state and will disappear when the state disappears."

In other words, it is a turnabout in roles. The bourgeois, the armed forces, bureaucracy, and the well-to-do are the oppressors. This class can never be reconciled with the laboring class, the heroic class, the toilers and exploited. Dramatically, they reverse themselves with the Bolshevik Revolution of 1917. However, it was only names that changed. Workers, the laboring class, the less intelligent, the mesomorphic section of society, the disturbed, the unsuccessful, the genetic servants — still remain the toilers, the oppressed, and the slaves of the new elite, bourgeois known as the Communist Party — and the most tyrannical, dictatorial, oppressive, suppressive, and murderous organization on earth. It probably was not the intention of the three "kings" of communism to substitute a ruthless dictatorship as the instrument of state, a dictatorship in which oppressiveness is its chief role. The primary role was thought decerebration of the masses.

Unbeknownst to the kings of communism was there is no salvation for the oppressed masses as they envisioned. For they are genetically born toilers, workers, marvelous in their patience, steadfast in their devotions and loyalties. Their false philosophies were predicated in their own embittered minds. The kings had no idea of modern biology demonstrating social relationships designed by nature, in which dominants within society is the essence of existence. Nor had they the least intimation that the noble precept of the American Constitution, "All men are created equal," was a colossal antibiological fantasy. Their wildest mental orgies could never have predicted the biological variances of men, races, and sex, measured in terms of neurological abilities and muscular propensities.

As Marx had stated in a letter in 1852, no credit was due him for the discovering of the existence of classes in modern society; this had been done by bourgeois historians in describing class struggle.

Observe human society — capitalistic, socialistic, dictatorial, or communistic. It is apparent that the large mass of working class, those at the bottom of the social political and economic scale, and who live poorly not by design, not by lack of proper environment or education, but because they are placed by the God of chance — DNA combination — into the role of toiler and follower. They are not blessed with ability to rule, but must themselves be ruled. No state understands this better than the communistic state with its hierarchial control of masses.

Socialism for Lenin meant a dictatorship of the proletariat workers over all political and economic matters by dedicated professional revolutionaries. Biologically translated, Lenin, a sub-dominant primate, is to take converts — bachelors, homosexuals, workers, soldiers — out of the tribe to challenge the existing order of the tribal dominants. Challenged and successfully put to rout, Lenin would move into position as a dominant, with his own chosen, reestablishing social order. His was no crusade of benevolence, but merely the age-old struggle of outsiders moving into position of dominant.

Lenin cannot be regarded as a dominant. Rather, he was the jackal that was given enough dominant genes to enable him to challenge, but not enough to rightfully take a position of dominance in society, as historically we witness our own revolutionary, George Washington. Lenin would destroy society to achieve the alpha order, whereas Washington would work within it to achieve his biologically inherited leadership. Lenin achieved his goal not due to his own powers, but because of backing of the German government that secretly shipped him from Switzerland to Saint Petersburg in Russia on April 3, 1917, to disrupt and withdraw Russia from the war.

Tragically, by the time of his death on January 21, 1924, Lenin had only succeeded in replacing one autocratic system with another. The state didn't "wither away," nor, as Engles had hoped, did the state become superfluous, nor, as Marx wrote in 1848, did the working class substitute an association which excludes classes and their antagonism.

No place is the legacy of class more evident than in Russia and China. The state class is supreme. And, as Marx continued, "There will be no more political power, since political power is precisely the political expression of antagonism in civil society." Had Marx sensed biological politics, we may have had a modern definition.

As one reads the mumbo-jumbo of these fiery revolutionaries, one is impressed with the absence of logical thought expression in seas of confusion. Their obsession was to kill leadership. What would follow in the wake was submerged in the emotionalism of the contemplated deed.

For humanity it was unfortunate the communistic trilogy was not more aware of biological facts. Had this been so, instead of replacing bourgeois capables with garbage collector inferiors, the revolution would have taken a more traditional line and specific types within the species would have been utilized to their maximum efficiency. When the new revolution comes to Russia and China, as it must, society will be biologically and class-structured according to the occupationally designated genes. Biologic individuality will be the constitution. Future successors of Marx, Engles and Lenin will insure democracy because it is biologically based on permitting free expression of individualism. Communism is based on arbitrary force which ignores inherent differences.

The concept of biologic democracy is not new. Workers move into lower class sections as if on clue from a controlling being. Entire educational systems do little more than sift the human sands into occupational niches they are designed for. There are exceptions. One cannot be but amazed at the normal class sorting throughout all societies. When the Communist Party is dismantled, into its place will rightfully move the oppressed bourgeois who have abnormally been thrust into working class roles. Again, in this present vacuum shall move the elite of biological heritage, the artists, writers, composers, poets, officers, professionals, business people, leaders, and statesmen. Workers will be truly workers. They will be benignly governed by biological superiors whose roles are innate to dominance and human progress.

Throughout Lenin's writings, as he speaks for himself, Marx, and Engles, there is that persistent theme, the recurring obsession, that once the dictatorship of the proletariat comes into being, there will be a "withering away of the state." It is a concept so utterly absurd, so illogical and so impossible, that it demonstrates lack of intellectual faculty. Yet it further demonstrates ignorance of biological science. They would only have had to look at the social organization in species. Some information was available in a rudimentary form on bees, wolves, lions, baboons, and birds.

Essential to any society, of whatever species, is a basic form of state in which dominants command, soldiers protect, sacrifice and are sacrificed, and the multitude work. Anarchy is the final absurdity if it is carried to its purest form in which government and state are abolished, and in which the individual returns to a free and unrestrained society. But converts are available within the dim-witted of genetic structure. They may carry recessive genes. These genes represent the purity of individual nature without control.

Anarchists are a throwback of millions of years ago to species ancestors before the formulation of society. Pre-social recessives are still being thrown out today. They continue to serve a function in society. In evolutionary ascent, colorful conflicting "isms" and classes serve as buffers over historically difficult periods in which environmental changes demanded the severest of social adaptabilities.

Many times in our developing primate society we may have been saved from extinction by anarchistical genes. Witness millions of years of drought in the Pliocene. We have only fragmentary record, but here all forms of developing society may have disappeared only to have the species' bloodline preserved by antisocial rebels who split out on their own to find a more favorable environment supportive of less social group demand.

When the three communist firebrands spoke of "the dictatorship of the proletariat," they could never have dreamed that they were on one piece of solid biological territory. Although, by some mysticism, they all agreed the state would "wither away" and disappear, and in its place would arise some worker type of controlling substitute which would not be a state, but which would serve the functions of state. They were quick to point out that they would only control temporarily the state they revolutionized against, until this new blessed organization would come into being.

We now all know that once the communists take over, the state does not "wither" or disappear. Instead, there arises a tyrannical, paranoidal oligarchy unparalleled in animal history. So we cannot know exactly what they were blubbering about when, after half a century, this final blessed toilers' organization, not a state, was to come into being.

The biological territory they discovered was niched with workers — the proletariat as well as the bourgeois — the courts, the legislatures, the executives, the army, the police, the business managers, bankers, professionals, etc. The workers needed and assumed a dictatorship which would then oppress the oppressors, the present bourgeois. Yet to have this dictatorship, obviously the workers had to set up dominants, which were the leaders and commisars of the communist state. They had to set up military rank with authoritarian generals and officers. They had to establish courts, even if only sham and subservient to their dictates. Finally, they had to set up bureaucracy that outdid anything that was under the leadership of Tzars.

What Marx, Engles and Lenin actually provoked was not a revolution of the proletariat, but a revolution in which they substituted for bourgeois gencticism, the best worker geneticism. In positions of governmental dominants, which were the classical natural inheritance of the bourgeois, were moved incapable workers.

Bourgeois bloodlines had been established over the ages. As these superiorly-gened people intermarried, they rightfully gave forth a high percentage of higher-classed individuals. In like fashion, the working class and toilers intermarried and the workers' gene pool, the serfs, remained pure workers.

These two groups, by trial, error, and class struggle, which is a biological struggle in which the rightful geneticisms assume their predestined occupational roles in society, are already moved into position in all societies.

It is an irony that communists created a bourgeois revolution, substituting inferior dominants, while killing off their better germ plasma and hereditary superiors in the White Russians. Were it not that western politicians in the Second World War aided and abetted this genetic castration, true Russia would have emerged.

Incredibly, the bloody holocausts spawned by Bolshevik biological ignoramuses, proletariat dictatorship, but succeeded in what they despised —

a bourgeois revolution in which one group of bourgeois succeeds the other. In this case, the successors were petty bourgeois, those of inferior geneticism which were propelled by force of arms and terror into command of Russia to suppress and eliminate the society of biologically dominant superiors. It is because of this colossal fallacy in comprehending human primate structure that one day soon, the world shall witness a second great Russian revolution.

Within the military, the biological hierarchy is in position. Such writers as Solzhenitsyn and others, the revelations of the Stalinist era are preparing the masses for new freedoms. There only needs to be war miscalculation as with Chinese or American, or biological superiors of the army moving to assert their control, to reestablishing the benignity of a free state — free press, free assembly, and freedom for religious worship. This is the nightmare of communists.

Vladimir Ilyich Ulyanov, known as V. I. Lenin, was born April 10, 1870, and died January 21, 1924. While in prison in 1895, he began his work, *The Development of Capitalism in Russia*, which was published in 1899. In Chapter VIII he comments that capitalism's historic role was an increase in productive forces of social labor and the socialization of labor, the latter which destroys small economic units, concentrates production, squeezes out forms of personal dependence, creates mobility, diminishes the number of agricultural workers, increases the need for union and changes the spiritual makeup of the population.

Capitalism was his obsessive "bug-a-boo," which created poverty and misery of the masses and social antagonisms that must be destroyed through revolution. The transformation of competition into monopoly was the most important phenomenon of modern capitalism. Imperialism was the highest stage of capitalism, dominated by finance capital.

What Lenin was railing at in his biological ignorance was not a manmade force of socio-economic order known as capitalism, but was rather a natural force of human primate development. In the evolutionary development of the human primate order, a system of economic benificence, namely capitalism, was necessary for survivorship, being none other than biological capitalism.

Studies have pointed out the socialization of labor in the non-human primate groups. Females were gatherers of roots and vegetables, and reared the young. Males divided into hierarchies for hunting groups far away from home base. Bachelors and homosexuals were employed within the hunting party and became expendable by the "bourgeois" dominant apes.

In insects, we see the division of labor among workers and drones, the queen and attendants. Over the broad spectrum of the socialized animals, there is an unequaled distribution of productivity and leadership talents.

As the modern species of man — Homo sapiens — came into being, the major precepts of Lenin's enumerated capitalism was developing in natural form. In smaller economic units, the group and tribe became obsolete. Production became concentrated through new forms of livelihood such as farming and its supportive sciences.

Personal independence was squeezed out as the broader horizons of social advancement entered the marketplace. It became obvious that agricultural workers would decrease as their productivity increased. A need for union has been a hallmark of animal society, from starlings to porpoises. The spiritual makeup of human society has undoubtedly changed within evolutionary history, from one of complete unawareness of spiritual existence, to the complete geneticized compulsions of religious fervor.

The economic form, capitalism, is nothing more than components of a geneticized society. It is neither abnormal nor oppressive. Capitalism did not arise out of the minds of philosophers or the industrial revolution. It arose from programmed genes in evolutionary advancement which required social order as a means of survival.

There has never been a human society of moderate size which is not representative of biological capitalism. It is a comedy to imagine that in either Russia or China, communism is an economic force which has supplanted capitalism. In Russia, as in the capitalist countries in the west, there is hierarchy and privilege within the structure of the military. There is a privileged police class which mercilessly suppresses the working masses. There is the state dominated by the privileged Communist Party which directs and dictatorily oppresses the proletariat. The wealthy class is represented by the power privileged of the Communist Party and its Politburo. The state is an absolute dictatorial oligarchy and far from "withering away," conducts foreign affairs in normal capitalistic manner.

Communism presupposes a classless society. This is farcical. If one believes Solzhenitsyn, in *Gulag Archipelago*, a huge class of Russians are prisoners which Marx-Lenin communism was supposed to eliminate. In Russia we have illustration of class struggle if one peers beneath the false window-dressing of communism. The delusion is held together by Leninist double-talk, while the real recognition of class separation goes unchallenged.

If the wealthy bourgeois of the west are oppressing the proletariat, then the privileged and powerful Communist Party members in Russia, in translating wealth into power, are the true capitalistic exploiters of toiling workers. Both groups are equal. Both are biologically constituted in genetic sovereignty. Illustration of the biology of political science is the Russian Revolution. Nowhere is the mentality of the revolutionist better shown than in Lenin's book of 1919, *The State and Revolution*, as he buttresses his argumentative propaganda with reverential quotes from Marx and Engles. We are able to psycho-deduct the genetic composition of himself and his two high priests.

Psychiatrically, one can consider this triumvirate of revolutionaries to be mentally ill. They all possessed delusions of grandeur and persecution. It is in the latter form, as paranoics, with their hatred for authority and the state, and their violently reacting obsessions of persecution that distinguishes their instability. In the American Revolution, George Washington and the signers of the Declaration of Independence had few of these emotional abnormalities. It was a revolution, to be sure, but it was benign, fought in the interests of the people. It was not carried out with pathological hatreds.

For our communist revolutionists, the goal was destruction. They succeeded in destroying the state and the bourgeois. Their successor, Stalin, was even more successful in the annihilating bloodbath of compatriots. All had

utter disregard for human life, a callousness toward a police state and imprisonment. Present-day Russia is a manifestation of these deranged mental
faculties.

Delusions of grandeur are readily apparent in Lenin's work. Not only
from the idolatry with which he regarded Marx, but from his missionary zeal
of revolution, that he shall be the savior of oppressed mankind, a thought
shared by Marx and Engles. Behind the bloody calculating lines one reads the
ego-mania of these beings. By revolution they were destined, divine-like, to
avenge and destroy, as an Angel of Death, humans whose only crime was
their biological superiority.

Elements of serious mental disease appear in the works and lives of
Marx, Engles and Lenin. They had delusions of grandeur. They had rabid
phobias of persecution. They were intent upon senseless, murderous killings.
Black clouds of destruction filled their subconscious. In an enlightened
society they would have been committed to a sanatorium.

If we discount mental disease as the motivating organ of their actionary
venom, we are left with the rare but frequent enough genetically programmed revolutionary. To this class we should add assassins who challenge
dominants -- individuals such as Lee Harvey Oswald and Sirhan Sirhan, who
murdered the Kennedy brothers.

Possibly no more than a fraction of a percent of the male populace is
coded genetically as a killer-usurper of state function. There is a basis for this
social programming. A society with continuously fixed dominants would,
over long evolutionary periods, run into despotism and inefficiency. One perceives this in the lineage of royalty. Because of restrictive inbreeding tendency toward superior qualities, oftentimes a rotten apple enters the
sovereignty and leads the nation to disgrace, ruin or poverty. The alternative
is the overthrow of the government.

In evolving hominid society the revolutionary disruption, on occasion, of
the state governed by the dominants, would lead to new adventures, new
areas of shelter and food, and possibly to isolated enclaves where new pressures would enhance the marginal gene pools.

In communist Russia, the working class, the toiler and industrial gene
pools, have been expanded at the expense of the previous bourgeois components. There is less intellectualism, creative works of art, music, literature,
less pure science and scientific dedication to the humanities. These facts are
colossally apparent.

Not only is the ruling class communistic oppressors of the masses in
genetic contraction, but since they have eliminated the flower of White
Russian DNA after the revolution, there exists a paucity of quality cerebral
structure. Thus, communists have succeeded in biological alteration of a
large populace — not for the better, mind you, but for the worst. Human
social evolution can travel blind alleys on the path to extinction. Who knows
what a rightist revolution of the army might accomplish? The worker could
remain the same, as is his historical and readily-accepted role, if bread, vodka
and sports are freely provided. The new rightists would charge off in eugenic
splurge, which Renaissance not only bourgeois quality would improve, but
the arts and humanity as well. New rightists would devote less energies to

weapons of destruction, imprisonment, and creeds of suspicion, to provide true advancement in biological social science. These men already exist, if but scantily, in the gene pool. It is inevitable that their rightful biological roles should emerge expressed in the revolution of the dominant class.

The following are quoted from Lenin's *Class in Society*, in which both symptoms of mental disease and underlying biological genetic compulsions exist. (We have italicized portions of the quotes to give you the key.)

Lenin: "During the lifetime of great revolutionaries, the *oppressing classes* relentlessly *persecute* them." (See 5X)

Engles: "The State — is cleft into *irreconciliable antagonisms.*" (See 3X)

Lenin: "According to Marx, the state could neither arise *nor continue to exist, if it were possible to consolidate classes.*"

"According to Marx, the state is an organ for the *oppression of one class for another.*" (See 6X)

"The state is a special repressive force for the suppression of the proletariat by the bourgeois, for the suppression of the millions of toilers by a *handful of the rich, must be superseded* by a 'special repressive force' *for the suppression* of the bourgeois by the proletariat (the *dictatorship* of the proletariat)." (See 6X)

"Revolution *alone* can 'put an end' to the bourgeois state." (See 4X)

"*Every* state is a 'special repressive force' for the suppression of the oppressed class." (See 3X)

"The Communist Manifesto, with their proud and open declaration of the *inevitability* of a *violent* revolution." (See 1X)

"The necessity of *systematically imbuing* the masses with this and precisely this vein of *violent* reaction lies at the root of the whole of Marx's and Engle's doctrine." (See 2X)

"The substitution of a proletariat state for the bourgeois state is impossible without a *violent* revolution." (See 2X)

Marx: "Political power is precisely the *official* expression of antagonism in civil society." (Change official to biological) (See 5X)

Lenin: "The state is a special organization of *force;* it is the organization of *violence* for the suppression of some class." (See paranoid)

"The proletariat needs state *power,* the centralized organization of *force,* the organization of *violence,* for the purpose of *crushing* the resistance of the exploiters. . . . " (Symptoms of delusions of grandeur since the speaker is identifying with the proletariat and murderous aggressiveness.)

". . . the more clearly the oppressed classes, with the proletariat at their heads, become conscious of their irreconciliable *hostility to the whole* of bourgeois society." (Fixed delusion of persecution by an entire class.)

". . . *compels* the revolution to 'concentrate all its forces of destruction' against the state power, and to regard the problem, not as one of perfecting the state machine but one of *smashing and destroying it.*" (Anarchistic aggression.)

". . . in transferring the ownership of the railways, the factories, land and so forth, to the entire nation, to the whole of society." (Land and property redistribution is referring to abnormal territorial rearrangement, which biologically would be controlled by the stronger bourgeois dominants.)

"Marx deduced from the whole history of socialism and of the political struggle that the state was bound to disappear, and that the transitional form of its disappearance [the transition from state to no state] would be the 'proletariat organized as the ruling class.'" (This denotes an immature attitude toward parental state authority which would indicate mental disturbance.)

Engles: ". . . and the victorious party, if it does not wish to have fought in vain, must maintain its rule by means of the terror. . . ." (Pathologic, sadistic aggression.)

Lenin: ". . . capitalism . . . calls for *seas of blood* through which mankind has to wade in slavery, serfdom and wage labor." (See 5X)

Marx - Engles - Lenin — Mental Disease

1X*   (Compulsive paranoic persuasiveness to incite violence.)
2X   (Fixity of single solution by violent aggression.)
3X   (Delusion of limitless persecution.)
4X   (Cerebral fixation in violence as a solution.)
5X   (Persistent persecutory delusions.)
6X   (Fixity of persecutory delusions involving huge masses.)

Marx admits he did not discover classes. It was bourgeois historians. Actually, there was no discovery. Class is normal genetic constituency in society. Whatever its size, it is programmed evolutionary through survival pressures operating upon social composition. When Marx speaks of the final classless society, he is in wild philosophical conjecture due to his biological ignorance. Evidence of class society has not only been omnipresent, but it is well represented in communist Russia.

The state which the revolutionary triumvirate hoped would "wither away" and which never has, is the rule of the inherent biologically dominants, designed for order so that the species could be evolutionarily furthered. The state is the primary component of biological society to assure survival and progeny. It is based upon DNA coding of class supremacy, to minimize intragroup competition for general welfare. Laborers and leaders are born. Communists are fabricated out of the thin air of terrorism.

It is apparent we have been severe in analysis, psychiatrically and biologically of three revolutionaries. One should be amazed that defect in thought would provoke such massive movement within a society. Yet, if we examine history carefully, we will find that it is ofttimes the mentally aberrent with abnormal zeal that moves more complacent humans.

Joan of Arc was undoubtedly a hallucinating schizophrenic when she led the French armies against the English. Attila the Hun was a cold-blooded Asiatic assasin as he swept over Europe. Hitler displayed psychoses in innumerable brain divisions. Some have said that Christ was a schizophrenic, suffering delusions of grandeur, believing himself of divine origin.

The list of mentally defectives who have altered society and have temporarily captured the cooperation of the populace, is a long one. It illustrates that the great majority of the toilers are genetically geared to accept dominant control. That is why it is very easy for a few agitators to readily capture the minds of large groups of factory workers, while within the medical, legal, or upper echelon businesses or professions there is rarely, if ever, unanimity of agreement. Bourgeois society, the society of the dominants, has too great an abundance of diverging genes. Whereas, the working class can easily be grouped in trade unions or mustered into armies because of the unchallenging similarity of their DNA composition and their lack of dominant traits. The laborer is said to be led and cared for by the dominants. Russian communism has certainly shown that the masses are led by the party. It is not demonstrated that they are properly cared for.

There is a tendency to regard political ideologies as manmade and culturally determined. Yet remember, the premise that society, the actions and the institutions, are already grouped into place by virtue of underlying genetic dispositioning and coding. Human societies, when isolated, regardless of composition, settle into common denominator basics. They manage to envisage the supernatural, the mystic or a religious pattern. Marriage and incest taboo codes fall into position, rulers and disciplinarians emerge, workers are designated.

It's genetic mathematics. Begin with 1000 gambling dice, throw them out on the table repeatedly, and come up with consistent patterns. Humanity, being of the same "nucleic acid" speculation, can never rise above chemicalized mathematical potential, which is restricted and predictable.

So we find traditional socio-economic action emerging in the genetic mutations, spawned prior to the industrial revolution, notably capitalism. Capitalism is an economic system whereby materials, factories, mines and ships are provided by citizens known as entrepreneurs, leaders or gamblers, for the opportunity of others to voluntarily work capital assets to receive wages. Capitalists are those who own, risk and direct the assets. The laboring class are those that work the assets. What makes the system so fantastically successful, viable and unchallengeable, is a directed geneticism based on the original society precept of divisions of hominids in their evolution.

Here we see the fruition of society on a grand scale, mimicking its ancestral inheritance of the smaller group. There are few societies, if any today, in which it is not immediately apparent that dominants control. This was a necessity as we emerged from the trees, commencing to utilize technology of the hands we had gained from branch-hopping millions of years in the African savannas. Our emergent political coding was that dominants should lead and make decisions. Workers should follow and be expended for the good of the group. It was further imperative there not be persistent intragroup feuding. Homosexuals satisfied 20% of this requirement. Others, like the workers, were docile, not in courage of fighting but docile toward leadership.

Neurogenic programming of the worker class was one of the first great mutational advancements in anthropoid society. By necessity a large group of both male and female had to be designed to be unchallenging. Troops were as necessary as officers — natural selection making it so. That is why we see huge national movements being captured by fanatical ambitions of a few dominants. The masses, the proletariat, do not think, they only listen to the orders of the dominant, Gurus.

The French Revolution was a group of philosophically, hysterically dominant liberals leading a motley organized group of proletariat workers. Within a generation they were no better off than before, morassed in crippling wars of an ambitious dominant, Napoleon Bonaparte. Only a small number of fanatical dominants from left and right, with outside help, managed to split Spanish workers in the Revolution of 1936 down the middle like a field of wheat. Before it was over, a million innocents had perished.

A bumbling prejudiced magpie like Roosevelt was able to galvanize the American workers into World War II, which left Christian Europe in ruins. It elevated the Soviet proletariat to the first true challenges for survival that the American people in their history had experienced.

Animal studies demonstrate pecking order in chickens, each submissive to the one above. Vervet monkeys in Rhodesia demonstrated, within a captive troop, a top leader, younger and smaller. And in monkey colonies in Japan, one high-ranking male was 35 years old and had not been in a fight in a decade. Within the fish world is hierarchy of rank order. Tropical swordtails, under environmental change, struggle for status even above sexual interest. From the baboon to kadu bull, from the beagle to the wasp, there are illustrations of dominants.

What the antecedents of man forged on the African savannas was society, which they evolutionarily selected and programmed within their DNA coding. Dominants to run the show and workers to obey. It was capitalism. Springs and water holes were controlled by dominants. Females groomed the leaders in homage. The best fruit trees were owned by capitalists. Workers were permitted access by virtue of their submissive work — watch duty, vanguarding, flanking.

In the early time of Homo sapiens we see more illustrations of capitalistic emergence. Royalties — dynasties of Egypt, Asyria, Babylonia, and Persia — similar royal dynasties in China and India, and wherever the elements of civilization were combining — rightfully took determined genetic positions as protoplasamed dominants to control the helpless working muscle, mesomorphic class.

However, royalty was subject to one inconsistency. The role of the dominant was to be passed from father to son. This had excellent genetic backing, because the dominants, the higher bourgeois, do have "dominance" traits. By normal laws of heredity, one expects to find their propagation. Their propagation was buttressed by another factor — that royalty tended to intermarry. To reach the initial position of royalty, "strong men" became by force and prowess leaders of nations. These powerful genes were passed down. A further strengthening of the gene pool occurred by hybridization, resulting in so excellent a royal line as the Ptolemy's of Egypt. The inbreeding they practiced was a hoarding mechanism to preserve their superior genetic pool.

Two forces — one inbreeding and the other intra-royal marriage — contributed to early successes of royalty. A third factor contributed strength to the regals' well-being. That was the violent introduction of a usurper, a challenger or a conqueror who introduced his own strong bloodline.

Acting against these forces was the monarch who married a peasant girl. This may not have been very important because the dominant genes may be expressed only by the male. However, there are startling instances in history when genetic aberrations may have taken place to produce strong feminine leaders such as Elizabeth I of England and Catherine of Russia.

What was more important was when the royal line, by a dereliction of morality, introduced worker genes which resulted in heterozygosity — from some chance encounter with a stable boy. A series of kingly saps ensued which has been the undoing of royalty and required the frequent parting of heads from the bodies. They had neither the resolve nor ability to control or the strength to govern because of their inherent genetic pollution.

Dominant genes are a form of capitalism to accompany evolution of man. They represented control of the best territory, food supply, mates and progeny. But they also represented something more than the Russian Bolsheviks and their successors have been willing to admit — communists themselves, an example of privileged power. Higher echelons of the party, in their ability to control working classes, possessed privilege, which Lenin realized was an artificial creation. It was justified in that the party was always right. This insatiate revolutionary struggle for absolute power, the enormous privilege inherent in this political dictatorship, is so capitalistically genetic in scope that factory owners of the past pale to insignificance.

The fundamental concept of capitalism is control, utilization and exploitation of resources. Communist party domination is the highest of bourgeois capitalism. It not only exploits minds, initiative, and the lives of its subjects, but it exploits to its will, machinery, factory, and agriculture of the nation for its selfish purposes. The act of political power itself is privileged and possessive.

When one sees Khrushchev, Brezhnev or Gromyko dressed in fine business suits quaffing champagne or munching caviar in diplomatic hostings, when one sees the same well-fed men living in comfortable daccas, hotels, embassies and offices, when one reads their directives to the proletariat, issued in authoritarian format, western capitalistic factory owners marvel. When one sees their suppression of the workers' right to strike or the repression of culture, one cannot but conclude that these men wield the highest arbitrary capitalistic power on earth. They are the new Russian bourgeois which have carried capitalism to an ugly height. It was not destined to be held together by terror.

Within mental processes of revolutionists — socialist, communist, or anarchist — there is quandry, elements of social order never fits Utopian concepts of the "isms" they espouse.

A recent example is Daniele Cohn-Bendit, a young anarchistic leader who played a significant role in the May 1968 disturbances in France. Known as "Danny the Red," he co-authored a book concerning his political observations — *Obsolete Communism: The Left Wing Alternative.* It contains the usual immature, unrealistic chatter of the leftists, along with some disillusioning observations concerning the Soviets. What it contains most is a complete lack of knowledge of bioism, which is the science in political science.

The basic unit of any political body is its biologically programmed DNA. A faulty conception of the neurogenic basis is bound not only to invite quandry, but eventually complete failure in the aims of any of the promoted "isms." In other words, one must first be a biologist to interpret society deriving from genetic composition.

"Danny the Red," in describing the upheaval in 1968, says it ". . . failed precisely because the workers themselves failed to take the next logical step; to run the economy by themselves as free and equal partners." He quotes Condray, "It should be said firmly and calmly in May 1968 in France, the industrial proletariat, far from being the revolutionary vanguard of society, was its dumb rearguard."

Danny goes on to say that the failure cannot be explained in terms of treachery by working-class organizations, nor can you condemn the ideological sibmissiveness and servility of the wage-slaves. And he goes on to bemoan the fact that the working class has been split into distinct strata: unskilled workers as robots, then skilled craftsmen, then technical experts, science and management, differing from the Marxist concept of a vast mass of impoverished workers on the one hand and a few wealthy capitalists on the other.

What Karl, Friedrich, Ilyich, and "Danny the Red" have failed to comprehend is that the workers are born workers. They couldn't lead if they wanted to. History is replete with examples of the conquest of the proletarian mind. It was not the proletariat working class which enslaved themselves in Russia, it was the dominant bourgeois Communist Party with its bloody commissars who mustered force to kill White Russians and return to economic slavery the working masses. "Danny the Red" couldn't understand the lethargy of the French proletariat because it is inherently lethargic in the field of dominance and leadership.

That is not to say that the working class lacks muscle power, patience or endurance, nor is it to say that they do not make courageous and brave soldiers, noble in sacrifice and heroism. Nor is it to say that they are dumb clods without feeling, emotion, humanity or humility. To be sure, they are not without love, charity or mercy. What they do lack, however, is initiative and leadership.

I recently saw 2,000 aircraft workmen stand obediently in a cold parkway of a northern factory to hear their president upbraid them for laziness and faltering production. Had there been only a few dominants in the group, they would have pulled him from his perch to mete out righteous indignation. Labor leaders know that unions are created, cemented, and homaged by small groups of paid gangsters, agitators, foreigners and hoodlums, hired to direct and wield the unchallenging masses. This is biologically the way animal society arose. It is no different today, whether the chiefs be capitalists employing Pinkerton guards or employing professional hoodlum agitators. The masses follow — the few direct. It has been wisely observed that present-day labor leaders wield more tyrannical power and live in greater luxury than most of the older hard-line capitalist factory owners.

"Danny the Red" noted that the communists as well as the Trotskyites and Maoists look upon the proletariat as a mass that needs to be directed from above. Even Lenin argued that the proletariat is unable to reach an understanding of society and tends to adopt bourgeois ideology. Therefore, the party is to be its natural spokesman and the defender of the working class.

What they have observed and not stated is that the working class stands apart. It cannot respond as they hope it should. The lack of initiative is not due to any fault of education, opportunity or indoctrination. What underlines the docility is stark genetic inheritance which has programmed the workers for a passive role and which is responsible for the main innocence they exhibit in union affairs. Britain is finished unless a leader from the right terminates the present leadership by the irresponsible labor party.

Equalness, or equalitarianism, is the erroneous foundation upon which the classless society has been predicated. At the commencement of the 20th century there was the supposition that men were created equal. This was historically bolstered by its inclusion in the American Declaration of Independence. The thought basis, although charming and charitable in nature, arises out of 18th century philosophies and revolutions, but has no actuality in science.

Men are not created equal. They never have been and they never will be, unless it be rare similarity of identical twins, and even they have fundamental, environmental differences. Still unrecognized is the stupendously shattering organic chemical revelations of human genetics. There is no longer opposition to the emerging fundamentals of this titanic science. Man from the very moment of reduction division and crossover, from the moment of recombined amino sequences, altered, mutated, and influenced the fertilized egg or zygote, egresses into being creating new and radically different individuals.

We recognize human differences — that no two of us are structured equally. Yet there was a tendency with the socio-communist movements to regard all as potpourri of classless soup, wherein minor variations could flourish and develop. Much as one regards an evergreen forest as a unique plant species, the human forest was to be regarded with equal measure. Destruction of monarchies and aristrocracy, challenges by democracy and republicanism, the snide reference to dictatorship — are all a part of the "we are all equal" principle.

Great movements, communism, socialism, and even anarchism, dictatorship, autocracy, fascism, Maoism — are instruments of political science in the control of human societies. All are based on theory and philosophy, not on biological fact. High credit must be given to democracy, capitalism, and the free enterprise system, for here, in reality, the floration of the individual is permitted, duplicating the historic anthropologic and evolutionary nature of man. Political science is a most inexact and temporal field dissected by hypothesis and riddled by supposition. On the other hand, bioism, the science of genetic combination, is rooted in definitiveness of the mathematics of the amino acids. What is emerging from physiological and physical testing is that it will shortly be possible to catalog humans on a numerical basis.

What shocked Bolshevik revolutionists was that they succeeded. The prize fell to them with hardly a shot fired. They were standing on the right corner at the right time when the historic bus pulled into sight. Its Russian conductor, who was old, tired, war-weary, riddled with confusion and dissention, was merely shoved aside in the November 7, 1917 armed insurrection which, according to eye witnesses, resulted in no more than a dozen casualties.

Through the ensuing years of the Civil War, 1918-1921, when the Red Army was finally to dominate Russia, the world was trying to explain the success of the people's dictatorship theory, having rooted itself in the backward feudal state of the tzars.

According to revolutionary theology, mankind progressed from a feudal serf-state to the bourgeois democratic stage to achieve socialism. Something evidently went wrong. Back in April, 1919, Trotsky tried to explain it by saying that the erroneous conception arose out of the original sin of Menschivism. England, and then France, then Germany, should have been the first to succumb to the banners of communist dictatorship, yet who was to argue with success? They had achieved their springboard and now the rest of the world was to be redeemed.

Something did go wrong with the theory. There was an inverted order. Communism and the dictatorship of the proletariat did pass facilely, directly from the feudal-serf stage in the backward nation of Russia, without having to go through the bourgeois democratic stage — the stage of well-developed capitalism, democracy. This was unforseen by the revolutionary prophets.

Nevertheless, new formulae held true when, after the great Chinese Revolution, the People's Republic came into being in 1949. It was a worker-peasant coalition in one of the world's most backward nations which suddenly thrust itself out of the feudal-peasant stage directly into the celestial abode of socialism. Two great masses of people and land had emerged from the Dark Ages into the light of absolute tyranny and controlled thought.

What is significant is that no other nation that is capitalistically competent, adopted the communist-socialistic schema. There are many nations that fly the Red flag, but they only do so because they were sold out by politicians, or came to power with help of capitalists such as Castro's Cuba, where he treacherously deluded backers that he was fighting as a democrat for the people. There are those within capitalistic nations who do not understand the menace and murderous tyranny of communists. Therefore, they innocently aid and abet the formation of the mass prisons. If we examine closely the formula for three stages to develop government, it could not be conceivable that the true route of humanity in evolutionary progress is from feudal serfdom to capitalistic democracy to socialism; the latter being nothing more than a 20th century authoritarian device to control the masses.

Khrushchev, the late Soviet leader, bombastically bragged that the communists would bury the capitalists. He intimately believed — as do all communists and socialists — that they will one day inherit the earth. It may come as a stupendous blow to them to know that capitalism is the final and only destination of society, because it is based within the actual chemistry of the genes that reside in all human beings. It is possible, in the late 20th century or early 21st century, that we may see both Russia and China convert to capitalism in the wake of smoldering cities and decaying economics following territorial and ideological struggle.

Their people will have had enough of war and oppression by dictators to be ripe for the resumption of a humane society within the mold originally intended, namely, to judge each man his worth according to his biological inheritance and productivity. Class strata is the expression of anthropological development. To eliminate it, Red armies will have to line their officers against a wall and liquidate them. Consider Russian hierarchy from this newspaper article:

Soviet Reds Undergo Purge

"Millions of comrades are being investigated to determine their fitness to carry the little red card that labels them among the elite members of the Soviet communist party.

"It's the first party purge in 19 years. Everyone of the nation's 14,455,321 card holders is subject to the purge. It will take two years to complete, and no one knows how many will be expelled from the party.

"A tame version of Mao Tse-tung's Cultural Revolution, the 'card exchange' was devised by party chieftain Leonid Brezhnev two years ago to 'cleanse' the party of 'passive and indifferent' comrades.

"Special investigative committees have been set up at every level of society, from the small state farm to government ministries, to study members' 'everyday behavior and ideological, political and professional standards.'

"Behind the ideological rhetoric is a determined Kremlin effort to boost the stagnant economy, revitalize party ranks, crush growing corruption and strengthen the party's influence in Soviet society.

"Members have had to turn in their cards for renewal. Only those whose records meet the required standards will get them back with the stamp of approval as the 'finest, worthiest representatives of the Soviet people.'

"Party members control virtually every aspect of political, military and economic life in this country.

"Numbering only 6% of the population, they wield at least 95% of the power.

"The main targets of the purge are those who have contributed to the failure of many of the party's national economic plans.

"A few party officials are immune. They include Brezhnev, his 14 colleagues on the Politburo, the military leadership and scientific elite.

"The purge, which began last fall, is the sixth in Soviet history. The worst was one of Stalin's in the 1930s, when nearly a million party members were shot. But Brezhnev has assured the people that 'under current conditions, the party can keep its ranks pure without resorting to such measures.'"

Biological base is the hope of the future. Western nations must ready themselves to exploit it. Instead of wringing hands and shaking heads when a capitalistic dictator comes to power, as in Chile and in Franco's Spain, they should reflect on the hells of communistic socialism, and thank God for men such as Franco who gave the Spanish 37 years of peace and prosperity and saved magnificent people from slavery.

What may happen is that the liberals, the criminals of biological society, will hand the padlock to communists without firing a shot. Severe taxes discourage initiative of higher-class biological producers and rewards the slovenly with little tax, foodstamps and welfare programs. This leads to socialistic imprisonment. Without question, the masses must be cared for, fed and housed adequately according to their genetic contribution. To equalize economically and legally, the resplendent range of DNA coding is a great injustice. The station to which men are born, by and large the great majority, appreciates the limitations of their biological positioning. They only resist it when some socialistic agitator succeeds in falsely propagandizing them.

Communism, anarchism, and socialism would, indeed, be the wave of the future if human DNA coding was identical. First priority for existence is wide genetic divergence. It is for this reason "isms" and schema ebb and flow across the pages of history. The true and final government shall be that which recognizes inequality and class structure.

An error of supreme magnitude in the struggle to dominate minds and bodies by political "isms" was the failure of capitalistically successful nations to realize they were being challenged. There should not be a square in any Russian city that is not dedicated to the memory of Franklin Delano Roosevelt. He can rightfully be regarded as the savior of communism. He was chief architect of Russian survival in the Second World War.

One cannot say that communism succeeds on its own merits. Lenin was transported in secret by capitalistic Germany to Russia in 1917 to commence the Bolshevik takeover under an impression that he would shorten the Russian participation in the war. That he did, but the capitalists, by aiding and abetting this criminal renegade, initiated a road to their own doom. Without capitalistic aid, communism would never be a threat. Roosevelt, Churchill, and the capitalists of monarchial Germany can be thanked for its initiation and perpetuation.

Beyond communistic collaborators in the western democracies is a great naivete in the capitalistic world concerning the ambition of communism. Never for one second have communists relinquished desires to dominate the earth, bury capitalism, and subject people to the yoke of Marxist-Leninist.

Yet, even if a certain number do understand these forceful motives, they sit back complacently without making the least efforts to counteract this nefarious political philosophy. They are content more often to excuse and defend communism, proposing that it isn't the same type as it was sixty-six years ago. Or, more facilely, merely compare arrays of statistics showing beneficisms of the capitalistic-democratic systems.

Never is the heart of the threatening beast attack. For that one must get down to solid refutations of the Marxist-Leninist venom. Capitalism never had to defend itself before. It is time it faces up to the impending conflict. Where communism scores its points is within the prejudices and stupidities of the proletariat, that large group of great muscle power and sweat and of small intelligent quotient and thought. Communists score point after point to lead by giving labor false impressions of power, pitting their small minds in jealous hatreds against upper classes or rewarding and eulogizing their roles, paying them off in tin medals.

Hatred of the wealthy is not a difficult place to begin. It's extremely easy to covet thy neighbor's largess. The privileged passing-down of fortunes is something that particularly rankles in the gullets of the poor. Even when the inheritance of wealth is on solid and good genetic ground, when it is abused it cannot but anger and alienate the lower classes.

To transfer one's possessions from parents to offspring at the moment of quietus is not only a nobility of human consideration, but it is also strong genetic programming rooted in the evolutionary biology of society. In a society organized and moved into the manufacture of stone, wood, and bone implements, even hide clothing, it became obvious that some of these manufactured articles would outlive their owners. What commenced were communal inheritances to the whole tribe. With genetic refinement, private property passed to the descendants' heirs.

Hand in glove with the favoring of offspring is the development of society which demands selection-survival from all its members. So, while society with its interdependence of members and their inequalities is of high importance, genetic legacy can result in none other than false social programming.

A striking example of the genetic compulsion to provide survival for offspring posthumously is the Rockefeller family. Their fantastic wealth from the 19th century has been transferred and enlarged to ensuing generations. This is natural with the rest of capitalistic society, which in like fashion, transfers that which they have to their offspring. It is a remarkable observation that within the firmly established capitalistic societies there is little reaction to these massive transferrals of wealth from generation to generation. Partially because they are glossed over by the creation of philanthropic imagery in the wealthy, a devotion to civic betterment, and the fact or not the fact that high inheritance taxes are paid. These are some of the ways to deceive the poor proletariat that the wealthy are his benefactors. It demands good public relations and funds being doled out to news media. So be it. This is one of the things that makes capitalism and entrepreneurism magnificent. Men can be wealthy, strong and successful, and can pass funds unto their descendants.

Yet, if it is something we admire and are not jealous of, it is only because we are in relatively fortunate economic position. Here is where communists make time. Where poverty exists, where grievances are rampant, communist agitators move in to poison the minds of the masses. Leon Trotsky felt it would only be a matter of time before America went communistic. His philosophic followers believe likewise today. The disastrous great Depression of the '30s and the defeat in the long, irritating Vietnam War with its massive American people's protest, makes us wonder why communism has not made greater inroads into American society. Yet the communists say, "We shall be patient until capitalist society makes an error it is bound to make — a long, protracted, unsuccessful war from which results national dissention and privation." They're waiting! But for them to succeed in communizing America they will have to gain control over the philosophic thought of the proletariat.

I was renting an apartment to an associate college professor. He was bearded, wore a band around his straggly, unkempt hair, smoked much, was recently divorced. It was after the oil boycott and after the price of oil had shot up. I mentioned that in the future heat in the apartment would have to be curtailed. There could not be waste. I explained what I did personally to conserve energy. He shot back at me angrily, "Do you think for one damn second that rich people are going to conserve heat and lower their thermostats?" I never forgot that, or the defiance with which he presented his point. It had never occurred to me that wealthy people did not have to conserve energy. It had never crossed my mind that while I had to conserve energy, with their money the rich didn't. Here was a hippy-style college professor living on the beneficence that a great state was allowing him, far out of proportion to his productivity, and he was poisoning, I am sure, every class he taught with insidious seeds of class hatred.

It was a strange psychological revelation. I went back to my apartment, turned up a thermostat, and said to myself, "If they have heat, I can have heat." After reflection, I turned it back down, thinking that if some people want to be pigs, they can be just that. Yet the seed had been skilfully planted. It was rich people who had their thermostats set at 80 degrees, while I put mine at 68 degrees and put on a sweater.

Class hatred is so easy to engender that the communists have used it as their major tool in acquisition of power. What has to be thought about seriously is how does the capitalistic world improve their image and especially its glaring abuses. Inheritance taxes have failed because they are side-stepped by foundations and batteries of rich attorneys who only the very rich can employ. Neither are the super-rich about to reform themselves. The errors of the few being so glaring and privileged may bring down the entire house upon the heads of the educated, intelligent, moderately rich, property owner bourgeois.

The subtlest of all forms of socialistic propaganda is the repeated revelations concerning wealth, holdings, and privileges of the super-rich. They are too strong and powerful to dismantle their empires; nor is anyone in the capitalistic systems going to ask them to do so. England, unfortunately, has gone along that downward economic trail by destroying the economic advantages of her upper classes with severe and unreasonable taxation.

It is a cross on which the entirety of capitalistic society will be nailed if it is not reformed. No public relations teams, no governmental propaganda is going to take this weapon from the socialistic agitators unless in every capitalistic nation there are limitations to the size of capital acquisition, and this limitation can be very generous but not excessively so. There, too, must be a limitation and a cut-off to inheritances, at least a third generation from that of the first. In good times no one need worry, but in troubled times and with the advent of rising communistic penetration into capitalistic society, this situation has to be resolved — to remove one of the strongest converting tools in a communistic ideology. It is undoubtedly against the spirit of the entrepreneur and the highly successful that a ceiling be placed upon acquisition of great wealth. But such is the case, and without it the proletariat may run rampant.

In primitive societies there was an obligation which was enforced by social pressures that the wealthy distribute and share their material advantage. Whether it be conquering heroes traversing European Roman roads throwing out coins, or the elderly billionaire, Rockefeller Sr., a kindly old man, passing dimes to children, or be it feasts, alms, bonuses, philanthropies, donations or income taxes — society demands excessive wealth be shared. This is genetic inheritance and prudence.

Philanthropy masks man's avariciousness and acquired estate, but further provides protection. For the wealthy it's good business to share wealth ostentatiously. Nothing infuriated lower-class Americans more than when they learned that hundreds of millionaires paid no tax — President Nixon paid none — working an evasive scheme. Jealousy is rooted genetic instinct. In cultures that are limited economically and where few own anything, anthropologists have detailed communal living in which property is shared equally. Yet the underlying premise here is that there is no great gap in material possessions.

Liberty is a word that carries revolution into being. Underlying impetus is disparity of wealth. Beggars and starving people can never be regarded lightly by wealthy masters. Our own revolution paid lip service to liberty. The great cry was "taxation without representation." If there was no taxation, it would have gone past the board. Freedom and representation are magnificent words. Yet our civil war with a shouting to end slavery was fought to coerce the South back into the Union, an economic matter. The South fought to maintain its economic position by way of cheap labor, namely slaves.

When one says that the root of all evil is money, it is certainly the supreme adage of war. We weren't in World War I to save democracy. We were in to save the economy of England to beat down worldwide encroachments of German commercialism. World War II was another goof-off with a homogenous people wishing to expand their territoriality. That required subjugation and annihilation of conquered peoples in the manner Anglo-Saxon American colonists won the West by genociding the Mongoloid natives (Indians.).

Germany's march for land in World War II and the American conquest of the West was in the spirit of evolutionary tradition. One succeeded. The other failed. These massively violent eruptions of modern society are natural selection techniques, multiplied thousandfold in which survival of the fittest and the most prolific achieve goals incorporated within body chemistry by group action.

The two super-powers, China and Russia, will engage in titanic apocalyptic death struggle. They are on biological collision course. Their territorial disputes will be resolved by conflict. Their racial antitheses, yellow and white, are the heart of the antagonism. A yellow-white war already incipient has instinctive traits going for it — territoriality and racial antagonism. One can forget communist mumbo-jumbo concerning Marxist revisionists and who interprets the role of communism best.

Within society is the instinctive jealous hatred of wealth by the "have-not" proletariat. So long as there is inequality in wealth, as the proletariat are made aware and agitated by Marxists, it will be number-one problem when comes depressions or long, unsuccessful wars. Do not imagine that the proletariat will fight on the privileged side of the upper bourgeois. Years ago communications were poor. Today the populists can be incited rapidly. If America is to win against communists, socialists, sick liberals that are ensconced in the legislature and highest courts, then this problem must be dealt with hastily. Prohibition that wealth may not descend to the third generation. It will be a weapon in revolution to the right. The right must reform itself before it can gain loyalty from the broad proletarian mass.

The most profound political event in history was the coming of Christ and the radiation of Christianity. Based on Divine Trinity, God the Father, Christ the Messiah and Son, and the Holy Ghost, that ethereal being, the spirit of religion provided mankind with first-rate characters to play out underlying religious genes which were selected toward in societies' evolution. Religious genes provide solace and metaphysical interpretation of abstract spiritual value. They have little to do with physical nourishment. Merciless wars raged over the interpretation of spiritualized chemicals.

In the 19th century, another cosmic event of a similar trinity erupted. This trinity, unrecognizing biological religious components within man, concentrated upon an opposite tract; namely, the control of man's production. The key point was the physical welfare of mankind — unshackling him from the more successful groups of humans who were established in power — who were primarily a capitalistic economic system and who exercised severe control over peasant-worker elements.

"God," in the name of Karl Marx, was Jewish — a bitter, bearded, fat German. He wrote concerning a new economic system, although he was never successful enough to make sufficient money to care properly for his family. Possessing hateful obsessions against the wealthy and successful, he advocated the abolishment of private property. In 1852, living in London, England, he had insufficient funds to bury his young daughter Jenny and, in the same year, for ten days, he fed his family only bread and potatoes. From this neurotic hatred of the capitalistic system came the most vicious literature of all time, that proposed abandoning religion, capitalism, private property, and placed workers as supreme dictators above the successful and established business people and government. His works are a crazy quilt of venomous propaganda against everything decent, advocating change by bloody revolution.

Little did the world know that this "God of Vengeance" preaching hatred from his failed existence would incite the ignorant, would arouse the malcontents to spawn protracted revolutions that changed the political nature of earth. His economic theories have since been widely discredited, even among the intellectual Russians today. Yet Marx remains the "God with the Bible" to millions of fanatical followers.

The "Son of God" was Vladimir Ilyich Lenin, who swept to power in the Bolshevik Revolution of 1919. He lies deified today in a mausoleum in Moscow, where the faithful pay continuous tribute to this supposed liberator of the masses.

Lenin was followed by Stalin, "High Priest" and liquidator of the masses. What rounded out the Divine Economic Trinity was Leon Trotsky, the

"Holy Ghost." It is through the eyes of his writings that we see the true nature of communistic movements, for he was the one who led the October revolution. After being exiled, he haunted Stalin and the bloody oppressive bureaucratic regime. Stalin succeeded in having a Mexican drive a pick-axe through his skull.

What is so fascinating about Trotsky is that, apparently, the man was totally sincere. He truly believed the Marxian system was the ideology proper for the salvation and welfare of mankind. What he did not know, nor did any of the "Economic Trinity," was that equality of man is myth. Great scientific advancements, biology, genetics, and anthropology was not theirs to formulate a rational ideology. Their oppressed workers were not equal with the bourgeois. To speak of a classless society is to speak with philosophical wishful thinking. Mankind is spewed out with varied genetic abilities and coded into classes. The workers will always remain workers, mesomorphic, lesser intelligenced, less searching in goals and motivation, more primitively adaptable and culturally slavish. Through no fault of their own, they cannot compete with the upper classes. It was not intended they should compete, but merely perform their tasks within society so that society could be advanced.

Such great human inequality does not mean that workers should be oppressed, harassed or exploited. No society wishes this upon its lowest half. It was a matter of economic conditions which set the stage. Both capitalism and communism are dedicated to the working class. The former recognizes biological truth of inequality, while the latter insists on a lower-class dictatorship over better-bred elements. One sees coal miners and garbage collectors persecuting Nobel prize winners.

Leon Trotsky typified the soul, the beauty — if there is any — in permanent revolution of the communist movement. He was a true liberal-leftist-socialist — a fact which is camouflaged. Liberal U.S. Senators and liberal Supreme Court judges are as much communist bent as the "Divine Economic Trinity." These synonomous words — liberal, socialist, leftist, communist — typify the groupings today.

Leon Trotsky, a Ukrainian Jew, was born in 1879. By the age of 19 he was a confirmed Marxist and union organizer leading strikes and demonstrations and printing subversive literature. He landed in prison and was deported to Siberia for four years. By 1902 he had joined a team of Marxist radicals in London. At the outbreak of the first Russian revolution, he hurried back to St. Petersburg to participate. By 1907, defeated, he was sentenced to life imprisonment in Siberia, but succeeded in fleeing to Western Europe.

From the foregoing, at so early an age, we are able to surmise the tormenting genes of criminality and anti-social behavior that surged within Trotsky. He was a compulsive revolutionist, a staunch agitator, and a propagandist. Such behavior is rare. It originates in the breakup of established society. There was survival value here in evolutionary social selection.

Emissions of these rare recessive genes permitted overthrow of dominants with new pioneering horizons being engendered. Individuals moved their tribes out of established but drying-up wastelands or moved them further south when the glaciers descended on Europe. More than that, it may have been this revolutionary sport that took us out of the trees down unto the dangerous predator — infested savannas.

Too many times in history we have witnessed the success of social radicals throwing entire nations into bloody, senseless, murderous chaos to achieve a new type of political base. These rare bourgeois descendants grant a geneticism replete with drive, killer genes, and aggressive compulsive genes. In Trotsky's case, these were combined with genius, in the field of organizing and writing.

The "Divine Economic Trinity" — Marx, Lenin and Trostky, who fervently hated the upper classes and espoused the dictatorship by the proletariat of the bourgeois, were nonetheless themselves excellent examples of first-rate bourgeois. It was only Stalin, who came out of the peasant-mudded proletariat, as well as later, Nikita Khrushchev.

Yet how were these men to know that they were excellent examples of the bourgeois, with their good intellect, drive, and fight for possession of capital property? The highest type of capital resides in political control of human beings. Unfortunately, the biologic science of genetics was not far enough advanced, nor were those who could prophesy, from what the science had offered to date, that humans issue forth in specific unequaled class structure.

It is somewhat akin to the Periodic Table which Dimitri Mendellev discovered. Elements known to date fit into a mathematical regularity. Unknown elements were forecast and later discovered where the blank spaces existed. So it is today with the classes of men. It was Karl Marx himself, as well as other philosophers, who acquainted us with class society and numerated percentages. It simply remains for future geneticists, psychologists, and sociologists to fill in the grey areas.

Classless society was good philosophical propaganda which could delude anyone who didn't have education in biology. No one is going to admit they are unequal, even when they know it. It was a fantastic sales pitch, and still is for communists. Even with formal education, workers of the proletariat have but to look around into areas of excellence wherein bourgeois owners reside. Inequality was countered by the false assertion that the proletariat did not have the opportunity for proper education and career promotion. This stance has been disproven by studies which show that not only do some races do poorly and have greater percentages of proletariat, but that entire sectors of the population are non-redeemable to higher achievement, no matter how much first-rate education they are provided.

Trotsky was aware of this problem. He observed that the human race has the right to be proud of Aristotle, Shakespeare, Darwin, Beethoven, Geothe, Marx, and Edison. He asked, "Why are these people so rare?" And then he answered, "Above all, because almost without exception they came out of the upper and middle classes. Apart from rare exceptions, the sparks of genius in the suppressed depths of the people are choked before they can burst into flame."

Here was his error in conception. Intelligence tests and personality tests have been in valid use for a quarter of a century. The workers simply don't

have the I.Q. Parental genes have to be excellent to promote genius. If, by
occasion, genius does emerge in a poor working family, you may be quite
sure that before that life is ended, there will be a change in some phase of
society which will express his superior code. "Genius will out" — the adage
goes. . . . Never fear it.

Marx, Lenin and Trotsky would roll in their graves if they knew that
they typify the highest of the bourgeois class. And that Stalin and Khrushchev who later denounced them, were both dyed-in-the-wool, non-intellec-
tual, manure-booted peasants. It devolves upon future biological study to set
the screwed political spectrum back into realistic form and dignity. Revolution to the right does not mean that the worker will be oppressed. It means
that all will contribute according to their genetic inheritance and each will
receive the fruits according to his contribution. Liberty is not for those who
will destroy classed society, but for those who will preserve it.

The Chinese communists are unswerving Marxist-Leninists and have not
revised its ideology. More emphasis is placed on the agriculture peasantry
than in emphasizing the industrial proletariat. It follows the same totalitarianism as Russia. Like all communistic regimes, it is obsessed with class
society. No matter how the words are uttered, including the national bourgeois which Mao envisioned to be part of a democratic dictatorship, later to
be followed by complete socialism, the thesis is erroneously based, as is all
communist doctrine, on the equality of man and, therefore, the necessity
to destroy class structure.

The founders of the United States of America, in the 1770's got sucked
into this philosophical nonsense. Both out of biological ignorance and a flare
for democratic propaganda carried to an extreme, they issued the now
famous phrase, "All men are created free and equal, . . . " This was, of
course, a lie, and it is doubtful if they themselves believed it. It made good
and startling copy for the beginnings of a nation. Being aristocrats, highly
bred and educated, some even possessing slaves and who, in the majority,
would have been shocked to feel that their words would have meaning which
would relate them to the Negro or the backwoods peasant. A half a century
later, even the great Darwin was not certain of the human relationship between the Negro and the white.

Nevertheless, the damage was done and a biological anomaly was proclaimed in the same name of legal equality. Namely, what was meant was
that all men were equal in the eyes of the law. This, too, is a sociological
disgrace because men of variously gened backgrounds do not receive similar
treatment before the law. Social workers have for a century deplored the
fact that the poor are improperly represented. In a nation like Russia, there
is no law which provides equality. The law is exactly what the communist
party and its dictators intended it to be.

There is a second factor which operates against the equality of men
before the law in any nation. Whereas the law may be concise and clear,
humane and just, it is standardized. What evokes the problem is that consistent standard is to be spread over and cover inconsistent and unstandardized
elements. This is not possible in even the realm of twisting facts to fit an
ideal. Varied genetic traits which characterize every human being cannot be

subject to uniformity.

You would have a hard time building a machine which would harvest at the same time tobacco, corn, and apples. It is here where the judge has been placed who tempers justice and individualizes edicts. In judgment we find not law that deals with equals, but that which fits the law to each individual.

How, then, is one to have true democratic justice if people may not be regarded as equal? First, one recognizes the postulate concerning human biological inequality, high genetic variance, and different organic propensities to commit crime or be amoral. If justice was really based upon American equality, President Nixon and the Watergate gang would have been serving long terms in striped suits.

A few places in which inequality before the law is recognized is where the defendants have psychiatrical problems or where the individual was acting under the influence of alcohol — these two states set apart the defendant as equal before the law. While we recognize these two conditions, there are hundreds of other normal genetic variances which can also be considered as inequalities and that should share equal deliberation.

Obviously, the law breaks down in such areas as homosexuality. These people have been persecuted, jailed, murdered and disgraced for none other crime than the normal dictates of their bodies and genes. Prostitutes have been flung into prison, shunned and ostracized when they did little more than what their natural biological instincts prompted. Take a woman of lower mentality with normal sexual drive away from an impoverished family, a social condition founded on genetics, and you can't expect her to act like Queen Isabel.

Youths who commit horrible crimes of aggression are not impelled necessarily by deprivation, but are unstably urged by their proletariat genetic constitution. You place here a pinch of mesomorph, a lowered intelligence, a quotient of neural aggressivity, a heightened flashpoint hormonal network, and you have ingredients of the habitual criminal. Forget society and its supposed cultural creation of criminals. Once the placental cord is tied, you may have on your hands a potential criminal. In the congestion and slums of large cities there are environmental pressures which bring forth the underlying genetic expressions.

Years ago it was felt that by examining a series of pictures or making a series of measurements of the head, one could detect criminal types. Such theories were roundly rejected, but that was only because the information ventured was not sufficient. If, instead of pictures they had used colored television of movements, expressions and mechanisms of a person or a battery of personality, intelligence and morality tests, one would have no trouble recognizing the criminal type without benefit of a police record. Criminality is in the genes, the type ranges throughout the social classes according to their expression.

Communism is the absolute form of labor exploitation and oppression. Whereas, in the western world, the biological genetics of citizenry has stratified according to capacities acting within a free market society, the communists render the majority of its citizens salt-and-pepper porridge, floating as unidentifiable specks within an ocean of oneness and despair.

Rarely has it been realized, with justification to the Leninist principle of oneness, that the majority of humans are of proletariat stock. They are the serfs of the tzars, the foot soldiers of the Caesars, the slaves of the American Southerners — they are the workers of Detroit, the longshoremen of Britain, the olive-pickers of Italy. They are a homogeneous group which, in the development of society from the time of emerging Homo sapiens, were entrusted with mesomorphic subservient tasks.

Outside this group, as was recognized by Lenin and Marx, is the bourgeois group, the supposedly oppressive capitalists, military hierarchy, religious hierarchy, and bureaucracy. It is from this predetermined group that come the directors of society, for better or for worse. It is also within this group that the widest human variations exist and where erupts continuous problems.

It has always been easy to structure society by tests as intelligence. Here the multiple-gened cerebral coding takes the form of a normal probability bell curve flaring out to a few geniuses at one end and a few morons at the other, the majority remaining in the center. Regardless of what this curve measures, it is not society. From the phone book listings of the Yellow Pages to the programs broadcast on TV or radio, to the amount of pages of the newspapers that are devoted to sports, serious books compared with trash, it will be gleaned that human success does not lie in a bell curve.

Class cleavages appear in the fashion Lenin and Mao rant about. The sweaty proletariat is there with beer, bread and cheese, its coarse language, inane sports events, fantastic stupidity and lack of drive, right across the board for at least a good 60% of the western world and up to 80% or 90% in the communist slave world. This group is homogeneous, predictable, and leaderless, possessing all the tragico-comic range of human emotion, all the supreme faith and devotion of servants. They have none of the higher attributes to control their spontaneous excesses . . . and so herein resides the higher percentage of crime.

Within the bourgeois one finds wide variability necessary for social evolution, exploration, and radiation. This variability blocks itself into distinct classes and occupations. Although religious genes permeate strongly into proletariat mass, in higher exponents of society they remain sparse or live a suspended existence. Military leaders come directly out of the mold. Yet it does not mean they are true dominants. For example, Eisenhower was a military leader, but MacArthur was both a military leader and a born dominant. His nemisis, Harry Truman, was a cunning politician who jackal-like always circled outside the dominants, awaiting opportunity. Politicians are genetic freaks which, by ruse rather than force, permit their evolutionary selection to give the world its gravest challenges.

A large imbalance came out of the tribes of prehistoric man where they had formerly depended upon two or three dominants to formulate the policies of their small societies. Cleverness and cunning rivaled honesty, strength, and determination. It was a light quarterback running the ball against brutish, heavy, and not-too-bright dominants. Emphasis was placed on survival, and this depended upon ruse and clever brains. So we selected toward the deceitful and treacherous, which operated with love and family within the group. Dominants are still produced today and are to be found majorily within the academic world and the business communities. The politician has few genes of conscience or morality. He is universally distrusted. Politics outranks honesty, sportsmanship, and reliance.

Mao diverged from orthodox Marxist-Leninist doctrine concerning which should be the revolutionary vanguard. He chose poor peasantry over the urban proletariat. Both are of the same genetic constitution; yet in Mao's case, it was a matter of strategy, the peasants being more readily aligned into the cause. Lenin used land hunger of the Russian peasant as a prompting agent. The propaganda force was important, as was the recognition that this was a huge homogeneous, gullible geneticism which, when cut adrift from hereditary leaders, could be molded in the most abusive totalitarianism.

There is a historic tendency to feel that from the writings of Marx and Trotsky that their ideology, the fight against oppression, their land reforms and promises of a classless society, were important facts in the march of the socialist Red banners. Nothing could be further from the truth. A half a century after the revolution, the standard of living in Russia is far below western nations, and they are still trammeled in the mire of a police state — human liberties having been suspended.

In 1917, if the Bolsheviks had promised followers green cheese, buttermilk and free brothels, the proletariat masses would have fought just as well. The proletariat was not fighting for Marxist and Leninist ideas. They were fighting like they have always fought when led by properly coordinated leaders. When they have something to overthrow or destroy which reminds them of their poverty, their devotion is superb.

In the bloody Civil War which ensued after the October revolution, there were plenty of White Russians fighting just as hard for the rights of capitalism and democracy. Chiang Kai-shek's armies strenuously withheld the communist force of Mao. As in all struggles with large masses of the proletariat, fortunes of war favor one side or the other. In this case it was the communists. Yet no one should be deluded that their victory was an ideological one. Had the Allies foreseen the specter of communism and understood it in 1917 and 1918 as it reared its ugly dictatorial form, there would have been no Russian communism. Too, had Franklin Roosevelt been less communist-socialistic, the Chinese would have never succeeded in their swing toward communism. There are other communist regimes today . . . but here again, the proletariat are pawns within the plans of the bourgeois. You can substitute any double-talk for communism. If properly presented, the proletariat will bite at it because they have no sense. They await only incantations of high priests, passions to be incited by self-promoting press and labor-gened rabble-rousers, and they are off.

One of the problems raised during the American Vietnam War was the frequent comments that no one knew what they were fighting for, including the soldiers. Yet they fought, and bravely, too. The cock-and-bull theory from some nit-wits in the State Department concerning a domino theory — one down and the rest fall — was proved to be utter trash. The great mass of proletariat had been aroused. Forward they marched to the pleasant hum of armament and weapons' factories, to cash jingling in banks and to militaristic adventure-seekers. It wasn't until the proletariat and a goodly portion of the bourgeois, after seven frustrating years, said "Enough!" that through student riots and public protests, they were able to drive President Johnson out of office.

It was tragedy. Brave men forced into a bottomless quagmire of Asiatic war in which over 50,000 perished. And for what? Final defeat. It points up the extreme resiliency and unswerving devotion in which the proletariat may be mustered for almost any cause, just or not. Now Americans are calling that war an unjust war. It was not the lack of ideological propaganda that brought defeat and an end to the war, it was that the proletariat can be taken just so far, so long. Any Madison Avenue slogans will suffice — any propagandized press and TV media lies will prompt and any lying president will set the mass into motion. That mass has a limit to endurance. But it has no true basic ideology, be it communistic or democratic — it merely obeys.

Men will wage long and cruel wars for the slimiest of reasons. Take religious wars as an illustration. Religious funds go one way — that is, into the hands of robed soothsayers who deal out the mystifying supernatural unknown not-to-be-questioned testaments. In honesty to those that pay admission fee and contain within their genetic structure religiously-oriented metaphysical thought, these people receive spiritual sustenance, comfort, and hope.

Aside from counseling, nothing material derives from religion, excepting those fortunate enough to administer its earthly coffers. So when you take large bodies of men in the poorest of times, surrounded by plagues, send them across half the length of the known world under the most arduous conditions to rescue the tomb of Christ from the Infidels, one can say that such men fought not so much for profit but for the mere act of placing their proletariat bodies in armed conflict to serve willingly bourgeois dominantly-gened masters.

It was not only the Crusades that were the farce of the Middle Ages; there were massacres such as those of St. Bartholomew's Day. The French Catholics slaughtered ten thousand men, women and children, the Huguenot Protestants. Add to that religious wars which ravaged Europe in the Dark Ages and emerging Renaissance, even up to the present day, it is good copy to ring into the moral justification for mass slaughter, some form of standard religious sponsorship. One day again, we shall effectively use it as Christian and Jewish banners are unfurled flying high the Cross and Star blazing in nuclear light as we righteously counter Godless Red drapes of communists.

Men march forth not out of slogan or reasoning, but because of underlying genetic composition. The strongest forces impelling men into wars doom are genetic — the salvation of tribal and national biology, characteristic culture, and language resulting from that biology and, finally, instinctive receptiveness of workers to be mobilized by dominants. Lenin, Trotsky Mao, and the like, could as easily waved a lemon-tree banner proclaiming some absurd slogan as "Humans united for humans and forward to oppres the oppressors," and still succeed.

The Soviets are pointing with pride to industrial and military accom plishments and raising their standard of living. With such a large nation, Russian success may have little to do with the precepts of Leninism, Marxism or communism. It could have been a backward geneticism which was ready to ignite in the same manner the U.S.A. mushroomed in the early 20th century.

Even when one compares today the per capita of gross national product of the United States [in 1975], $6200 and only 2% illiteracy with the USSR of a per capita GNP of $1530 and 1% illiteracy and communist China with a GNP of $170 and an illiteracy of 75%, one may be sure that beside the German scientists they stole to give them nuclear and space knowledge, with the help of the Rooseveltian American communists, they are far in arrears. Capitalism proves itself as the superior system. There isn't a single free Western European nation that doesn't outdo the communists.

That which would make Karl Marx and Friedrich Engles recoil would be the knowledge that it was characteristic for ten million years in man's history the bourgeois was father to the proletariat. Not father in political thought, but full-blooded hierarchial father.

One of the reasons the proletariat class has so degenerated was observed by Carrel: Lower classes mixing genes among themselves provide little opportunity for human advancement. Though eugenics sounds like a nasty word because it would deprive someone of equalitarian plantings, never forget that the human race evolved by privileged mating of dominant males with almost a totality of child-bearing females.

Examine such ancient customs as the *Droit du Seigneur*, whereby the owner of the castle spent the first night with the peasant's new bride. Or in the Southern plantation where the white master commenced the process of white-izing Negro blood to a percentage wherein the American Negro today transports 30% white genes. Consider the perpetual jokes about Turkish harems or the wives of King Solomon, right down to Brigham Young's polygamous Mormons, there is a strong genetic compulsion underlying dominants controlling sex.

A breeder of fine animals picks stock dominants. In human breeding, this is undemocratic heresy. Whether Marx or Lenin likes it, the upper bourgeois sired the human race. If any nation succeeds in liquidating their bourgeois, permitting paternity alone by the proletariat, it is duly bound to be the unique exhibit of garbage collectors, chambermaids, and stable boys. The masters of communism were behind the times. Gregor Mendel's treatise on inheritance was on the shelf. Unfortunately, there was no one to translate it for them.

Never fear, the proletariat "Reds" shall rule the earth. So long as divergent genes exist, there shall be capitalism, democracy, freedom, and socialism. Communists recognize class as oppressed workers and peasants — those who have overcome and displaced the bourgeois. This is fantasy. The proletariat exists, but they are incapable of eliminating the natural gened dominancy of the bourgeois.

In the western democracies we don't recognize the word "proletariat" as much as we understand its synonyms: agriculture class, working class, lower class. Ownership of property does not exempt them from being genetically proletariat, nor does educational achievement. In the checkout counter of any supermarket it is no task to spot the proletariat. A nicely-dressed black lady in front of me in a Puerto Rican market had run up a $93 bill, paying it with food stamps, the gift of northern politicians seeking votes. One half of her order was unnecessary, nothing to do with food sustenances — wines and liquors, paper towels, wrappings of all types, cartons of soda, junk food, etc. Had she not had stamps, she would have purchased prudently. But the proletariat does not have the mental power to purchase prudently. When excessive money is handed to them, they spend it like drunken sailors on shore leave — and you'd better believe that drunken sailors can spend!

Genetic incapacity of the proletariat is better understood by communists. Wasted muscle is wasted prosperity for all. If nothing better can be thought of, workers can be enlisted in government projects such as construction and reparation of slums. It is the underbelly weakness of the democratic system. Its muscle is permitted to atrophy because of the economy. By and large, workers are not asking for handouts. It is an obligation of good government that there be no such thing as unemployment — or unemployment benefits.

In communism there is small opportunity to be wasteful of workers. The maximum amount of work is attempted to be withdrawn from citizens, and they are given in return what the communist leaders want to give them. No back talk tolerated. It is excellent economic strategy. For in this class of people one is dealing with children that must be fathered and directed.

In the western democracies, since each person is equated with one vote, the economic attitude is that there should be almost equal distribution of wealth. Bear in mind the communists do not equate people as equal, nor do they distribute the power equally or wealth equally. Yet here, the capitalists say, "You don't have to work. We will pay you when you're unemployed. We will give you money and you may spend it as you see fit." — forgetting all the time that there are two gross errors in such logic. One, the mental combinations are not there to properly handle money due to biological inheritance. This is historic in the development of society where the majority of supervision of the lower class derived from the dominants. Unemployment benefits did not originate with the proletariat who needs constant, closely supervised fathering. It is capitalistic insanity.

Wealth in any nation resides in the brain of the bourgeois and the brawn of the workers. Once you pay them for unemployment, which is a type of enforced paid vacation, they contribute nothing toward productivity or the welfare of the citizenry as a whole. Seven million unemployed soon become parasites living off the government and other workers. Since money is given for nothing, only inflation, recession, and depression can follow.

If proletariat geneticism is properly used in the free world, as is forced labor in the communist world, there would be boundless prosperity. The saddest monopolistic privileged institutions in America are the hospitals and medical profession. Beds are scarce, labor is exhorbitant, and the prices cost an eye of the face. How extremely simple to say to a percentage of the unemployed, "We have sent your relief check to the hospital. Report there and pay the equivalent in labor. They in turn will deliver your unemployment check to you."

That which the western world has not comprehended is this large homogeneous genetic group is willing to work and obey. But they must be supervised by traditional dominants of their biology. You can't pass money to them under the guise of unemployment or social security. If they are capable, they must earn it. To pay for nothing, as the vicious practice of unemployment has developed, is an economic blind spot which can lead to inflation and recession. Kooky welfarism developed with the New Deal Rooseveltian click.

As society evolved there was not only stratification of class, but division of labor. There developed an economic system. Since man's success came about as a social animal, the selection and survival was toward tribal units which were most efficient. This led to the survival of those that had better hunters, fishermen, and gatherers. To achieve this important genetic advantage, there had to be cooperation.

Imagine society made up of dominants in which no one stepped aside. Suppose that there wasn't a mechanism which would determine "pecking order" or command. Or still better, think of armies going into battlefield facing one another with corporals and sergeants as the only commanders. Of course, they might do better than some armies with their rear-echelon elite. But in general, it would be chaos; an immediate internecine contestation for who should be supreme commander. One immediately will say that leaders will arise from the ranks. This is not so. Good geneticism of leadership has already been spoken for. It is why it is rare, in modern-day armies, to find leaders other than those that were carefully selected and trained in military academies.

Arbitrarily, the communists didn't do such a bad job when they grasped at class distinctions to erect their ideology. Their concept of the proletariat and the genetic concept of the proletariat could run anywhere from 60% to 85% of the total social mass — the remaining being occupied by the petty bourgeois. Top-ranking bourgeois possibly do not occupy more than 5% of the population. Here are high-ranking priests, soldiers, captains of industry, academic and scientific communities.

Newspaper editors, reporters, and politicians are seldom of this group. In America, when you deal with 5% of over 200,000,000 people, it gives you some 10,000,000 top-rank bourgeois. Cut it down in a city of 100,000 to come out with 5,000 which represent the genetic cream, is about right. Check phone books, courthouse records, and the banks for "Who's Who."

That leaves 10% for petty bourgeois. These are the knaves that commit white-collar crime, the politicians that embroil nations in wars, whose characteristic quality is deceit. They were selected toward outside of the dominants by Machiavellian abilities against others. Within this group also are professions such as teaching, nursing, police, white-collar workers, supervising and managerial personnel. Most professions are within the bourgeois rather than the petty class.

Is it strange that society should come up with three major classes? Since they are unequally divided, it makes good sense. Many armies have been structured in approximately similar fashion — 85% privates, corporals, sergeants, petty officers, 10% and 5% at the top.

From this we can see that in structuring an army, the underlying geneticism came out the exact way the underlying population genes dictated. When one examines society, he does not look at culture and foibles of man, he is looking directly at genetics.

Back in 1927, Mao stated that "hundreds of millions of peasants will rise like a mighty storm, like a hurricane, a force so swift and violent that no power, however great, will be able to hold it back, forward along the road to liberation." And so he was right. Unlike Lenin who regarded peasantry as only an auxiliary force in the proletariat revolution, Mao saw them as the vanguard. Here again, it was not a question of strategy, but a question of geneticism, the Russian urban working class being of a more advanced programming, while in the great sprawl of China, selection had been toward agricultural units.

Although the Chinese have high regard of themselves when they would take on a white race power such as Russia, they had better think more in terms of arms than population. When conflagration between these giants erupts, it will be settled by weapons. We see a similarity in the small island of Japan that had excellent homogeneity and the development of an isolated genetic pool providing drift from mainline China. With explosive violence and success, this warlike seed erupted upon the world scene in power and dominance, only to be nipped by superior technology of the Pacific East. Genetically, one can predict the Soviets will win. It is for this China reopened the door to America to counterbalance not only the paucity of technological and industrial development, but retardation within their masses.

In their civil war, both Mao and Chiang Kai-shek put on a good war show. This would not be the same as the yellow race confronting the white. Should America stay out of this impending conflict, which it will not because it is dominated by mild-minded politicians, it would be one rare opportunity in history to erect from ashes a non-socialistic biologic democracy. There will be no winners in that conflict. In the reconstructive process, mankind should think genetically and preserve its better strains.

Chinese communism was from the beginning obsessed with feudal landlords who were privileged for years. New York for decades held the same obsessions and tried to control the problem not by free enterprise, but by rent ceilings and restrictive controls which resulted in discouragement of construction, poor maintenance, and consequent slums.

One asks, what is the salvation for the bourgeois against the flood of the biologically inept? Each man can carry a gun. In sheer numbers it's almost an impossible contest, even with superior knowledge and skills. Yet the swing to the left in America has been avoided. Instinctive makeup of the proletariat is a willingness to follow upper-class leaders. After the October revolution, the Russians squared off in a bloody civil war; White Russians against Red Russians — the proletariat fighting on both sides. When the Red Russians ran up the victory flag, they had eliminated as many of the bourgeois as they could and embraced the remaining proletariat. This was revolution to the left. In Spain, in the 1930s, it was revolution to the right. Exactingly, Franco carried out the same system, eliminating proletariat, sparing bourgeois.

In both instances the proletariat masses nestled beneath bourgeois masters — the Communist Party and the Franco bureaucracy.

Early during the rise of Mao he classified peasants into three groups. Poor peasants he considered the main force in the bitter fight for the countryside. These were good "Red" material for propagandizing, for they were not afraid of losing anything. Many of them had "neither a tile over their heads nor a speck of land under their feet." A survey of Changsha County showed that they comprised 70%. This group was subdivided into two groups — 20% utterly destitute: mercenaries, hard laborers, wandering beggars, and 50% less destitute: with a little land, a little money, eat more than they earn, live in toil and distress.

Poor peasant class called by the gentry "riff-raff," was fertile soil for ideology. If Christian missionaries had been armed with rifles instead of Bibles, and had the backing of munition makers and militants rather than docile church groups interested in salvation, they could have led this mass of proletariat on a Christian crusade of force that would have shook the earth.

Of the highest 30% of social strata, Mao reserved for middle peasants; 20% of the landlords; and 10% of rich peasants. It is about the way social structure is divided in the west. What is forgotten in the biological social process of humans, no matter in what land or nation they are situated, no matter what ideology, they will space themselves in social stratification according to their underlying geneticism. That which permitted communism to root was not the social stratification or the abuse of it, but paucity of land, resources, and the challenge of the environment. There is an added collary: wealth of the genetic pool.

A right to unionize and strike are errors that democracies have committed. Little have they understood the underlying humanity. It is similar to telling high school students, "You don't have to come to class if you don't want to. You can have meetings or protest, close down the school, go on strike, or do what you want. This is your right." It would result in chaos. The dilemma of freedom in the high schools is skirted by the attitude that they are children, minors and consequently must come under rigid supervision. Yet, when we carry this principle to laboring masses who have little more intelligence, a smattering of knowledge and experience and because they are not of minor age, we say, "Que Bueno! Let them have their rights. Let them be at liberty to bring down and decrease the economy."

It is an error of social biology. The laboring class cannot be given freedom to do as it wishes. Within the mass of social organization they are adult children. They have far less intelligence than the bourgeois or capitalistic leaders. But they are so constituted that demands, goals, dreams, and ideals are far inferior to that of the upper classes. They go "gung-ho" about sports such as boxing where supposedly normal individuals pull on pairs of hard gloves and try to pummel each other into unconsciousness. If that isn't accomplished, they produce small petechial hemorrhages within the brain which later heal to produce punch-drunk morons. Their diet of TV and theater is indicative of mental reservoirs. So it is abnormality to permit those who for millions of years have been subject to leadership to bring leadership to its knees from childish whims. Politicians have thus created a monstrosity by permitting the stupid to lead. Industrial strikes are conducted by collectivized idiots and rarely do anything for economic welfare of a nation. No one understands better than the communists that these dumbheads — really nice people — are most fertile to incite to disturbance, rebellion, and destruction. Collectively they have no brains. A few Mafia agitators can work them at will.

Paradoxically, the nemesis of democracy shall be the "one man, one vote" idea. Under this ideal but false ideology, politicians play toward the masses, responding to their every whimper. It is not to say that the masses are not deserving of the best society can offer — that their grievances should not be properly adjusted — but that the emphasis is at the wrong end of social organization. Biological equality does not exist. To permit government by the majority in which at any time can be a coalition of uninformed citizens, is nothing more than "tyranny of the masses."

Minimum salary and limited working hours, extra compensation, laboring rights granted by leftist politicians. These legislative concepts conflict with biological rule. How can there be a minimum wage when each individual is unequal in production? It negates the most stunning creativity of all time. Human evolution is not ceilinged by edict, but prompted by the survival of the fittest — the rewarding of the ambitious and successful. Some men thrive on tremendous amounts of work, relish it. Others are downright lazy. Where is democracy when it is legislated what a man should be paid?

In 1937, Mao said, "In human history antagonism between classes exists as a peculiar manifestation as the struggle of opposites consider the contradiction between the exploiting and the exploited classes. Such contradictory classes co-existed . . . struggle with each other . . . develop to a certain stage . . . and develops into revolution."

What occurs in this quotation is that Mao shows how childishly ignorant he is. First, nonsense about contradiction is double-talk. It is a "mumbo-jumbo" of Marxism-Leninism similar to liturgy. It is something you say as a cover-up for a scientific explanation. The class of party communists are the world's leading example of the exploitation of class. Notably, the proletariat, by bourgeois and the petty bourgeois. There is no contradiction here. There is nothing but unexpurgated slave ownership with complete authoritarianism. Secondly, the concept of class struggle of opposites belongs in "Mother Goose" rhymes. From the remotest unto the distant class struggle is the method of society. What is interpreted as struggle is genetic inheritance which permits reign of dominants and specialists to assume control and direction over lesser gifted masses.

Whether it would be a blessing to have all relatively equal in biology and an exploitationless, classless society is of small debate. Unto the heavens we give thanks for the rich diversified geneticism which evolved, both individually and collectively in stratified groups as primates became socialized.

Mao sums up. "The law of contradiction in things — that is, the law of unity of opposites — is the fundamental law of nature and of society and, therefore, also the fundamental law of thought." How do you like that? Nowhere in nature is there unity. It is an environment which is constantly being challenged by organically chemicalized beings under laws of free competition by adaptability to the immediate problems. Revolutionary it is to be sure, but it has always been "revolution to the right" in which the capable evolve.

Marxism-Leninism bogs down in philosophical abstraction. They consider that so long as a state remains a state, it must bear a class character; it cannot be a state of a "whole people." When society becomes classless, there will no longer be a state. When the higher stage of communism is achieved, which is still not a reality in socialistic countries, then each will give according to his ability, to each according to his needs. Mao grants that it will take a long time to eliminate class differences between worker and peasant.

Such absolute dislogic as the absence of a state of classes within human society comes about by peculiar cerebral wiring. Intelligent people do not know what they are talking about. Yet they actually believe these exercises in false thought. There is something within the minds of many people which has an honest fixity which cannot be changed by the process of logic. These people have genetic receptors outside the mainstreams of normal cerebral physiology.

You don't have to look to communism alone to see divergent mental selectivity. All you have to do is read the writings of Sigmund Freud to conclude there are grey areas in normal-appearing people which preclude complete understanding of a situation. Yet they are intelligent, healthy, and often successful. Most outstanding examples originate in bourgeois class, as Lenin and Marx, yet it appears that Mao is pure proletariat. These grey-matter cerebral blind spots that occur in the intelligent and educated with fair frequency diffuse throughout the proletariat. If you listen seriously to their opinion, a high percentage of this defect is noted throughout.

Mao's village encircle city strategy for carrying out worldwide communist revolution may be successful in the Orient where the bourgeois live within the cities. Yet, if he were to apply this system to America geographically with suburbs and capitalistic status of the American farmer, it would be a fiasco. If an American communistic movemment did evolve, it would do so along lines similar to Russia, namely, from factory workers.

Linn Piao, in 1965, commented that the Chinese Revolution was but a continuation of the great October Revolution in Russia. He enumerated what the two had in common: (1) both led by the working class with a Marxist-Leninist party as its nucleus; (2) both based on worker-peasant alliance; (3) both seized power through violent revolution and established proletariat dictatorship; (4) both built the socialist system after victory, and (5) both were component parts of the proletarian world revolution. What we know is the underlying chemical formula which promoted this catastrophic shift in society. It may be regarded as: take the lower class, the proletariat, with low titre genes and mesomorphic overload. Choose them from over-populated, undernourished, hard environment where destitution and despair is the rule. Add intelligent bourgeois agitators whose nuclear chains are well organized. You then have a basic worker-peasant mix catalyzed by Marx-Lenin. Shake violently by revolution to precipitate proletariat dictatorship. This compound will fertilize a socialistic system.

Analysis demonstrates that what passed in the foregoing formula was a substitution of dominance. The broad group of bourgeois and petty bourgeois — 15-20% — has been jettisoned into the common with all their skills and abilities. An extremely small group representing the Communist Party has moved into traditional leadership. In many ways communism is fascism. It is merely that dominants gain power through revolution and suppression of human rights. Cries of socialistic and philosophy are pablum to quiet the masses and to disguise the totalitarian facade. Mao couldn't have put it better when he stated, "Political power grows out of the barrel of the gun."

Communists have excellent war-like genes. They use them in their obsession with assassinations, pogroms, and liquidation of millions of innocent people who happen not to agree with them. To obtain these admirable inheritances there has to be paucity of humanitarian genes, genes of compassion, charity and feeling. Here we notice the stark contrast in thoughts of Soviet greats such as Sakharov who was not permitted outside the country to receive the Nobel Peace Prize, and Soltsenitzen, the great critical writer who was exiled, and the leaders of the Communist Party such as Khruschev and Brezhnev. Unfortunately, both types — the killer and the savior — have their roles in human evolution. We are the supreme species who evolved rapidly because of killing ability. Too, we needed those of compassion and love to adhere society, bind its wounds, and preserve the wisdom of the aged.

Sometimes Mao comes out as a fairly decent biological strategist. He pointed out that one must have the courage to despise the enemy. It is elementary. Hate is a normal emotion. Other animals hate their tormentors and, when the opportunity presents, turn on them and kill them. Yet it is not long-engendered and is soon forgotten. But man has classical ability which, after a few re-enforcements such as Chairman Mao proposed, it can bloom throughout a lifetime.

Nor is hate a passive thing which happens to be incorporated into our neural structure. It is aided by internal hormones from the thyroid, pituitary and adrenal, and maybe a chromosomal aberration such as the XYY. Hate is a miserable emotion rooted in the neurogenes through the process of evolutionary selection. All along the competitive ascending road there were challengers. He that could remember them could despise his enemies — could retain hate until the auspicious moment arose when he could deal the despicable object a crippling blow such as he survived.

Hate is obviously not manslaughter, nor is it second-degree murder in which passions for a moment flare. It goes to the top rung of the ladder, cold-blooded, premeditated murder in its worst hour.

To carry this odious "crown of thorns" hate was a biological competitive advantage. Here one may note that women rarely have this long-sustained quality when compared with men. After all, it was the men who did the fighting, delivered justice, and repelled attacks. For women to have been heavily programmed with such genes would be self-defeating, for they were in the center of the group. Although it may sometimes happen, you don't often find a woman who pulls out a revolver and shoots her rival. Women's hates are small and in time forgotten. On the other hand, men may carry hate with them to the last twitch of their muscles.

Startlingly, the Chinese communists have established a formula for conquest of the earth by the proletariat. Mao's theory is the establishment of
rural revolutionary base areas to encircle the cities and conquer them. This is
to work well in Asia, Africa, and Latin America. It already worked in Indo-
China. Since the peasants constitute the main force of the revolution against
the imperialists and their lackeys, it is only the countryside that can provide
broad areas in which the revolutionaries can maneuver freely. Carrying the
logic further, if in regarding the entire globe, North America and Western
Europe are called the "cities of the world," then Asia, Africa and Latin
America constitute the rural areas of the world. Therefore, it is the internationalist duty of the socialist countries to support the peoples' revolutionary struggles in Asia, Africa, and Latin America.

It's a good plan with all those masses of depressed, rag-tailed, poverty-
stricken, overpopulated peasants out there. And do you know what's going
to happen? The American people, with their weird secretaries of state, their
bombastic leftist senators, the church by its population programs, are going
to help them accomplish it.

The opening curtain in Angola and the relinquishing by Europe of its
colonies, the criticism of Rhodesia and South Africa — all will contribute to
communist-power takeover. Instead of trying to feed them, loaning them
money and humanitaringly spending billions to develop their economy, we
should be sending them birth control pills by the shipload and specialists to
show them how to use them. What kind of nonsense is this, to develop one's
potential enemy? Not only should there be no aid, there should be negative
and meaning sabotage to their development.

That which is diabolically clever in the scheme is that we are not dealing
with class distinctions within a nation, we are dealing with the earth. The
enemy is western civilization, excluding Russia. Mass geneticism of all classes
of western civilization, Europe, and North America will be targeted for
extinction for no other reason than wide variance of the proletarian class
genes which are found indigenous to the civilized developed world. If the
proletariat of Europe think they will escape extinction by this incredible
documented scheme, they are misled. Future biological fight shall be western
civilization against the peasant workers of the three depressed continents —
bourgeois genes versus agrarian serf-worker genes.

An interesting sidelight in the life of Mao which almost backfired, was
the "Great Proletarian Cultural Revolution of 1966" when the 30,000,000
youthful Red Guards marched across the face of China shouting Mao's
slogans. It was Mao's ploy to utilize the fanatics to attack his power structure which he didn't trust. It just about paralyzed the country, but it did
succeed in staunching the capitalistic wounds. It is the enigma of communism. Since it is spurious ideology, it must wage war against the successful
economic system of capitalism and biological supremacy of the bourgeois
who seek expression. Target of the movement was capitalists who wormed
their way into the party by taking "the capitalistic road."

In April 1969, Linn Piao reported to the 9th National Congress of the
Communist Party of China. "The Soviet revisionist renegade clique has com-

pletely betrayed these brilliant teachings of Lenin. From Khrushchev to Brezhnev and company, they are persons in power taking the capitalist road who have long concealed themselves in the communist party of the Soviet Union . . . turned the world's first state of the dictatorship of the proletariat into a dark fascist state of the dictatorship of the bourgeois.''

That which communist and socialist hate most is its members taking the road to capitalism or converting from rigid regimes of Leninism-Marxism to more practical procedures. What Linn Piao is saying is that true communism isn't working in Russia.

Communism is confronted with a serious problem. Its founders felt a new philosophy granting equality of the masses. The masses are not equal; consequently, any ideology erected upon such a basis is a contradiction to traditional biological evolvement and society as genetically constituted. Capitalism keeps rearing its ugly head in social camps because it is the pattern of true human behavior — that is, to reward the intelligent, ambitious and hard-working, and to permit those that are inherently programmed to gravitate into their normal niche at the bottom of the social scale.

Mao himself prophesied that the class struggle between the proletariat and bourgeois will be long, torturous and acute. Ignorant of biology, he could not foresee that capitalism can never be relinquished unless the world succeeds in laboratorily rearing individuals from a single egg to displace other competitive beings. In that event, have no doubt, socialism will become supreme.

Mao made another forecast, saying that with certainty, from experience in the two world wars, if a third war erupts, the people of the world will revolt and send the whole pack of imperialists, revisionists, and reactionaries to their graves. This makes genetic sense. In the past, the flower of bourgeois was strewn by millions over fields of Europe. The recuperation of such excellent genes cannot be achieved overnight. It would be a propituous time for the proletariat — that huge population — to take over.

An interesting aside concerning the communist giants Mao and Lenin is an analysis of their physical being from their writings. Lenin comes out clearly upper bourgeois, while Mao remains peasant and typical proletariat.

In the revised Constitution of China, 1971, one may glean small breakdowns in original theory. For instance, members of a people's commune, if they don't disrupt its economy, may operate small pieces of land for private operation. All western freedoms are guaranteed — speech, press, assembly, strike, religious belief, of the home — but, as always, they are nothing when subject to the sanction of public security.

Capitalism is normal biological mechanism fixed within genes by evolving society. This is inequalitarianism, survival of the fittest, stratification with privilege. To increase efficiency for defense, lessen intragroup competition and prevent overlap specialization — these were factors selecting toward man's modern society. Then how does an abnormal political philosophy, as communism, rear its bestial head?

In the followers of Marx, "class society" was their obsession. They could see only that there was a dominant ruling class which was hostile to the people. They were supposed to destroy the ruling group and advance to socialism.

Obviously there must be a ruling class, so society rules in the name of the proletariat, democracy or aristocracy. It matters little. The proletariat are mentally equipped to be led and not to lead. Modern observers inside Russia have reported the emergence of definite class structure, especially in the army, bureaucracy, and Communist Party who obtained privilege and power. It is the cross to which communist doctrine is nailed. Humans are biologically determined to slot into occupational position. No amount of rhetoric can change the underlying amino acid sequence. The ritual we must remember, communism is pure fantasy, hatred, retribution, self-availing profit and power.

Trotsky was committed to classical Marxism, especially to permanent revolution. He was possessed by an extreme drive to convert the world into Utopia. Men become fixed in ideas, especially those that have been emotionally reinforced. Once the computer has been fed and the mind has reached conclusions, the plug is sometimes pulled and no further information will be accepted. It's akin to a good Catholic who has been raised strictly in the faith. When he comes to the university faced with sciences of evolution and anthropology, they go into the ears, circle the brain, and seat themselves long enough to pass the examination. But then they disappear without having unbudgeted neurons fixed early in formative youth concerning original faith. Trotsky was a crusader — however blind.

History repeatedly betrays Marxism. The assessment that "the revolution will either be the work of the workers or will not be at all," has patently flunked. All the upheavals, including the October revolution, have been the accomplishments of closely-knit military organizations or bureaucratic coups. These forces have incited the workers; that is, the proletariat who do not have the requisite amino sequences to carry off a revolution.

Although they have the minimum of brains, the working classes of Europe drank socialism like cheap wine — French communists, English chartists, German workers, Polish socialists. For the century, 1850-1950, they organized, rebelled, and actively engaged in goals which were inflamed by agitators. In past history nothing like that had occurred. But never had there occurred inhumanity of an industrial revolution.

Genetically, willingness to accept false schism was the result of displacement of the working element from the agricultural environment to which they had adapted over a hundred thousand years, to bleak prison-like, restrained and non-territorial existence. It was inevitable that political dissent would root. It was unfortunate that the industrial world was entering a period of high productivity and not granting the worker the shares in that prosperity.

Trotsky stood for dictatorship of the proletariat because he took it for granted that landlords, capitalists, and bureaucratic overlords will not yield their powers without a savage fight. In this he was correct. We see this in the capitalistic world today. Disproportion of wealth and power is awesome. Devices as income and inheritance tax to equalize biologies never fully succeed. With lawyers, politicians and agents, capitalists will retain power in spite of socialists that would divest them, in either capitalistic or communist worlds. Communists are as capitalistic as the western world. They mask their avarice under lofty-sounding titles. Nelson Rockefeller, one of the wealthiest men in America, struggled admirably to portray himself as a liberal, with which he succeeded.

Where Trotsky took off from other leaders was that he believed the proletarian dictatorship should be a proletarian democracy. Working classes should have the benefits of the democratic process in the selection of leaders and not be subject to a select self-perpetuating ruling class. This was a dream. Even in democracy working classes do not control. For if they did, the structure would fall apart, as is beginning in labor-infested locals such as England, Puerto Rico, and Argentina.

Lenin disagreed with Trostky's concept of the working class. They both saw the historic mission of workers as the agents of socialism. Trotsky felt that the working class was homogeneous, socialistically aware, and possessed a high capacity for political action. Lenin, however, saw it as highly stratified, each having its own level of education, capacity, origin, background, relation to the petty bourgeois, and with varying degrees of receptivity toward socialism. There was a mix of everything which needed the party's guidance.

Lenin makes an interesting point. Although the working class, 70% of society, can be grouped, there are many divergencies. That is why the corporal and sergeant exist. It is why mesomorphs and homosexuals abound, why politicians exploit people. The politicians are hardly proletariat — they are outsiders who have availed themselves of an opening niche in the dominant pattern, freaks playing all sides toward their ego center.

Moving into the glaciers of northern Europe were the dominants, the chiefs. There were the heavy-boned, squat mesomorphs who served as beasts of burden. There were sergeants who with loyalty obeyed commands. There were those that stayed with the women shaping stone-tooled projectiles, or those that sewed skins with bone needles to make clothing. Society selection bestowed virtues upon the tribe that was more efficient and would mean specialization. To pass newly-discovered adaptabilities forward it was imperative that germinal plasma be modified by natural selection or by direct germinal alteration. Darwin spoke about various types of selection which were imperative to evolution. We may consider social selection a strong force.

The Age of Permanent Revolution, a Trotsky anthology by Isaac Deutscher, is a great book. In his introduction, Deutscher states, "The Soviet working class has been exhausted by Revolution and Civil War, catastrophically reduced in size, disorganized and demoralized through the collapse of the entire economy. It proved unable to safeguard proletarian democracy and to control the party in power. Within the party, too, the rank and file failed to control their rights and to control their leaders. The Bolshevik regime took on a monolithic character which it was to maintain for decades."

Deutscher is speaking of the ultra-centralization of Stalinism rather than Lenin's democratic centralism. He concludes that it was Trotsky who represented the consciousness of the revolution in advocating a democratic party as opposed to dictatorship. In other words, Stalin sold out the working class to substitute his own authority.

As brilliantly as Deutscher may interpret communism, he misses the essentials of biology. The proletariat never will be able to safeguard democracy, no matter how democraticized they are. They can't be bothered with the task of management, nor do they wish it. No fault of theirs. It is the glory of modern man that this mass of people are sympathetic and patient with rulers by inheritance. Imagine what chaos and anarchy would result if they did struggle for power — if all beings were equal.

Under Stalin and later Soviet leaders, workers really took a lacing. They were deprived of the right to protest, strike, express opinions, and were punished for trivial offenses when they opposed "labor discipline." Trotsky opposed this policy. But what about the workers' counterpart in the United States, where ofttimes they strike unnecessarily, defy authority in the courts, lower production, perform mischievous acts to private property, cause disruption of the economy as well as cause inconvenience and financial loss to innocent outsiders? Is there a genetic resemblance?

You may be sure there is. Only dictatorship is further down the line, and has been repeatedly exposed by crusading journalists who have linked labor movement hierarchy directly to international communism, Mafia, and organized crime. Crimes committed by American labor leaders read like the "Who's Who" of bribery, extortion, and assassination. Occasionally, big fish get caught, such as Jimmie Hoffa and Tony Boyle, the United Mine Workers union president who had the Jablonski family murdered.

The worker, a strong and magnificent being, does not have the requisite genes to speak for himself. In both nations he is exhorted by a ruthless leadership. What is unfortunate in America is that the laborer can't see out. Within his programmed occupation it takes but few agitators screaming higher wages and better working conditions to ignite the critical load he carries, and he's off on a stupid campaign.

Speak with men who have gone on strike. One after the other they'll tell you they didn't want to strike. You'll feel they are lying to you. They're not. They are little chickens when they sit in an auditorium and listen to a smooth-talking bourgeois, one from high in the racket, from a different city, who couldn't care less about them. The laborer who could kill an ox with his bare hands, trembles in his shoes at the thought of standing up and saying "Boo" to his captors.

Throughout history workers have been "up for grabs" by dominants. Be they capitalists, socialists or communist leaders, or organized labor Mafia. Labor is there for the taking — strong, lovable, dumb brutes who cannot add the score. They succumb to a few well-chosen slogans and cleverly-placed needle grievances. In unionization, what occurs is the abrogation of government and private enterprise to dictatorial forces of the underworld.

Trotsky made an interesting racial point in which he felt that Negroes of North America would one day rise in a body against their oppressors. He had a good sense of political movement, but here again, he lacked anthropology. In the past, Negro slave revolts have occurred on a minor scale in both the Roman Empire and the American South, which were quickly subdued. What Trotsky failed to realize was that, fortunately, they do not have wicked genes of their white brothers, the Caucasoids of the north. They had no necessity as African residents to develop the art of mass kill. Negroes never had opportunity to select toward these genes. The climate was contrary to adaption of mass military movement. No great Negro armies have been fielded, and none will. Negroes are too individualistic and too gentle a people. It isn't that they are not brave, nor that they are not physically strong and capable of war in mass movement. It may just be that they are too damn smart to get sucked into the continuous nonsense. Whatever it is, it resides squarely within their genetic structure, as attested to over millennia.

Social genetics of divergent societies in countries as Russia and the United States must be aware of three factors; one, a common denominator of social inheritance in all races and subraces; two, unique social divergencies which are innate from the isolation of genetic pools . . . environmental adaptation gave them passage to survival; three, a factor that often confounds us — the territory in which the genes are operating.

No quantity or quality of genes of a subrace or nation can compensate sufficiently for poorness of resources. The Spanish are an example of the finest subrace on earth. Yet they have a tough time economically and must make do with meager soil, small amount of metal and energy resources. On the other hand, the United States is blessed with cornucopia. It is superfluous to enumerate the vast agricultural, metal, coal, oil and gas resources — water, timber, variable climates, and immensity. The genes of Anglo-Saxons and later southern Europeans turned it into the powerhouse of the earth.

When we question why American workers did not adopt socialism or why it isn't about to adopt it, we must remember factor three is operating in which the worker's lot is quite substantial. There is no need, as in the Soviet system, to purchase the grain for daily bread from abroad. Contrarily, if genes are badly mixed, that is, newly mixed, as in South America where three major races come together — the Mongoloid Indian, the Negroid and European Caucasoid — no amount of valuable resources such as they have will serve them to erect a strong and viable society, one that is highly civilized.

Racial mixing is a gross abnormality within the social revolution. These majestically spiraling tiers which are indigeneous to each race and subrace, once they are mixed, produces a product which is something of all, but none of one. It is racial bastardization and mongrelization. The product, although honorable, sometimes brilliant and wonderfully human, now has a talent range that does not fit the specific evolutionary adaptability that his ancestors forged hundreds of thousands of years ago.

It is the same with animal breeding. If we permitted all our dogs in all kennels to mix freely, we may be sure we would come out with some great friends of man. But in the process we would have lost the distinguishing features of the many and would have a lot of funny-looking, misshapen canines, incapable of executing the abilities of the pure breed.

Our new homogeneous mongrels, as some anthropologists would have races of the world become, would no longer be able to deploy as police dogs, sentrys and attackers. Beagles would lose their sense of smell and tracking.

Pointers, setters and retrievers would be morphologized out of business. House pets could become vicious and unruly.

A veritable genetic holocaust results in mongrelization, whether it be that of animals or humans. The chain of forward evolution for a specific adaptability and consequent survival is broken. There appears a jack-of-all-talents but a master-of-none. It is for this reason, in the racial mix, there has been so little contribution to civilization excepting, perhaps, poetry and mediocre novel-writing.

Whereas, factor three is territory wherein adaptability of the genetic group operates, factor two, or the individualism and uniqueness of the genes above the social common denominator of humans, is supreme value. It is for this that the earth should protect its genetic interest. The Jewish people have probably been the wisest in not inviting outsiders into their culture and by discouraging subracial intermarriage. Unfortunately, in America this barrier is breaking down, with increasing numbers of Jews and Gentiles entering wedlock. This can lead to nothing beneficial for the Jewish subrace, their identity, and their capability. What it will do to the Gentiles cannot be determined. But there is one thing that is certain, and that is, whereas separately the two subraces have contributed mightily to the advancement of civilization, the mixture will turn out to be mediocre. It's something like mixing French champagne with Canadian whiskey — mixed they are atrocious, separated they are magnificent.

Isaac Deutscher, in his concluding introduction to Trotsky, says, "In sociopolitical ideas, American conservatism seems unshaken. Yet it is in the field of ideas, Marxist ideas, that Americans have most to learn, if they are not to land themselves in a grim historical impasse. And in the field of ideas, Trotsky, I am sure, is still a superb teacher."

In reply we should like to say, we have reformed this in this work, *Genetic Basis of Society.*

Trotsky has said, "All classes and groups of people are permeated with hatred toward absolutism and that means with sympathy for the struggle for freedom." This is a 100% false interpretation. With the proletariat, the great mass of people, they are quite content with absolutism. That is the underlying ability for totaliarian communism to succeed in Russia and China. The proletariat especially solicitate dictatorship and leading — whether it be from a powerful bureaucracy, their gangster labor organizers or a dictator, they huddle their genes beneath the spread of authoritarianism. They are programmed to be led.

It is only when the leadership becomes oppressive, or when conditions are so vile their very existence is threatened, that they can be incited to revolt. In that process, if they succeed, they only fall under the directorship of new leaders. As the child in the family seldom enters into permanent revolution of long continued rebellion, so it is with the working class, who actively seek the upper bourgeois as supportive gene structure.

It is why the wealthy, able, and successful are adulated by the working class. It is their inherent geneticism that permits them without the least flinching to freely address one as "Sir," which, for a high-ranking dominant, carries a few neurons of inhibition.

When the telephone company goes on strike or an industrial plant, in which the managerial personnel takes over, such as the strike some years back at the *Washington Post*, you have manifestation of genetic dominancy genes. Both sides respect the other for what they are. And what they are is bourgeois and proletariat. One cannot live without the other. The proletariat does the factory work and the bourgeois the directing. Nor was it intended that their roles should be interchangeable. Evolutionary adaptation selected them for specific occupational duty.

Back as far as 1905, in the aborted revolution, Trotsky recognized the proletariat as a class which obsessed Red leaders. Yet, interestingly, he also recognized its social homogeneity, not knowing that it was a product of biological inheritance and not economic frustration.

He recognized also something that is unrecognized in the western world, and that is, the power of government. "The greater the anarchy created by the strike, the nearer the victory. . . ." But when communism achieves goals and enslaves workers, its attitude toward strike is to take dissident labor leaders forthwith to the first cow pasture and pass bullets through their heads. Yet, they watch cunningly, aid and abet strikes in the western world. Democracy's leaders, being weak politicians, attempt to deal instead of outlaw an instrument, which can be their undoing. Jazzed-up sympathy for the poor and the unions is liberal-leftist-Bolshevik propaganda that will pull down the house to substitute their own brand of terror control. Under communism, the word "strike" is a non-word. Its utilage is for democratic subversion.

It is emphasized that in 1905 the Soviet was a class organization. This was the source of its fighting power. Those striving toward a better life were instinctively on the side of the Soviet. It was understood that the worker group was up for bids. The bid would not come out of the proletariat, but out of the bourgeois, the communist party, which would shut the proletariat out as soon as their select dictatorial power was consolidated. The Tzar was exchanged for Lenin. All else remained the same.

During Trotsky's exile, after 1906, he formulated a theory of Permanent Revolution: a feeling that society keeps changing its skin, that alterations in war and peace, in economy, science, morals, and family, and that democracy is only a prelude to social revolution. Thus, between the democratic revolution and the socialistic reconstruction of society, there develops a permanent state of revolution.

Trotsky, obsessed like a medieval peasant, ate his bread contaminated with ergot concerning demands of revolution. Yet he is correct. Great nations and empires do fail, fall, are absorbed or vanquished. Time alters all political structure. But it is not from permanent revolution — it is directly related to genetic coding, its pollution, purity, hybridization, and numbers of assimilated offspring. Had England truly colonized its colonial gains over the centuries with pure English blood instead of military power, and had they succeeded in genociding their territories like the American Anglo-Saxons, they would have had one whale of a nation.

Poor Trotsky is going out and free all those non-genetically-related workers of the earth. It is bound to failure. It shall possibly be, once the

Chinese develop proper technique, they will sweep easily to the Atlantic. And Russia, with its heterogeneous peoples beneath an iron yoke of false creed, will shatter into insignificant pieces. Nations march on genes. They can be fattened on alliances and allies, but these are merely fed into the dominant force whose DNA structure is "up" for the task, such as Napoleon avalanching into Moscow.

Trotsky misinterpreted the role of innate biology. He speaks, "From the extraordinary significance which Lenin's arrival received, it should only be inferred that leaders are not accidentally created, that they are gradually chosen out and trained up in the course of decades, that they cannot be capriciously replaced. . . ." This appraisal of Lenin's 1917 appearance is nothing more than Watsonian behaviorism in which Watson said in effect, "Give me a normal healthy child and I will make him into whatever shall be desired — poet, doctor, leader, criminal, etc." It is the obsolete theory of behaviorism — so beloved by politicians and pedagogues. Lenin had it in his genes — leadership, drive, organizational and speech ability, and obsession with his cause.

Contrary to what Trotsky believed, leaders are accidentally created when one of a half-billion sperm succeeds in climbing the fallopian tube-fish ladder to meet an ova and penetrate its nuclear intelligence — where the miracle of chemical mechanisms transpires, and they pair up. From that moment forward, leadership has been irrevocably decided. Even before that moment, at the time of reduction division of the germinal cells, there has been the miracle of the gambling wheel in the choosing of which amino acid chips will be retained to go forward in reproductive effort. This latter, although evolutionary science does not wish to believe it, is under environmental control, as the influence of plasma and blood elements, drugs, and chemicals umbrella and alter selection at the uterine conference site.

Here is the true tragedy of communist ideology and of the weak-kneed western capitalist politicians. They understand one vote, one man, and one man, one gun. Yet, for them it is inconceivable that above that equation there is a myriad of individual differences to make humans the most unequalled of beings within any species.

At a parliamentary meeting, October 25, 1917, Trotsky made a casual observation concerning the democratic group present. It concerned clothing. Officers' chevrons, the eyeglasses and neckties of intellectuals were absent. Present were "trench delegates, no means of pretty picture: long unshaven and torn trench-coats with heavy fur hats on their disheveled hair, often cotton sticking out through the hole . . . buttons torn off, belts hanging loose, and long unoiled boots wrinkled and rusty. The plebeian nation had for the first time set up an honest representation, made in its own image and not retouched."

As the old saying goes, "A man is judged by the clothes he wears and not the company he keeps," in today's analysis, has good genetic basis. It is not necessary for the proletariat to speak or act. Their clothes are self-revealing, and that is what Trotsky was realizing in the observation. No amount of money turns a sow's ear into a silk purse. A Hollywood designer, early in 1975, as one of the worst-dressed of the year, named a teenage daughter of a

President. It proved, once again, that genetic groupings are inherent, are a matter of chance combination.

It is not that the poor do not have money to dress well. It is because they are proletariat and have neither perception of good taste nor desire to effect it. It does not necessarily mean clothes — it can be such things as automobiles or furnishings. The artistic neurons are not present to dictate aesthetics. Taste has little to do with education or training. A light cord, when exposed and running across a ceiling, will send an upper-bourgeois into shudders, but to the proletariat it goes often unnoticed. What we are saying is that clothes are an outward expression of the mind and genetic occupational level of the individual within.

There are exceptions to this in which promoters, poorly educated and poorly minded, put on classy shows in clothes and cars for the sake of sales. Yet, if one looks closely, the appearance is flawed by overcompensation. The sartorial sequence is not natural. The rag-tail part of the army that Trotsky and Lenin put together succeeded admirably. But it succeeded because firebrand Bolsheviks such as Lenin, Trotsky, and Stalin, were cunning, dedicated and upper bourgeois, taking advantage of a historical quirk with false slogans.

Since the French Revolution there has been a flood of equalitarian falsehood. It has only been in the last ten to fifteen years that geneticists have taken a second look at this glib analysis of human behavior. Trotsky handled it admirably. But within two lines you can read the error. During the Russian Civil War he instructed Red Army men in infantry regulations — "You are an equal among Comrades. Your superiors are your more experienced and better-educated brothers. . . . You must obey them."

One cannot imagine an intelligent mind submitting and believing the unexpurgated rot of such double-talk. It is not that the superiors are more experienced or better-educated. Not for one second! It is that the superiors are blessed with superior genes, with extra genes, with genes put together in proper sequences. They have genes that can act as dominants and not lie inactive, because of the instructions they received in the reduction division. Students come out of Annapolis or West Point not because they are more experienced or more educated — they are graduated because they have cogs upstairs to integrate properly abstractions and technicalities fed into them.

In those few sentences of Trotsky's one sees why Marxists and Leninists' communistic ideology will fall into tatters once threads of terror and dictatorship that hold it together part at the seams. In America, the Constitution may proclaim liberty and equality for all — and we may believe it as far as the judicial system goes — but we know full well from the first grade on that no such thing exists biologically. By the time students are separated from high school, the social classes have already been segregated.

With the third quarter of the 20th century there appeared a new weapon, formerly seldomly used internationally, and seldomly employed as part of war, excepting World War II, that was terrorism. Today it is worldwide. Its major seeds can be traced directly to concepts of Bolsheviks and communists.

During the Civil War, Trotsky attempted to justify terrorism. He stated, "Terror can be very efficient against the reactionary class. . . . Intimidation is a powerful weapon of policy, both internationally and internally. . . . War, like revolution, is founded upon intimidation. Our extraordinary commissions shoot landlords, capitalists, and generals who are striving to restore the capitalist order."

He continued to say that a successful war only destroys part of the conquered army and that the remainder is intimidated by breaking their will. A revolution kills individuals but intimidates thousands. So the reasoning goes that Red terror is as armed insurrection, a continuation. So concluding the premise, terror is amoral because it is violence. War is violence. A war is just. A revolution is a war and, therefore, that which is just is moral — or thoughts to that effect. Terrorism is o.k. Use it.

What we see in these pronouncements is a truly dominant, high-class bourgeois. It represents a throwback to early primate society in which the dominant determined life and death, and in which there was no sense in mercy or compassion. It represents genetic groupings that are thrown out in modern societies and whose coding has remained unchanged. Trotsky's thoughts differed little from the thoughts of later terrorists, the Nazis.

Menschevism had a theory: for the countries of Europe to reach socialism, they had to pass through both the feudal substage and the bourgeois-democratic stage. This can be translated genetically. The feudal substage was normal from the beginning of man's first society. To understand the emergence of the bourgeois-democratic stage is merely to shuffle the same genetic hierarchy under capitalistic expanding prosperity. Feudal elements transferred into the bourgeois. They were held together with neo-rich and successful which had been sieved out of the proletariat by their drive ability, cleverness, and acquisition of property. They were leaders. Only the names changed.

The democracy tid-bit emerged more as a ruse than true political philosophy. There is no true democracy. Every parliament knows that. Proletarians are given robes of participation which are meaningless because they must pass the tickets of government to higher echelons whose educations and influences are sufficient to guide their destinies.

Were it otherwise, you could never have permitted a president like Johnson to wage a long and bitter war which failed. The vast majority of the citizenry and a great portion of the military were opposed to it. It is where the poor little devil of the proletariat will be short-changed. He must pass command to someone in the bourgeois class, one who is able to implement it.

The final farce to the three-pronged theory to arrival to socialism, genetic biology is ignored. These are legislative and dictatorial efforts to equalitarianism.

Marxist doctrine indicates that class relations originate out of economic production. And further, that these relations correspond to a level of the productive forces. No one can quarrel with this. There is an aristocracy of labor when we consider privileged labor unions. Yet more than that, beyond production, in the whole of the economic milieu, humans are cast fairly accurately according to their abilities and skills.

Whether the Marxist realizes it, production economics is only the chaffing screen through which the good seed is properly localized, and the residue is placed on lower social rungs, entirely from inherent genetics. This has nothing to do with ideology. It is the Achilles heel of communism. Go to any American high school, pull its graduates' records, then page through the Yellow Pages of any telephone directory and you'll find educational experience and business correlate to provide society with class structure via genetics.

Trotsky, in *The Revolution Betrayed*, scorns the Soviet system. As they say, "It takes a thief to catch a thief." This old Bolshevik in the 1930s did some fancy and accurate upbraiding of Stalin's totalitarianism. It's too bad Franklin Roosevelt or Winston Churchill didn't listen. Trotsky speaks of the revolutionary vanguard of the proletariat being devoured by administrative apparatus, demoralized, and almost anihilated in the Civil War. He berates the bureaucracy, those privileged officials and commanders of the standing army, which represent a compulsion, which the masses cannot exercise and to which is directed against them.

Trotsky's interprets social class with its levels of society as being something that can be artificially corrected. Light never dawned on his idealistic zeal that whether a revolution was betrayed, or of what form of government is aegis to the people, within time society will stratify according to its genetic componency. It is high comedy, this Bolshevik bellowing like a wounded bull that bureaucracy is the protector of inequality. Mind you, he is speaking of the Soviet Union under Stalin. He rails at the poverty and cultural backwardness of the masses, who have again become incarnate. "The deposed and abused bureaucracy, from being a servant of society, has again become its lord." He laments the privileges of the new aristocracy — a backslide to capitalism is possible — bureaucracy has converted itself to an uncontrolled caste, alien to socialism, a new differentiation in society exists.

With communists, leftists, and liberal legislators which permeate free democratic governments, there is a horrendous wail when one mentions "Fascism" as matured in Italy, Germany, and Spain. Indignation arises not in the facts of the system, but from its unswerving opposition to communism. Media and literature are highly prejudiced by leftist and Jewish people. Jews had rational sufferings under Nazism. Hatred does not have a right to distort facts. They have the most to lose by attacks upon systems which confront communism. Even more, Jewish people suffered tremendous persecution under the Russians, and still do. So we should tolerate fascism even though we do not agree with its unseemly aspects.

Through Rooseveltian propaganda the world derived a false picture of fascism. We will reiterate that the Nazi treatment of the Jews was vile, brutal, and contrary to all that is civilized and decent. Amen. Yet we should never forget that in the late '20s and '30s, these nations were forced to the brink of disaster with totalitarian communism. Their people were being terrorized by positions of Marxism-Leninism. Structure of their capitalistic society was being attacked — labor unrest, sabotage, and even the firing of a cherished building, the *Reichstag*, German Parliament, was done by a young communist. A conspiracy could not be proved. A fair judicial trial permitted other communists accused to be released. Marinus Van der Lubbe, a young Dutch-German communist, confessed fully his arsonist deed and retraced his actions in unquestioned detail.

What was not well known, before 1933, 60,000 Red Banner Front communists paraded in Berlin. All over the nation, torn between ideologies, were daily bloody fights between communists and Nazis. In France, in 1936, a million and a half workers occupied factories and raised Red flags over them.

Spain had become a land of anarchy in which hundreds of churches were set ablaze each year by godless communism. Contrary to what had been told, the republican government of Spain was a Red government. At the first opportunity, when threatened by Franco, it allied itself with the Soviets, sending extensive reserves of gold directly to Moscow, which was never returned to the Spanish people.

In September of 1920, revolutionary movement in Italy exploded. It resulted in seizure of the factories and industries by the workers. Proletariat dictatorship was fact. By November, it was arrested by the emergence of the fascists. In two years, under Mussolini, fascism had come to power.

It should be without argument, had Hitler not persecuted the Jews, nor forced their exodus, nor deprived them of rights, properties and titles, the course of history would have been far different. He was not reasonable when he emphasized persecution of this cohesive group of subracial Caucasians. Yet the persecution served him politically, by working through normal racial biases of all peoples — genetically fixed.

Trotsky defined fascism as a governmental system which is based on the uprooting of all elements of proletarian democracy, within bourgeois society. Its aim was to destroy the communist advance by holding the classes in a state of fragmentation.

None of the western democracies could certainly quarrel against a form of government that opposed terroristic, ruthless, and totalitarian establishment of godless communism. Further, how could anyone oppose the right of a people to maintain their characteristic culture and evolutionary advancement rather than be garroted by a sick economic doctrine as Marxism?

Nationalities do have these rights. What was objected to under fascism was its autocracy. Its leaders, in their efforts to combat the vile enslavement, had to resort to the strength of martial and dictatorial powers. It was only through this means that they could combat the evil. They had to bypass free election guarantees and democratic constitutions. Unfortunately, this choice may one day come to the western democracies, including the United States. The obsolete democratic redouts of Portugal, Italy, and France are soon to fall under the hands of socialists.

This is a poignant decision for democracy. It can no longer succeed in its ancient forms and combat communist tyranny. It should be clearly noted that Hitler, Mussolini, and Franco knew how to defeat communism. They were the last free nations to do so. Their defeat came about only because of their brother capitalists aiding and abetting communists.

Grievously and disappointingly, the centralization of power, which was needed, carried with it tremendous abuse and the loss of civil liberties. With the fascism that one day may emerge in the remaining strongholds of democracy, it is to be hoped that as many as possible constitutional guarantees and liberties can be maintained. Yet it is the very constitutions and liberties of the democracies that the communists are counting on to bring the free nations of the world to defeat. Long before the strong man assumes power under a crisis and does not relinquish it, it behooves examination of how the basic tenents of democracy can be re-altered to combat the challenge to existence.

Such measures could be prohibition of strikes, incarceration of labor leaders and agitators, restriction of the press when contrary to the national good, registration of firearms, and a merciless crackdown on crime and terrorism.

Back in 1914, Mussolini made a class observation. He considered society as reciprocal between two classes, the proletariat and the bourgeois. Between them were the intermediate layers, the joining web. These layers, during periods of crisis, would gravitate upward or downward depending upon their interests and ideas. Mussolini had the formula, yet he did not know why it existed. Had he studied anthropology he would have seen the mass proletariat workers, the expendables and muscle mass, the lowest levels of intelligence, devoid of leadership. We have described the bourgeois as the dominants, political jackals, intellectuals, skilled artists and technicians as representing the cream of neural capability.

The huge feminine mass, because of evolutionary adaptability programmed to child-rearing, educating, protecting, gathering, food preparation, care of a mate, did not require excursions into technical skills or political science. Intermediate group, which Mussolini advantaged himself, was nothing more than evolutionary divergency found in all species, as they probe by offspring to establish themselves in adaptable niches — in this case, social. Strong selective factor makes this possible, in that the major groups do not interbreed extensively. The farmer boy marrying the queen, or the peasant girl Cinderella-ing the prince, is the exception. Feudal overlords anthropologically guard their supremacy. Under-privileged wallow within the same genetic pasture.

Hominids had opportunity to select geneticism toward abilities specialization and efficiencies within society. Man's success was not individual, but social more than any other facet — rising up erect, to be able to run on two legs, or development of the hand. Within each human there is programmed extensive DNA directive devoted to social relations. Man's sociology is innate and relatively unalterable. For this he wages holocaustic wars for no obvious gain. For this he permits dictators and terroristic oligarchies to rule over him. He is acting in a modern world with mental equipment designed for a million years ago.

One of the originators of communism, Friedrich Engles, wrote that the state, including the democratic republic, consists of detachments of men armed for the defense of property; everything else serves only to embellish or camouflage this fact. Again, biological ignorance is laid bare. What he states is true. He does not understand the reason, being territoriality and sovereignty thereof, which is rooted in the peasant with a quarter-acre vegetable plot, to the British lord of a vast preserve. Repeatedly, communism stubs its toe when it nobly declares obvious truth and ignores the underlying point of biological takeoff. So we are to get rid of the territorality instinct by dictatorial compulsion?

In 1935, Trotsky, in speaking, "Should America Go Communist," stated that civil war of a revolutionary nature isn't fought by a handful of men at the top — 5% or 10% who own 9/10th of American wealth. He questioned who would fight against communism. Your corporal's guard of multi-millionaires? Your Mellons, Morgans, Fords, Rockefellers?

Again, the master of the proletariat did not understand it. But the proletariat of France and Germany stormed into filth and death by the millions to trenches of the First World War for four long years. Their spirits were relatively unmodified by their capitalistic, feudal, and aristocratic leaders. Elan of the French troops sent them screaming, naked bodies against the withering fire of machine guns, to crumble in the barbed-wire hell of no-man's land.

The proletariat are genetically leaderless. They will always be "up for grabs" when the right slogans, propaganda, and incitation is disseminated into their willfully obedient neurons. Men defend their hovels, wives and children with the same ferocity as the duke defends his palace. Trotsky did not understand this.

It is pleasant music to the capitalists' ears to hear the Bolshevik state, "Mankind would not tolerate a totalitarian abomination of the Kremlin pattern. The political regime of the USSR is not a new society, but the worst caricature of the old."

Although Trotsky hit Stalinist Russia, communist leaders argue that the greater number of countries in which the capitalist system is broken, the weaker will be the resistance offered by the ruling classes in other countries. For this reason communist aid has been given to Cuba and Hungary. There is further extension to this doctrine. If communists can acquire bases and establish communistic countries in Africa and Asia, they will outflank Europe and the West in the same manner they outflanked the country from the cities in Russia, and from the country the cities of China. Their opening African offensive is to be noted in Angola and Ethiopia.

Revolutionaries have excellent timing for actions. In western democracies it should not go unheeded. They feel that since war is the mother of revolution, because it rocks the established regime to its foundation, weakening the ruling class and pressing the masses with indignation, it is fertile soil for governmental overthrow. Therefore, America and France will never again engage in protracted wars as World War II and Vietnam. For the ideological blueprint to mobilize the proletariat has already been filed.

When the terrorism of Stalin reached its summit in the Moscow trials of 1936 to 1938, killing millions of innocent victims in every walk of Soviet life, Trotsky, in exile, was accused of plotting to assassinate Stalin and of killing masses of Russian workers. Trotsky struck back by saying a new aristocracy had been formed in the Soviet Union, lamenting that the October Revolution proceeded under a banner of equality while the bureaucracy of Stalin was the embodiment of monstrous inequality. . . . "The Revolution destroyed the nobility, the bureaucracy creates a new gentry. Stalinists are traitors to the interests of the Soviet masses and the world proletariat."

Poor, poor Trotsky. To him the Russian Revolution had been couped by its palace guard. They had not only reinstated capitalism, but bureaucratic inequality as well. If we are to believe Trotsky, and there's no reason why we shouldn't, the bloody socialistic mess reverted back to normal biological, political science in which the true dominants assumed historic role. The masses precipitated into classes according to their genetic programmings.

Before Stalin's assassin drove a pick-axe into Trotsky's head when he resided in Mexico, Trotsky had written, in 1940, a few things about the Soviet Union. In them he is struggling hard to understand how the revolution could have been betrayed. Never the faintest glimmer of genetic light dawned in his revolutionary soul. His higher neurons were floating in clouds of human equality. We get rid of classes which are artificial, get rid of oppressors, destroy the bourgeois, and presto! — workers run the government, a classless society emerges, and soon there is not even a need for the state. It was such a childishly beautiful conception that begot communism. But the roots of its tree never considered genetics, in which the driving force is not revolution, but genetic evolution. The tree rooted in sand will ultimately topple.

Trotsky spoke of the Stalin group as a greedy, lying, cynical caste of rulers, and if the population was to rise to higher levels of culture, it must free itself from the humiliating usupers. Revolution haunted him and he saw it as the only means of removing bureaucracy. This evil that he helped coronate, that became a bureaucratic autocracy, must give way to Soviet democracy. It is tragic to hear the old revolutionary speak of restoration of the right of criticism, a genuine freedom of elections necessary to further the development of the country; when, as the archangel of death, in the October Revolution and the ensuing Civil War, he ruthlessly suppressed the very forces that would ensure human freedoms.

Trotsky spoke of growth of social wealth giving way to socialist equality — that ranks would be abolished and tinsel decorations melted. It was his compulsive blind spot — equality. No society on the face of the earth, however remote, has achieved equality, for there is always the head man or tribal elders, or the wise matron known as queen. Trotsky viciously attacked the Soviet Union, saying that the apparatus of the workers' state was transformed into a weapon of bureaucratic violence against the working class — that the bureaucracy was transformed into an all-powerful, privileged caste — that convincingly repudiates socialism.

He foresaw what never came about — a new revolution in the USSR against social inequality and political oppression, tearing down the privileges of bureaucracy, Soviet aristocracy, its ranks and orders, and inequality of labor's wages.

Here we have insight into fixed neurogenes of Trotsky. His obsession with equality was electrolyzed in his subconscious and conscious mind. No amount of afferent inlead could breach its rampart. He struck wildly against his tormenter, who was soon to do him in by proposing another revolutionary uprising of oppressed Soviet masses. This was to be led by the Party of the First International, proclaiming, of all things, "Long live Soviet Democracy."

The misplaced cerebral wiring is apparent. You cannot equate communism and democracy. The one is absolute dictatorship, so formulated by the prophets Marx, Engles, and Lenin. The other recognizes the right of the individual to participate in his government, something that has never occurred in a communist country, where it is the oligarchy of the few that decide the fate of the many.

Stalin was accused by Trotsky of having murdered the old guard Bolsheviks, all the collaborators and assistants of Lenin, all the heroes of the Civil War and October Revolution. It was possibly when he proposed the purging of the parasitic bureaucracy by armed insurrection of soldiers, sailors, workers and peasants, that Stalin decided to liquidate one of the last of the Bolsheviks.

In his testament, Trotsky proclaimed that he should die with unshaken faith in the communist future. Right up until the end, only a neurosurgeon's scalpel could have removed the crossed circuits. Stalin performed it with a pick-axe.

Yet we must pause and pay tribute to the man. He was a great thinker, idealist, and he did move worlds. For lack of knowledge of genetics, his vision was distorted. Some men will be compelled to devote their lives to physical toil. They are so constructed, and under most conditions, enjoy it. Their life span and well-being is enhanced by engaging in the biological schema.

Trotsky wrote of the rarity of genius. He noted most geniuses come out of the upper and middle classes. He deplored the fact that the sparks are choked before they burst into flame. What never occurred to him was that genius is a product of genes of the bourgeois class, as he himself. The proletariat seldom beget giants.

In 1926, Trotsky had his hand on the throttle, but dismissed it. He stated that he discovered the "Darwinian's utterly naive and unscientific attempts of applying the conclusions of biology to society." The falsity of his reasoning is the failure of communism's permanency and the achievement of its ideals. Society is biology!

Two young writers, Karl Marx, age 29, and Friedrich Engles, 27, published in 1848 a pamphlet which in the history of social force ranks with the Bible, the Magna Carta, and the Constitution of the United States. A treatise of less than 50 small pages termed "The Communist Manifesto," proclaims to the world the theories, aspirations, practices, and programs of a new social order.

Marx was born of a Jewish family in Germany. Engles' father was a manufacturer and Calvinist. Both had been converted to radicalism in Berlin. Together they collaborated in one of the world's leading democracies to issue their instrument of destruction. Marx died in London in 1883. To his dreary tomb Marxist pilgrims visit yearly. Because the implementation of his doctrines came long after his death, he was never to know the hellish scourge he wrought upon humanity from his embittered life.

It is important that we speak of the Manifesto, not so much that it has value today, excepting to having incited millions of non-thinking masses and their opportunistic leaders by its false logic. There is one phase that may not be denied. The authors of the Manifesto were apparently sincere in their efforts to benefit humanity and especially the working classes. Yet benefit was to come about by dethronement and subjugation of upper classes, to destroy them, to permit them to sink into the same abyss as the lower classes and even to deprive them, as well as everybody else, of private property. In short, the proletariat, that is, the worker masses, shall become dictators over all, and by some ruse fully unexplained, the state, bureaucracy, and the bourgeois, that is, the upper classes, will simply wither away.

If so much hadn't resulted from this mixed-up, fiery, romantic, illogical, nonscientific piece of declaration, one would say that it was the work of a couple of grade C high-school students, and dismiss it. But a miracle was in the making, half-truths and slogans served to galvanize the lower social echelons and especially revolutionary radicals. This was to go directly overhead of nationalistic tendencies. The workers of the world were to unite.

The first sentence of the first chapter begins with: "The history of all hitherto existing society is the history of class struggles." Marx attempts to explain it, free man and slave, patrician and publican, lord and serf, oppressor and oppressed, stood in constant opposition to one another, that society is split into two great hostile camps, two great classes, the bourgeois and the proletariat facing each other.

This was written before Darwin published his *Origin of the Species*, before Gregor Mendel's significant discoveries in heredity was recognized, before anthropological and primate studies, and before the science of genetics. Credit must be given to Engles and Marx that they did perceive two large classes of society. There is no question about this. It is why workers, soldiers, sailors, farmers, etc., exist side by side with management, generals, admirals, bankers, etc. Yet the American farmer, in his land tenacity, is by no means the proletariat as defined in the Manifesto.

In recognition of class, which was obvious, they were surveying the animal world, especially primates. We have pointed out the biology of hierarchy and status. In evolution of society, selection was reinforced by class efficiency and noncompetitiveness, causing inheritable genetic programming. In their first sentence, had they substituted the word "genetic" for the word "class," they would have been on solid fact. It would then read, "The history of all hitherto existing society is the history of genetic struggles." This is revealed by territorial instinct in the waging of war. It is manifest in the strong nationalism resulting from genetic pools. And it is evidenced by the very categories of classes that have arisen within civilized nations, including the communistic nations, as Trotsky so poignantly pointed out.

From Pickett's glorious and vain cavalry charge in the Civil War battle of Gettysburg to the absurd French mincemeating defense of Verdun in World War I, to the German encircled doom in the icy rubble of Stalingrad, back to Norman the Conqueror's invasion of England — in whatever field aggressive banners are unfurled, it has been nothing more than the ultimate expression of genetics seething within the nerve center apparati of the combatants.

The great First World War, holocaustic, horrendous, and infinitely cruel, was a clean, classical example of the forces of biology on the march. Not only was it testament to the blind obedience of the foot soldier and a great many bourgeois officers, it was a revelation of their paucity of intellectual scope and primitive animalistic compulsion.

No matter on what field of butchery a great engagement has ensued, it is a tendency of historians, military writers, and veterans to glorify the site as hallowed and sacred rather than to speak of that which it was, animalistic savagry led by cotillions of fools. Out of honored respect for the departed and brave, the cunning and deceitful, the ruthless and merciful, we enshrine with laurel wreaths the heroes and the valiant.

Should a higher civilization from outer space investigate our history, they would not ripple the liquid in their teacups at its most gory or glorious pages. With clarity they would recognize the fundamental tenent of history's wars as being a mere extension of evolutionary selection. They would comprehend that these hysterically mobilized masses — the French, Germans, Russians, English, Italians, Americans, Turks, Bulgarians, Greeks, Poles, Austrians, Cheks, Hungarians, all that fought in one age or other — were compulsed to preserve or expand the genetic pool that characterizes them in speech, literature and land, and especially the coding of their genes. That varying subracial pools fought as allies or extinguished one another in civil conflict, did not mean prescriptions of sovereign was being obeyed, it meant that each group was fighting to further his own seed, in a same manner as a husband is protective of his wife's issue. It is why no military campaign has succeeded for long with efforts of mercanaries.

Nations maintain identity and cohesiveness. It is a powerful force in protecting that which they have or their advancement. History's pages are replete with the downfalls of nations when they permitted massive seminal invasion. This is what brought the Roman Empire to heel — not Christianity, but the interbreeding with slaves and barbarians, which did not increase their subracial *esprit de corps*. India has never come into Caucasoid greatness for the very same reason that their individuality was integrated with various races. Atilla and the Huns possessed great power and drive, until they sparked out over the decades and centuries by interbreeding with the barbarians they had conquered. Prizes of ancient war was the capture of women, taken into slavery, but also into childbirth. This was the genetic fifth column. It has been the Achilles heel of every nation that permitted the ingression of a divergent subrace. This is what Hitler fanatically railed at in his hatred of the Jews. Yet the Jewish people over the millenniums have managed to preserve a great and intellectual identity. Other nations were fortunate. A rally of Christian forces at the Battle of Tours, 732 A.D., defeated the invading Moors, that saved western civilization.

It is not that interbreeding of races and subraces is morally wrong, or that one race or subrace is superior to another in varying traits — it is that the breeding process is not directed. What emerges are not thoroughbreds, but human mongrels.

Whether it be the noble defense of the Greeks at Thermopylai, 480 B.C., shutting out the Persians, Charlemagne at Tours repulsing the Moors, the French at Verdun, or the Germans at Tannenberg in 1914, in all instances, where the great battles have been waged, territory was an instinctive consideration, but it was not unique. What was basic was the underlying genetic preservation and propulsion of its own identity. Marx's and Lenin's Communist Manifesto states. "Masses of laborers, crowded into the factory, are organized like soldiers. As privates of the industrial army they are placed under the command of a perfect hierarchy of officers and sergeants." This is, of course, an established fact, both in communistic and capitalistic regimes. Hierarchy is not only an instrument of the state, it has been the very basis of society from its beginning. Indelibly, it is registered at the moment of the match of ova and sperm.

Marx bemoans the fact that after the laborer is exploited by the manufacturer, he is set upon by the landlord, shopkeeper and pawnbroker. Unless the laborer is an infant in his mother's arms, which communists like to believe so they may play the mother's role, he, of course, must look after a part of his economics. It is communist contempt for worker's ability, that he was terrorized into the collective farm. This resulted in failure of Soviet agriculture, having to buy massive amounts of grain from the free capitalistic world.

"Thus the proletariat is recruited from all classes of the population." Wrong! The proletariat is never recruited, it is born. Over the centuries, the upper classes have maintained consistent interchange of genetic abilities. Whereas, workers beget workers. There is a salting downward of an insignificant number of higher classes into the worker group and a small invasion of the capable from out of the proletariat into the bourgeois, where they amalgamate.

In western capitalism liberals have strong difficulty understanding what unionism is about. Hubert Humphrey, Ted Kennedy, even Rockefeller, extolled the American labor movement. From the late Humphrey's liberal eyes you would think the labor movement was the future of the age, not just lush votes and privileges that ensues to one of its champions.

Marx had no doubt about it. He wrote in the Manfesto: "The real fruit of the worker's battles lies not in the immediate result but in the ever-expanding union of the workers. It compels legislative recognition of particular interests of the workers." That is blueprint of the communistic road, to equate unionism and legislation with aiding and abetting of communism. Marx states that the bourgeois itself, "supplies the proletariat with its own elements of political and general education; in other words, it furnished the proletariat with weapons for fighting the bourgeois." — meaning, in effect, the mass education as envisioned in America is a useful tool to communistic slavery. It is not that workers do not need education; they most certainly do, but it must be programmed to the needs of working classes and welfare of the total society. Make no doubt about it, unionism is synonymous with communism, outside Russia.

American representatives shove legislature edicted from the Communist Manifesto. Marx deplored capital and described it as a condition for wage labor, saying, "Wage labor rests exclusively on competition between laborers." If you wish to be a good communist, get rid of competition between laborers. That has already been done by the American minimum wage law. This piece of socialistic legislation, out of the Bolshevik Bible, ties the hands of free enterprise, promotes inflation, nourishes inefficiency, stifles competition to foreign markets, and puts millions of workers on unemployment. It is unnatural biologically and nationalistically stupid, serving the interests of vote-gathering politicians. A man's labor is worth exactly what the open market is willing to pay him, no more, no less. An attempt to legislate equality of gene components is self-defeating to all.

Members of Congress and the Supreme Court do not belong to the communist party. They merely carry out Marxist-Leninist dictates. One such rip-off is the watering of the American dollar. Marx had particular aversion to capital. So, when the U.S. government spends far more than it takes in and purposely inflates the value of the dollar, it is not the proletariat that loses, but the upper classes. They are the ones that have saved their money because of their peculiar genetic initiative. A solid dollar — an unchanging dollar — that would, year after year, buy the same amount of bread or beer, is unthinkable to the leftist thieves. Thus, older people who have saved their money throughout their lifetimes find the worth of their dollars decreasing from 11% to 18% a year. This is a very effective method for destroying the power and resources of the upper classes and making them dependent upon the largess directed by Bolshevik-type socialists controlling from a bureaucratic desk.

In the second part of the Communist Manifesto, they make no bones about what their program is. They are to form the proletariat into a class and overthrow the bourgeois political power. Following this, they will abolish private property ownership. The overthrow of political base is old genetic hat. The abolition of private property, which may be considered territoriality, is contrary to instinctive traits. This is coming out of the studies of biology. Nothing so moves the human soul to outrage as an invader occupying sacred soil of the nation. Dissecting the well-based emotion further, it has resulted in a great body of law, centering around the concept: a man's home is his castle.

Communists have nothing to lose. They are dividing the upper classes' wealth. They are taking from the wealthy and successful to distribute to the leaderless. It's a good ploy, even God's servants in the pulpits utilize the same tract, in disguise. "A rich man can't get into heaven." . . . "The poor are blessed." . . . "The meek shall inherit the earth." . . . and so on. Their pronouncements are pre-Marxian sour grapes.

What the men of the cloth are sermonizing is fundamental nature, jealousy. Those who've got it are derided and those who haven't are to be praised. Yet there is another factor — in the proletariat there are a greater number who possess religious genes.

At the time of Marx, during the 19th century, the new industrial world made conditions extremely difficult for the poor. But what was creating the poverty in harsh urban life was not economics, but rather the increase in population. Between 1790 and 1820, in America, the population shot up from four to ten million people. Thereafter it almost doubled every 20 years. This rate of growth was paralleled in contemporary England, where Marx wrote the Manifesto in 1848. America had wide open spaces to absorb this enormous increase, and basically, the proletariat are happiest when on the farms. England and Europe, lacking such space to care for their burgeoning population, could react in two ways — one, relieve lack of agricultural opportunity by crowding them into the cities in miserable row houses where the industrial revolution with its early evils was in full swing; and two, permit people to emigrate. Until the time of the industrial revolution, mankind never had to contend with the intricacies that overpopulation brings.

Vast plagues of the Middle Ages had been halted. Although many great discoveries of medicine — knowledge of bacteria and anesthesia, for instance — came after Marx's death, there were advances in all the fields of medicine which, in turn, permitted rapid expansion of population.

Too many babies meant they had to find work and shelter upon maturity. Consequently, they gravitated to the cities. The sheer weight of numbers produced scarcity and poor labor market competition. This same specter of population explosion is with us today. Unless it is checked, a new Marx may emerge and write from within the social tragedy.

Marx shows adolescence in the field of love, in comedic fashion. His Manifesto reads: "The communists have no need to introduce free love; it has existed from almost time immortal. What the communists might possibly be reproached with is that they desire to introduce, in substitution for a hypocritically concealed, an openly legalized system of love." Indeed, our primate forebearers engaged in a great amount of free love, but only within the structure of dominancy. From primate studies we learn that male dominants possessed females at the time of estrus. Before that period, bachelors snuck in to plant their ineffective seed.

Marx did not understand women. Contrary to opinionation, women will never hold fast for a system of free love, even if legalized. Throughout recent social evolution there has been too much bondage, individual to individual, to reverse the process. Although prostitution is the exception, it is not the true nature of women. Rather, it is a conciliatory gesture toward the proclivities of man.

When the Manifesto declares, "The workmen have no country," Marx shows ignorance of history, thinking that the working people of earth will unite. Roman standards to the French flags of liberty proclaimed solidarity of subracial groups which comprised the nation. Workers showed in valorous deed, from the plains of Prussia to the fields of Andalucia, that men will fight and die needlessly or gloriously for the gene pool they represent. The power of nationalism is so intense, especially when the people are relatively homogeneous, it overcomes all efforts of erasure.

"In proportion as the antagonism between classes within the nation vanishes, the hostility of one nation to another will come to an end." This assertion from the Manifesto is manure. Also from the Manifesto are measures to come in advanced countries:

1. The *abolition of property* is a biological anomality and can only succeed through dictatorship.

2. The *graduated income tax* that is recommended, a reality in most countries, is being legislated by the Reds.

3. Abolition of the *right of inheritance* is a cruel thing when one considers it is the non-organic complement to the organic issue.

Nevertheless, in numbers two and three of the above, nations have seen fit to adjust toward equalization of human rights. In America, adjustment three does not appear reasonable.

Points 4, 5, 6, 7, 8, and 9 are communistic nonsense based on dictatorship. But point 10 has merit in advocating free education for all children in public schools. This is a noble concept, but it has been highly abused. Liberals in nations as America have erected a gigantic wasteful industry for salaries and socialism. They have attempted equal education upon grossly unequal biology, fitting the square peg into the round hole.

The Manifesto concludes with an urging sentence: "Working men of all countries unite." To which we would add, it will do no good unless you have the brains of bourgeois to back you up. So the rallying countercry should be: "Intellectuals of the world unite. Make certain you take care of your brothers, the working people."

As Francis B. Randell, in 1963, in his *Introduction to the Communist Manifesto*, said: "Lenin founded a very unorthodox Marxist party. . . . Lenin learned to be an atheist, a revolutionary, and a socialist from other native Russian revolutionaries, not from Marx. Of all the theories that Lenin combines in his Bolshevik program, the only specially Marxist ideas were that: 1. 'The scientific notions of the inevitability of a social revolution,' and 2. 'The emphasis is on the proletariat.' . . . Nevertheless, Lenin and all the communists ever since have had the unshakeable conviction that they alone are true Marxists. Marx's chief claim to historical claim is the use the communists have put him to."

One cannot retreat from cautious observation that the whole of the communist schema is the proposal of violent revolution with a takeover of nations for gain under the bandit masks of socialistic welfare.

Even Trotsky states: "The error of Marx and Engles in regard to the historical dates, flowed on the one hand, from an under-estimation of future possibilities latent in capitalism. . . ." Humorously, he laments that capitalism has ruined the petty bourgeois at a faster rate than it has proletarianized it — thus creating a middle class buffer zone.

In summary, communism under the light is a political science based upon misinterpretation of biology — that it is a false assertion of the principles of human nature and has succeeded only through tyranny by profiting zealots. Outright fraud in the communistic doctrine is its incapability to recognize genetic inequalities which comprise the human race. Human genotypes cannot be altered by force, nor can the normal hierarchy of dominance-submissiveness be eliminated from the populous. Its concept of a classless society is propagandized skullduggery. The worker is born a worker. No amount of environmental opportunity will change the DNA codes within his organic makeup.

No one knows better than the worker himself that he is incapable of leadership or of entering into the upper classes. He does his special thing, and he does it well. But so do the rest of the human spectrum. Failure of communism to recognize vast individual differences, to chastise and persecute their intellectuals, and to disenfranchise the total mass out of greedy bureaucracy and selfish power-hunger, presents the bogus movement of the century. That it has succeeded is testament to the gross stupidity of the majority of the people. It stands as an obnoxious monument to the leadership of cunning, ruthless dictatorship.

Chou En-lai, beloved late Chinese communist, who exchanged toasts with Nixon, presided over the killings of hundreds of thousands of landlords during the reforms of the early 1950s. Mao was a butcher, and Stalin rivaled in every category the atrocities committed by Hitler. One has but to look back at the anthropological development of society to realize that the human primates are highly susceptible to command and blind obedience. Without leadership society is non-existent. Unfortunately, it is the excesses of leadership that have been the Achilles heel toward a stable political science. Dogmatic principles of socialism, in the hands of bloody totalitarian dictators, has been to appease the masses and hide their own terroristic power.

However, the communists do not have a monopoly on political-biological stupidity. *Time* magazine, January 6, 1976, reported that the District Judge in Chicago ordered the police department to hire 400 new officers — 50% of them black and Hispanic males, 16.5% women, and 33.5% white males — aimed at ending discriminatory hiring practices. Obviously, the judge was a poor biologist and an even worse geneticist. No one can legislate anti-discrimination.

Instead of rebelling at discrimination and inequality, we should welcome them with open arms. Without them there is no society but anarchy. They are the saviors of mankind, not its destroyers.

Communistic ideology is a fleeting political science. It demonstrates how masses of the world's people can be pulled into non-biologic venture. The very fact the communists lay so much emphasis upon classless society points up the underlying biology of class hierarchy.

To combat dangerous challenges to freedom there needs be alteration in democracy. The right to vote should be curtailed to those that have achieved sufficient educational background that the franchise may enjoy its fullest flower. New requirements for politicians are necessary. They should complete prescribed courses in universities, factories, business, and the armed services before they are permitted to run for high office. Before the president of a university, a general in the army, or a Supreme Court Justice is chosen, there is careful consideration of his qualifications, past performances, and ability. On the reverse side, any numbskull can be elected President of the United States, provided he has done no more than succeed in the art of politics.

The greatest issue facing democracies today is recognition of the inequality of citizens and their inherent class-determined nature. Too long this emergence from studies in universities has been ignored with pomposity of old clichés as: "All men are created free and equal." Lincoln emphasized that the new nation dedicated "to the proposition that all men are created equal" was now "engaged in a great civil war, testing whether that nation or any nation so conceived and so dedicated, can long endure."

Lincoln was faced with an issue that had been dealt with peaceably in other nations. Everyone knew that one day slavery would phase out, the same as they knew in World War I and World War II that it was impossible for Germany to invade America. Yet in those times warmongers and those of special interest inflamed the populous into bloody and counter-productive wars.

In a few years after the assassination of Lincoln, the Constitution was amended so that no state could "deny to any person within its jurisdiction equal protection under the laws." Today, no one is regretting the wisdom of the abolition of slavery and the Fourteenth Amendment. What is being questioned is not equality before the law, but the legislative attempts to coerce the inequality of a biologic diverse citizenry into equal DNA alphabetized robots. This is false theory. Though noble in purport, it is impossible in reality. What we are dealing with in the 20th century, and which will be explosive in the 21st, is the resolution of biological diversity and inequality under a form of political dominance. With neatest of fashion, communists have resolved it with a renewed form of slavery, the masters being the Politburo and the communist party who have the authoritarian power and privileges thereunto — of life, death, clothing and shelter — over their faceless masses.

For democracies the issue of equality could denote their death knell. It is only recently that science is cognizant of the vast inequalities among humans. To legislate socialistically, grouping all into the same mother lode, is to court final disaster, whose only resolution will be military dictatorship from the right or the submergence into bureaucratic totalitarianism.

At stake is whether free societies will permit the normal expansion and privilege to which its higher classes are constituted and will benignly enfold the workers to the direction of their best efforts for production and happiness. Will they insist on discouraging initiative, promoting inefficiency and discord, and continue to legislate according to concept of equality instead of toward biological diversity? Will they prohibit desegregation so that genetic pools may remain strong and not be subject to the cataclysm of evolutionary mongrelization?

Millard W. Hansen, a professor of social science at the University of Puerto Rico, writing in the *San Juan Star*, January 1976, puts the issue of equality succinctly. He wrote: "Much confusion, hatred, and public conflict are rooted in this grave dispute. Tocqueville's analysis of the American democracy in the 4th decade of the 19th century found a passion for equality far more intense than a love of liberty. He also perceived that the passion for equality could move in different directions: toward self-improvement, striving to become equal to some now in certain ways superior to one; or toward envy of those now superior and a hatred to be satisfied by pulling down those now above one. Every society in its measure is a structure in which individuals have different, unequal positions of authority, competence, and reward. If this is understood, then equality before the law is a just opportunity for all individuals equally to seek for themselves that position in the social structure appropriate to their will and competence. If this is not understood, then equality can be the destructive envy Tocqueville observed, the hatred of those above which persuades one to pull them down rather than to improve and raise oneself. The fury of many political leaders in the new nations of Africa seem to be sustained more by envy and hatred than by a drive for self-improvement.

"The new admission policy approved May 1, 1975, by the Academic Senate as proposed by Chancellor Ismael Rodriquez Bou of the University of Puerto Rico's Piedras Campus and now under revision by a special committee, was justified by reference to the constitutional and legal provisions here noted. But the effect of the policy was to pull down private school graduates' scores on reasoning in the entrance examination while raising the scores of public school graduates. More. High scores per se were lowered while low scores were raised."

An interesting book, primarily two essays, *Imperialism — Social Classes*, by Joseph Schumpter (a German who died in 1950), is complex, but does give one an opportunity to examine the deficiencies of social scientists who are not cognizant of genetics. It is a work that could be profitably organically translated. At this time we shall point out the voids.

In the introduction to the two essays, Bert Hozelitz states: "Capitalism was based on slogans emphasizing the equality of all men. Yet social classes and class differences continue to exist."

A turn of 180 degrees must be taken from this premise. Capitalism represents the very essence of human diversity and inequality. Within its free framework it permits the individual's genes to express themselves to the maximum of their ability. Although capitalism is a science of economy, it has a direct proportional relationship to the quality, quantity, and disposition of the genes which are entered into its system. Thus, the self-made man is no idle boast as he passes from rags to riches, traversing all social class barriers by virtue of his amino acid codes. Further, social classes and class differences, retainers of authority and position, will continue to exist, even though disguised in communist states, due to the structure of society's underlying gene units.

One exception would be a nation originating from the split of the same human egg to produce identical tenants. Even this most magnificently conceived of socialistic eugenic experiments is destined for failure as soon as one of the citizens went sun-bathing or underwent X-ray examination. We mention one of the factors of evolutionary change resulting from mutational radiation.

Schumpter acknowledged the genius of Marx in recognizing capitalism as a stage in the development of society. Yet we are in error if we feel that in the 18th or 19th centuries capitalism first appeared. Capitalism in its more primitive forms dates back long before the earliest hominids.

Dominants in the earliest of human primate society were the first capitalists. Going back millions of years, their unique innate position of occupational status, or if usurped on contest by contenders moving across a social barrier by aggressiveness, these leaders controlled not only the actions of other tribal members, but had acquired capital in the form of the best territory with its consequent food surplus. They were privileged with preference to the tenderest morsels, the first water, the first crack at the females in heat, and protection on the march on the veldt by vanguards, rearguards, and flankers of their followers.

In the millions of years which followed, these special capitalistic privileges of the chiefs culminated in a blossoming of the first civilization on the Nile, designating full authority to a Pharaoh and his complementing nobility.

When only a few men in a tribe control the food supply, it is authoritarianism! When they dictate the working conditions, accumulate the females unto themselves, and command the best and safest territory, such practices are the very substance of modern capitalism — landlords and landed gentry, monopoly of food supply, political control over working conditions, profit derived from acquisition — all has the happy sound of industrial revolution's social inequalities, but all is based in the historic mission of divergent genes. To the victor goes the spoils, to the genetic capitalist goes the economic privilege. Capitalism is inseparable from biological coding. Not only will it rear its head in adverse societies such as the communists that wish to repress it, it has become and shall always be the alpha in social evolution.

Khrushchev was wrong when he said communists would bury capitalism. The only way capitalism can be buried is to bury the species. Social inequality which perturbs people can be viewed in the most simplistic of areas. Examine a few of the families you know intimately. Look at their tremendous divergence in offspring, where a black sheep, a rather common occurence, drives parents up the wall. Not only are one or two strangers to the group, but the children themselves are so widely parted that one can almost say, "Parents do not raise their own children — they raise foreigners."

When that slot machine lever is pulled in the boudoir, the product does show in many cases similarity to the participants and further similarity due to adoption of habits. But you can leave it at that and find similars in the nation which resemble the parents closer than do their offspring.

If theorists who maintain that germinal plasma is inviolate and that acquired characteristics cannot be inherited are correct, then this lottery game that takes place with offspring is nothing more than mathematical chance. No one need seriously consider offspring as an issuance of his own. We don't subscribe to this and feel germinal plasma is altered by parenteral conduct.

Schumpter speaks of those who contrive to have a declaration of war issued because they gain financially, or because they need a war as a diversion from domestic political difficulties. As we have elaborated, wars are primarily genetic. Genes have interests of their own. They will not fail to express their programming, even though it means holocaust, war or suicide, if their purpose is threatened or if advantage is to be had.

"Most nations furnish an example at some time or other," Schumpter continues, "that seek expansion for the sake of expanding, war for the sake of fighting, victory for the sake of winning, dominion for the sake of ruling." This neatly describes strong inherited patterns, notably territoriality genes, hunting and killing genes, contesting genes, and genes of the dominants. All these factors were selected toward in social evolution and are a consequent part of the body.

Mention is made that from the Punic Wars to Augustus there was an imperialistic period, a time of unbound will to conquest. Throughout recorded history we see surging movements of people seeking land and domination. Thus Attila, Genghis Kahn, Alexander, Caesar, and the European conquest of America demonstrate strong leaders. Yet underneath was a propulsion in the explosive force of the gene pool. Wars are not a cultural epidemic that infects nations. Their powerful outward surges result from increments of gene patterns. It may be these violations of normalcy are the outcome of shifts in gene constituency, reacting to adaptational pressures within short periods of time. Thus, national aggressiveness could be fueled by direct gene change in the germinal cells.

Oftentimes a writer states a genetic truism without realizing it. Thus, Schumpter's "War policy of the state is explained from the necessities of its social structure and from the *inherited* dispositions of its ruling class." There is no doubt upper bourgeois, the ruling class, possess and have inherited the genes of war and aggression.

In speaking of the wars of the 17th and 18th centuries as commercial wars, the surface has not been penetrated. Beneath the economic aspect is the drive for genetic expansion and survival which selects commercialism as an adaptational vehicle.

In a rarely-found reference to nationalities, Schumpter observed, "That the Slavic masses never showed militancy or aggressiveness," and that "there was never imperialistic trends on the part of the Russian peasant. Triumphant tzarism rested on Germanic and Mongol elements." Some day, if it has not been done, war colleges will have texts outlining the potentialities as far as war-making and aggressiveness is concerned, which resides within ethnic racial groups. It will detail the level of innate attributes, in comparative studies, residing outside training; in short, the physical genetics of soldiery — military genotypes.

Schumpter again, "Non-rational and irrational, purely instinctual inclinations toward war and conquest play a very large role in the history of mankind. It may sound paradoxical but numerous wars, perhaps the majority of wars, have been waged without reason. . . ." Without the instinct basis above mentioned, wars could never be waged.

A rising and falling of families within a class is enumerated by Schumpter. Surplus value does not invest itself, but must be artfully reinvested, plowed back into the business to blaze new trails. With astuteness comes the disposition to save. And Schumpter noted how successful families live with curious frugality. Leadership is of prime importance, demonstrating concentration, capacity for work, and self-discipline. Not to be eschewed is risk, trial and error to seek new markets by new business combinations. Contrarily, husbanding resources is characteristic of a declining position.

What Schumpter is saying is that those successful in business are successful because of their innate abilities such as intelligence, drive, stamina, discipline, leadership, and problem perception.

In the majority of capitalistic wealth creations, hard work and cleverness are more responsible than the luck of sitting on top of a farm with oil strata beneath. Ruthlessness, chicanery, bribery, theft and cunning all play their genetic part. One of the most characteristic features of the proletariat working classes is their absolute inability and refusal to risk their sacks of potatoes in business ventures. They can be loaded with encyclopedias which they'll never open, go into debt for junk that makes them poor, and buy over-priced automobiles and gadgetry. Yet to involve them in a solid business venture such as maintaining and renting apartments, buying land or operating their own enterprise, takes super-human effort. Proletariat women are the worst offenders. They are devoid of the genes to see out of their situation. By denying their husbands risk, they continuously relegate themselves to a life of mediocrity.

One can observe from experiences the relative stability with which people born to a class remain there. However, a college education and businesswise knowledge does help many proletariat to move across class lines. Yet what is moving across is not the economically successful, or politically capable, but individuals possessed by their classed genes.

We never did say that the proletarait cannot produce higher classes. What we did say is that because of lower gene structure they produce an extremely high number of their own lower class. It is the same with the upper classes, which produce majorily their own kind. This is aided by intermarriage within the class. Class structure has nothing to do with educational, economical, or environmental opportunity. It is determined at conception. People born to a class often remain there by virtue of parental guidance. There is little gene-class shifting. Over the centuries there has been a consistent tendency for populations to be sifted genetically into their classes.

Classes exist mainly because of division of labor and occupation. The requisites are entirely genetic. We seldom find true mesomorphs as college presidents. The composition of any factory is from bottom to top intelligence, measured by its many faculties. The scholastic system is not devised to promote equality of opportunity, but to screen out the wheat from the chaff, the brilliant from the stupid. Presentation of a sheepskin in a good college is not certification of study, but a testament of genetic ability. It is why American education is the crime of the ages, wasting manpower and funding for the training of the inept. It is only outranked by the waste of military venture.

There are wide class differences in ethnic and subracial groups and in various geographical areas. This difference resulted out of social selection which directed itself toward the adaptability to native environment. Whereas, we find Eskimos of little class distinction, we find the caste system of India abundant.

Isolated duress in the tundra did not permit the luxury of social diversification that the subtropical continent affords. If we were to move the Indians out of India and supplant them by Eskimos, we would have the rare privilege of witnessing a classless society develop genetically into a caste system. Conversely, the Indians in the tundra would sustain their caste programmed acids for only a short period.

Schumpter concludes, "The ultimate foundation on which the class phenomenon rests consists in differences in aptitude. . . . Aptitude may be natural or acquired. Function alone is not the essence of class. Class position and capacity go together."

In Schumpter's analysis of class one has the feeling when he speaks of aptitude in his complex reasoning that he speaks on the periphery of the genetic locus of social organization. He bounces around the object of class without being able to penetrate fully its organic mystery. But in contribution to political science there can be no doubt that he clearly foresaw the physical qualities which stratify the institution.

In the spring of 1978, evidence was coming out of Cambodia that in the past few years they had murdered and maltreated in such a way the non-communistic adult population, that majorily there remained young teen-agers and children, cared for by the state.

This indicates the biological naivete of the Red leadership. The party ploy, in eliminating those with capitalistic indoctrination, is to cleanse the state of the antagonistic and rear good unquestioning, little Red slaves. Yet you cannot be too hard on them because the church, over the centuries, has maintained a more humane policy directed at the religious brainwashing of youth.

Where communist comedy shall unfold will be when the cherished youth reach maturity and many will become "capitalistic roaders" through their underlying gene structure, uninfluenced by tutorage, and become a potent nucleus for the overthrow of the hated regimentation.

Time's essay, January 4, 1982, should be translated into Russian and other languages of the Soviet states, edited to a range of intelligence and flooded into the nation. This perspective analysis, by Strobe Talbot, Erik Amiftheatrof, and Richard Hornick, is magnificently scholarly. As we have deduced in this book, so they come up with communism as being little other than a *ruthless dictatorship*.

"Draconian control . . . zealotry . . . dogmatism . . . bullying . . . acquisition, consolidation, preservation and extension of power . . . self-perpetuating elite . . . power politics . . . coercive methods, and totalitarian precepts that have attained their apotheosis in the USSR. . . . They will not give it up . . . pits the commonwealth against the individual . . . an adversarial relationship between the rulers and ruled . . . suppression of dissenters and the extermination of opponents . . . dictatorship of the proletariat . . . absolute authority . . . bureaucracy, terror and militarism. . . . Party is maintained by every form of violence . . . secret police . . . Red army . . . Stalin presided over the extermination of at least 20 million 'class enemies,' 'enemies of the state,' 'enemies of the people,' and 'traitors.' . . . Brutal way power is often obtained and maintained . . . privileged and self-perpetuating caste. . . . Russians have over the years dominated the leadership . . . produces neither social justice but promises to bestow power . . . controls its subjects by keeping them poor. . . . Priority given to power over prosperity . . . overriding preoccupation with preserving that power . . . political system impervious to economic failure and social demoralization. . . ."

The article gingerly skirts the real issue we maintain — that communism is a perversion of normal evolutionary biological society. They say, "Communism stifles the best while rewarding the worst. Imagination, initiative and man's natural inclination to improve his own lot have been sacrificed . . . true equality throughout an entire society is unattainable, the doctrine of all-encompassing equality can be maintained only by illusion and pretense."

Quite simply, people are superiorly or inferiorly gened and their abilities should be permitted expression and rewarded. This can come through Genetic Democracy, where everyone is represented according to his social value.

"The instinct to acquire, to own, to protect and ultimately to pass on what one has built in life is neither alien nor sinful." In other words, private property — capitalism. *Time* magazine hit that on the nose! That is a true biological instinct: acquisition of materials and territory and the drive to defend them.

Time confirmed a thesis we presented: "Stalin seized an opportunity . . . by the shortsightedness of his allies . . . notably the Americans. By default, they had conceded Eastern Europe to the Soviets as a postwar sphere of influence, and thus to open-ended military occupation." Roosevelt and Churchill were dunces.

IX Class and Democracy
Class is Evolutionarily Mandated. Democracy is Dictatorship by Proxy of the Masses

PEASANTS

ORDON A. CRAIG, in *Europe Since 1815*, states, "Imperial Russia . . . inspired thousands of young men and women of the educated class to go as missionaries to the peasants to preach the cause of revolution; they found little response, having much the same experience as Bazarov in *Fathers and Sons*, who, as Turgenev tells us, prided himself but never suspected 'that in their eyes he was all the while something of the nature of a buffooning clown.' The Populist movement of this period made the mistake of idealizing the peasant and expecting wonders from him, ignoring the fact that he was too illiterate and brutalized to comprehend its message."

The substance in the foregoing is good, but the conclusion is not correct. It was not because peasants were illiterate and brutalized they did not comprehend messages of liberty, freedom, and social revolution. It was the genetic composition of the proletariat is incapable of revolution. Lenin found that peasants would not lend him support, so he relied on city workers. They, too, were proletariat.

The genetic formula which they lacked was supplied by dedicated and ruthless leadership of a comparatively few Bolsheviks. Criminals supplied the spark to genetic lethargy of the masses. Lenin recognized this, and Craig further states, "Lenin believed that the Socialist movement must be led by an elite of professional revolutionaries, since the mass of the workers, without the discipline that such leaders provided, would lose their revolutionary elan and sink into the swamp of reformism."

Right from the beginning communists recognized workers and masses as a bunch of dumb, untrustworthy slobs, and that a dictatorship should be set up to control them as so much chattel of the party.

Even before Lenin, Tchakev taught that successful revolutions depended less upon the action of the masses than upon the vision and determination of a revolutionary elite. We cite these as illustration how formulae of *Genetic Basis of Society* can be used for interpretation of historic movement. History is replete with genetic fact. It is for future historians to re-examine records and bring them to life by genetic interpretation.

DEMOCRACY

Alexis de Tocqueville spent nine months in the United States, from May 1831 to February 1832, studying its political institution. An extremely astute and intelligent observer, this young Frenchman, of an aristocratic family, wrote his classic work, *Democracy in America.* His concern was freedom and democracy should go hand in hand without minority groups, as the aristocratic, being subjected to the tyranny of the majority.

Democracy is a relatively new form of political science, not pre-dating the art of writing. For millions of years before that it was a matter of biological dominants assuming command. It is not to say the democratic process did not appear in consultation with dominants by taking the people into mass acceptance of things as migration or an act of war. De Tocqueville visited at a time when political institutions were being shifted from power of descendants of the founders of the nation — those of aristocratic birth, education and wealth, to common Americans. If we were to define it in communistic terms, the upper bourgeois was being replaced by dictatorship of the proletariat.

President Jackson drew with him into office the lower strata of American society, in a social reformation by proclaiming equalitarianism that was never to depart from the American scene. It resulted in crooked boss-machine politics in major cities where the unscrupulous could wield lower classes for gain.

What was not meeting the eyes in the 1830s, when popular democracy was gaining foothold, was the biologic divergence of people and the necessity to permit the elite, the moral, and the intelligent to govern. De Tocqueville dimly perceived that there was something amiss. Yet, being inbred with the era of liberty and equality, it could not occur to him that beneath the skin of men was where the true solution in politics lay. He saw Americans being pulled into a faceless crowd in which no one stood out excepting an image of the people-at-large. He saw that Americans had forfeited their individual freedom to be ruled by the mob. By this process the majority became king — it imposed its tyranny upon the minority.

Sometimes de Tocqueville missed badly, and as he stated, "I am aware that many of my contemporaries maintain that nations are never their own masters here below, and that they necessarily obey some insurmountable and unintelligent power, arising from anterior events, from the race, or from the soil and climate of their country. Such principles are false and cowardly."

Whoever his contemporaries were, they had it in the bag. The "unintelligent power" which they couldn't place their fingers on was none other than the subracial isolated genetic pool, adapted to the resources of their locale that would express themselves in a manner of selection according to the laws of social evolution, notwithstanding the major vicissitudes of life, strife, climate, and catastrophe.

At no time does *Genetic Basis of Society* disparage the magnificent institution of democracy and its basis in economics, or capitalism which permits individual genetic expression. There is no such thing as a static political institution which can serve man perpetually. Further, it is not democracy which is objected, it is abuses which have attached themselves to it, endangering its existence. We can no longer assume that some basic principles are healthy as racial desegregation, minority rights, and right to strike which can thwart economic growth and the nation's future. Nor can democracy afford lack of discrimination and open immigration policies. Every man cannot be regarded as biologically equal with the equal right to vote, when vast numbers are not qualified for the franchise and are manipulated by the unscrupulous to serve private political interest. Future of democracy should be devoted to repair of its weaknesses.

A realterization of democracy does not mean depriving citizens of happy and fulfilling lives. It means, merely, that benignity shall be directed intelligently and not by mob rule. It means that when a great issue arises, as population explosion with consequent social disruption — war, poverty, chaos — it cannot be left for the populous to decide, incited by foreign religious leaders acting under biological ignorance. They propel mass subjects to emotionalize concern and pressure politicians to eliminate birth control and abortion. Repeal of abortion permitting decision by the Supreme Court would illustrate de Tocqueville's observation of tyranny by the majority becoming reality. The Right to Life, a group opposed to abortion, is improperly named and should be called the Road to Death and Disaster, because this is what will come about if such forces prevail.

De Tocqueville writes of a concern that was ignored in the long Vietnam War: "All of the nations that have been obliged to sustain a long and serious warfare have consequently been led to augment the power of their government. A long war almost always reduces nations to the wretched alternative to being abandoned to ruin and defeat or to despotism by success. War therefore renders the weakness of a government, most apparent and most alarming."

CLASS STRUGGLE

A warning is issued by de Tocqueville that among civilized nations only those that have nothing to lose ever revolt. Marx later picked this up with the cry, "Labor has only its chains to lose." It should be well heeded. Institutions in America as the savings and loan institutions which make it possible for every man to have a piece of territorial action, is wise national stability action. On the other hand, free-wheeling labor can bring America's economy to heel as it has done in England, once national resources run low and world competition is a problem. This, with the demand for anti-abortion law revision and population explosion with overcrowding and smaller job market, could spell real disaster. Genetics involved in the foregoing is a biological inversion in which the majority, the proletariat, become dictators, and the bourgeois, with their talents, become submerged. No crisis is imminent, but the leftist movement is on collision course with U.S. biology.

A strong warning has been issued by de Tocqueville: "If ever the free institutions of America are destroyed, that event may be attributed to the omnipotence of the majority, which may at some future time urge the minorities to desperation and oblige them to have recourse to physical force." Clamor for equalization means not bringing the proletariat up with the bourgeois, which is genetically impossible, but pulling the upper classes down. This could be the cue to dictatorship on the right which would be successful because political power will depend more on technical and mental skills than upon masses for cannon fodder. Thomas Jefferson said, "The tyranny of the legislature is really the danger most to be feared and will continue to be so for many years to come."

De Tocqueville was a fabulously good prophet. He clearly saw a hundred years ahead when he spoke of manufacturing aristocracy which was growing up. Cautioning democracy to keep its eyes peeled in this direction, he said, "For if ever a permanent inequality of conditions and aristocracy again penetrates into the world, it may be predicted that this is the gate by which they will enter."

Not knowing genetics, he could hardly have surmised the biological inversion of the Russian Revolution, placing labor in power, nor the counter-revolutions that place kings, sovereigns, and intellectual oligarchies in command. The gateway to the future will be the genetic revolution and instead of one great happy polyglot family of equals similarly colored, there will be a wild race to evolve genetic superiors, separating forever the idea of equality in human biological progress.

Instead of a greater intermingling between classes, those select groups of humans treasuring their better genes will intermarry and, under the auspices of genetics, will diverge rapidly from the mainstreams. To do otherwise would be to flaunt the entire range of human evolution. Mankind is now passing through a brief period of ideological fadism, which will terminate as nations begin the most difficult and dangerous of human experiments: controlled breeding and rejection.

Britain's lesson is to be heeded. At the turn of the century her capital savings began to diminish. At the end of World War I she had to repudiate her war debt to the United States. By the end of World War II the downhill progress was precipitated. Governmental spending had become unnecessarily excessive while productivity was stagnating and exports receding. When the labour government took over from Churchill's wartime coalition, it envisaged a socialistic Utopia.

What went wrong with this colossus of nations in half a century out of her magnificent centuries past? Where were her great but in tombs of Westminster crying "Hold!" This splendrous citadel and custodian of highest form of politically-scienced art — democracy — is entering mediocrity, the panacea of socialistic commonness — the end of greatness.

That which wrought this degradation was not lack of courage on battlefields, nor valor on high seas, nor defeat — that did not return her battle standards intact. Neither was it an act of pestilence, infections or epidemics, nor did strong muscles of workers relax or resourceful quick minds of its citizenry fail. From the funeral procession of the giant to the coronation of the queen, no one seems to have witnessed the landmark.

But it was there. Rest in peace, brave England. Thy mission upon the earth has terminated. Thy historians have recorded similar exodus of civilizations as sheafs of hieroglyphics to be filed neatly in library rooms of ivy-covered universities. That the majesty of England should come to pass few men visualized the real cause.

Basic to the tragedy was biology. It was genetic programming that had permitted bastardization. Not only by an influx of foreign bloods, but by a more subtle form of biological anarchy; that is, inversion of normally programmed class structures, a denial of biological force which springs from strong dominancy and hierarchy relationship.

The plague bacillus that invaded England centuries past, carried by flea-infested rats, sending a third of the population to their graves, was no less insidious than adoption of unqualified democracy. Exacerbating the malady was a labor government and liberal proponents in the body politics with spurious notions of socialism and human equality.

As long as human inequality existed, at whose social injustices great writers as Charles Dickens railed, England would be forever mighty. It is not inhumanitarian to treat people as unequals. What is inhumane is when lesser-gened individuals — proletariats, liberals, laborers — are permitted to run government and exercise powers by tyrannical rule of the majority by simply counting heads instead of assessing what is within them.

The Decline and Fall of the British Empire was due to acedence to hysteria of proponents of unrestricted democracy — liberty, equality, and socialism. No nation with such an escutcheon may maintain for long its identity of greatness unless its lands are underlain by vast resources of hydrocarbons, its mountains flush with timber and fresh water, mines of copper and iron ore seemingly endless, its shores abounding with fish, and its farmlands fertile and moist. That alone is a prop to any people under any form of government, until the wells run dry.

For England to forsake privileged class status, for her to penalize the ambitious and brilliant, for failure to yoke the worker whose geneticism is geared to the plow and not to the throttle of government, for the error in not recognizing democratic equality pertains only to legal necessities, was contrary to biological social thrust and greatness. Human equality equates with human absurdity.

BASTARD CAPITALISM

There has been a bastardization of classical capitalism in the participation by workers in management policy of corporations. In majority of instances, it has resulted in failure — especially where biological guidelines are not observed. The worker in gene programming has inherited subdominant structure, and his lower intelligent quotient is incapable of managerial ability as well as foresight and analysis. So what happens is that workers' vote is delivered docilely into hands of a few bourgeois labor leaders who are only interested in lining their pockets.

In England, in the steel industry, it takes three men to produce what one man does in Germany. In capitulation to the worker who is represented by leaders, there has been injected increased costs and failing competitive position. There resides a subversive power, strikes, work stoppages, slowdowns, favoritism, and seniority with sufficient force to cripple industry.

Where participation of labor is valuable is in the field of health, safety and working conditions. For wages labor should not have the right to strike because they already have the prime right individually to refuse work and to work for whomever they please; contrary to communist system where occupation is determined by hierarchy bosses.

Does labor have a right in the boardroom to share in profits of industry? Biology says not, because the industry is not of his making; it has not been constructed from his genius, initiative or imagination. It has succeeded not because of him, but in spite of him. Its blood is the capital that has accrued from stockholders. Decisions can only represent capital entrusted to industry. Since labor has not contributed, since he has not bought his ticket, he has no right to ride the train.

CAPITAL

Consider what this much maligned word "capital" is. It is the additive values of human effort. It is not an insensible precious metal, bales of cotton or barrels of petroleum. It is not grey-bricked factory walls, railroad sidings or overflowing warehouses. It is human tangible asset. It is as much a part of communistic countries as capitalistic ones.

It represents amassed human effort, from the geologist's discovery of the mineral, to the fellows that staked them. It represents the laborer who forewent extravagence to invest. Mother's hands contributed their part of hard work to educate the intelligent who went forth to invent, innovate, and compete successfully in the markets. Soldiers, fathers, educators, ministers, pioneers, and promoters — all contributed their share of pain, thought, and sweat to this mass of liquified labor. For those who blazed the industrial trail, who stored this precious commodity for utilization in creation of jobs and derivement of profit must go homage. Without capital there is anarchy. Man's first capital derived from stone projectile points created by artisans who were repaid for their lithic efforts in profit of game. Capitalism came into being with man's first society. Those of skill, industry, initiative, thrift, foresight, and leadership were rewarded. These savants provided for the welfare of all and have historic right in control of this acquired human effort — capital.

The most rabid capitalist agrees that there has been injustices and monopolistic practices under the system. But these offenses have been minusculine when compared to the avalanche of advantages provided by capitalism, spreading abundant wealth, opening doors to opportunity, permitting personal freedom — to worship God without recrimination.

INNATE DRIVE

Drive has been indicated by John Pfeiffer in his *Emergence of Man* — "Most Americans are 'low achievers' in the middle class educated. They behave as if they do not care about getting ahead. One out of a hundred exhibits a strong urge to achieve. A quarter percent are moderately ambitious." This ties in nicely with proportion of population we designate proletariat.

Not being ambitious doesn't indicate laziness. The majority of people work like ants. They encase their lives in single occupational endeavors. They do everything to make their lives miserable. A symphony concert artist practices, rehearses and rehearses — there are sessions of criticism, praise for but a few performances. True, also, with the medical profession. Instead of making life easier, they make it more complex with regulations to keep them busy, agitated and in conflict. They are like the worker bees that know only how to work. The laborer resists violently when faced with a job wherein he must think. A ridiculous classification of a "laborer" being a deprived person by education, not by "genetics," is myth.

THE GRINDS

There is a group of dedicated individuals, "the grinds," born to all classes. They feel they are gift to humanity: work long and tedious hours, refuse to be supplanted, carry intolerable conceit, do not drink often. They are socially bland. Like social insects they toil incessantly. Others regard them with amusement, respect or pity. From childhood to death they are compulsed to do their thing that they know best. Mere automatons of tissue, usually financially successful, but dreadfully boring and uninteresting. Their work compulsion results from mesomorphic energies and low sensual abilities. They were important genotypes in our prehuman past. One of their stereotypes is the miser. At the other end are happy workers — competitive, highly dependent upon dominants, and properly supervised in jobs fit to them.

LEADERS

In chickens there is progressive linear dominance among the group members. Referred to as the "pecking order," upper class dominants are permitted at the feed unmolested. No one challenges the leaders. Everyone pecks below them, according to rank. If a leader is removed, another immediately assumes alpha position and the others permit this dominance as if by consent. Acquiescence to behavioral dominance demonstrates similar situation in humans.

Only leaders contend leaders. Masses of society docilely line up to cast ballots in secret timidity. It is the ruling class, the aristocracy, royalty, politicians and economic leaders that direct their whimsies, while the majority of populous fall into step no matter how tragic the direction. It is essence of the term, "hard core." Revolutions are directed by few strongly-gened dominants. Wars are waged by the upper portion of a percent of combatants, the followers dying without notion of the rational. Inane clashes of world wars were machination of dominants. National honor, economics, rivalry, rage, territorial aggression were mere wisps in the hurricane jealousies of strong leaders. World wars were "people pawns" sacrificed to unbearable egoisms of Hitler-Roosevelt-Churchill-Mussolini-Stalin-Tojo dominants. Few came forth to challenge leaders. It was chicken acquiescence to behavioral dominance ingrained within human structure. If it were not so every nation would have met with its own revolution, contending the insanity.

Clearer still is the pecking order in military establishments. Dominance hierarchy of a biologic nature is reinforced by punishable codes. Few privates challenge generals. Yet there is a new liberty mechanism emerging in art of "fragging," wherein a subordinate displays his opposition by hidden attacks upon superiors — being none other than hierarchy challenge.

INEQUALITY

Fundamental point in social evolvement is inequality. Mutation and variance may be the fine scientific writing, but biological progress and evolution is due entirely to production of unequals. Within society we see stately order of hierarchy and inequality. Unfortunately, fools attempt to legislate human equalness when underlying genetic codes are unequal and strive mightily for unequalness.

More important inequalities within societies are not chance happenings, but purposive programming of occupational and rank roles, to further harmonious advancement of the entire group. A society without caste and privilege is no longer a society, but a tower of babble which cannot exist.

When we abandoned food gathering for hunting prey and subjected ourselves, outside tree protection, to greater predatory risks, we acquired genes of socially structured necessity. For example:

(1) Leadership... DD
(2) Homosexuality .... hh
(3) Workers.. WW
(4) Feminine protectionism................................ MM

(5) Autocracy leadership. . . . . Dd
(6) Submissiveness. . . . . ss
(7) Cooperative - Gregariousness . . . . CG
(8) Killer. . . . . KK
(9) Explorers and pioneers . . . . PP
(10) Caring in disease and charity CC
(11) Rage inhibition R1 R1
(12) Occupation . . . . O^{1-20} O^{1-20}

A prehistoric clan's genotypes from a hundred male individuals may have been composed with the following: 2 leaders, 5 autocrats, 15 killers, 2 explorers, 65 mass, and 11 technicians - cooks and flint artists.

An advertisement by Continental Assurance Company points up rarity of true leadership when a key executive is gone, "and with him go the magic. The quick mind, the irreplaceable insights. The priceless contacts. The ability to inspire people. The rare charisma of a born leader. Without him things don't seem to work anymore. Your number two man remains a number two man . . . even in the number one position. Then it begins: morale drops, etc."

What in effect is being said is that a leader is innate, possessed with unique unexplainable qualities, obviously non-equalitarianism and non-environmentally or opportunistically produced. Most, if not all, number two men have had equal or even better educational opportunity. The critical distinction is that, as the ancient saying goes, number one was a born leader — the parental genes spewed out a type to dominate others.

THE MASSES

In the middle '70s there was a popular country music TV program aired Saturday evenings. It was infuriating to those of I.Q.'s above 100. But it appealed broadly to the lower-class labor and farmer market. With a format of corny jokes, supportive backdrops of pretty sexy girls, and "gitar" vocals, it rolled them in the rural aisles. One item was outstanding. Intellectuals couldn't get the jokes. It was as if they were speaking a foreign language. To be sure, some jokes were obvious, but they were keyed to unlock lower-class ears. Likewise music programmed itself to hill-billy recipients. There was a further incongruity to the upper classes in that fat, slovenly and ugly humans were glorified.

Future Lenins seeking the proletariat may well poll similar programs which so effectively separate class audiences. They are absorbed in sports, beer, children, wages, and fun. They relinquish their minds by proxy to clever bourgeois politicians. No revolution was ever won by the masses. Always in forefront of chaotic governmental change are genetically born leaders. It is why communists consciously but without being aware of the basis, jail, liquidate, make insane or eliminate true leaders and dominants.

POWER

In a capitalistic society there is opportunity for the individual to drift into economic slots which benefit his inherited geneticism. With communism and equalitarianism there is little area for individual genetic expression or entrance into a normally programmed social niche. Outside the party one finds great minds as Solzhenitsyn's and within boot-black clowns as Khrushchev.

In dogma of communism is drive to overthrow vested authority by revolutionary means. It is a sorry page of history because it is promulgated by biological heresy. Instead of liberating masses, it yoked natural dominants of society to garbage details. Rather than creating a classless society which is genetically absurd, it inverted society which will one day be bound to unravel. It is reason official Russians are insanely suspicious of outsiders and why they are unpredictable. Those that have power did not come to it by the natural biological sifting. In consequence they react from high insecurity and inferiority because they are not truly dominants but have been thrust into their roles by vagaries of history.

An equally unfortunate bastardization of social biology was seen in fascist dictatorship of Hitler and Mussolini. Although a considerable floration of individual capacity was permitted and class levels allowed to colonize, there was extremely false imposition of a single absolute master at the top which dominated. This was out of proportion to biological sensibility. Consequent defeat was its final result.

General Franco of Spain was exception. He came to power as a nation was being torn by anarchy and communistic subversion, at a time when Spain was in throes of worldwide depression, and at a time when agitators were poisoning minds of workers. Within this maelstrom emerged a truly strong soldier-leader. That he was dictatorial and vindictive is not to be denied. Yet the Spanish had excellent memories of their horrendously bloody civil war. It is tribute to the man, be he fascist, a dictator, Franco gave his nation thirty-six years of peace and elevated it from a devastated, desperate land to one of prosperity.

George Orwell, author of *1984*, excellent perceptional novel, went to Spain to fight on the communist side in 1936. Disillusioned, he wrote *Homage to Catalonia*. He was no prophet. Although he came to understand treachery of the communists, who didn't care for the people but only their own aggrandizement, he relates how he felt the Franco regime would be worse than the government-backed communist group. Further, under government communist group there would be distribution of land. For so excellent a later-day writer, it was a very naive viewpoint. Yet it is interesting the manner in which communists sold ignorant proletariat, liberals, and intellectuals.

LAND AND CAPITALISM

The communists never gave anything to anybody, especially land. They take it unto themselves, utilize it for their own selfish purposes, command its direction yet proclaim its ownership to be shared communally. How can there be communal ownership? "Ownership" means that title and control of the land resides with individuals, groups or corporations. "Ownership" does not mean the control and utilization of land, as residual within the dictatorial edict of government.

Nonetheless, the communists did stumble quite by accident upon a biological gem of which they had no knowledge of its basic value. Flying in opinionized dreams, they envisioned land reforms. They don't own the land. Since it is not theirs, they can gleefully incite others into rebellion to partition it freely. To the lower-class laborer this is heady drink, excellent basic propaganda. Besides being an excellent sales tool, he never understands its tremendous elevating power.

Within any culture there has been and will be land abuse. In nations as South America and colonial Mexico it was a severe injustice. Yet one cannot from the history of a few instances compile a dogma of land distribution or equality. It is far more complex.

Like blind pigs, communists stumbled upon a big acorn which was biologically significant. Their loud protestations against bourgeois and fervent interest in alleviating oppression of masses hit juicy kernels when they spoke of redistribution of land on an equitable basis, or merely a no-land policy in which everyone owns everything and shares it as comrades. Their stars rose before the new biological science discoveries, that throughout species in the animal kingdom, territoriality is an instinctive genetically programmed compulsion. From birds to dogs, seals to kudos, the possession and defense of one's own territory not only brings rewards, mating opportunity as well as substance, but provides basis for evolutionary selection.

Quite by accident the communistic manifestos fell squarely into the money when they appealed to the basic bio-inheritance of territorial ownership. Not being scientists but politicians, they understood the response but not the mechanism. And, as usual, this led to their half-assed theory of communes.

They made it on the first premise that territoriality does appeal to each individual. This must be qualified because there are large quantitative differences within individuals. We find tremendous drive toward ownership of land and material objects in the upper classes. On the other hand, communists fall flat on their faces when they parley land reform into communes, communal effort, and national agriculture. It is why they are the world's worst farmers. Despite years of unimpeded efforts, they look to capitalistic nations to provide them sufficient foodstuffs to prevent widespread famine. In Soviet Russia there are few small plots farmed by peasants on a semi-capitalistic style which because of the initiative provided, put out high productivity in comparison with the larger communal units, much to the embarrassment of the government.

A premise that since human geneticism is oriented positively toward territorial ownership, group ownership would be superior and more efficient. Here is where the egg is laid. Group ownership has been proven without doubt to be less efficient because it lacks individual motivation. Nobody protects their home and possessions better than the owners. In grouping of the instinct of territoriality, one moved away from biology into theoretical politics. This abnormal move was done because groups can be more easily dominated than individuals. It was hoped by destroying individual ownership, there could be no blossoming of small capitalists, in which would be found inequalities in wealth and position.

The communists don't care whether people are fed or whether they perish by millions, as has passed with their famines and purposive famines in their short history of dominance. All that matters to Soviet masters is they exert control, even though capitalism will bring greater prosperity. To embrace capitalism they must admit to the great biological flaw in their doctrinal ideology. It is their point of no return. None of their double-talk of contradiction can pull them out of this biologically false tailspin.

In the early formulating years of society communal effort was of utility in group protection. This institution went on to evolve into tribal and national armies. From the beginning the dominants had their special tree and females. This evolved into small groups with their own caves in a location that might not have been to their choosing but was certainly theirs to call their own.

If one considers the absurdity of multiplying individual nuclear family unit in millions into a biological bureaucratic monstrosity, abnormal to genes as communistic collectivism dictates, one can perceive why communism must alter basic precepts or forever be nailed to the cross of tyrannical despot of the masses.

Fortunately, capitalism owes its incredible agriculture productive success not to fertile lands, nor to nationalities which farm them, but to freedom of genetic expression. Excepting for national defense and home ownership, very little excepting farming may be an expression of territoriality programmed genes. "Communalism" blocks initiative and stifles innovation. Capitalism provides productivity and progress. If it is left alone by socialists who infest democratic parliaments, it will continue to lead.

Humans are born capitalists, not communists. Their innate drive is toward their own betterment and that of their immediate families. It is not to be subservient to bureaucracy. As certainly as a great nation's constitution proclaims liberties, rights and freedoms, just as certainly DNA codes proclaim biological rights of individualism, of inequalitarianism, of religion, and freedom from mass tyranny.

FEUDALISM

Feudalism is classically designed as a triumvirate of authority, consisting of sovereign royalty, military leaders, and a religion hierarchy. From this base of dominance, commencing with the early Dark Ages, they established small city states which radiated power into the outlying countryside. Feudalism was not authoritarian dictatorship in which masses were incarcerated in serfdom. It was development of a symbiotic relationship between classes of society, which leveled themselves according to genetic capacities.

Not as Candide envisioning satirically that the world was the best of all places, feudalism was for its time and place, for its era of technology and medicine, the best of all possible systems. Mao Tse-tung had railed against the evils of feudalism that war carried tardily into 20th century China without considering it was the only system that could achieve satisfactory livelihood in the level of technology, education, and resources that were available in so backward an agriculture base.

What made feudalism successful for so long was not that it was an oppressive dictatorship of the people, but rather a protected defensive island in which the abilities of all were used to their maximum. Formation of walled cities and castle complexes was a necessity to survival of all within the feudal unit. Protection has been a major effort of civilized society, and feudalism, with turrets, redouts, massive walls, moats, gates, and armed hierarchy, satisfied this prime consideration.

The military had "class" stratification, as it does today. There was no problem for the valorous, strong, intelligent, and proven to move forward — the lesser geneticisms remaining at lowest levels, accepting command in the same fashion of early primate social groups. There was tendency to consolidate geneticisms into national groups. This spilled over as colonialism in which diverse genetically isolated drift groups were subjugated by national imperialisms.

In the 20th century, imperialism or exploitation of colonies was too big a bite for foreign geneticisms to swallow. This led to retreat by major expansionistic nations to fortresses of their own people. Colonialism could only succeed where the governed were of similar geneticism as the governors.

This has been the fallacy in colonialism by which the blood of the conqueror did not preserve pure lines. In the United States, no such error was made, and rather than integrate with natives, the Mongoloids were wiped out — prices indiscriminately placed on their heads — to be displaced by whites.

Feudalistic leaders, although small in number, represented dominants. In animal societies, dominants achieve majorily leadership from genetic inheritance. One would suppose from the ruling class that a large percentage of offspring would be dominants. However royalty may beget royalty in the political sense, it is the Achilles heel of the monarchial system that a successful king as often as not begets a soppish son. The inheritance of dominance is biological and it was non-recognition of this fact that eventually unseated the majority of royal houses in Europe.

On the other hand, within democracies is ability for dominants to advance into sovereign positions. This has been bastardized by substitution of weak and treacherous political characters gaining power by chicanery and incitation to roles which they are not biologically destined.

Within the small complexity of the feudal system, royal sovereignty was not as tyrannies of today. What feudalism did provide was a stable center of administration, law and armed forces. Masses would have perished, huddled in thatched hovels, fearful of bandit raids that perpetually harrassed groups not protected by lords of the manors.

BOURGEOIS DISUNITY

Outside of communistic "classless" division, classification of people is roughly 90% proletariat - the workers; and 10% bourgeois - the owners of capital, land, education, brains, ambition, drive, and money. This is a division that poses serious problem in the "Revolution to the Right." It has not been a difficult task for revolutionaries under banners of Leninism-Marxism to unite ignorant masses of proletariat. But imagine bourgeois with their intellectually warring factions, supreme disloyalty, hatred of one another, marching shoulder to shoulder to regain communistic territory. It is the bourgeois having too many brains, opinions and differences to achieve unity of uneducated workers dedicated to a cause. One needs to attend political and business sessions of doctors, lawyers, educators, to know that they are filled with selfish people.

Mao Tse-tung screamed against rich peasants, landlords, local tyrants and evil gentry representing 10% of the population and, finally, killed or displaced them. It is with this upper 10% wherein the benign political future of the world resides. All communists have done is to substitute their bloody dictatorial selves. In identical fashion where dictatorship is in effect a small group to the right perform this same governmental structuring, but do not have the suavity of mass propaganda originated by the leftists. Leftist dictators are of inferior genetic structure, because they originated within the masses. The rightist dictatorial groups are of higher gene caliber and education, granting a greater degree of freedom and envisioning their political world with greater biological accuracy. There are exceptions.

The form of government native to man's genetic disposition is a sovereign or dominants who achieve power by right of birth — or by physical prowess. Good genetic inheritance which provides physical superiority places these individuals in leadership roles. We see in primate society dominancy is genetically inherited. Individuals in primitive societies subservient to dominants, upon occasion challenge their position. But, by and large, 90% of society, be it animal or human, is willing to follow tranquilly. Not only are they willing to follow leaders readily, they are at a complete loss if not led. Within their genetic structure is groupings subjecting them to obedience. Revolutions and capitulation of established regimes have never been won by the masses. The masses fought bravely, but only because they were inspired by the very few that had proper genetic composition.

QUALIFIED DEMOCRACY

Pure democracy is unnatural because it contains no qualifications which consider inequalities in genetic inheritance and consequent contributing roles toward good of the entire society.

Why should a few male discontents have ability to tie up a city because they belong to a transportation union? Why should workers frustrate production because they are misled by Mafia-style leadership? Finally, why should the worker have a vote when he does not understand issues on which he is voting? It is little better to say that when he votes, he designates one who will make decisions for him. But how can this represent society when politicians' consent derives from the unenlightened?

In a qualified democracy those that vote, those that run the affairs of the nation, have earned such ability by their level of education, achievement or contribution to said society. England once had been a qualified democracy and reached great achievement. For it was manipulated in such a way that regardless of democratic practice, upper classes were clearly entrenched in the management of affairs.

Recently, with advent of socialistic schema, granting of equalitarian rights, and concept of Utopian welfarism, the masses, who are incapable of government, have disrupted the economy of Britain with strikes, welfarism demands, and shifts to the left, that they have made what was a first-class nation into a second-rate, inflation-ridden, almost bankrupt power. A temporary reprieve has been effected by North Sea oil discovery and shift to the right with the conservative government.

Many have understood the danger in socialism winding up in communistic dictatorship. Socialism enters by the back door of the democratic process proclaiming benefits to the people. It is the work of traitors that wish to destroy government for the aggrandizement of their own power. Some day democracies will understand that they cannot afford the liberty of socialistic components under name of free society. It is folly in the name of democracy to permit those whose intent it is to modify democracy that it becomes enslaved within liberalism — which is non other than communism.

POLICE

They are proletariat in origin and bourgeois in service. Their genetic disposition gives them certain uniqueness. Mesomorphic in character, they are brave and commendable. No civilization has been able to succeed without their effort. While they are not of intelligencia, they possess severe loyalties to dominants. Their genetic composition was formulated in selective evolvement of man's society, that is, his political society. This could have gone back millions of years. Dominants necessitated assistants they could trust who were loyal and who carried out commands for the integration of society.

This group — disciplined, courageous men, often target of criminal attack work for comparatively low wages for the risk they undertake, donate fidelity to the state — could come into being by none other than programmed genetic occupational type.

For communist parties to have enveloped this magnificent proletariat into their own scheme, elaborate it into a sinister secret police, confuse it with their own dictatorial power, then say society is classless, is a comedy sentence. In actuality, the Communist Party is one giant police force.

RESTAURANT GENES

In the advancement of primates, food-sharing was imperative. Male hunting groups needed to return meat to the tribe where women gathered nuts, fruits, roots, and vegetables. A pregnant woman could not hunt, neither could a woman with children effectively participate in the chase. So sharing developed. In coordination of raising the family, fathering and hunting, natural selection gave preference to individuals who exceeded in these arts. Charity genes are a part of restaurant gene complex. It was necessary to provide for the elderly and sick. It paid dividends by providing a source of aged wisdom and salvage of labor power. Charity was fruitful in aiding neighbors, who would reciprocate.

Malicious restaurant genes are what involves people in the shaky business. It's one thing to cook well at home, but to transfer the architecture from that drawing board to a screaming cook is quite another matter. All over the world there is a glut of restaurants, and indeed, a very few are good. Yet people flock into this act. Restaurant genes have gotten to them.

Take note, cooks are genetically born. Obviously, too many cooks spoil the soup. Natural selection recognized that. Evolution selected toward, say, two good cooks per hundred individuals. These cooks were primarily women. These CC dominate genes are to entrust to a few individuals' daily menus — supervise ingredients and cooking. Lesser people with the recessive cc and the heterozygous Cc genes were needed to tend the fire, collect beetles and nuts, dig roots and bring in half-spoiled meats.

To make something tasty from grasshoppers, dandelion, or overripe fowl is evolutionary priority. Survival occurred more often with capable cooks. It is not a rarity in foreign countries to find putrid fowl or fish so skillfully concealed beneath herbs, spices, garlic or onion. One is unaware of the deception — until later. Possibly this type of cooking is not the worst. It may be benefit to one's intestinal tract following historic procedure. Slaughterhouses and food-processing plants could be too sanitary. We may need contamination within foods, excluding pathogens, to give us healthy intestinal flora rather than being dependent upon harsh chemical laxatives.

The majority cannot cook, no matter how well-trained. Like Einstein had mathematical genes specifically unique and rare, cooks likewise have sparks of genius. A real cook has great sense of taste and smell — expert sense in judging quantities of ingredients. She has a fantastic memory for quantities of food involved, and unbelievable skill in culinary process. There are a few ways in which these CC genes can be recognized phenotypically — good cooks are usually fat, suffer from arthritis, are short and short-stepped. They have unwielding opinions, plus laboring class genes. Rarely are they drinkers. They have laboring type's stamina, make good citizens and mothers, are religious and, above all, eat well and consistently. We salute these excellent CC genes that will soon disappear as we direct toward fast food and mechanically-processed items to bypass these heroes of palate.

SOCIAL GROUPING

In evolutionary ascent we selected toward small traits that provided survival. It was millions of years over which we straightened our vertebral column, altered our pelvis, and stood upright. This gave us advantages — ability to see from greater height, ability to run, ability to have our upper arms free from locomotor activity to be used in carrying objects, fighting, hunting, and manipulating skills.

In the thousands of things we selected toward, there was only slight advantage each century. It is not unreasonable that we selected toward desirable components for the group. Socially-grouped life advances because social order outweighs the sum total of individuals composing it, a Gestalt. Wasps, bees, ants, and wolves have inherited instincts relating not to physical characteristics but genetically programmed neurogenes which determine culture of their social order. It is only a small reference from here to envisage that as social primates developed, small variant advantages in discrete individuals could be extremely advantageous.

Most of us have the compassion gene, sympathy gene, paternal-love gene in a basic form. Some may have the healing component. This was passed to about one in fifty males. He became the Shaman, witchdoctor, priest healer, the modern medico. In a hunting party, in event of injury, if only one possessed this remarkable gene it would figure highly in survival of the group. A wounded man would be tended, carried back to base and nourished unto health. The healer, even in blatant fakery, does endow measures of comfort. Within medical school, internship and residency, there is idealism and sympathetic humanitarian effort. It is only when those of healing bent radiate into the world of money and politics that a more detached individual emerges. It appears that money and authority, emanating from medical associations and governing bodies, sour the true projected development of the gene complex. In the small hospitals which I know, one surgeon belted another in the mouth, another sued a colleague for slander, and acrimonies by the truckload took place among members — not because of healing effort but because money, success, and power were involved.

Conduct of doctors contrasted sharply with conduct of nurses, who are paid a fixed fee and who, creating unnecessary surgery or pampering care, have no renumerative advantage. One notices a higher dedication. This arises through the complex set of maternal genes and fulfillment of their role.

However, in fairness to the medical profession, there is a basis of charity, sympathy, compassion, and good medicine. It is not permitted to flourish because money is an eternally dominant prod and because organizations are selfish in purpose, not wishing free enterprise or competition. Medical organization is monopolistically-oriented. They will spend a fortune to track down some poor unlicensed charlatan, but not a nickel to relate medically-induced diease, "iatrogenic" disease, or the huge malpractice to health engendered by the drug industry, aided and abetted by the medical profession. If clever and smart socialized medicine were forthcoming with limitation and equality of fees, then medical costs could be cut by a half with equally good results. Hypochondriasis may be considered as a paradox. In this instance, as in those possessed with thieving genes, survival takes place because of feigned illness. You can tell a hypochondriac that he is not ill, and he'll not believe you. That is because it is on a subconsciousness genetic basis. One who inherits these genes, Hy Hy, travels life with a never-ending series of illnesses, most of which are false, and travel from body location to location. The holder of these society parasitical genes, no matter how intelligent, can never be convinced or treated out of their phantom symptoms.

In the development of social order, compassion and medicine were necessary to salvage injured members. Hypochondriacs soon developed, were selected toward, knowing they could ride this phase throughout life. Who gets the grease? The squeaking wheel. They perform no useful function to the social group. They enter by way of the back door, known as parasitism. One might mention that it is a very dangerous diagnosis for any doctor to make because, if he is wrong, it could be a fatal error. Yet over the years, if one carefully observes these people, he becomes amused and deaf-eared. Then, too, one should remember that beside the host of imaginary diseases they conjure up, they do run the risk of all the diseases the rest of us are subject to.

BIGOTRY

The bigots, uneducated, those that look at a race and condemn it from prejudice — this is a difficult concept to comprehend. If we examine differences between whites and blacks we should find relatively the same number of occupational groupings, as dominants, workers, homosexuals, soldiers, pioneers, artists, prophets, and priests. However, there can be an offset between the two because, in the development in specific environmental niches, selective needs differed. Hunting in the north, the building of shelters, development of agriculture, fishing and seafaring, required different specialists than individual gathering and less developed hunting of Africa. There was less need of cooperative effort. Mobilization for wars was not of prime necessity in the retention of land.

Most white people are subconsciously bigoted against the Negro, as are all races likewise one against another. It is difficult for them to see other than a race as a whole. As the Mongoloid race has its share of criminals, misfits, laboring people, artists and geniuses, so do other races. Yet there is a tendency to condemn the whole rather than accept the individual. Colored professional people who, after prospering, moved to the suburbs away from their ghettoed brethren, find little difference in white counterparts who moved away from the working-class people. But there is a wide disparity of success between the races. This is not the fault of opportunity, but rather ecological placement in evolution.

One sees migration of Negroes from cold hostile northern cities back to the south. This is native to their geneticism and shall be rewarding. Races have propensities for specific environments. The Spanish never sent their conquistadores further north than California. The English didn't settle Mexico or Venezuela. It was like climate seeking like climate; it was pioneering genetics that was programmed to seek similar ecology. Imagine the Pilgrims landing in Brazil, the Spanish colonizing Massachusetts! Misplaced habitats are factors in bigotry.

HEARST

In the Patricia Hearst kidnapping there is genetic observation. There is the kidnapper General Marshall Cinque, who referred to himself as a "nigger'— "nigger" who was doing the hunting. There was the girl's wealthy father, well-bred, distressed, non-aggressive businessman who had inherited considerable wealth. Of still lesser aggressiveness was the girl's fiance, a moustached, bushy-haired, mild-mannered, thin doctor of philosophy. As the characters emerge on stage, one is immediately awed at the roles they engage in. This is being written in April of 1974, and the outcome is uncertain. But, in view of the risk against the overwhelming superiority of force, Cinque has determined to engage battle. There is small doubt that he could come out with viable anatomy. If he is not a hair-brain, drug-addicted psychotic, if he is in reality a rational, sane revolutionary, then one can deduce the following: he possesses strong leadership (LL) genes, combined with aggressive (Ag

Ag) genes. Political genes are also present. The character that has been revealed is a dominant male leader.

Understanding the distress and the play-it-cool technique of the father and fiance in an attempt to regain the hostaged daughter, their appeals to the kidnappers were submissive. Immediately capitulating, the father doled out two million dollars in escrow. Beaten up in the abduction, the fiance voiced a plea that he would not prosecute the kidnappers.

It shall be a legend kidnapping. What immediately strikes the genetic mind is not the personalities, their training or the circumstances with which they are trying to cope, but the basic action of inherited genes in confrontation.

Suppose we gave to the father and the fiance strong gene disposition of the marshall. Love and the protective factor would be secondary to other courses of action. "You will receive no tribute if my daughter is not released within five days. I offer one million dollars to officers who bring you to justice. If she is not released within ten days, I am offering a million dollars to the man who severs your scalp."

How should the fiance respond? "You xl!+Xz!! Only space on earth you'll be safe is stuffed in a sewer"? Strong opinion, but one can be reminded of an attempted airline highjacking in Spain. A colonel in charge ordered the highjacker out of the plane in ten minutes or they were coming in with guns blazing. That would mean death. He came out in minutes.

UPSTAIRS - DOWNSTAIRS

Jean Marsh, who played Rose in the eminently successful TV dramatic series orginating out of England, was also responsible for the concept. She stated in a New York interview that the success of the series was due to people appreciating a type of social discipline in which God, country, and a place in society was definitely set forth.

This magnificent drama, enacted weekly by British actors, covering the early 20th-century England, structured itself between the upstairs elite, privileged, and wealthy class, and the downstairs, housing some extremely notable servants, the working class.

What millions of people, especially the more educated, were enthralled with in this drama was polished delivery of play-acting, at which the English are superb masters, clever intelligent plots with sober, titilating reflection, nuances of understatement, audience discovery, plus historical backdrop.

By far the most important element was basic genetics. If one were to say that Hudson, the butler, or Rose, the maid, was less intelligent than Richard or James, it would not be true, because the document is highly skewed toward an array of servants with unusual abilities, talents, and perceptions. Intelligence division in the portrayal was false. Few households ever held so capable a servants' quarters. Where genetics does come in was in the strict theatric portrayal of human caste.

It is not a matter of education, wealth or titled inheritance that the upstairs was populated by upper-class genetic individuals. This is a fundamental fact of biology, that dominance levels emerge. In days of royalty we may have been prepared to accept these tenants without question. Then came revolutions of equalitarianism which attempted to distort biologic laws which were evident on every street in the city, namely, human inequality.

That which we were viewing in "Upstairs - Downstairs" was a happy, harmonious micro-society based on class difference. And that difference and distance was admirably maintained by Hudson, who never questioned the precept of operating within one's class.

In such an arrangement the social and economic roles were spelled out exactingly, each knowing their place and social limitation.

The immense pleasure derived from this series was based on strict class stratification. Although there was tragedy, there was never chaos. Each one performed in his particularly assigned orbit. Subconsciously, that which we recognized and identified with was the expression of our own genetic patterns.

It is not that this era has ended for a better one. Far from it. It is just that the social pendulum has swung outward. When we speak of equalitarianism, the end of the English class system or the end of royalty, we should review the Russian experience which traded sovereignty for tyrannical rule of bloody criminal communist masters. Today we know Russian people would be happier under the reign of tzars.

William Etkin, in *Social Behavior and Organization Among Vertebrates*, states, "Two factors which operate very widely in vertebrate social groups to control aggressive behavior are (A) Dominance hierarchy based upon individual recognition among the animals of a group and (B) Territoriality which confines aggressive and other behaviors to limited areas."

In "Upstairs - Downstairs" the dominance was observed and aggressive behavior was nil. Limitation of territory further decreased conflict, so we were looking at a perfect social unit, not the inane, confused, mentally ill, violent television affair presented to lower masses.

Scott pointed out in 1958 that when male mice raised in isolation were placed together, most individuals would start to fight. "Within a few hours or days a social rank is organized, and the mice have learned their places. Fighting then becomes rare since the subordinate mice no longer fight." Examples throughout the mammalian kingdom abound concerning hierarchy and dominance. By a freak of weird fate, equalitarian democratic perversion has attempted to disperse this biologic structure. A display of dominants is exhibited with a symphony orchestra. There is one true leader, the conductor, and possibly four dominants scattered throughout as first violinist. However, the hundred other members are genetically submissive, belonging to the proletariat.

An interesting study in 1976 was performed in the agriculture departments at the Pennsylvania State University. It was found that piglets within a few hours after birth established social order, as later reflected in weight gain and carcass characteristics.

Newborn piglets stand minutes after birth, explore their environment, grasp and suckle teats. Once having suckled, within an hour aggressive forces manifest themselves and they actively engage in teat-sampling to engage finally in defense of the preferred "fountain" territory. This early fighting determined future dominant relationships.

What is particularly devastating in such studies, to the proponents of human equality, and environmental factors being of supreme importance, is that within one hour of birth in which learning has no previous record, the genetic codes lying within the piglet permit the immediate establishment of social strata. While engaged in contest along the udder, it is obvious there was a dominancy scale already in effect pre-birth. All that was necessary was for the contestants to group on the battlefield to find their respective niches in society.

Human society, acting over a longer period in establishment of order, displays this same tendency, as any grade school teacher will bear witness to those bright-eyed youngsters that move to the forefront and those sad-eyed recessives that appear not to see the light about them.

INEQUALITY

Practically every educational system in the world would tumble were it not for the recognition of human inequality. What is more cruel than accepting in college only those students that were in upper one-fifths of their classes? What is more discriminatory than the collegiate grading system weeding out inferior seed, labeling it poor quality, and infusing good seed with honors and economic reward? Mankind is spiked to the cross of inequality. It is this crown of thorns that must be borne in political resolvement of the biological injustice. Yet biology has majesty and method of its own. Species could not have existed had they been composed of all chiefs or all privates.

For the lawmakers idealism soars when they sanction proclamation as Section I, Virginia Bill of Rights, adopted June 12, 1776: "that all men are by nature equally free and independent and have certain inherent rights, of which, when they enter into a state of society they cannot, by any compact, deprive or divest their positivity; . . . "

Section II: "that all power is vested in, and consequently derived from, the people; . . ."

Section III: "that government is, or ought to be, instituted for the common benefit, . . . "

Section IV: "that no man or set of men are entitled to exclusive or separate emoluments or privileges from the community."

We can proceed further to the Declaration of Independence, July 4, 1776: "We hold these truths to be self-evident, that all men are created equal; that they are endowed by their Creator with certain inalienable rights; that among these are life, liberty, and the pursuit of happiness."

May the foregoing political proclamation bear witness to the magnificence of equal justice. Beneath the idealistic brilliance there is jungle turbulence of evolutionary struggle. Fine words do not make facts true, for as then, now, and in the future, man will have to pay more attention to biological realisms of society.

If we were to arrange Section I, we would have to admit that men are not equally free and independent. He that possesses the greatest freedom is he that bears the best-gened constitution, be the adaptational situation power or the multiple components of intelligence. No man is independent, nor has he been independent since the time of Homo erectus and the formation of society.

The very substance of society is dependency. It is the structuring of the group into class orders that conflict may be minimized. It is placement of abilities into occupational niches that the greatest efficiency may ensue. And lastly, it is recognition of earned sovereignty and authority. To each does not befall the same lot. The bed of roses to one may be cold earth to the other.

In higher wisdom, the biological gods were not exactly inconsiderate. For some men, given a palace, their gened underpinnings may revert it in short order to little more than a pig-pen, whereas, the gardener's home may bloom with cheer, warmth and friendship to outrank the castle. With inequality of genes, nature attached such virtues as patience, endurance, and drivelessness to lower labored echelons. Throughout the social order there are compensatory mechanisms to permit the healthful survival of those within different classes.

Intelligent people would go rip-roaring out of their minds if they had to live in the noisy, raucously humored heated temperament, inconsiderate, and disorderly lives of many workers. They would reform such environment immediately. Yet the proletarian class thrives on inane slop of television, radio, newspapers and magazines. They eat sports as if life depended on it. Their ears are insensitive.

These qualities do not mean the proletarian class is not sensitively human, passionate, worshipful and gracious. It simply means the genetic bases of human beings in evolving society are varied and consequently requisite of separate needs. That is the ticklish challenge for the future. The communists have solved it by making the masses the slaves of the communist party aristocracy. Capitalism had the best approach, until socialists commenced to extinguish initiative and reward the inferior by equalizing all.

Power is not derived from the people. Power is derived from society which is separate from the people. Society is the biological mechanism which can grant power. It is composed of class, dominant-submissive hierarchy. People individually, per se, are babblers at the foot of the tower.

That men are entitled to privileges has been a strong part of American society which defenders of equality have failed to recognize. Great and secure fortunes of the Rockefellers and Fords are esconced in legally-protected foundations. Justices, legislators and presidents are amply rewarded with lush pensions, as are high-ranking officers in the military. Universities are capacity-filled intellectual snobhouses, feeding off monopolistic merchandise. Even the religious set forth their highest as well-fed living idols. Contrary to Section IV, especially in America, the restriction of privilege is hardly discernible and there should be small room for complaint that there is small opportunity for seed growth which excelleth.

As man folded woman into the web of social order, she was only considered equal as far as head-count went. Rather than being created equal, women were created for the competitional advancement of their nuclear group against environment and other humans. But that all should have life, liberty, pursuit of happiness, so be it, for the road of mankind has never been easy.

Livestock have been found to have space requirements defined by bubble-like shapes surrounding the head, according to Stricklin. When one animal moves into the bubble of another, the offended animal will either fight, move away, or submit. It is another example of the "pecking order" as seen in chickens. Yet what is coming into realization is that throughout the animal kingdom, even in minor societal organizations, there exists dominancy, which presumes class.

With examples from nature concerning inequality, social order, submissiveness, and dominancy, it is little wonder that man, who has developed the most complex society, is heavily committed to class structure — a fact that is reflected throughout history.

Stanley Salthe, in *Evolutionary Biology*, states, "Darwin's major contribution was to point out and document extensively in his book of 1868, *The Variation of Animals and Plants Under Domestication*, that population of living organisms are not composed of identical individuals. Indeed, as has become abundantly clear since then, no two individuals in a population are identical, not even monozygotic twins."

It behooves us in the 20th century to carefully consider the fragility of socialistic idealism. About us are ruins of 18th-century political equalitarianism which flared with the French Revolution. Nemesis to such noble thought concerning man's openness has been recent biological unveilings. No place in nature do we find intraspecies oneness. What we do find is limitless variation and ruthless competition among humans, nations, and tribes for survival.

It is not difficult to stimulate legislatures and sovereigns toward the maintenance of their nation and gene pool. Under the most tragic of wars and deprivation, this larger unit of intraspecies' force violently defends its perpetuation. Yet legislators, on the other hand, have not yet been fully appraised of the nuances in individual differences. They proceed according to categorized scribble with profound ignorance of modern biology. It is easier for them, seemingly, to equalize unequal components than to face up to facts of differences. To permit some to vote is an outrage because they have no slightest concept for what they vote. Although this appears as an injustice, it is the history of humanity that only few shall lead for the usefulness of society. It is not that democracy is bad, but rather that it is too superb and, as the biological and psychological revelations progress and as communism increasingly threatens, there needs to be subtle alterations to accommodate newer knowledge. Conductors of a transit system tying up a city or government employees striking are proofs of democracy's Achilles heel. No one is particularly enthusiastic about altering democracy, the idol of equalitarianism. Yet, if it is not refurbished, it will crumble by genetic mismanagement.

APE MEN

From *Hunte Illustrierte:* "*In einem japanischen zoo gelang erstmals die Paarung eines Leoparden mit einter Lowin. Ihre Nachkommen wurden auf den Nomen, 'Leopon' getauft.*"

If one observes the wide species difference between the leopard and the lion and the fact that they have now been successfully mated to produce offspring, one may truly shudder at what is in store for humanity from out the genies-gene laboratory. There is already a shift toward intermarriage of upper bourgeois, sovereigns, intellectuals and educated, and an opposing stabilization of working class-peasant masses.

What is out of the stage of conjecture is that human mating with the higher anthropoids would be feasible and, by subtle breeding techniques, we'll be producing subhumans who will be capable of waging many aspects of war, as well as perform much of the work of the factory and farm. They will be utilized as we utilize many animals today. Humanitarianism will become an explosive issue. Legislators will be confronted with greatest challenges earth will ever witness. Then there shall be no question of class structure. Man, subman, superman, and specialized man shall be strung out like droplets in a rainbow. Variability will be starkly visible, not philosophical. From wide expansion of our species will come problems more severe than nuclear devastation. Man's scientific ability will open more unresolved portals than it closes. We can only pause and reflect the fantastic precipice we shall traverse. Equalitarianism will be buried. Man's genetic surgery will neatly divide and radiate class society that originated millions of years ago on the African savannas. Politicalisms will amount to trash research. Class of men will be as radiant as rocks and minerals of the earth, from diamonds to coarse sandstone and bitumen. Biochemical reagents are at hand. They only await the crucibles and weird scientists who shall direct them.

DOMINANCE

Dominance is more conspicuous in animals in which situations are competitive. It is why in man societies are heavily spaced in class structure, excepting where dictatorship attempts to impose a one-class system. Since male chickens dominate female chickens, we must consider separate male and female hierarchies. A human simile in monarchy is that animals, as antelopes and mice, possess one dominant to each group.

Strong evolutionary pressures were applied to the birthing of social organization to make dominance a necessary principle. Within groups that has a high level of individual aggression it not only lessened intramural fighting, but provided undivided leadership to face enemies. In modern society, such as the defeat of Roman generals at Cannae, the advantage of unified leadership is apparent. That's what armies are all about — dominance hierarchy.

Unfortunately, authoritarianism and now law is still the driving power behind nations that would be great, powerful, and continuous. It is when political forces attempt to exclude normal dominance from innate roles that from out the woodwork comes havoc. Stratification of society is further maintained by permitting degrees of access to means of production, resources or commodities, and to the rights of property and territory. Societies are superior according to material ownership and accessibility. Fame, fortune, and rank are a shake of the dice. The dice are none other than reduction divisioned gametes. They determine tissue wealth which properly settles rank and value in society.

In *Early Dynastic Period of Ur,* at the bottom of the social hierarchy were slaves who were bought and sold by even ordinary artisans and minor administrators. It was recognized that there were differences in biological worth. Quite often capable slaves became free men. In spite of occasional insurrections, there was a docility, a submissiveness, that went with the practice of slavery.

Slavery went out of business because it had become economically disastrous, with less worry, one could get more work out of a free man once he was given a monetary incentive.

Students have been subjected to Marxian jazz about virtue of classless society. Class society was assumed to have originated in an oppressive form by results of the industrial revolution and wealthy bourgeois. Communism was heralded as the champion to dispel this despised development.

As far back as the Early Dynastic Period in Mesopotamia, social stratification has been the normal cultural rule. Class society has been the pinnacle of achievement in any civilized nation. Hierarchial forms are not a matter of crass stupidity that could not understand the value of communistic life. It was that biology of Homo erectus sifted into the proper niche with the dominance-submissive scale, like the majority of the animal world. Were Russian communism not an enslaving dictatorship one's head would spin with the rapidity to which it would return to stratification. This should be a sobering thought for crackpot socialists desirous of equalizing the unequal.

The French Revolution was falsely predicated upon rights of man and philosophies of non-biologists. French society, with its nobility, clergy, and military in the higher echelons, was not particularly wicked. What was at fault were the times, poverty, disease, and lack of industrialization. The revolution didn't change a thing. It simply shifted the power into a dictator, Napoleon, who gave the French a taste of good and bad wars. They were no better off than they had been under the monarchy.

There is a tendency to become perturbed with a class society since in its upper layers kinship plays a significant role. The son of a king becomes king and the daughter of a general marries the colonel. It is an artificial appearance, for beneath these closely-intertwined castes are heavy preponderances of normally adjusted genes.

CASTE

Although we do not have a caste system in America, we do have occupational and social groups which amount to the same thing. One difference is that the Asian Indian is born into his caste and his status is unchanged upward or downward. There is common to both societies the recognition of an order — superiority-inferiority.

It is not unreasonable that the caste system in India is biologic. Even though the orders are fixed by birth, the castes are genetically-isolated pools. It means there is a disproportion of talent, ability, and gene structure from one to another caste. Untouchable breed untouchables, which are similar to unskilled American laborers, and these groups, being isolates, do not move out of their biological niche.

On the other hand, the twice-born caste — Brahman priests and Komti traders — are possessed by genetic drift of genes for higher intelligence, leadership, drive, and dominance and passed to their descendants. This caste represents scientists, intellectuals and business leaders, which in America biologically struggle into positions.

In America there is a preponderance of better-gened children in descendants of the higher social order. They'll occupy the best occupational niches. This is not because of competitiveness. They come from superiorly intelligent parents and by inheritance occupy the higher caste positions. Children of college graduates go to college, not because economics is more favorable than the children of the poor but because they have by birth inherited genetic apparatus to continue the higher style.

Equal environmental opportunity is vote-getting platitude by cheap politicians. It has no bearing on DNA coding of favorable traits. Legislation can never level class structure, as communistic socialists would like. The child is born to his occupational level, and that is his destiny! He stands greater chance of higher levels if he comes from higher parents. No amount of education will make a thimble-full of difference in his DNA endowment.

Alex Carrell, in *Man the Unknown*, calls attention to social grouping derived from heredity. He states that distinguished men appear with greater frequency in families of intelligence, or aristocratic. On the other hand, peasants may produce the great, but not as frequently as the upper class.

We have suspected this for years, since geneologies of famous families are replete with scientific and cultural luster. Obviously, no one can quarrel with his contention that there is a worker class which for centuries tilled the soil, lacked imagination and spirit, and did not contribute fully to the evolution of man. When Carrell affirms social classes are synonymous with biological classes, he pioneers a delicate philosophy.

It is not quite that simple to divide classes into manual workers and intellectuals and expect them to beget similars. Benet was the first with his intelligent tests to demonstrate wide variances in human intelligence by scientific measurement. The intelligent, from whatever group they issue, float to the top class — "genius will out" — and those less fortunate remain proletariat.

MANMADE SELECTION

We are beginning with manmade selection. Economic isolation has produced biological isolation. We are breeding economic groups. As such, we should not be startled that similar to animal breeding we can have good or bad stock depending upon the components we join. By intellectual drift to the upper classes the lower residue is clearly not quality stock. Both on drift and the breeding produced by economic grouping which is a recent event with the agricultural revolution we have created two classes, workers and intellectuals, in which we recognize distinct hereditary factors.

When we emerged from hunter-gatherer, forest and savanna groups of small size — fifty to a hundred individuals, rarely over half a thousand social contacts — interbreeding was unrestrained excepting the sexual spoils that went to the strong males. These could have been mesomorphic workers rather than intellectuals. We did not beget classes millions of years ago but occupational types.

As we moved to cities, nations, complex industry and agriculture, we arbitrarily separated muscle from brain. Economics became the selective factor, and breeding became a matter of class wherein one was found. It is the human race being forged into biologically distinctive groups through the media of economic selection — worker-muscle genes begetting worker-muscle genes and savants begetting savants.

In all this, the mechanisms of heredity, genes, and selective factors are apparent, and obey laws employed in animal breeding. We can breed humans in various shapes, sizes, with various abilities and intelligence, but it is slow and oftentimes uncertain. How does the laborer shoot out an occasional genius and the aristocrat many? We are breeding human variables in what seems a pot of luck.

In Mendel we see the formula. Colors or wrinkled skins come out definite — not a blend. Apply this to social groups. A worker is a geneticism we have recently selected and developed. He is of Mendelian law and disposition, unchangeable, unalterable. Within the social animal species we see a division of labor. The classic worker, drone and queen of the honey bee colony. In species as the ant, or even the wild dog, functions are genetically designated.

WORKERS

When the Reds killed off Russian leaders — White Russians, the educated, cultured and historical ruling class — in the interest of the worker, they did not dispense with the despotic class. They eliminated an indispensable biological group of leaders, politicians, cultured savants, and intelligentsia. They had no other substitution other than to draw from the best of garbage collectors and janitors, form them into an exclusive clique, the communist party, and rule "liberated" workers. It was a tragic error.

Marx employed a false premise when he regarded class struggle as a manifestation of the economic system. He viewed classes as the resultant of politico-economic oppression — that capitalism is a manmade system. Entirely ignored and unknown was geneticism. Biogenetic structure adequately accounts for formation of class. A worker or chief is entered into the social order in the same manner as pink or white blossoms in a garden — by genetic law.

We see the pitiful sight of people sitting on park benches taking the sun into their thin tissues, awaiting life's end. Vast cities are filled with wisps of terminal flesh — such as St. Petersburg, Florida — catering to retired farmers who do not seem old but whose bodies are burnt out.

On the other hand, we watch to the last breath oldsters such as Winston Churchill, Frank Lloyd Wright, Picasso, Toynbee and, in fact, almost all successful people who seem to be impervious to mental aging. They appear old chronologically, but their bodies are active, their minds alert. There are three components of age. Chronological age is inevitable. In tissue age they seem to resist slowdown characteristic of the laboring class; and in mental age they are as wise as ever.

Evidently, the laboring class can be sacrificed to take sun listlessly in the twilight of their days. Their muscular work is done. No longer are they capable components of an energy-demanding society. They await death in serene acceptance. Not so with intellectual class. Death is a hideous enemy. With what they have their bodies move incessantly — seeking, drinking, creating, condemning, striving, retarding the inexorable hands of time. Meagerly they relinquish only what powers and rights which are imperative upon them. Until last fulminating pathology, they are rebellious and contesting death.

I have comforted *exitus* of hundreds of laboring people. I have never failed to marvel at the placidity with which they accept the hand of the Grim Reaper. Religion never appeared to be a factor one way or the other in their complacency in face of death. Their road had been hard, without brilliance, and its end is to be equally uneventful.

Yet, if the termination of the intellectual is nonprecipitous and not by massive stroke or cardiac arrest, if there is time to contemplate the curtain's descent, there is tremendous resistance. A hundred plans to foil the inevitable — a dozen doctors to offset the fleeting moments remaining. Here is the will to live, to persist. Psychologically, "will" means not too much — but for genes — drive, ambition, conquest, "will" — will to live — is a genetic directive. This powerful gene is fully developed in cerebral tissue — the neurogene. It originated with our need to preserve our wise aged leaders. It never developed in those that contributed only muscle to the social group. Will to live, a neurogene of the intellectuals and the wise.

SOCIAL CONTRACT

In Robert Ardrey's *The Social Contract*, he states, "Insect societies may include genetically determined castes, but among backbone creatures this cannot be." This fine writer goes on to explain that equal opportunity is the second law of vertebrates, whereas inequality is its first law, a society being a group of unequal beings.

We must regroup this train of thought. In human society we are highly unequal in traits and abilities. The ceiling at the time of our delivery is so definitely imposed by our restricted genes that one can never break through it, no matter what the drive. Who would not like to compose like Tschiakovsky, write like Hemingway, or sing like Caruso? Unfortunately, good components are sparingly distributed.

Even if one would contend that we were not issues in castes and occupational groups, there could be no denying that inequality in itself is the master sieve of social stratification. Take any high school class of teenagers. In a matter of minutes it can be determined who shall be whom. Ardrey does state that if his conclusion is correct: "Then the ruff exhibits the only genetically determined class sytem within a sex that I have ever encountered in the vertebrate world."

There are experiments that show rearing primates in isolation later affects sexual abilities and social cooperation. Here we could be up against not that they lacked education, but rather delayed time genes were not permitted expression. Many genes only come into being according to a pre-arranged formula, as walking, speech, menstruation, etc. In the isolation experiments, social genes prevented from interacting with the mother or companions could upset the timetable that one may not come up with socially normal behavior.

In the isolation experiments we are dealing with an irregularity that never took place within the evolution of the species. The tethers of sociality are so genetically interrelated to the individual, to the group, that one cannot pull one factor out and dissect it to analytical advantage.

W. C. Allee stated that, "Animals with exactly the same heredity may still develop, even at an early age, social differences showing one is not exactly equal to the other." What else is this but genetic determination of social hierarchy?

Ardrey stated, "In the organization of any society of equal beings (and all beings are unequal) to act as one, evolution has favored the mechanism of hierarchy." It follows that hierarchy is genetically structured in social animals because it is the only consistent way in which this treasurer of biological importance can be passed on from generation to generation. Groups having survived by the wisdom of hierarchy would of consequence pass the instinct forward.

Ardrey cites Wynn Edwards' statement: "Hereditary compulsion to comply must be the real key to social organization. If this were not the genetic case, how would it ever have been possible for the magnanimous achievement of packing guns and going off to murder one another by the millions? Such conduct has little to do with reason, but rather animal behavior acting under ancient outdated instinctive patterns."

Washburn presented: "Almost certainly every human society has regarded the killing of members of certain other human societies as desirable." A murderer gets hanged and a bloody warrior gets a medal. The mess of war defense and aggression can only be explained in genetic context. We must regard a group's gened pool, tribes or nations as being selfish and in competition with other similar units. Human genetic evolution is mono-directional. The biological pool seeks survival from other units, whether they are in competition or not. It is so structured that it fuels itself at the expense of other societies.

Throughout modern history we see how astoundingly nations line up into almost equally balanced forces, then go at one another. Hardly has the decisive smoke cleared from fields of battle than regrouping is underway to line up equally balanced antagonists for another holocaust.

Selfishness of the gened pool makes difficulty in cooperation. We rarely find instances where the United States and the Soviets decide to combine and rule earth. That human genes possess instinctive jealousy when it comes to matters of social pools is as unwavering as national flags and anthems.

"To he that hath shall be given unto, and he that hath not shall be taken away, even from that which he hath." This glaring revelation from the Bible describes a biological truism — namely, prestige and power of social genes. All the kings' men may never take of that profound treasury whose lot is forged at conception. Those with good genes shall succeed and live in comfort, while those of paucity will be pawns and fodder for wars, tillers of soil, and residents of slums. It's not that the future outlook of man is bleak. His future social structure is not predicated upon more education, but is firmly rooted in divergencies and quality of genes within the pool.

Tinbergen, in *Social Behavior in Animals,* discusses the peck-order, "Each individual learns by pleasant or bitter experience which of its companions are stronger and must be avoided, and which are weaker and can be intimidated. In this way, the 'peck-order' originates in which each individual in the group knows its own place."

In that statement there is a question. The pecking order does not originate through experience or education. Nature is far too shrewd in her evolutionary schema of social animals not to latch onto the principle of hierarchy and lock it into the genes to prevent confusion, in-fighting, and misdirection. Pressure toward the fixation of the social institution is tremendously strong.

VILLAIN

In the North Sea there is an anglerfish which has a bait on the top of its head. Smaller fish are attracted to it and are gobbled up. Within the plant and animal world there are numerous examples of deception, camouflage, villainry, and thievery. So it is no small wonder that man, with his immensely complex brain and social schema is the master villain of all.

Historically, it has been philosophers' and poets' quagmire when trying to resolve good from bad, noble from vile, sinner from saint. There is no need to belabor the point. Nature has provided us with the answer. Man is born bad and self-serving. He arises to nobility as his genes and customs permit. As we have spoken, thieves, murderers, killers, warriors, saints and Samaritans are genetically fashioned. Killers, the shrewd and cunning, all types, had a forwarding effect in social evolution and were consequently registered in DNA codes. Think how many times an alert, treacherous leader saved his nation. Bloody Joe Stalin, arch-Machiavellian, had few virtues, but he led his people into an era of victory and social enslavement. Selection pressures, rewarding dishonesty and deceit, were powerful forces in evolutionary advancement. It is why crime will be with us until it can be bred out.

Within the insect world, one of the finest examples of geneticized social hierarchy is found. Occupation is dictated genetically. There is a queen, males and sterile females or workers. Some are carpenters which build homes, others are gatherers of honey, others tend the young. Rather than being in one job, they are rotated throughout life. The job is indicated according to age. In other words, occupational promotion occurs. In human society, we have refined the system by placing workers in lifetime jobs without promotion.

More and more genes are being shown as agents of social traits. Korner, 1971, in *Amer. J. Orthopsychiat,* observed significant behavioral differences among newborns that parents should deal differently with their children as separate individuals. In *Behavioral Science,* 1971, Gerald McClearn recites that single genes determine a number of conditions of mental retardation as well as cognitive and personality functions. Influence of hereditary genes is shown in many traits as activity level, learning, memory, and aggression.

ANARCHY

Nations have reacted with savagry toward a political science known as anarchy. Unfortunately, anarchists have been stereotyped as bomb-throwers and terrorists. In the majority they are docile actionists, interested only in removing shackles of bureaucratic and authoritarian dictatorship.

Peter Kropotkin, an early anarchist, analyzed anarchism as a society without government, law or obedience. It functioned by agreement between groups for the sake of production and consumption, to satisfy the needs and aspirations of civilized beings.

There has been a tendency in America to relate anarchism with Marxism. Though in association, from time to time they had a joint purpose to achieve collapse of orders they both rejected. They were in final purpose, enemies. Marxism demands mastery and exploitation of nature for its own purpose. Whereas, anarchism viewed the relationship with nature as one of harmony and non-opposition — that social problems stem from the artificial constraints of free natural development.

In search for genetic propulsion of anarchism, we encounter a primitive reality. We note that for millions of years in our evolutionary history, anarchism was the rule. There were no laws. There were no large concentrations of society. And, of course, there was no industrial revolution to fester regulated blight. In fact, there was only the bliss of anarchy, save but for a local dominance hierarchy.

That in modern society many of the laboring class should retain anarchial genes is not surprising. We have retained the male breast and nipple, which have for ages become obsolete.

Anarchism fit perfectly in the political constitution of the evolving primates. Its emphasis on harmony with nature, spontaneous creativity and naturalness is the perfect backdrop for our first gleanings in social order. All our ancestors were anarchistic. What moved us out of the anarchistic age was the agricultural revolution which necessitated immobility and population density. Authoritarianism and law inevitably resulted. Free-wheeling lifestyles of the jungles were out. Since this collectivism was only a recent phenomenon, within the last 50,000 years, it is fairly certain there are residue anarchial genes within the genetic pool.

Although Negroes were the major race exploited by slavery, they are possibly the race which cherishes personal freedom most. One sees this in their attitude toward slums and unwillingness to respond to white people's value of orderliness. Rather, they pursue a wider sexual, less marriageable style. Having had of the races more primitive, less developed status, they retained greater proportion of anarchial genes.

Yet, oddly enough, they are not among the modern protagonists of anarchism. It was for the northern Europeans to carry the torch. These people attempted to untie bureaucratic enmeshment. As the white society evolved further into industrialism and consequent personal regulation, there was greater impulse to undo restraints. The disproportionate crime rate in ghettoes is not because of poverty or deprivation of opportunity, but rather the result of a genetic pool being displaced outside normal environment to be abnormally constricted. Ghetto crime is within genetic structure of the slum people, because they do not regard many things as immoral which white society seriously condemns; namely, drug addiction, alcoholism, prostitution, gambling, and petty theft. The latter is the only one in which there is a victim of action.

We may conclude that anarchism has a wide biological basis. Within this framework lies a great deal of crime. Man is not going to submit readily to falsities of his nature until they can be outbred, which is a long way off. Whereas anarchism wished to release the bonds of society immediately, Soviet Marxism is willing to look at historical development and exhort increased production. Marxism has a slightly higher genetic role than does anarchism. While it attempts to regard everyone as equal, it places a collective system of tyranny into the hands of the communist party. Nobel Prize-winner, Solzhenitsyn, poignant Russian observer and victim of his nation's oppression, spoke out June 30, 1975, in Washington, concerning ideology. "Marxism has fallen so low, it's simply an object of contempt. No serious person in our country today, even students in schools, can talk about Marxism without smiling. . . . All of Lenin's teaching is that communism considers to be a fool, anyone who doesn't take what's given to him. . . . Only firmness will make it possible to withstand the assaults of communist's totalitarianism."

This genius is not of inferior genetic stock, for Solzhenitsyn eerily details that 7,000 persons are in insane asylums in Russia with compulsory confinement, doctors going around injecting people with substances which destroy brain cells. Twice America has aided in the process of inferiorizing Russian genes. First, when she allowed communism to develop at the end of World War I, which permitted widespread destruction of the opposing white tzarist Russian armies containing the flower of the national genetic pool. This resulted in further systematic massacres of dissidents, democrats, and those possessing the liberal spirit of freedom.

Solzhenitsyn said, "In 1933 and in 1941, your leaders and the whole Western world, in an unprincipled way, made a deal with totalitarianism. We're still paying for it, and we're going to pay for it in a worse way."

Today, a modified anarchism may be acceptable. Compulsions of petty politicians, intransigeant legislators, mediocre leadership, lack of realism, sponsorship of the lower masses, innate knavery, and compilation of code and law, on top of code, law, and regulation, have so ensnared society that one day rebellion toward limited anarchy must inevitably transpire.

Not only would reunion of man with primitive nature be advantageous mentally, it would normalize institutions as the family, aid in lessening war, and permit human evolution with its component culture in non-aggression fashion. People are fed up with regulatory bureaucracy, accepting as matter of fact deceit. Politicians, with treason and guile, were part of the remote human tribe. If they had served no useful purpose, they would have been weeded out in selection. However, as thieves, they aided social survival. As tricksters, their cunningness outran bravery and was responsible for many inventions by primitives in conquest of environment — as traps, snares, nets, dead falls, pits, projectile throwers, and stick weapons. Politicians were authors of firing areas to drive out animals, which were later to be elaborated in fire bombings by Churchill on the civilian Dresden population, by nuclear holocausts of Japanese cities by Truman, and savage raids of Hitler. Employment of physical forces was supported by deceitful forces.

William Godwin, father of anarchism, believed that government corrupted society. Our bloody obsession with war has made the recital of history the "Killer's and Conqueror's Diary." From middle-strata political genes, those of Machiavellian cunning, once they usurped the role of the genetic dominants, who were true leaders for millions of years, earth engaged in a never-ending series of conflict. In recent history, false dominants are not a matter of strength, bravery, wisdom, and resistance to challenge. They are the Watergate conspiracy, Stalin purges, Hitler genocides. That politicians are born with ascribed qualities, double-facedness, faithlessness and perfidy, innately blessed, may come as a surprise. Yet follow the record of politicians after their demise. One cannot but marvel at the consistency of unscrupulousness.

Alexander Beckman was an anarchist who, in 1892, attempted to murder Henry Clay Frick, manager of the Carnegie Steel Company of Pittsburgh, during a strike. From a book, his *Prison Memoirs*, Beckman eulogizes, "To the People! To the beautiful simple People, so noble in spite of centuries of brutalizing sufferings! I am simply a revolutionist, a terrorist by conviction, an instrument for furthering the cause of humanity."

We note his enthusiasm to assassinate was DNA programmed. He exaltedly grabbed the role. Little preparation was needed. There was no sentiment of wrong-doing. He would euphorically kill, cold-bloodedly, in the name of anarchism, which alone could save the world. He only wounded Frick, but unfortunately, this rare throwback gene has a place within society — to remove dominants from dictatorship. We have learned of assassination attempts on Fidel Castro by an American president through the CIA. Even in higher echelons, this gene-prompter may be directing.

Many times in hominid history a new course had to be taken in violation of established order. For a fixity of culture, a normalization of society would inevitably result in extinction. Therefore, the rare assassin genes were an instrument in abrupt alterations — much as mutagenesis provides alternatives for survival selection.

It will be centuries before we can identify neurogenes. What is clear are the divisions of social character. They are distinct, obviously inherited. We cannot, as the old saying goes, make a silk purse out of a pig's ear . . . we cannot make leaders out of laborers, great physicists and mathematicians out of Negroes, or jazz musicians out of Chinese.

A wonder of political science is anarchism. It is structured upon communal life with voluntary association and autonomy to the individual. This is reversion to ancient hominid society, with simplistic tribal association, as hunting and gathering groups, acting under rudimentary social structure. In modern industry, it has appeal to those who would be unshackled from the abnormal demands placed upon their biology.

Anarchy is a rational form of well-being. Its adoption is within the limits of presently programmed genes. Society could rid itself of communist slave institutions, bureaucracy, zoning boards, coding officials, city managers, do-good groups, and regulatory legislative bodies. Predicated upon the minimum of regulation, regimentation, militarism, attention to foreign policy, return to primitive foods and lifestyles, then anarchial societies should have very few cases of anxiety.

We see in Daniel Guerin, exponent of anarchism in France, basic genetic error of this radical political science. All anarchists and communists exhalt in belief of egalitarianism. They are blind that humans are biologically unequal, and unequal by genetic inheritance, catalogued and locked into classes. In paranoial fashion they embrace the worker.

Guerin sees a revival to worker's self-management. One would set up a worker's general assembly, above that a worker's deliberative council, and above that an executive management committee. Communism has performed a similar feat by placing dictatorial bodies among workers.

Outside of Russia, the failure of this system is attributed to workers not mature enough, lack of education and technical knowledge, thinking in terms of wages, and willing to place their power into the hands of delegates which enables a minority to control.

What Guerin did not see is that the worker shall always be a worker. His genes have irrevocably designated him to the role of being subservient. Yet some workers emerge as true dominant leaders. These exceptionals were dominants in the first place. Because of environmental influences, they were not relegated originally to true positions. In the highest labor councils there may be a few representatives of genetic dominants. They play, eat, and luxuriate as potentates, they rule as capitalistic factory-owners.

Society cannot be managed from the bottom up. Totalitarianism in bureaucratic Russia has demonstrated that. It is a crucible where self-management has failed. "The worker's paradise" is dominant suppression of laborers by the chosen few.

In the general strikes in Paris, France, 1968, the workers tasted true power, but they couldn't follow through because they could neither run the economy by themselves nor be partners. What they were up against was that the managerial classes are true dominants and oppose revolution at every step. Workers are submissive, servile, accept economic oppression.

Today we see greater stratification within industrial society — lowest being unskilled robots, then skilled craftsmen, next staff managers, technical experts, and finally, higher echelons representing finance and corporate interests. All are genetically based with abilities they bring to their working niches.

Marx had a childlike image of impoverished workers on the one side and rich capitalists on the other. He was only viewing a transitional event in bio-industrial revolution before society was capable of sorting its genetic occupational groups. The gigantic inherent strength of labor has turned out to be no more than a muscle giant with feet of clay. He shall be exploited, benevolently or otherwise, by small groups of leadership, entrepreneural or dictatorship geneticisms. It is tragic that so few can mobilize so many for revolution, enslavement or good.

Aims of the socialists, communists, and revolutionists, in their fervent hearts, feel they are directed against oppression in favor of equalitarianism. They are bound to ultimate failure. Geneticism, with its emphasis on variability from feeble-minded to genius and occupational types, produces highly intellectualized specialists which are indispensible within social structure. These specialists demand continuation of power and social hierarchy. As science of genetics progresses to reveal DNA code components of human types, ideologies such as communism and socialism shall disappear just as the dinosaurs.

Broad class structure may be regarded in the following genotypes:

W^oW^o — Worker genes: the masses, ordinary citizens, proletariat.

I^nI^n — Intellectuals: technicians, professionals, specialists, experts — bourgeois.

L^lL^l — Leaders: managers.

G^eG^e — Genius: elite.

P^oP^o — Politicians.

From the following article we can see how unemployment has become widespread by not understanding inequality of men — by trying to legislate biology, price-fixing it.

Employment
LABOR

"Five million new jobs in 50 days: If Congress repeals laws enacted under great depression economic fallacies, millions of jobs are immediately available to the unskilled. Workers have been locked out by legislative loading. Too many legal requirements at too great a cost have separated non-essential laborers from employers who could utilize them."

In pre-Rooseveltian times it was not uncommon for those of limited means to employ domestics, handymen, cleaners, painters, carpenters, gardeners or firemen. Nor was it unusual for farmers to obtain cheap labor or builders to hire randomly and freely. Or for restaurateurs to have help flowing from all corners. Students could be sandwiched into dozens of jobs. Not so today. They have become casualties of New-Deal-sponsored Utopias which have failed to provide adequate employment. Minimum wage, social security, unemployment taxes, compensation costs, labor regulations, municipal, state and federal taxes, and bookeeeping have effectively separated workers from classic employer relationships.

For these "convenience" workers, social programming has eroded their value. No longer are they advantageous to the millions of citizens that used to employ them. In their place has been substituted muscle or sweat equity in which even professional people and the well-to-do carry out repairs and functions that once were designated to servants and handymen. A third of Americans, off and on, were employing the unskilled. Today, who can afford the unskilled? Casual labor has been priced out of the marketplace. It has been forbidden by a host of well-meaning but fuzzy socialistic schema which impose penalties and problems between workers and employers. How do you get millions of Americans to go back to work and, at the same time, make the rich, middle class, and the poor happy?

Let the middle class and wealthy commence hiring at pre-Rooseveltian conditions. Accessible labor for personal use gives them greater leisure and opportunity. Extra jobs bolster the spirit of the poor. It isn't only cash that a domestic or handyman carts home — there is a full stomach, leftovers, used clothing, odds and ends, and valuable items that are not useful to the employer.

Landlords can employ hundreds of thousands at proper price — upgrading property which has been too costly to repair. If welfare payments are withheld for improper upkeep of property, no governmental pork barrels will be necessary for slum clearance and public housing.

To reverse social schemania there is the unpleasant task of dismantling unobtainable Utopia. Out the window must go, for at least this ten-million group of workers, social security, unemployment benefits, withholding taxes and bookkeeping tyrannies, as well as compensation whose tab should be picked up by the government — a free labor market minus government.

Unemployment benefits do not cushion a recession but are majorily responsible for high rate of inflation and decline in productivity. It's a list into millions, the legal defrauding of the unemployment system. If it were sensibly pegged at 25% of wage rather than 90%, our gross national product would be soaring. People want to work. But not when they get 90% of pay and can do as they please. This outpouring of unemployment wealth earned by business squandered on unemployed, pumps inflation fiercely because the worker has become in effect a drainer and not a supporter of the productive economy.

Put five million people to work in fifty days?
1. Repeal — minimum wage laws - withholding taxes - unemployment taxes - social security taxes - all taxes pertaining to labor.
    Eliminate — bookwork and reporting.
    Outlaw — labor regulations.
2. Let the government set compensation fees and pick up the tab, which would result in huge savings to all concerned, eliminating legal rip-offs.
3. Give back employer and employee traditional relationship without governmental interference.
4. Make labor payments tax-deductible for the employer.
If such a simple but miraculous piece of legislation could pass the old Leninist guard of Congress, America would soon be a land of employed and prosperous. Individual human biologic ability and production cannot be price-tagged and fettered by the legislation of equality, but must enter the open market, be bid upon and utilized to good of all society. Socialistic motherhood has failed, creating endless waste of talent.

The Rooseveltian socialists who schemed that the bourgeois, the "proprietors," should keep the books for the proletariat, the "workers," were the masterful biologists. They realized the workers were dumb, incapable of accuracy, prone to dishonesty, and susceptible to fiscal irresponsibility.

Therefore, they instituted not a bourgeois hierarchy to supervise the less genetically fortunate, but a penal system on the proprietors, to force them to collect, withhold wages, and perform other acts in relation to employment of workers, without compensation. Clearly Congressional "commies" recognized inequalitarianism by saddling the intelligent with keeping books. The bookkeeping schema levied upon the intelligent and entrepreneural is a communistic ruse directly from the Manifesto and mouth of Marx.

GENETIC DEMOCRACY

The United States was organized as a genetic democracy. Its founding fathers were aristocratic and privileged. They were wealthy, educated, self-made, intelligent; some owned slaves. Furthest from their minds were rights of minorities or the common man. They were in rebellion against colonialism and England.

Their vision of the republic was that the capable could ascend to political prominence and opportunity would be available to all. They never believed for one instance that government would be composed of lower masses of society. They would protect the average citizen, but they would never become the dominant force.

Without sovereign dictatorship the people should govern. Who were the people? Gentlemen, the educated, the wealthy, the respected, the brilliant, the wise. The founding fathers of the United States envisioned quite clearly genetic democracy. Those riding the train could not be its engineers. Rather, the elite — the upper bourgeois — should givern in benignty. The masses — the proletariat — would be charges of governmental authority.

Yet the progress of genetic democracy was bastardized. People took the florations of the Constitution at its literal value rather than the intent of dedicated men to preserve their lands, wealth, and class style. If America is a true democracy, then it should be a classless society, which it definitely is not, and never has been.

What intrigues us most in *Genetic Basis of Society* is that original intent has been inversed. Attention to mass vote has permitted emergence of strong labor unions, union crime, decreased production, inflation, taxation of initiative, over-solicitation of minorities, continuous wars for prosperity, unbalanced budgets, and slippage of world prestige — all parcel to rule of lower classes, incited by the liberal-socialistic left.

Center-stage is no longer domain of bourgeois dominants, intellectuals, ambitious and creative. Too few votes on the right permits rampage of those whose biology was never intended to govern. With civil rights movements, busing, equalitarianism in all its biotic pathology, the dictatorship of the proletariat is coming into being.

Society never intended proletarian rule, only submissiveness. What came out of evolution was bourgeois supremacy, class structure. It is not that a new humanitarian breakthrough has been achieved; it is that the incapable are leading and could, with communists, drown all in the unholy mire of totalitarian dictatorship. Genetic democracy is biologically natural, not wily scheming of jackal politicians.

With the modern age, one-man, one-gun governmental power will succumb to the profusion of new weaponry, defeating for all-time strength by population. There is a treacherous horizon in new armament sophistication. It means elimination of proletariat as a class force, to be ruled by bourgeois brain power. It also means that by weapon implantations controlled remotely, the individual will be subject to the will of dominants, be they good or evil.

SUMMARY

Democracy is an abnormal form of social structure. It is anti-evolutionary — contrary to the organization erected in man's genetic history. Prime question in political philosophy is — who should rule? Dominancy is well-illustrated in animal studies deriving primarily from the expression of the DNA makeup of the particular organism. Because of superiority in intelligence, some are able to assert authority. It follows that the basic units for dominancy are inherited. We know that "leaders are born." What is more difficult to come by is that kings and politicians are bred through inheritance.

Democracy is a form of government in which representatives are elected by masses and majority decision rules. This is a contrary situation to biological development of the human species. Hierarchy, privilege, class, and discrimination were the formative ingredients of society. It was unthinkable that peasants, laborers, workers (mesomorphs or endomorphs) should enter into decision-making. This group is genetically programmed to be subordinate and unquestioning. They are programmed not to enter into political policy, but to obey natural leaders.

This form of social organization is oligarchy, fascism dictatorship or rule by juntas. It is also representative of monarchies and feudalism. These are normal systems of government followed by ancient men into the present. We can review the long line of Ptolemys, Persian kings, Roman emperors, and forceful leaders as Alexander, Caesar, Atilla and Charlemagne, who ruled with absolute power. Within the early city states of Greece, there was a glimmering of democracy. At the end of World War I, royalties toppled and there emerged socialistic and communistic forms of government as well as the strengthening of old democracies as in the United States and England.

Appeal of democracy is based on a new philosophy of equalitarianism. This false biological assumption forced political upheavals which resulted in lip service to the principles of equality of man. There is in reality no such thing as democracy. Lower, less intelligent classes proxy away their authority to elected officials in the same fashion as they submitted to dominants millions of years ago. These elected officials, in turn, being bourgeois, a great number attorneys, do as they please and the public is thrust outside political movement, excepting at election time. Catch words, slogans, tricks and deceit are proffered to a poorly reasoning citizenry as inducements for re-election.

There is the hue and cry that if the rascal doesn't behave to one's liking, he can be voted out of office. But the rascal is oftentimes too clever, understands peasants' whims and foibles, and soothsays their qualms. Then again, if the rascal is turned out of office, there is no better choice for replacement.

Democracies are controlled by the bourgeois, which represents the upper 10% of the intelligencia, and rarely do leaders arise from out the working masses. Wilson was a college professor. Roosevelt was a Phi Beta Kappa. Kennedy was a brain. Nixon was an attorney. Carter was an engineer. Eisenhower, Washington, Jackson, and Grant were generals. In every instance the presidents can be regarded as superior-intelligenced and of the upper bourgeois class.

Plato believed that a group of specially-trained intellectuals should rule. Thomas Hobbes held that one man should rule, a king — a monarchy. John Locke advocated democracy. John Stuart Mills was interested in the limits of the power of society over the individual, that the minority must be protected against tyranny of the majority. Karl Marx came along under an aegis of Hegel's metaphysics. He explained history in terms of struggle between classes rather than nations, as Hegel had done and, hopefully, was on the side of the majority ruling. Although present-day communism, an outgrowth of Marx's theories bastardized the concept, to rule by an elite oligarchy — Communist Party leaders.

From the foregoing we denote strongly dissenting views. Though these great philosophers' brains were functioning properly, they were not sufficiently supplied with tenants of modern biology to realize they were barking up the wrong trees. That is excepting Plato, who sponsored as rulers a trained intellectual group. He, in effect, foresaw limited democracy. He must have realized that equality of men is a lofty-sounding fable; and those that rule must be selected not as politicians, pleasant storytellers, confidants, heroes or consensus candidates, but selected as true biological dominants, trained and intelligent.

That which is needed for future political science to round out Plato's vision of a limited democracy is the qualifying formulae in which the genetically fittest assume their roles in government. We term this "genetic democracy" — the wave of the future.

The Best of All Known Forms of Government? 1982 Democracy in the U.S. — Freedom.

★ There is no war, but *youth must register* for the draft or face a $10,000 fine and five years in jail. The whereabouts of 99% of these youths can be learned within 24 hours by alerted communities.

★ Although *voters of the nation were not consulted*, President Reagan sides with the British in the Falkland War, supplying arms and services. Dropping neutrality which is tantamount to declaring war against Argentina, he angers South America.

★ Israelis invade Lebanon. Reagan greets Prime Minister Begin. *The Argentinians were aggressors* in trying to retake islands wrested from them by the British 149 years ago.

★ Watergate's 10th birthday. Ex-President Nixon, *forced to resign* under impeachment threat, was pardoned of all crimes by his successor, Gerald Ford. President Nixon, living and well, *receives hefty government pension.*

★ Congressmen, receiving *good salaries,* voted themsevles additional income. The public forgot the *giveaway under Jimmy Carter of the Panama Canal,* which the majority of voters opposed.

★ John Hinkley shot President Reagan and three others, one in the head, *goes free under a plea of temporary insanity.*

★ *Ten million people unemployed;* with no war in sight, the nation is spending *tens of billions for armaments* it doesn't need.

★ It appears Prime Minister Margaret Thatcher, *English,* and Menachem Begin, *Israeli, are running the State Department.*

★ Right-to-Lifers under church aegis are moving ahead. Since they *don't favor abortion,* no one else can have one. Looming tragedy of population explosion unconsidered.

★ *Violent crime* is rampant. People barricade themselves in their homes. Yet billions of dollars are spent to fight drug traffic and convict naive people of drug usage. Additional billions are spent by the public on prescription drugs, addictive and harmful. It's a Mafia and pharmaceutical rip-off. *But law enforcement goes childishly chasing citizens who have the genetic right to do with their bodies as they please.*

★ Voting time. Drunks, addicts, uneducated, stupid, proletariat, feeble-minded, the controlled by political bosses for past favors, arteriosclerotics, government recipients, indolent and the non-productive are hassled, cajoled, and *transported to polling places.* You must have a license to drive a car. To vote there are no skill qualifications.

X Political Genes
Art of Domination

LATINS Vs. NORDICS

MITTERRAND of France advanced a theory of Latin and *Mediterranean socialism.* This differs from Nordic socialism in an effort to explain the intimate collaboration with communists working toward a common program. He sustains his thesis that countries in Latino Mediterraneos, France, Italy, Greece, Spain and Portugal, have social economic structures very distinct from the countries situated in northwestern Europe where social democracy has been triumphant.

In Mitterrand's opinion, Mediterranean countries have not yet arrived at the level of economic development characteristic of the neo-capitalistic countries. Because of this, social democratic reform is not possible for them.

To a certain point, he considers these countries are in a basic chapter of the third-world stage. He accepts the theory from reasons of convenient politics.

That which the political scientist has observed is not a political nature but a biological nature. Latins act the way they do not because of regulations of their constitutions or dictators, but because they are genetically programmed similarly. The characteristics of their blood derive from Visogoths, Goths, Etruscans, Greeks, Romans, Arabs, Jews and North Africans, Spanish, Italians and Egyptians, Ostrogoths, Carthaginians, Mauretanians, Numidians, Assyrians, Persians, Turks, Sardinians and dozens of other sub-racials of the Caucasoid race, tinged with DNA of the Negro and Asiatic. They have genetically blended over the centuries. There was free intercourse in the Mediterranean. It was possible in early Roman times, as reported by Gibbon, to travel from Ostia at the mouth of the Tiber, with a favorable breeze, to the columns of Hercules, in a week; and in ten days to Alexandria in Egypt. Roman roads permitted travel of 100 miles a day, their firmness having lasted almost two millennia.

It was not only the ease of communication in the Ancient World and the widespread trade issuing from hundreds of ports, it was the system of Roman rule over a thousand years which uprooted and attracted the barbarians and the civilized into its armies and metropolitan areas. Human nature being what it is, it was not difficult to formulate a Latin-type subrace. There only needs to be a few encounters with dissimilar human genes to introduce them into the pool almost permanently. As some are dominant, they will continue for long periods, i.e., colored blood injected into yellow or white genetic pool.

We see a subracial type emerging within the nations bordering the Mediterranean. Spain exported and dispersed its blood widely to mix in the nations of the new world of colored and mongoloid Indian. One finds today in commonwealths such as Puerto Rico an assimilated suavely beautiful people in which the skin tone of the majority is almost similar. On the other hand, we remember that the northern tribes of Europe were not advantaged with multi-subracial and racial infusions. They were relatively isolated behind the barricades and provinces of the Romans. While they did spill into the Mediterranean areas sporadically to add their seed to the mix, the reversed process seldom transpired. So what Mitterrand is talking about is not political divisions in which the Mediterranean group are friendly toward a type of communism and are in third-world stage. How we interpret it is that the inherent biology of the Latins is more acceptable to certain forms of government.

Naturally, one expects to find in the northwestern nations of Europe people who develop democracies — who are intensely loyal nationally, who have not so much a higher sense of honor but have less propensity toward pilfering and treachery and a greater sense in the mass killings of war. This cleavage in behavioral traits resulted from the genetic selection in the evolvement of northerners toward those who had to cooperate in the hunts, share the duress of the climate and the meager food environment. This geneticism had to rely upon loyalty, honesty, leadership, and high stratification of society, from dominants to large percentages of submissives. Such programming inevitably expanded their talents to become the greatest organized killers on earth, notwithstanding the French and Napoleon. Yet the majority of the French, and a great portion of their blood, is brother to that of the Germans. France is not as good an example of Mediterranean heritage as the others, as she retained traits of both northern and Mediterranean; the reason being that France was the crossroads of Europe for thousands of years.

What Mitterrand's theory does point up is that political science may not be considered unless one takes into consideration the underlying genetic biology. Politics and governments do not derive from the thoughts, actions and whims of leaders, democracies or ideologies. They derive solely from programmed biology which expresses itself according to ability.

EXAMPLE OF A DOMINANT

Winston Churchill was undoubtedly the greatest statesman the world has witnessed. He wrote as if the world issued from a very few people that had managed themselves by birth, ruse or ambition into powerful offices. The little guy, cannon fodder, factory worker, was something to be swept under the rug as obedient flesh but at voting time to be pampered. History moves by the names of the great. Herein is obvious tribute to genes of high bourgeois. One of Churchill's notable achievements was capture and control of the President of the United States, Franklin Roosevelt, who wrote nothing of significance and whose egotistical pomposity was ready prey for the wily Englishman. Although Roosevelt was a Phi Beta Kappa, the only exhibition of ability was his possession of political genes. He lacked vision of socio-economic history and deductions for the future.

Yet, with Churchill's magnificence and charm, living most romantic of regal lives, he attended and was author to "the rise and fall of the British." Born in the Victorian age at the height of English grandeur, empire, civilized achievement, and first-rank power, he and his colleagues were to dismember the national structure. Great Britain became a secondary ally to the United States, cast its people into squabbling and striking labor disputes, jackass socialism and austerity. As a self-serving, ambitious politician, Churchill emasculated the flower of Anglo-Saxon dominancy genes and aristocracy. He left them dead upon worthlessly-fought battlefields. He drove them to Marxist-Leninist concepts masqueraded as labor government or socialism. Expulsed to other nations were the English bourgeois from oppressive taxation and the tyranny of equalitarianism. It created the British "brain drain," an irreplaceable art export.

History in retrospect is a saga of error and stupidity. Few men visualized direction of the future. Churchill, in his extraordinariality, and Roosevelt, as his vassal, had shortsighted predictions for the welfare of their nations. While Churchill guided his nation into descent, Roosevelt and his socialistic propensity precipitated the United States into a nuclear life-and-death threat with the largest land-mass, authoritarian nation on earth — the Soviets.

The two chums not only insured rise of Russian super-power and consequent threat, but also permitted its conquest of Eastern Europe. The dissemination of hatred and propaganda to subvert nations of the free world in the hideous ideology of communistic equalitarian dictatorship by the powerful party elite was to follow.

A statement such as that brings forth hue and cry about what should have transpired had Hitler's Germany succeeded to dominancy in Central Europe. The massacre of the Jews in concentration camps was a desperate move toward ending World War II. This would not have occurred had Churchill and Roosevelt been more diplomatic and accepted refugees. Further, the persecution of Jews in pre-war Germany, lamentable as it was, was in many instances no different from other European nations over the centuries or as they are treated today in Russia.

As far as power politics is concerned, European wars over the centuries have a way of shifting territory back and forth with subracially-gened people managing to keep their identity, culture, and language. This is true from the Polish, Flemish and Ukrainian to Catalonian, Irish and Basque or Puerto Rican. So, whatever the outcome of the conqueror, it would merely be a re-alignment of boundaries, a regrouping of opposing force. Within a period of time, forces of subraces would be expressing themselves and boundaries re-altered again.

Where Churchill and Roosevelt made prime error was in permitting authoritarian international communism to succeed to tremendous stature, permit it to acquire satellite states such as East Germany, Rumania, Bulgaria, Poland, and Czechoslavakia. It was diplomatic madness to aid communism in the destruction of free capitalistic, Christian-oriented, white-raced northern nation. There was no need for the entrance of either the United States or England into the Second World War. Between France and Russia, Germany would have fed on bones too large to chew and a balanced peace would have ensued.

It was the same situation in Japan. If the egoed Roosevelt had permitted Japanese expansion into Asia and stayed out of Asiatic matters to delete provocations, there would have been no Pearl Harbor, no Korean War, no bloody Vietnam fiasco, which now shall encourage communists forever. Witness Moscow and Cubans in Angola, in the opening guns of Russian-African imperialism. What would have resulted would have been Japan, another capitalistic power, being bogged down on the huge Asiatic mainland by the sheer weight of the Chinese masses with their guerrilla tactic abilities. By 1980, the world would have witnessed an equal balance of Germany, Russia, China and Japan, and resultant prosperity. That the Churchill-Roosevelt schema was gross asininity is demonstrated today by the fact that a gutted Germany and Japan are now allies eagerly sought and wooed by English-American victors. Not only that, the shortsightedness, as the Treaty of Versailles in 1918, sets the stage for the greatest of struggles to come.

Genetically, there is one certainty. Unless the conqueror can genocide, hopefully by birth control, the racial or subracial group occupying the territory, and supplant it not so much with the culture or language of his own people but with the gened blood codings of his expansionist nation, the victory will ultimately be fruitless. Conquest will submerge within a short time to the DNA expressions of the isolated pool. Examples are the British in India, the Indians in North America, the French in Algiers, and the Spanish in South America.

Thus it behooves us to search in random sample writings for orifices to genetic revelations. In the great democracies, Churchill says, concerning 1820 in England, "The mass of the country was instinctive Royalist and the personal defects of the Sovereign had little effect upon this deep-rooted tradition."

If one substitutes geneticism for tradition, one could translate that in the early 19th century there was a loyal laboring class. Today, the ratio of higher bourgeois individuals is too small to the masses to keep them in stabilized submission. It is when this historic biological chain is broken, the hierarchy shattered, that social innovation for the worst results.

Within the 150-year period, there was a severe "brain drain" of the finest dominants and those of pioneer spirit to English colonies and other countries by high classes. On the reverse of the coin there was permission for the immigration of a great variety of subjects of the English colonies, notably the lower classes who selected toward England as a step upward, sufficient enough for the first time to provoke racial animosities within the nation. Both groups selected upward. The lowest to England, the highest away to greater opportunity.

This was not the only imbalance coming to this island nation. Proletariat under superior medical advances and higher income were breeding like uncaged rabbits. Their ranks heavily taken in wars were easily replenished. On the other hand, landed gentry, aristocracy and upper class, as is the tendency of the cultured, voluntarily limited growth. Nor were the upper-classed patriots replaced from battlefields. From such gened turnover, it is small wonder the empire disintegrated, socialization and nationalization of industry surfaced and lower-class, unscrupulous labor politicians under banners of equalitarianism and unionism were able to throttle a great people's destiny. It is doubtful Prime Minister Thatcher can turn it around. Discovery of North Sea oil will aid for only a short period.

Churchill was not sympathetic to Wellington when he spoke in the House of Lords against reform, saying, "A democracy has never been established in any part of the world that has not immediately declared war against poverty, against the payment of the public debt and against all the principles of conservation. Property and its possessions will become the common enemy. We shall lose colonies and foreign possessions, and with them our authority and influence abroad."

That was in 1831. Wellington, a strong believer in benign aristocratic authority and undoubtedly cognizant of genetic sociology, contrary to Churchill's sense of democracy, was prophetically brilliant in his stance against the onslaught of the peasantry and workers. The cave-in to those who were never intended to rule and to whom Churchill abetted through political necessity, did indeed lose the colonies and foreign possessions and British influence abroad. Wellington, hero of the Battle of Trafalgar, saw genetics. Churchill ignored it, and rode on his special luxurious wave.

In the 1840's, Prime Minister Peel said, "The fact is, people like a certain degree of obstinancy and presumption in a minister. They abuse him for dictation and arrogance, but they like being governed." Churchill grasped the changing times. All that is necessary to complete normal schema is place proper dominants above them. Proletariat are born to be ruled, as the Russians have aptly demonstrated and Peel sensed.

Again and again, Churchill fondled genetics without recognizing it. The "Poles, Swedes, and other hereditary enemies of the Czar." You had better believe that subraces in isolated genetic pools such as Swedes and Poles are hereditary biological enemies of the Russians, and always will be as long as they exist in blooded groups.

Churchill wrote of the Civil War in which genetics was a causative factor. Immediate issue was liberation of the Negro race, which a great many white leaders believed was a subhuman inferior species. One of the strongest propaganda elements to bring slavery down was interbreeding, which provided individuals of white content. Where should the line be drawn? For many reasons the slave system was being phased out on moral grounds. It had long served Greeks, Romans and Egyptians as a readily available form of intelligent energy. With mechanization, it was pricing itself out of the market.

McWhiney and Jamison, in *Attack and Die*, detailed Southern culture as Celtic: "The American Civil War was basically a continuation of the centuries-old conflict between Celts and English." — SPT, Nov. 14, 1982. This supports our contention that all wars have a genetic population base. Political elements are only expression of gene-related groups.

Churchill: "Those who hold that the fortunes of mankind are largely the result of the impact upon events of superior beings will find it fitting that Lee's famous comrade-in-arms 'Stonewall Jackson,' should be mentioned at this point." From the way Churchill writes, we can introspect his mind that he was one "of those who hold . . ." that he recognized genetic's ability to produce superiors as himself, a magnificent example.

Another observation made by Churchill was that the Civil War would have done a lot better for the North had Lincoln kept his lawyer's fingers out of the action. Churchill states, "But Lincoln's vacillations are a classic instance of the dangers of civilian interference with generals in the field." It was errors of Hitler, President Johnson in Vietnam, and other politicians who attempted to direct wars from their incapabilities. Politicians have one set of genes and generals another. Rarely do they blend in brilliance. Churchill concludes: "But should a great general appear, the civil government would be wise to give him full scope at once in the military sphere."

Political genes have a quantity of treachery and deceit residing in their code. When speaking of Lincoln, Churchill said, "In order to placate or confuse the pacifist vote, Lincoln had encouraged unofficial peace parleys with the South. Horace Greely . . . the President's representative. Greely soon discovered that he had no authority to negotiate a peace." It was akin to Franklin Roosevelt's pre-election declaration that he would not send American boys to war overseas when he was already laying the groundwork to do that very thing — much like Gerald Ford's pardon of a president; we shall never fully know what crimes President Nixon committed. But he was responsible for making Ford president. It is this genetic peculiarity in politicians that makes the public universally suspicious of their honesty.

FUTURE POWER OF NATIONS

Milovan Djilas, ex-chief of the Parliament of Yugoslavia and Vice President of that country, was expulsed from the Communist Party in 1954. He was in prison 1956 to 1961. He speaks of what will happen in the world in the next 50 years. There will be less changing of frontiers and more sociopolitical activity. Different from the 19th and 20th centuries, future nationalism will be ethnic and cultural rather than economic and expansionistic. The nation and nationalism will be much stronger than the ideology or economy.

Djilas foresees the disintegration of the imperial Soviet because all other imperialisms have collapsed. Further, that history sneers at Lenin because imperialism, instead of being the most advanced form of capitalism, is in reality the most advanced form of Sovietism and Bolshevikism. Soviet states will separate into independent national states. And, too, one cannot discount a war between China and the Soviet Union. So much for the forecast to the year 2025.

The forecast makes good genetic-politic sense. Evolutionarily, we expect isolated genetic pools having their characteristic distinctions to remain through the mechanisms of underlying genetic coding and adapt to the environment where they reside.

The swing toward nationalism is nothing more than a return to former biological basis of evolving society. Similarly, related genes with their perceptional qualities provide cohesiveness. It is why nations get into trouble when they introduce foreign genes into their national pools.

Nationalism shall be the wave of the future. The Basques of Spain, who fought long and hard and whose blood-type ratio is unique, give full testament to the driving power possessed by large unitized human societies which came out of isolated evolvement.

That which prevented nationalism from occurring in greater measure is totalitarianism of Russia, which forcefully combines disparate segments of races and subraces to congeal under single dominancy — much as Abraham Lincoln oppressed the desire of the genetically-developing South seeking to leave the Union.

True conquest of the world will take place by a homogeneous racial population, which will displace all others. The Catholics have made a good try at spiritual domination, but taking in many different racial geneticisms flaws the effort. It was why England broke off from Rome and established her own church. The English are English and the Italians are Italians; never the twain shall mix.

As far as Milovan Djilas' prophesy of war between China and Russia, he has DNA fed perfectly into the computer. The white race and yellow race will some day class to the death of one or the other.

There is impulse to conflict which resides in their common borders besides different genetics.

We have seen in recent centuries how genociding formulates nations — the United States killing off Mongoloids, Hitler dispensing with Jews, the Jews trying to eliminate Palestinians, the Arabs attempting to eliminate Israelis. The recital is but examples of innate compulsions.

PATHOLOGIC DOMINANTS

Unlike the sullen, criminal Stalin or wily orator of England, Winston Churchill, Roosevelt and Hitler exhibited pathological emotionalism in political fervor that placed them into dictatorial roles. It may be contended that Roosevelt was not a dictator because America was a democracy in which people could freely choose. Grossly it would appear that democracy existed. Yet here we have a man who against precedent felt himself super-godly enough to defy the two-term rule of American tradition and continue into a fourth term. He would have continued as long as life permitted, in defiance of precepts of a democratic society. This was true dictatorship as many would interpret it. It was evidenced by the fact that within a short time after his death, Congress saw fit to limit tenancy of presidents to two terms.

Roosevelt, by political chicanery, power, and privileges of his office, and by taking advantage of the great depression in the same manner as Hitler, moved into fixed position. Elections were shams. Roosevelt's opponents were pushovers. Hoover was victim of depression. Al Landon, a squeaky, mid-West farmer contesting the "savior" of working men's munition-making jobs. Wilkie was a "me-too" who failed to comprehend world issues. And Dewey, a lack-luster gangbuster, was forced to run against a war in progress and a loaded political machine. There was no contest. Machiavellian charisma of Roosevelt thoroughly duped the working classes. War economy delighted upper classes who were manufacturing weapons of death and laborers who were fed good-paying jobs. Hitler had thrown world Jewry and their wealth into Roosevelt's power. Roosevelt was a capable politician — a diabolically clever one. This is the true ingredient of dictatorship.

Roosevelt had the best of dictatorial worlds. From election in 1932 until death in 1945, it was a continuum of authoritarian power. Only the Supreme Court stood defiantly in his way. But in reality it didn't matter because he did exactly as he pleased, Congress rubber-stamping his every whim.

On the other side of the Atlantic, another dictator arose out of ashes of democracy in the manner of Roosevelt by appealing to unemployed and economic slump. Both dictators rode to power on economic misery and maintained that power by spending for instruments of death and preparation for war. It is ironic that the depression was cured by preparation for war and war itself. It is further ironic that in both instances, democracy succumbed to the rise of these dictators, whose stars ascended in the early '30s and whose horrendous careers ended in 1945. Thus, death reinstated democracy in the lands of victor and vanquished.

We do not feel as others that the poliomyelitis virus that attacks the spinal cord and paralyzes the lower legs (as was the case with Roosevelt) does not also do actual damage to higher brain tissue. However, one can undoubtedly subscribe to the fact that such physical handicap will carry with it mental aberrations which must be compensated. To be reasonable, we realize that any part of the body which is grossly altered produces psychologically compensatory adjustment or over-compensation and re-directment. A physically normal animal functions differently from one which is paralyzed.

Another factor with Roosevelt was how long did he possess the reputed leukemia which carried him off in form of massive stroke. Leukemia alters all tissues of the body and is especially disturbing to mentality. When drugs are administered, this heightens mental peculiarities. Here we have a man, a cripple, subject to polio virus when he came into the presidency and who departed it with leukemia. Both are viral episodes. Consequent somatico-psychic changes had to influence political decisions. To what extent they influenced behavior will be forthcoming from open archives and non-biased psychiatrists. Read John Toland's *Infamy*, 1982.

What one observes is a manic-depressive personality. The hypermania in speeches, broad egomanical smiling, incessant juiced-up psyche, God-like deliverances and pure lies when Roosevelt said he hated war and would not send American boys to die abroad, then he forthwith got into war as quickly as he could. He was taking sides long before Pearl Harbor by lend-lease and other ruses, which actually placed America as an ally within the war and which made a situation such as Pearl Harbor a foregone conclusion. According to some, Roosevelt sought Pearl Harbor, knew in advance the attack was to take place, and did not warn his commanders, General Short and Admiral Kimmel. Then he made them the scapegoats for infamy. These emotional traits and behavioral deeds relate to a cunningly unstable, paranoidal type of mind.

When one compares great Rooseveltian exuberancy when things are going good, to the depressions of some of his favorite programs such as NRA or unsuccessful packing the Supreme Court, it demonstrates manic-depressive syndrome. All of this went unnoticed because of the depression, preparation for war, and the war itself. His inordinate hate for his enemies, his false compassion, his God-like egoism and, finally, his lingering illness were hidden from the electorate. Pictures of a cripple being wheeled were deleted by the controlled media. It was pathetic to see later, whenever the chance arose, George Wallace being portrayed with all the incapacities common to a paralytic by those disagreeing with him.

Hitler's career was every bit as meteoric. Rapidly he assumed dictatorial powers. His persecution of the Jews and his final solution to exterminate them is a sickening episode of history. Because we portray Roosevelt in Hitlerian terms, let no one misquote that we agree with the Nazi conduct which shall forever disgrace the German people. On the other hand, war monsters existed on both sides. Merely directing crimes at the enemy has never solved guilt which may be equal. America did not profit from the war. It ended up facing, for its very survival, a ruthless communistic giant dictatorship. The victors planned badly.

Mania in Hitler needs no great detailing. His actions up to the end are proof. He was probably no more maniacal than Joseph Stalin. In defining the word "mania," what we mean is emotionalism so intense, barbaric, ego over-powering, with such self-glorification coupled with delusional drive which produces mass murder, atrocity, war continuation, negation of compassion and charity, a personality which seethes with hatred. This wanton destruction of life and culture, this insensitivity to reason and compromise, is mania in its finest hour.

Roosevelt, wealthy and educated, inherited laboring-class genes from which he launched his socialistic drive. Hitler, a badly-educated painter, corporal in World War I, demogogue, was born with genes toward the right. Both Roosevelt and Hitler had super-complement of political knavery genes — obtaining power by chicanery. They differed in what constituted direction for Homo sapiens.

Hitler, with dominance genes, wanted to carry the Germanic gene pool into expansive power and territory. Roosevelt's genes were lowest class laborer bent on racial mixing, economic chaos, and rule by the proletariat — a reversion of normal evolution. He attempted to disrupt the historic genetic composition of society by favoring the masses with a few dominants, thereby crippling the highly evolved upper classes.

Roosevelt led the Democratic Party coalition, minorities as Negroes, Jews, Catholics, laborers, plus welfarers, against white Anglo-Saxon Protestants who found themselves in the minority oppressed by tyranny of the majority, de Tocqueville style. In March 1976, the *St. Petersburg Times* reported how Roosevelt risked impeachment by backing Churchill's secret offensive against Hitler before the United States entered the war. Churchill went behind the back of Chamberlain, then Prime Minister, to seek alliance with Roosevelt, and Roosevelt, the egoist, went behind the back of the American people.

"I am your biggest undercover agent," remarked Roosevelt in his outright deception to the American people, in favor of his linkage to Churchill. In 1940, he was actively conniving by intelligence coordination with the British the entrance of the United States to the side of England. The rest is history, with England a second-rate nation today and the United States facing nuclear eternity. Had the American people been permitted to judge properly without English, Jewish and Rooseveltian propaganda, they may have supported the religious capitalistic state and Hitler would have eventually ended, as do all dictators in time. But into the equation, unfortunately, went the justifiable Jewish hatred of Hitler, with their tremendous wealth, power and influence. It is sad, indeed, that beneficiaries of the war, the Russians, are violently anti-Semitic and anti-Zionist and have persecuted the Jewish minority in the same fashion as Hitler but with less notoriety. We cite the war and its promotion to illustrate the incredible ability of a few screwed-up humans to involve millions in unnecessary holocaust via mal-gened human hierarchy.

In examining the mind of Roosevelt there were vicious characteristics which prompted his retention of power. After a 1940 national defense speech, he sent to J. Edgar Hoover the names of 128 people who had sent telegrams to the White House criticizing the address. For the FBI to investigate those that had the courage to oppose this pompous defective was the height of democratic disenfranchisement. This was before the United States was in the war! It illustrates the considerable number of paranoic and egocentric genes manifest in leadership roles. Roosevelt was the worst president this country has ever had, by his action leading the country into the Second World War, with the debacles that followed (ascension of communism, Korea, Vietnam, Cuba, Eastern Europe, China, and now nuclear threat to America and the entire free world).

SUBRACIAL DRIVE FOR LIBERTY

Communists are securing a United States beachhead while American people sleep and politicians are engaged in broadening civil rights. In *El Nuevo Dia*, Puerto Rican newspaper, December 1, 1975: "*El Partido Socialists Puertoriqueno se esta preparando para la lucha armada como uno do los medios para conseguir la Independencia para Puerto Rico.*" Translation — "Puerto Rican Socialist Party is prepared for an armed struggle as one of the means for getting the independence for Puerto Rico," expressed by the representative, Carlos Gallisa. He further said that independence was not going to come to the island by electoral vote but from armed confrontation; that the Socialist Party endorses acts of sabotage and that he, personally, hopes Puerto Rico converts itself to communism. And added is the old Marxist-Leninist line concerning the abolition of private property and each receiving according to his necessity.

Reported in *El Mundo*, November 20, 1975, Nicholas Medina, President of the Federation of Universities for Independence, appeared in the quadrangle of the University of Puerto Rico defying a court order prohibiting him from entering. He said he was saluting the Second Congress of the Puerto Rican Socialistic Party and described the decade from 1960-70 as one of violence, agitation, and student struggle against ROTC, which obligated ROTC to leave the university. He saluted birth of the revolutionary paper, *Claridad*. His act was summed up in a headline "The Leader (President) of the Federation of Universities for Independence sees revolution as a stage toward liberation." A third Red, Juan Mari Bras, Secretary General of the Socialist Party during the Second Congress of the party, December 7, 1975, in the coliseum in San Juan in which some 8,000 attended, stated that he had been asked by the government to change some of the principals in his organization, namely, to renounce their relations with the internationalist communist and liberalize their electoral laws. His answer was that P.S.P. (*Partida Socialistica*) would never renounce the right of an armed struggle for the independence of Puerto Rico.

At the same meeting of Reds there was a representative of the Palestine Organization, Assan Rahman, as well as large portraits of departed despots, Lenin, Che Chivara, and the founding god, Marx. They sent messages to the Communist Party of Cuba, the Socialistic Party of Iran, and daughter of late President of Chile.

Two hundred, fifty-six children filed into the coliseum with their fists raised carrying placards. The Secretary expressed the thought that these children will see dawning of communism in Puerto Rico. What was most important in 1976 was not to gain or lose elections, but to create the first Leninist-Marxist party in Puerto Rico. The demonstration ended with all present singing the "International." Elections were agreed upon by the party, but only for the purpose of political propaganda. The Reds obligingly made a resolution of aid to the North American labor force, as well as to the government of China, and recognized the Soviet Union as the most powerful base of the socialist camp. As was expected, they repudiated the fascist dictatorship of Spain and the monarchy.

On Sunday, December 7, 1975, at 11:00 a.m., in front of the Conservatory of Music, a few blocks from the coliseum, where the Puerto Rican Symphony Orchestra was tuning up for their concert, we observed the triumphant heady and spectacular march toward communism. In the warm sunlit morning, passenger cars, autobuses, and tow trucks, honking their horns, shouting and in unmolested pride, proudly flew from their fenders brilliant red flags with a single gold star, precipitating themselves to their meeting with destiny. It was right out of a page of the October Revolution in Russia. And one fully expected to see Leon Trotsky at its head.

Within the conservatory, a 65-piece orchestra rendered magnificently and stirringly Tchaikovsky's "Overture of 1812." Only between 100 and 200 appreciative listeners, well-dressed, neat, applauded vigorously. Have no doubt about it, here were true bourgeois. Half of the seats were unfilled. Tickets sold for a pittance — $1.00 to $3.00. Here was a great legacy of culture from their founder, the renowned Pablo Casals. Where were the intellectualized society of San Juan, Santuce, and Rio Piedras? They were certainly not at that delightful symphonic concert.

But 8,000 proletariat were next door screaming for independence and armed revolution. They were subscribing directly from the book to the bloody tyrannical principles of Marxism and Leninism. They spoke of sabotage and revolutionary presses, of the confiscation of private property, of the defeat of capitalism, of the idolitorization of socialist founders, of sly election tricks solely to promote venomous subversive propaganda, and of affiliation with the international communistic movements.

They employed the usual Bolshevik props — red flags and stars, large portraits of their gods, and even utilized the children gimmick. It brought back memories of Joseph Stalin, the man who killed millions of farmers and their children or imprisoned them, being surrounded by well-dressed children passing flowers back and forth for newsreels. The toe bones of children "Bloody Joe" sent to their deaths would have filled the stadium to overflow! Yet here were the communists up to their old tricks, cleaning their image with manifestations of children, poisoning their minds toward rebellion and disorder.

A Hollywood script writer could not compose a more realistic scenario concerning the initial advancement of communism within United States territory, excepting, of course, American Red senators who gave away the Panama Canal in 1978. Here it was for all to see, hear, read, and feel. The communists had established their first beachhead on American soil without firing a shot!

By permission of Congress, the communists are about to take over the American territory of Panama and the island possession of Puerto Rico. Only a small percentage of the people of Puerto Rico desire independence or care to be members of the Communist Party. However, it is not the way the communist handbook works. Communists are dedicated addicts, supported by foreign aid, who spew forth false logic to overthrow any nation in their way. They are organized and ready to move in, not by electoral policy but by disciplined revolution. They are patient. It is why America lost the war in Vietnam. America had not the least concept of what communism is. She simply had not read the texts that fill the free libraries. China was handed to communists by lunk-headed policies of Roosevelt and Truman. America sincerely does not want to stop communism because it is living in ethereal mysticism concerning virtues of pure democracy.

Liberal thinkers in the land's highest offices have not only pave the way for the communist beachhead in Puerto Rico, they have made its communistic capture a near certainty. If we are sagacious enough to sit on the sidelines when two communist giants, Russia and China, go to it, providing arms but not men to both sides, we may be able to bury communism. If we rid the State Department of minority heads more interested in preserving their ancestral roots than advancing the cause of America, and instead substitute shrewd Yankee traders who will work not toward peace but toward a Russo-Chinese conflagration, we may see the return of true capitalism, a return to democracy, and the end of totalitarian communism.

Peace is paramount; but only peace for the United States of America. We must play their tricks, those masters of intrigue, revolution and incitation to world revolution. Our policy should not be detente but military belaboring of China and Russia that they finish prostrate, susceptible to Western reconstruction in benign terms with firm political direction.

FASCISM FOR MEDITERRANEANS

One of our successful cloak-and-dagger adventures was the CIA intervention into internal affairs of Chile where the communist government was overthrown. It was replaced by the only type of government which will provide a degree of freedom and democracy in today's world, where one is dealing with South American blood mixture, that is, a benign fascist regime controlled by military dominants.

What we fail to understand is man is bred in the nations of South America with a tri-partite mixture: Spanish and Portuguese white, African Negro, and native Mongoloid Indian, the three races mixed to create a genetic constitution which cannot accept democracy. Only hope for this type of blood grouping is communism or fascism; but democracy is an impossibility. You have the "proof in the pudding" that over centuries it has never been successfully instituted in South American countries for long. Within this tri-partite racial mixture we have biological receptiveness to certain forms of dominance. From out of evolutionary development of races there resulted characteristics indigenous to their society and to perpetuation of their genetic pools. Once these are mixed, you have a potpourri that will not behave in the manner in which they were originally developed.

Building on a priest autocracy, the Mayan civilization reached great heights. It could best be compared to fascism of the pre-World War era. Negroes that were injected into the New World from Africa brought with them an anarchistically-gened society. Whereas, the whites — and these were special Mediterranean whites in whom a complement of the Moors and Phoenicians flowed — brought with them a long history of monarchy ruled by caesars, kings, and caliphs. These special white genes were selected toward rule by dominants directly out of Pleistocene evolution.

Combining fascism and monarchy does not add up to democracy. Democractically disposed subraces obtained their coding from the great challenges of northern Europe, as periodic glaciation, massive problems of providing shelter and clothing to withstand the northern cold. Added was prime work to obtain sufficient food by hunting under harshest conditions. Northern races, to survive had to evolve a form of expert cooperation. Dominants were not as important as the coordination of the tribe. The environment was too hostile to permit anarchy, *laissez-faire* type of go-it-on-your-own social order. It was too challenging to permit luxuries of feudalism and sovereignty. Northern Europeans selected toward those individuals of society in which cooperation was a greater element than the few who captained.

DEMOCRACY

That is why democracy never moved outside the bloodstreams of northern Europeans. That is why, as we travel south from England and Sweden, we end up with increasing amounts of anarchy and tribal rule — excepting where we come to the nation of South Africa, which is dominated by northern whites; that is where we find democracy flourishing within the blackness of anarchism. It is why a leader as Ian Smith did not relinquish right to proper government in Rhodesia, even though world opinion, communist-backed, boycotted him. Smith fully knew that once white rule is superseded by black democracy, it will end up with chaos, terrorism, and dictatorship. However, the Anglo-Saxon socialists in England betrayed him.

Pages of history are replete with examples of genetic foundations of government. It is not that one race is superior, it is merely that for the climates and environments in which the races and subraces evolved, they selected toward the type of government that would provide them with survival, or rather their governmental gene propensities were bequeathed them in the advancement of the fittest. What was fit for Africa was relative anarchy and slavery. The Africans themselves developed a high system of slavery incorporating their own people. It was not northern slave traders inventing slavery; all they did was funnel an established fact into an economic market.

What came out of the struggle for survival in the cold wastes of the European north was a society that selected toward cooperation, ingenuity, mastery of killing and hunting techniques. It is biological inheritance that is responsible for the spectacular development of western civilization. Its magnificent culture, as well as its horrendous and highly technical wars, are gene-programmed.

Pay small heed to emerging wealthy Arab nations. When their oil is exhausted, they will recede to bare-footed sheikdoms. Pay little heed to the entirety of Africa. These marvelous and resourceful black people are not genetically coded to erect powerful nations, wage sustained wars or develop a competitive economy.

When the political locos of the United Nations speak about aiding the underdeveloped countries, they display a wonderful ignorance of human genetics. They are underdeveloped, and shall continue to remain so, unless sustained by northern economies and northern developers. They are what they are because their genes have determined what they shall be. Do not expect any miraculous evolvement of any of these nations in the way Russia evolved under communism. Long before the Bolsheviks took power, Alexis de Tocqueville, in 1832, prophesized the emergence of powerful Russia and a powerful America would control the destiny of the globe. He did not understand genetics but he was reading the message.

It would be far better for the nations of the north to forget about under-developed countries and send them birth control pills. One day Catholics themselves, for their own welfare, will have to muzzle their church's hier-archy in relation to birth control. In the days past it was a swell idea to have Catholics outbreed other denominations in the interests of theology. High population would provide not only survival for the church but its eventual domination. Today the picture is changed. Population explosion, as well as communism, threatens the very existence of Catholic society. Bulging under-fed and deprived populations are fertile fields for communism, the moral enemy of Catholicism. It is time the church reversed its policy lest they be engulfed by the selfish policy of the past.

We have reviewed the basic organic requirements in political structure. We see how absurd are the edicts and laws of our leftist-leaning legislators and presidents. Roosevelt and the "New Deal" was nothing more than the application of communistic socialism attempting to throttle it upon a viable, white, northern European, capable, democratic geneticism. As Governor of New York he had the experience of dealing with a large population of pro-letariat genes who were highly susceptible to anarchism, welfare, and dominancy.

Roosevelt's incarceration of a northern European biology which was capable of handling its own affairs, keeping its house in order, and providing decent standards of living, contrasted with the southern biologies in new habitat gravitating to slums. Certain subraces, when transplanted to northern environments, demand a welfare state. Unless the state is clever enough to demand productivity and maintenance of property and domiciles, Harlems spring up, not so much by culture and racial barriers, but because their genetic pools demand adaptation to an environment to which they are accustomed.

The welfare state, socio-communism with a flavor of political dema-goguery, succeeded in permitting the anarchistic biological units to become low productive, non-contributory, and free-loading off the better northern adapted units. This process caused polarization, giving rise to the left — the minorities, democrats, workers, proletariat, socialists. It succeeded in pulling out from the northern European ranks the worst elements to place them into a degenerating section.

It had been previously believed that the problems of the ghettoes and slums were a product of poverty, lack of education and opportunity. It is now revealed that when one places a concentration of people whose genes are non-adaptable to northern cities into a fully-equipped, modern city in A-1 condition, if you educate them to the levels of their talents — within a few generations the metropolis would regress to slums and chaos, providing you removed the directive genius of the northern Europeans. What is bad for America is the imposition of a welfare state upon strong dominant biology which can handle its own problems. If left to its own resources, it would dole out humanitarian assistance as needed, without political inefficiency and waste.

Yet what was worse was to carry the system to Puerto Rico, with its unique bloodlines and Spanish culture. In the food-stamp program there has been great fraud. Although only a population of three-million people, it received $550-million in food stamps, or a massive 12%, of United States total in 1975. Not understanding the Latin temperament, it's a joke not to expect them to utilize the food stamps for items as tires, appliances, beauty treatments, and what-have-you. This is America's method? Are we going to prevent inroads of communism by welfare?

In the back of our socialistic schema is none other than Karl Marx. Yet we differ from Marx in the application. We don't give a damn about the productivity of the chiselers receiving welfare. We simply give them checks so they let everyone in peace. Before it is finally over we may be a second-rate power as England, burdened by huge welfare costs, harassed by labor organizations, and depleted of capital and human brainpower. The colossal error is in the fact that the productive ability is negated by leftists in the Congress. They, it appears, would rather see a descent to socialism which they can control rather than a jubilant diversified stratification of class which they cannot.

There is no evolutionary parallel to the welfare society. Parasites that did not produce were selected out rapidly. We are in a competitive world, and one day, if we cannot replace our advantages and resources, we will have marched into the camp of communism voluntarily, brandishing flags of equalitarianism and the slogan, "All For All."

NEGRO VOTE – One-on-One in a Democracy

The real Southerners — the Negroes. Excepting a portion, place them in any Northern city and watch immediate regression of Northern standards. This is always blamed on slum landlords who oppress and gouge the poor. Nothing could be further from the truth. Negro property genes have been abandoned to carefreeness. They have a better sense of vandalism than do Northerners. Rarely do you see them engaged in maintaining tenements. Again, it is not that they are not charming and clean people; it simply does not occur to them that the cracked plaster, the blotched walls, the leaking faucet, the scuffed floors, are an inferior style of living. Their genes are programmed for Southern living where apartment maintenance is unimportant.

If we examine two groups of approximately the same type-blooded Spanish residing within the United States — one in New York and one in Miami — it is immediately apparent that those in Miami's "Little Havana" prosper like kings while those in New York's Harlem live in miserable circumstances. It isn't because one is Puerto Rican and the other Cuban; it is because genes they transport are located in improper environment. A second minor factor is a goodly proportion of Cuban refugees are from the upper bourgeois class which does carry superior intellectual genes. The New York setting with relationship to the Southern Negro adds heavy weight, since they are both within an abnormal environment to which they are not programmed to adapt.

It's no small wonder that the City of New York was on verge of bank-ruptcy. New York is the largest Jewish city outside Israel. Jews are the wealthy educated masters of the metropolis. The city is almost divided into genetic thirds: Negro, Spanish-American with a flavoring of Mongoloid, and white Mediterranean-Judaic — all relatively isolated within their own cultural enclaves. Sprinkle as well a portion of all types of subraces, including Irish, and you can be sure you're headed for chaos.

America the melting pot? Not on your tin-type! The first thing a stranger to New York thinks when he encounters a new face is what group to identify it with. Economical, educational, racial, and cultural segregation have never permitted the melting pot to even simmer. If New York was a genetically pure form of any northern subrace, which are the only people adaptable to that terrible climate, it would be one of the finest cities. People would not stay indoors for fear of their lives or, when financially able, flee to the suburbs. The city would not have to beg the federal government to bail them out of impending bankruptcy. Tourists, once again, would be willing to visit a fun and cultural city.

Assimilation and aculturation of Puerto Rican people into Northern American society will be difficult because of inherent genetics which adapts perfectly to Puerto Rican environment. In the North, in spite of central heating, adaptation of Negro and Puerto Rican has never been successful. Puerto Ricans do perfectly well in their own land with social security bene-fits. The shield they are provided includes defense and a democratic liberty, which no other Latin American country possesses to such extent.

Puerto Rican reluctance to utilize English is a natural cultural adhesion. The clamor for autonomy, the road to independence, is also natural pheno-menon. It would be nice if the United States would go away, let them alone, provide trade and billions of dollars in economic support. The genetic politics of the whole affair is that they can't make it on their own econo-mically any more than any other Latin American country. Nor can their political structure remain stable and not gravitate into a type of Cuban communism, Argentinian chaos, or Chilean dictatorship. If Puerto Ricans are left to their own merits, their economy would collapse and liberty would take wings.

Tragically, this is the constitutional geneticism of the Latin American and Caribbean nations. This type of racial mix does not have the technologi-cal nor the "ambitious" drive genes which one finds in northern cultures. It is not that they don't have natural resources; it is that they don't have genetic combinations to create Western civilization.

You can read a library of books concerning politics and economics of the Latin Americans. You will come to one unmistakable conclusion: They are a world of disruption and emotionalism, with little cooperation or adequate discipline toward maintaining democracy. On top of this is a high rate of crime, gangsterism, workers' strikes and civil disruptions, with a turning inward toward the sanctity and reverence of family and church.

In 1975, in the small area of San Juan and surrounding communities, there was someone shot to death every day and at least a dozen armed robberies. At one time sociologists thought that heat of climate irritated people and that, consequently, in warmed-up passion, they committed thoughtless, spur-of-the-moment crimes. Actually, crime incidence has little to do with heat, although one may point out that Northern riots took place in the summer months. Mass communication and assembly are easier in the summer. Culprit is the highly unleashed genes of the southern races and subraces. In evolutionary evolvement, personal, violent, small-group aggressiveness was a more common means of survival than was northern races' emphasis on group strategy, cooperation, and restraint.

People do not determine politics; genes do. Oftentimes there is perversion of genetic adaptability. Yet, in time, the political spectrum will separate according to the underlying coding. There is no greater cold-blooded killers in history than the northern white race, whose intelligent group ability comes naturally by selective heritage. One could survive in Africa with an occasional feud or dispatchment of one's neighbor. Food was provided for the gathering. Yet, in the north, natural selection chose the best animal killers. It is no accident that northern civilizations arose out of the aggressive challenges. It is doubtful that within hundreds of thousands of years a true democracy will exist among the totally black nations. Whether they have dictatorship or communism, it is one and the same — both are dictatorships.

Democracy sprang from northern European people. Its purest floration was reached in the United States when white English aristocrats rebelled and penned a Constitution which has been in effect for two hundred years. That Constitution was designed for white northern Europeans. There was not the slightest thought that it would accommodate large minorities of other races. Attempts to alter this "white" Constitution to include other races by civil rights additions, laboring rights, and anti-discrimination, can lead to disaster.

MONGOLOIDS

China, a feudal, agricultural, peasant society, has not moved into modernized mold of Western society. Attribute this backwardness to evolutionary selection which gave priority to the proletariat classes. Then there is reason to understand the facility with which communism has taken root and communal propensities which characterize the Chinese and their seeming obsession with equality and minding each other's business.

The climate and soil disposition of the Orient provides a better setting for the selection toward mesomorphic, proletariat, hard-working, equal-in-suffering individuals. Overpopulation prevented the development of a class system, whereas, in the Western world there was a greater dispersal of tribal units, giving their isolated gene pools a chance to develop a more stratified divergency.

It is worth noting that any time the Chinese or Mongoloid race radiated out of their native origin to North and South America, when they set out on waves of conquest to the West, with Atilla storming the gates of the Roman Empire, and invasion and conquest of Russians, their genetic thrust eventually receded. In America, their genetic programming proved an absolute disaster when they were confronted with European whites. They were ostracized, isolated, and annihilated by the United States. In other nations of the American continent they were conquered and dominated by Spanish rule for centuries. Here their preservation was dependent upon breeding with Spanish males forming the Mestizo. Later, the Spanish descendants became the exclusive ruling class, regardless of revolutionary turnovers. To this ruling class upper bourgeois was added — Portuguese blood in Brazil, German and Italian blood in Argentina and Chile, and a smattering of European blood throughout the lower continent. The peasant, proletariat-serf class retained a high percentage of the Indian-Mongoloid.

Mongoloids who hunted their way into the New World and created great civilizations such as Mayan and Inca, represented a development of culture equivalent to agriculture revolutionary society of Mesopotamia. Their genetic peculiarities were no match for the Western European invaders. Although resistance was severe and bloody, in few instances were they able to resist conquest, domination and humiliation by the Europeans or by those whose progeny had mixed with Europeans.

It was not a question of Western technology or of the few Western horses imported by Spanish conquistadores. Cortez easily conquered Mexico by intrigue rather than force of arms. Without the aid of dissenting Indian tribes, none of the Spanish would have been able to conquer. The great failing of the New World Mongoloids was that they could not coordinate their efforts, even going to guerrilla-type warfare. Had they been cohesive and disciplined, they would easily have driven the white man out of the continent. It had nothing to do with will or drive that they were driven into the sea, deep forests, deserts, and frozen plains by the white invasions commencing in the 16th century. They had shown themselves to be excellent hunters and moderately capable agriculturists. Too, they had shown themselves to be brave warriors and, like Iroquois, oftentimes inhumanly cruel.

The problem was natural selection; they had never come up with proper genes to compete with abstract social intelligence of whites. There was no exception. For 500 years, regardless of their protests and insurrections, they had been subject to the rule of white Europeans and mixed descendants. Here one has the firmest of empirical science and the strongest of deductive logic. The genes of the Mongoloids of America were no way capable of resisting subjugation by Europeans.

Black Africans have to search diligently to provide meager history to compare with the culture of the northern Europeans. Yet, even with white colonialism, the same subjugation did not occur in Africa as it had occurred with Mongoloid natives of America. This was because of the Negro's superior adjustment to a hostile environment. In diseases such as malaria there was less native susceptibility. By and large, the Negro, with his temperament, physical ability, skin, nasal and lip structure and hair, completely outranked the white race without so much as a shot being fired. His adaptability to this hostile African continent was supreme.

White beachheads in Rhodesia and Southern Africa are no more than that. Highly developed transported cultures are held in place by white man's technology and capital, Apartheid segregation and discrimination. The insidious venom of communism, inciting the workers, will soon bring the final issue into solution. For a nation to succeed and to perpetuate itself, its geneticism must be relatively homogeneous. The distance between the whites and the pure blacks of Africa is light years greater than the distance between the Mestizos and Indians of South America. In this context, the United States is fortunate to have over two-thirds of its population of Western European stock. Today, communist incitation pecks at this historically successful citadel by trying to group minorities such as Mexicans, remaining Indians, Puerto Ricans, and Negroes in racial onslaughts against the system.

If a nation is wealthy, it is so because the geneticism of its pool is capable to rise to such status. Nations of poverty exist because their geneticism is incapable of adapting modernly. Freak accidents such as oil, mineral or soil wealth are excluded. What we are today is what the geneticism of the last few million years had determined we should be. We look about us to see the evolutionary solution, then deduct genetic formulae.

POLITICIANS

In evolution of social groupings, dominant apes could be challenged, but unless physically weakened, they were rarely overthrown. However, when we moved from a less physically dependent society to an intellectually mobilized one, doors were opened for the cunning. Strength was no longer a prime item. It remained for dirty infighters to promote dissention, connive and construct intrigue by which they could obtain power and self-reward. Such individuals are basically weak men. They are rarely loved beyond their tenure in office. To obtain power they need numbers. Their altruism into human society was the solicitation of the weakest, unprotected members. The sheer number force of weak allies of the stupid was sufficient to overthrow the truly born leaders. It is both conspiracy and coalition that forges their insensitive directions.

Politicians are born. They are genetically programmed. They evolved not as representatives of good government, but as usurpers of traditional leadership, filling the void created when we moved from muscle and strength to deceit and cunning. Democracy is a false shield that politicians carry. In a democracy everyone votes. Yet the majority are voting by whim, tradition, ignorance, submission. As hominids, our leaders were born and we obeyed. As Homo sapiens, political jackals conspiratorized mass flesh. Leadership is sacrificed on the altar of deceit.

If we examine the American scene, only two true leaders became presidents in the last century — Kennedy and Eisenhower. John Kennedy: regard the man's face, deportment, bodily attitude, brilliant mind, speech, and dynamism. Look at those in the political field of his times: Humphrey, Muskie, Nixon, Roosevelt, Truman, Johnson — you do not see leaders here, only politicians. The soldier president, Dwight Eisenhower: a leader in the field and for his country. The only two leaders of the century — Kennedy and Eisenhower.

A leader begins with proper physiology — and we mean to include physiognomy. Political parties have not learned from Hollywood. They insist on foisting a weathered, malshaped face upon the voter when they have millions of well-directed geneticisms to choose from. Voters are not above selecting toward a thin, physically well-shaped Adonis such as John Kennedy. There are too many cute games. Parties fear real leaders — they want intrigue and profit. Last thing they desire is a man of true and capable leadership because that cut of human may prove difficult to handle.

King-makers in the political party system have never realized that if the eyes are beady and sunken, chin receding, teeth bucked or nose goofed off, big ears and little hair — all are facial characteristics we do not respect. We are gene-programmed to honor facial and physical attributes of beautific qualities from evolutionary selection. We select toward masculine beauty; but in politics we are usually not given a chance. Screwed-up facial features may be a cartoonist's delight, but underneath the intellectual may say those big lips, distorted teeth, funny nose are genetic imperfections, are DNA goof-offs. How do I know the mind beneath it is any different? George Wallace, who was regarded as a racist, came off with about 10,000,000 votes — about 13% of the total — and the candidate who won had a mere 43%, in 1968. Obviously, none of the three had wide appeal.

Externalism of perfection in genes is difficult for the old-line political bulldogs to accept. Their attitude is, "The devil with what the guy looks like. How does he wheel and deal, and what can I get out of it?" There is a correlation with the perfect physiological male and high intelligence. Leaders have strong geneticisms. Consquently, they are bypassed because they are not readily controlled. Their interest is in the future, the nation, humanity, not in private groups in which the majority ordain power.

Some feel that in our two-party system there is small difference. Being in a liberal or conservative movement is apt to exchange itself by the next election. No such thing. Our parties are solid manifestations of genetics. The democrats sponsor the minorities — southern Europeans, Latins, Africans, Semites. Their bulwark is the Italians, Catholics, Jews, Puerto Ricans, Negroes, and workers' votes. Republicans, on the other hand, traditionally favor the English, New England, German, Scandinavian, early settler farmers and intellectual groups. The Democratic Party is regressive evolutionarily and leaderless, a representative of the masses, and has a tendency toward liberalism and socialism. Republicans, possessing the intellectuals, northern Europeans and further advanced cultures, tend toward conservatism because of greater ability to care for themselves and fewer proletariat.

Four of the largest wars found Latin democrats represented by Wilson and Roosevelt taking off on a castigation of Germans; and the republicans, Abe Lincoln and Teddy Roosevelt, charging Southerners and Spanish. The Mediterranean democrats of World Wars I and II were determined to do in their ancient northern enemies, the Germans.

Historic coalitions between Southern aristocratic democrats and Northern republican conservative whites was a blood not political tie. When the true democrats emerged, they reached for the worker-peasant, uneducated classes to be represented by fabulously wealthy opportunists — the Roosevelt, Harriman, Kennedy line.

In short, the art of politics is the art of handling genetically-related groups. Or why would the word "nepotism" exist?

XI Social Genes
Chemicalized Behavior

INTERPRETATION OF HISTORY

WITH THE advancement of social-genetics one can re-examine masters as Toynbee and Gibbon. They misinterpreted history because they lacked modern tools. Arnold Toynbee, British historian, died at age 86, produced prodigious works. He was one of the first to interpret history, which at the time was an act of academic heresy. His belief was that history could best be described as a tree in which the branches were separate civilizations of the world. The rise and fall of and the collisions between these civilizations became the focus of his scholarly attention. "History, in the objective meaning of the word, is the process of change."

Applying the view that comparison of civilizations or societies was the way to write meaningful history, Mr. Toynbee devoted the first six volumes of his study to searching out the pattern of genesis, growth, and breakdown of civilizations since the emergence of man.

Some of his civilizations had developed universal churches and universal political structures, and had been obliged to meet barbarian threats. He suggested that spiritual rather than material forces controlled the course of history and that individuals played creative or destructive roles in the unfolding of events. Mr. Toynbee argued that the end of history is the Kingdom of God and that history is God revealing Himself.

Few modern historians profess to find divinity in human affairs, and this contention, subtly argued, further served to set Mr. Toynbee off from others in his craft. His vast erudition also put him apart.

Toynbee did not know genetics. Consequently, he could not translate an ethereal concept of God into reality of human organic chemistry. One stark evidence of genetic effect produced the Dark Ages. Although it is fashionable today that the ages were not quite so dark, they nevertheless represented, between 400 and 1400 A.D., one thousand years, a sort of resting phase of human cells. Nothing spectacular ensued in arts, literature, culture or national organization. Something truly dramatic was being phased into the European genetic pools.

Disruptiveness of culture and stability results from interracial mixture, which destroys the traditional adaptiveness of both parties' offspring. In Europe, between 375 and 550 A.D., the Germanic migrations took place. It was as if a sorcerer's wand was stirring a genetic witches' brew in territory stretching from Gibraltar to the Black Sea and from Sweden to Carthage.

No stranger, a mixture of dysgenics had been produced in the world before. New injecting participants were radical: Mongols from the east and Negro slaves from the south. They did not contribute heavily to the admixture. What was of consequence was upsetting subracial mixtures which had been living in relatively isolated genetic pools for whom specialized adaptable traits had developed.

From the territory of modern Scandinavia, northmen swept down through Russia as far as Constantinople. They sailed west to Iceland and Greenland, and even to Sicily and Crete, in 850 to 1000 A.D. Anglos, Jutes, and Saxons invaded England. Northern Goths followed the Vistula south in 150 A.D. to the northern Black Sea. Ostrogoths from that area, in 454 A.D., migrated westward to Italy and Yugoslavia. Visogoths, in 397 A.D., traveled north from Greece into Italy and over to France and Spain. Vandals came out of southern Germany in 170 A.D. into Romania and Bulgaria, and in 401 A.D., commenced a circular route west through Paris to Spain, across Gibraltar and then east into northern Africa to arrive in Rome in 455 A.D.

Whereas, Negro slaves had been injected into the Roman Empire for centuries, Mongoloids swept out of the east in 375 A.D. The Huns were halted in Gaul in 451 A.D. by an allied west Roman and German army under Aetius in the horrible battle of the Catalonian fields. Repelled, they invaded Italy, but upon the death of their leader, returned to their Asiatic homeland. Some were assimilated, and we may today observe the slanted Mongoloid eyes in the Hungarian areas.

More than constant blood-bathing, rapine and destruction, inhabitants of Europe received a massive shot of foreign genes. Feudalism, exhausted and shocked from the ordeal, the bourgeois, nobility, bureaucrats, clergy, and skilled tradesmen retired to castle strongholds awaiting it out while listening to strolling balladiers, reciters of the Song of Roland, and amused themselves with chivalry, which ended when Miguel Cervantes ridiculed its follies in the great literary text, *Don Quixote.*

Outside, the castle remained calm as peasants crudely tilled land, husbanded sheep and cattle, lived and died in unbelievable filth, squalor, and disease. Great declarations by Karl Marx and Charles Dickens against the evils of the industrial revolution were penny-ante when compared with the Medieval Ages. Mankind survived it in a mixed-up genetic slumber.

Once mating catastrophes had subsided, adaptation and selection could gather the pieces, and the Western world broke out into the magnificent civilization which is still with us today.

What had happened was that intraracially, wild, strong, and hybrid types had, for the first time in Homo sapien history, been injected rapidly into diverse gene pools. How promiscuous those gene pools had become can be witnessed by the rapid spread of syphillis throughout Europe once Columbus's sailors had brought it home from the New World.

Following this intraracial orgy of tribes and nations, the boundaries of Europe, although not settling in peace or position, demonstrated a relative fixity according to genetic components. This permitted the rise of nations, national loyalties, and restricted subracial genetic pools to produce the identifiable characteristics. Its culmination ended in the racial horror of Hitler and the Nazis. Earlier, nations as England, France, and Spain had cemented their subracial identities. A true hold-out was the Irish, for the British never did succeed in subjugating them. The Irish question for the English was never one of territory, governorship, or religion, as they may suppose. It is that the Irish are a tough, determined-characteristic subrace who are not going to have their genes diluted by foreigners, come hell or high water. Even after their forced emigration by famine to America, they have succeeded in maintaining their characteristic and charming attributes.

Thomas Jefferson said something to the effect, "The earth belongs to the living." Brilliant, he did not know genetics. For the *earth is of the dead who live.* We are but chemical codes of the deceased who have selected our combinations.

A historian who focused his lifetime on one epoch of civilization was Edward Gibbon. Neither Gibbon nor Toynbee was privy to social genetics or anthropological studies. History revolved in a world of personalities, economies, and intrigue, in their eyes. However, rather than logical purpose, history is directed by inherited biological forces and by the strong innate drive of territoriality.

The social genetic approach to history contends that events originate and are propulsed by the underlying DNA coding. History acts, especially, through racial and subracial pools that are isolated and which give movements' identity. A second factor above intelligence and special inherited skills is geographical location in which adaptation unfolds. Obviously, races and subraces that were privileged to have good climatic conditions, minimum of pathological antagonists, and bountiful flora, fauna and minerals, had exceptional advantage in imprinting rules and deeds upon pages of written history. Material resources, evolutionary adaptability, cohesiveness of language and culture resulting from the foregoing forged nations' dominance is what makes them worth recording. Allies have been important, but great issues were settled by the formula of the genes rather than acts of outsiders.

A great work was to occupy over twenty diligent years of Gibbon's life — *Decline and Fall of the Roman Empire.* Gibbon was born in Putney, Surrey, England. He completed 2½ years of military service, finishing with rank of Lt. Colonel. He never married, and died in 1794. He saw irresponsibility of Rome's militarization, barbarianism and dissipation by sectarians; plus internal bickerings of Christians. There were different masses, venal soldiery, weakened frontiers, purchase price, mercenary troops, and abandoned provinces. He felt that the largeness and the eminence of the empire was its fatality, that it was inevitable effect of greatness and prosperity. It was a structure crumbling under its own weight. Gibbon described history as little more than a register of crimes, follies, and misfortunes of mankind.

Although the Roman system was formulating for 700 years before Christ, Gibbon begins his treatise with the rulers in the years following Christ, which ended in the West in 476 A.D. and in the Eastern Empire in 1453. What caused this great civilization to be washed down the drain was the object of twenty years' research.

Gibbon says, "Trajan was ambitious of fame; and as long as mankind shall continue to bestow more liberal cause on their destroyers than on their benefactors, the thirst of military glory will ever be the vice of the most exalted characters. The praises of Alexander . . . had kindled a dangerous emulation in the mind of Trajan."

It is true, we lavish praise upon the military hero in larger proportion than that levied upon the scientist. It is not from a lack of common sense, but from neurogenic constitution in which dominance is a strong factor. This was one of the social revolution's greatest achievements. Masses submitted to a central authoritarianism reaching its strongest movement with advent of agriculture and urbanization. While we praise the brave hero and neglect benefactors, we are evidencing our position in submissive dominants' hierarchy of genetic society.

There is a second factor. All is not centered in leaders. Throughout history there has been a tendency for those who record it to focus on the principal character as if it was his will that precipitated change. What is less frequently recognized is that Atilla, Alexander, Trajan, Napoleon, and Washington were merely the ultimate symbols of movement. Beneath were the masses of people marching genetically toward destiny. Any one of the leader's subordinates could have replaced them. Grant never won the Civil War, nor did Lee lose it. The gush concerning their prowess was fine writing. Without them, Vicksburg and Gettysburg would have been fought in similar fashion. This is not to say that the supreme commander is not an important factor in the methodology of conflict — rather, it is not to say he has been highly overrated. Commanders are only as good as what they command.

It is what is in the genetic mass that is propelling from beneath. It is their support and their moral that primarily determines battles.

Thus, when we look at this rapid succession of emperors — good and bad — we should not forget what was occurring within the constitution of their subjects. Roman legions under Caesars were a far different blood than those in the centuries which led to folding the great civilization. By blood we are not talking about hemoglobin; we are talking about genes which control such factors as muscle ability, endurance, even obedience and loyalty. There isn't a military commander that cannot recite from the top of his head the efficiency of troops of various races and subraces, where they excell and in what capacities they fail. As important as quality and quantity of armament provided to fighting legions is the quality of their genetic codes.

Although Gibbon speaks about the use of arms being reserved for those ranks of citizens who had a country to love, a property to defend, and share of enacting laws which it was their interest as well as their duty to maintain, he also points to biological factors when he states, "In all levies, a just preference was given to the climates of the north over those of the south; the race of men born to the exercise of arms was sought for in the country rather than in the cities. . . . It was presumed that huntsmen would supply more vigor and resolution than the sedentary trades which are employed in the service of luxury. Armies were commanded by officers of liberal birth and education, but the common soldiers . . . were drawn from the meanest, and very frequently the most profligate of mankind."

Military men, Gibbon dutifully noted, of the north possessed superior military skill which has been consistent over the ages. Conscription in the country provided better military material than that obtained in the cities. Both qualities are genetic as evidenced by the northern races developing killer ability from early organized hunts. Country boys made better soldiers than those of the city because, in the latter, slaves infiltrated bloodstream of the populous. Further, Gibbon observed the hierarchy that goes to make up armies. He did not attribute it to genes but, instead, to liberal birth and education.

An error is made when Rome is considered as an original homogeneity of Italians. The civilized Etruscans were powerful as well as the area of Lombardy which, before the Roman conquest, had been occupied by a colony of Danes. The strength of the empire resided in key genes which supplied it with intelligence, loyalty, and drive. Once these strong genetic selections were diluted by those of lesser temperaments, as inevitably happens with great civilizations because they bring into their midst slaves of conquest, profiteers and admirers, disaster is the end result. It has been so in Egypt, Greece, and Rome. It is similar courting of national disaster in America. Attempts of liberals to integrate children in the schools and then the marriage bed has propagandized racial intermingling as harmless.

Oddly enough, Gibbon saw it otherwise. "The narrow policy of preserving without any foreign mixture the pure blood of the ancient citizens had checked the fortune and hastened the ruins of Athens and Sparta. During the most flourishing era of Athenian Commonwealth, the number of citizens gradually decreased from about 30 to 21,000."

What the author was forgetting was the legality of infanticide, severe epidemics and diseases that resulted from urban life with lack of public health. We should remember that they did a good job of their civilization for a number of years. Had they worked vigorously at populating the countryside with their own, their tenure may have been longer.

One advantage the barbarian had was that he was relatively isolated from contagious disease. When they were ready to form armies, they could pick from healthful and expanding population groups. What did in Athens and Sparta was the hordes of foreigners displacing their genetic genuis. Mongrelization, either in animals or men, in large dosage and selected at random has never successfully fielded a good product. The rate of genotype change has overwhelmed the adaptability of genes, which both of the participants carries, making for freak structures. If one mates a Congolese with an Eskimo, a very pleasing human should result, but by such heresy the abilities now apply neither to north, south, nor even mid-way. Adaptability has been ignored, which to each of them took hundreds of thousands of years to achieve. It is why blacks do miserably in northern cities and why whites fail in Central Africa.

At the time of Claudius there were twice as many provincials as there were citizens. Slaves were at least equal in number to the free inhabitants of the Roman world. With such a genetic mixture it is small wonder that the empire radically dissolved through the effects of intermarriage and disloyalty of interracism. People often point to the diversity within the United States. The great surge westward, conquest, acquisition, and economic growth was directed solely by Caucasoids of northwestern Europe. It was only after the spill-gates were left open in the late 19th century that divergent floods of immigrants filled the already formed niches of the culture. Most adapted, but millions have not been assimilated to this day.

To travel a hundred miles a day on Roman roads was not unusual in the days of the Roman Empire. And with favorable breezes, the seas carried vessels within a week from Rome to Gibraltar and in ten days to Egypt. For the first time in the ancient world communication was excellent. This factor, plus the slave importation, created havoc in the strong genes which had originally and brilliantly carved out an empire.

Gibbon attempts to make a case for the non-biological aspects of culture as a cause of decay and corruption. He cites a long peace and uniform government, reducing men's minds to the same level, extinguishing genius and military spirit. There was a lack of love of independence, sense of honor and habit of command. An indolence arose when bold leaders became content as citizens and sunk into the indifference of private life, love letters, and refinement. On the other hand, brave and robust soldiers of Spain, Gaul, Britain, and Yugoslavia supplied the legions for Rome with excellent soldiers.

As the point is argued we see the dilution of the original gene group who were content to hire mercenaries to do their fighting. Who succeeded in the final analysis? Was it the heterogeneous race or subraces who preserved in their genes love of country, which translated by the DNA factor is the physical affinity and loyalty toward others of the same isolate? What resulted were great nations as France, Spain, Germany and England. Had the Romans been true to their genes and expelled the invasion by barbarians from all winds of the Mediterranean, there would never have been a Dark Age. Existing today on the peninsula would be headquarters of a powerful nation which may have preempted much of northern Europe and Africa.

The battle of gene preservation may not be as dramatic as results of great military victories. But genes, through centuries of discrimination and careful watchfullness, are far the most important force in the advance, decline, or survival of a civilization.

Gibbon puts it bluntly, "The Roman world was indeed peopled by a race of pygmies; when the fierce giants of the north broke in and mended the puny breed, they restored a manly spirit of freedom." Yet the "pygmies" had been genetically polluted. What the northerners brought with them were innate characteristics. And, though they mixed-mended the blood of the puny breed, there remained in their northern headwaters pure and un-adulterated strength.

If we flinch from biological interpretation of history by action of sub-racial masses, we can never discount the extreme importance of programmed genes within individual rulers. To cite Commodus, Emperor in 180 A.D., who was noted for his unprovoked cruelties which at length became a ruling passion of his soul, is to examine a 12-year reign of terror. His mind was possessed with fear and hatred against the whole body of the Senate. He suspected secret enemies. He valued nothing in sovereign power except indulging his sensual appetite, expended on a harem of 300 beautiful women and as many boys of every rank. Education had never been able to infuse into his rude and broodish mind the least tincture of learning. He fought 735 times voluntarily as a gladiator for the spirit of spilling human blood. He was irritated by hatred and envy and suspicion. He had shed the noblest blood of Rome. Dreaded by his servants, his life was ended by strangulation in bed as he slept.

As one muses upon actions of Ivan the Terrible, Hitler, or other cruel rulers, one may be dealing with paranoia or schizophrenia, which denotes peculiarity of DNA coding. These monsters that appear all too frequently upon the pages of history are propulsed by geneticisms outside amenable qualities of charity, compassion, morality, and love. It is as if their neuro-genic formulae had been deprived of inhibitory genes selected toward in the erection of society. Their bestial combinations were slotted in chance lottery.

Septimius Severus, a native of Africa, by acclamation of the army, was proclaimed Emperor in 193 A.D. It was not long after the empire had been sold at public sale to Didius Julianus, whose reign lasted only three months. Severus instituted a policy of bringing distinguished soldiers from legions of the frontiers, placing them in Italy in the service of guards. The capital was terrified by the strange aspect and manners of this multitude of barbarians. The Senate was filled with polished and eloquent slaves from eastern provinces. It is for posterity to consider Severus as principal author of decline of the Roman Empire.

In retrospect, it was not only utilization of foreign troops and mercenaries for defense and conquest which placed the skids beneath Rome. What was crucial was subracial groups were breeding at liberty. All sorts of genes were contesting the isolate magnificent pool of the true Caesars with its strength, loyalty, honor, jurisprudence, and architecture. Genes came from Africa - pure black; from east of the Mediterranean and Russia - pure yellow; and from barbarians of the north - purest white genes. With these were the subracial mixtures of the Mediterranean coasts. This was the cause of the fall and decline of the Roman Empire.

Imagine if France, in her two great wars of the 20th century, had elected to defend herself by men of her colonies. Or imagine if France itself had become as polyglot as the Roman Empire. What would have been her chances of survival? Some time, when you visit Italy, view the statuary of the Romans. Examine the faces carefully, notice the general physique of the carved marble testament to the era of their empire. Glance about you at the Italian people, and search for resemblance. You will not find them. Those folks that commenced the Roman Empire and won it were of a far different geneticism than those which participated in its fall.

At the turn of 200 A.D., Antoninus Caracalla edicted to the free inhabitants of the empire, name and privileges of Roman citizens. It was similar to the act by the Americans in 1917 when they made citizens of several million Puerto Ricans whose culture was not oriented to the Anglo-Saxon world. As Puerto Ricans stream northward to settle in New York City in vast numbers to an environment not native to them, one witnesses the fiasco of massive unemployment and welfarism.

America had no trouble in assimilating the majority of European subracial elements that came to her eastern shore. They were fed into the gene pool in moderate numbers over a period of time. There was much territorial expanse to absorb them. Others remained in small enclaves harmlessly retaining their own culture and interbreeding, posing no threat. Two groups remained — the Mongoloid group, which was systematically annihilated, and the black group, which was socially ostracized.

Gibbon, in a summary of 248 A.D., puts his finger squarely on the issue without sensing which key he was punching. Since Romulus' first four centuries the Romans of poverty had acquired the virtues of war and government. In the next three centuries they had vigorously established an absolute empire over the countries of Europe, Asia, and Africa. Quote: "The last three hundred years had been consumed in apparent prosperity and internal decline. The nation of soldiers, magistrates, and legislators, who composed the thirty-five tribes of the Roman people, was dissolved into the common mass of mankind and confounded with the millions of servile provincials, who had received the name without adopting the spirit of Romans."

This great author needed only to have substituted the word "gene" for "spirit" and his analysis of the debacle would have been biologically correct. Syrians, Goths or Arabs were exalted to the throne of Rome and invested despotic powers over the country of the Scipios. The decline of Rome did not mean the people's vigor had fled; it indicated that the compelling DNA propellants of the strong isolate pool were diluted. It resulted in murder of many emperors. Polyglot genes do not cohese in the fashion normal to the evolvement of biological society. We see continuous and violent revolutions after the Roman pool was infiltrated, the same as we see them in the South

American nations, and the same as we witness their relative absence in the northern nations whose genetic construction is undiluted.

After 250 A.D. it is futile to examine in detail the deeds, follies, glories and defeats, the intrigues, revolutions, murders and turnovers in the Roman Empire. By 476 A.D., when the Western empire terminated, more than fifty emperors had been elected, some reigning but for a few months, the last being Romulus Augustulus. In the east, the empire concluded in 1453 A.D. under Constantine XI by siege and sacking of Constantinople by the Turkish army under Mohammed.

If we are to learn anything from this magnificent book, *The Decline and Fall of the Roman Empire* — if we are to comprehend the demise of this most glorious of civilizations, after which the world fell into the thousand-year slumber of the Dark Ages — we should be advised that no nation, empire or civilization may survive unless the genetic genius that originated it is preserved and propagated in pure form and its ramparts and territories remain unmanned by mercenaries or foreigners. Civilizations fall not from force of arms but from frailty of genes.

KILL THY NEIGHBOR

Within the genocidal genes are genetically-programmed annihilatory compulsions directed against those of isolated, divergent, ethnic strains. We don't learn to hate — we are born to hate — to express our first law of the living. It is *my* code, *my* family, *my* tribe, *my* nation, which is always of uppermost consideration. *My* code meaning the tiny god of chemical combinations in the DNA brain which demands the fullest of expression and continuance. One person going his own way would be difficult, so a moderate tempering of the rigid "one-god-code" was in order. After all, a mate must be accepted and a reasonable number, a few hundred of other humans, to avoid the penalties of inbreeding. Nevertheless, even in a group more than two, rivalry exists with increasing frequency. The god-code had to submit to genetic-exchange breeding. Of all human conflict the least is found in the man-woman bond and their loyalty.

For the full blossom of genocidal genes, hatred had to be engendered against other self-species and recognitional patterns inserted. Slight divergencies such as type of hair, color of skin, facial characteristics and disposition, were fixed within the code to determine the enemy. We fight wars on a genetic basis. If not purely genetic in portraying contesting armies, we create racial symbols for psychological exploitation of underlying hatred.

Germans were portrayed to Americans in World War I as Huns; in World War II as Nazis — both are breeds of criminals. In our revolution the British were Redcoats, obviously not of the same species. Mexican and Vietnamese, as Mongoloid descendants, needed little symbolism to establish them as the racial enemy. In wars, the other army, if it cannot be readily racized, is propagandized as their leaders being abnormal humans so that the opposing army can effectually respond with underlying genocidal genes.

It has been shown by animal experiments of Zing Ynag Kuo that 85% of kittens raised in rat-killing environments became matadores. But half the kittens raised in isolation killed rats without learning. If raised in togetherness, kitten-mouse, they did not kill their cage-mates. Non-rat-killing kittens could be trained as killers by witnessing killer cats performing the act. We can conclude that environment and learning are formative factors in creating kitten matadores or bosom pals, and that killer instinct is recorded and programmed within the genetic code of the kitten.

CHEATING FOR SURVIVAL

In 1951, a cheating scandal rocked West Point. Fifteen cadets were expelled for violation of its honor code. Again in 1976, a hundred cadets were being investigated on similar charges. Within the innate system are genes relating to morality. They had strong social values in evolutionary ascent. Honesty was of greater value in hunting tribes of the north where cooperative organization was important and where food, clothing and shelter resources were shared. In the south it had less value because clothing and shelter were less important and food was obtained on an individual basis. A little deceit here or there in the individual proved advantageous. The HH gene is rather rare while the heterzygote Hh is in great supply; and the hh is present in the population at approximately ten to twenty times the number of people convicted for offenses relating to its usage, such as perjury, evasion, treachery, exemplified by the pathological liar.

Closely allied with honesty-dishonesty genes are thieving TT and loyalty LL genes. As with honesty, thievery has strong selective factor, especially in the southern climates. In humans its greatest emergence is Mediterranean peoples, all Caucasoid: Arabs, Jews, Italians, Greeks, etc. Although piracy is frowned on, appropriation of other peoples' lands and possessions is fair game in war. If there wasn't advantage in thievery it would not be with us. If we are naive enough to think that Homo sapiens invented the art, we have not looked at the animal world. Experiments have been conducted with hidden sentinels monitoring college students in examinations or children in file situations. The results show a large percentage of thievery to natively exist if subjects are given the opportunity and think they can get away with it. Loyalty genes have stronger root in those people who challenged glacerial conditions and were organized hunters — namely, Mongoloids and northern Caucasoids.

Cheating at West Point is reflective of poor education. Armies, well-trained and led by true and honest men in frontal attacks with banners unfurled, end up in rout and defeat. Whereas, smaller armies led by conniving, thieving, deceptive and cunning generals employing elements of surprise, enemy bribing, deceit and unfair play, strode from the field as conquerors. From the Trojan horse to Washington's crossing of the Delaware to the sneak Japanese attack on Pearl Harbor, "cricket" has never been an ingredient in warfare. One wonders why the erring West Point cadets who possessed the undesirable genes were not rewarded.

Whether it be doctors or congressmen, they will rarely punish one of their own, regardless what a knave, drunk, incompetent, criminal or fop he may be. The Watergate gang got off with wrist-slaps and the "Big Cheese" was pardoned. When is the last time you heard of a judge being expelled from the bench for incompetence? LL genes were marvelously advantageous in cohesiveness of society and its smooth functioning. No one will trample the shield which bears "Loyalty to Family, God and Nation." But, as this is carried into occupations and corporations, the expression of these genes is contrary to good public policy and social advancement.

The ABSCAM stings, 1980 — bagging of a U.S. senator and several congressmen for graft — was not done by colleagues but by FBI agents in an entrapment. It demonstrated prevalence of hh genes in Congress and the FBI. It was reported that had they expanded the game properly, half of Congress could have been sacked!

OCCUPATION

In acquirement of genes under pressure to survive various occupational forms of class are passed forward. A human worker shall as worker bee remain immortally a worker. He shall remain an underprivileged class, a toiler, an incomprehending commonplaceness, and all educators shall never put him forward. Tyrannies as communism-socialism shall exploit him, take advantage of his scarcity of rebellious, creative, and intellectual genes.

One of the first observations is in architecture and dress selection. Laboring people dress as laborers because of limitation of funds. However, there are certain underlying factors that serve to distinguish laborers even when funds are not a factor. Both in architecture and dress there is a lack of color harmony. There are strong and unreasonable contrasts. Ordinary iron pipe will be utilized with wood. A beam can be orange but it may have black molding. One can witness garish red linoleum running from the floor up the face of a bar and covering the top. There is no suavity. All is confusion and contrast. It is why laborers are susceptible to purchasing cars with weird, non-functional features that appeal only to a sense of incoherency. Clothes follow the same format. One sees every combination but rarely restraint or simplicity. It is exceptional to find matching colors, plainness, and cleverness. It is as if the world they see demands confusion.

You'd have to be deaf not to know when you're in a laboring-class bar! What would strike you most is the bar patrons' acceptability of noise. The jukebox blares, joviality is raucous with nervous and repetitively monotonous laughter, billiard balls click, coin machines jingle, bowling balls thunder, waitresses shout, and guffawing is all part of their art. The high noise level is incessant right up until they jump in their cars, race their engines, and accelerate loudly for everyone to pay attention.

The worker as a genetic unit is not difficult to recognize. He has stubborn mentality. He can be presented limitless opportunity and, jointly with his wife, will not avail himself of it. They will rarely risk capital in an enterprise in which the distant future is concerned. Workers' desires are now, today. Tomorrow is a language he does not understand. Socialists realize this defect of character and provide for his old age and life problems.

Neither can the working class handle money. No matter how much they have, they overspend, load themselves with debt, and buy foolish items with no regard that the next day their money will be exhausted. It is not that they are without fair intelligence or ambition. They can never develop a theme to its logical end. They have no insight into their shortcomings.

In unions the worker feels strength. Yet such strength has a tendency to destroy rather than to build. They are leaderless, needing definitive control. Russian communists immediately realized that workers are half-witted. Therefore, they imposed dictatorial control over them. Unfortunately, the free world — England, France, the United States — not recognizing the infant mentality, the rigid cerebration of the worker, permit them rights to strike to disadvantage of the majorities. The biological rights of workers are few. They were born to be led, directed to fit into their niche.

It is not that one is opposed to the worker and wishes to exploit him; it is that they have genetic limitations which should be recognized. When this is done, the worker shall produce sweeter fruits for himself and others. We see worker groups constitute over half the population. Education or environment will not change this composition. They are genetically determined. They perform those tasks their geneticism has prepared them for.

How is it possible to genetically issue occupational status? In miosis reduction and recombination there is a complete shuffling of gene cards. This results in wide human variation and new types. Yet it is not all random chance. There are certain units to work with. The game is run by the house. It may be likened to the crap table. You are dealing with dice but on a grander scale. With conception may come up one dot on each dice — snake eyes — feeble-minded morons or slightly better. Suppose "box cars" come up — double sixes? Here you have the top-echelon society and genius. Obviously, they don't come up too often. Seven is the most common throw of dice. To make it, three or four on either dice will do, or five and two or six and one. This is the great mass of proletariat — the common working people. Evolutionarily, it is not that the dice are loaded; it is merely the way the game has been played to provide variable range of humans to fit neatly into occupational niches, diminishing competition, confusion, and conflict.

Demographic statistics show a relationship between occupation and class, I.Q., and size of family. In the comparison of three countries — England, Russia and the United States — there is a descending order in the I.Q. of children: from 118 whose parents are professional, down to an average of 94 in children whose parents are unskilled. Semi-professional parental offspring runs 110, retail business 106, skilled 102, and semi-skilled 97.

In these large nations educational opportunity is provided to all. So what must be concluded is that a society stratifies its occupations in relation to intelligence. Individuals in occupations possess superior or inferior genes as regards intelligence, and are able to pass them onto their offspring. This should have been obvious to communistic founders when they railed at the bourgeois who were the repositories of better genes and consequently better jobs. In their haste to idolize the proletariat — the workers — they ran roughshod over the facts of human diversity and inequality.

This was Marx's supreme error. The capitalistic structure with its managers, bureaucrats, professionals, clergy, and armed services were in place not because of privilege or opportunity; they were esconced in social structure because of genetic superiority. At the bottom were workers relegated to their position by genes and continued in lower offices by propagation of lower-intelligenced children.

It is the fatal ideological error which remains uncorrected to this day in the USSR. The old Bolsheviks buried the flower of Russian geneticism to substitute its dregs. One day, as it will invariably happen, in Russia and all society, the sifting genes will stratify in historic capitalistic fashion.

Family size is in an inverse order in the study of the three nations. Higher skilled and more intelligent people have less offspring. This is a function of intelligence rather than sociological pressure. With lower-intelligenced classes there is less restraint. In studies of adopted children, their IQ rating correlates with their real parents rather than their foster parents. Such indicates strong genetic components within intelligence. It lays to rest the hullaballoo about environment and importance of educational opportunity. Genes will overcome adversity, be expressed, and will succeed according to merits in spite of billions of dollars wasted on uniform educational systems.

Lerner spoke of species becoming extinct because they selected in a direction advantageous to the individual but disastrous to the species — an Irish elk, for example, with overburdensome antlers. However, with man, his rapid achievement was due to his social nature. In the same manner an anatomical part might be selected toward, be gene-registered in consequent offspring, man selected socially toward beneficial group traits, and these became lodged within genetic programming. Thus, the vast majority of man's culture is chemically-recorded within him.

INTERPRETATION OF CULTURE

We are able to interpet the *Genetic Basis of Society* because laboratory materials are in existence. Solutions are documented. We have the end of the formula for society, but not A and B factors that went into its composition. There are common denominator elements and behavioral patterns that result from gene coding. Factors are known by four amino acids within sugar and phosphate molecules known as DNA and RNA. Society is no less than arithmetic deriving out of a chemical code.

Take man's innane preoccupation for swatting a ball — a soccer ball, football, basketball, baseball, softball, ping pong ball, tennis ball, golf ball, jai alai ball, badminton ball, volleyball, rubber ball, silly putty ball, marble balls, puck balls, and so on and so on. When you consider the sweat, effort, and wasted time devoted to these games, you'll have clear conception of the magnitude and power of the BB homozygotic dominant genes devoted to this modern non-academic folly. Whether it is Eskimo with snowball or ancient Iroquois with rounded stone game-ball or Englishman with his cricket ball, there is chemical coding at work beneath surface humano to be expressed. It is not that the human hand is admirably suited to hold a ball or is skilled in wielding a stick to hit the ball, nor is it that there are no other diversions to substitute for ball-fiendness and its representation over the "boob-tubes," it is a facet by which society evolved that the "lowly sphere" came into prominence.

Our closest primate relatives are not adverse to pitching a few. Before man left the trees, with his hand he passed succulent fruit, or even popped big ground-cats in the eye. One thing for sure, his weaponry was not in his teeth or claws. By an evolutionary fluke we developed hands, climbed the trees, and descended from them to be the first to utilize detachable weapons. If you watch the inefficiency of a dog burying a bone with that rough, black, blunt nose, you can understand the incredible leap toward mankind in the development of hands. The hand and stick had double value. It was protective and also a killing instrument whereby hunting came into existence. The ball, in shape of a jagged rock, to men equipped with stereoscopic vision, excellent muscle, coordination, and opposable thumbs, became a first-class missile. Early in society selection operated strongly toward wielders of stick and stone. That is why we have so many today who devote their entire lifetimes to little more than the pursuit of this art.

As selection moved us toward a mesomorphic club-wielding, rock-throwing society, there was strong gene fixation. There is no more vital force in evolution than the open roads to abundant food and the conquest of one's enemies.

Fortunately, society is a genetic mosaic and there are some who are born entirely without the BaBa genes. There are a few heterozygotes that devote their attention to less sportive arts, Bb's. And even less recessive, bb's, who almost vomit at the mere sight of such unproductive and wasteful effort. That is why there is vanilla and chocolate. It takes all sorts to weld units into a cohesive whole, the sum being greater than individual parts. Society exists because collectively there is superiority.

Next time you witness a football or baseball game, consider that they are not playing for the sport, money, trophies, or entertainment. The foregoing elements are only garnishings. The game takes place, including the Olympics, because the BB's lie within the athlete and the spectator. Their expression is imperative. One day, if we select toward non-athletic college professors whose research has saved us from nuclear holocaust, we may have beaten the ball-trick by substituting test tubes and library texts. But BB gene obsession with balls originated by natural selection in ability to provide protein supply and to protect against predators.

Ball fixation was necessary so the lesson should not be forgotten. Millions of years ago, in warm Central African plateaus, species resembling man were out-surviving related brothers by throwing hard objects. Since the time the chemical code was fixed, it has not been outbred. Although the necessity is no longer important, it continues to manifest itself in social behavior as sports relating to balls.

Montague defines culture as the learned part of the environment. There can be little quarrel that a portion of behavior is passed on by traditions and learnings from generation to generation. But this is only garnish on the salad. Vast proportions of behavior are undeniably rooted within neurogenes. *There exist through all civilizations and cultures common denominator effects. Taking such common denominators, then that which is divergent is learning and true culture.*

Culture is composed of innate, unlearned behavioral patterns. Culture is further an environmental factor capable of modifying heredity. Higher animal life is not a blind lottery dependent upon radiational mutations for evolvement. It is a slow adaptation to ecological niches by sexual competition, sexual preference, natural selection, occasional mutation, selective breeding, and environmental demand.

Carpenter speaks of primates organized into dominance levels. High-ranking males have priority to food and sex. Their sex drive is satisfied while subordinate males are inhibited. Selective mating may be operating here to cause the persistence of dominant qualities. Man's social stratification, his inevitable hierarchy system, within any nation or group, does of itself produce high selective mating. Communists marry communists, laborers marry laborers, rich marry rich, college student marries college student.

SUMMARY

Culture is not what it appears. It is little more than accommodation for historically innately-programmed genes. Members of the highest primate society emerge not as so many grains of wheat to be sown into the social fields, but rather like the balls that adorn an old-fashioned Christmas tree — multi-colored, multi-sized, expensive and cheap, hidden and displayed, lighted and obscured — each one individual and forever limited.

Science, May 1981, explains cultural diversity tied to genetic differences. Genes and culture are limited. Cultural differences may be genetically based. Wilson and Lumsden, in *Genes, Mind and Culture*, attempt to trace development from genes through the mind to culture.

Fifty generations, a thousand years, is sufficient for genetic shifts; so, since the agricultural revolution ten thousand years ago, there has been time for genetic bias in cultures. Units of culture are termed "culturgens." We have termed those units "neurogenes." Genes, the same as they build bones, also build the nervous system and its special intricacies. Different genes — different brains. And different brains are essential for efficient society. It is why we, in *Genetic Basis of Society*, deplore equalitarianism interpretation of social order as biologically perverse.

Thus, different gened makeup explains different cultures. But most important, social order, hierarchy, and political science are explained by divergency of genes — by genes granting roles to be played as leader or serf, scholar or ball player, staff or worker. We are no more or less than what our genes from birth dictate.

Society has no longer become the rich against the poor. It is the intelligent against the ignorant.

XII Religion and the Arts
Genes of God

GENETIC DILEMMA

O N ONE SIDE we hear evangelists like Billy Graham cry, "We must have a God — some type of God — be it Jesus or not." On the other side we have communists who, after the Bolshevik revolution in 1917, established official atheism, and cried to their young, "Close your eyes, pray for candy." Open. None appears. "Close your eyes, pray to Lenin." Open. Candy is on the desk. It is an ingenious device to discourage spiritual worship. Carried steps and ages further to reveal the scientific absurdity of worship, intelligent atheists are produced.

Believer and scientific non-believer, both are guided by innate genes. Believers are compelled to religious expression by their inherited biology.

Scientists repel religion because logic and physical law make it meaningless. Dominant homozygotes, RR, are the religious genes. Testimony to these powerful genes is the large number of people compulsed by them. Up the evolutionary ladder in the most miserable of animalistic human times, its selective value was enormous. Imagine what a magnificent tool with which to put people at rest, solace them, explain the unknown and death, decrease intrasocial tension, eliminate selfish competition and substitute charity, co-operation and "turning the other cheek." Little wonder the first people sought out, after police or military, in any great emergency, are religious leaders. They play powerful roles in becalming a society whose order is in jeopardy. All those with faithful RR genes obediently follow church dictates and contribute adequately time and tithe to their phenotypes.

A true RR would have great difficulty to press the nuclear holocaust button first. In retaliation, there may not be too much stress because other genes buttress RR as personal, familial, and national survival. Our presidents, to be elected, may be truly sincere concerning religious conviction or they may fake it. The tenacity of these genes is remarkable. The proud bearers lack scientific insight and fight like gamecocks among each other over specific creeds. The many religious throughout the world attest not only to basis universality of the genes, but that innate spirituality exists.

RR genes may not be found on specific loci of chromosomes. And there is more sophistication than that of polygenes. Consequently, their etiological center for expression would be a cerebral network devoted to the super-natural derived from advanced neurogenes.

Conversion, the acceptance of Christ, the born-again, or the "I've-got-it" emotion which seized Paul and Luther, is a profoundly interesting psychological phenomenon. Anyone with scientific head knows Christ doesn't suddenly enter the cerebrum when one professes belief. It is not that the emotion is faked; it is an actual emotional experience, accepting consciously a matured underlying gened complex.

Some describe their RR genetic manifestation very clearly. They may have been 15 when it occurred as they were placing a ladder under an apple tree. There is a physiological flush of well-being and security. Thus, they date religious commencement of their lives from this episode. Whatever it is, few laboratories have recorded the emergence of RR genes. It is similar in nature to zealous exuberance of faith-peddlars. The Bible is held as un-questionable authority. Scriptures are used to buttress argument, and there the debate ends — between the pages of that printed book. One goes no further. Investigation is referred to faith. And if you don't possess faith, obviously you can't understand it.

As girls at puberty begin to menstruate and boys have orgasms, so do religious genes manifest themselves after years of dormancy. In religious con-versions they come into full flower under various stresses. The genes involved are dominant homozygotes, RR, the religious genes, which await neural input in order to function. Exposure to a good series of church indoctrina-tional meetings, an older mind under duress, or fervor of an evangelist, sends impulses to the brain center to be locked into action philosophy. It is not unsimilar to allegiance to king or country.

Heterozygotes, Rr, are lesser in intensity than the homologous RR. This group may go either way — toward religion or atheism and indifference. They do not make good Christians or Moslems. But they are sought after by all denominations to enlarge the flock and enrich the temple. They are the ones who infuriate ministers by only showing in church during "big sales," Christmas, Easter, weddings, christenings or funerals. Here reside the religiously fraudulent — politicians and professionals who pay lip service to the church for community acceptance and gain.

Often a bona fide scientist is programmed with Rr genes. Two sides of his mind are incommunicado. He understands, "You don't have to go to hell if you believe in Christ. So I will receive Christ to be my Lord and Master." He also comprehends, "Religion is superstition — an opiate for the masses and the ignorant. Its miracles and cures are faked. It is non-existing hogwash." Dichotomy of thought doesn't confound him. He floats harmlessly with myths irreconciliable to logic. Religion, because it has natural selection survival value, is passed on heriditarily. Possessed with Rx, he is boxed into an ideology undergoing adaptation, since logic and therefore science have been injected into evolving man long after the establishment of religious genes.

A problem arises from a miracle of evolution — development of the human brain. Selective value of religion fixed the concept into inheritance scheme. As man advanced to higher brain capacity, it became possible to self-examine components of his being. It is an odd twist to philosophy of mind-body concepts. Religion, a corpulent gene, and mind, a reasoning inquisitor. Although these two loci of cerebration exist in contradistinction within the same brain, their accommodation to one another is a marvel of double-think.

Recessive homozygotes, which carry the rr genes, are not hard to come by. They may be violently atheistic and antagonistic, such as communist leaders. They may be mousey, deceptive, and religious only to further economic gain and social status. Or he may simply be a tolerant scientist who has not been blessed with beneficence and who regards those of religion with humor and skepticism. This group is not to be wholly condemned, because some see in religion magnificent societal force for good. Then again, our more ruthless warriors, by necessity, must be possessed of rr genes because they are the only ones compatible with the KK killer genes.

Russia has adapted toward these rr Godless qualities. Yet they have been unsuccessful in stamping out religion because the majority of humans carry heterozygote Rr. When Marx said religion was opiate for the masses, he was for once on genetic target. Lower social classes possess abundance of RR genes — the same as they possess lower I.Q.'s. It may be that RR genes are compensatory for lowered I.Q. with its increased burdens.

Cracks in Russian programs to repress religious genes have begun to appear. The *St. Petersburg Times,* Florida, reported on Russians celebrating Easter. Only a few churches are allowed to celebrate this holiest day of the church calendar. However, people who have abandoned beliefs and rituals of Russian Orthodoxy still observe Easter as a holiday — from habit, from nostalgia, or as a gesture of respect for parents or grandparents. The offspring latter group could be heterozygotes which are not too sure in the expression of their genotypes. Flickering of religion in communist Russia is testament to innate biology of the sacred genes. It is a light to future freedom.

RR   Homozygous dominant - very religious.

Rr   Heterozygous - mixed and indifferent.

rr   Homozygous recessive - atheistic.

KK   Killers - men of the sword, unrepentant.

Kk   Killers - by edict.

kk   Conscientious objectors.

What genes would you give Harry Truman or Churchill? A few to choose from — KK, Kk, kk, RR, Rr, rr. How about Lenin, Stalin, Hitler? The Pope? There are also patriotic genes — those that demand subservience, loyalty to tribe, nation, race or subrace — PP, Pp, pp. Benedict Arnold?

One day, while traveling through a coal belt with cancer-induced trees, I was fascinated by pleadings of an evangelist. I've witnessed the tirades of Billy Graham, the faith cures of Oral Roberts, and heard the word from pulpiteers. Every man has his little game and has to make a dollar. They don't harm anyone. No one with scientific training has to take them seriously. I had thought they didn't believe their own words — peddlars of gospel — a profession selling superstition and magic. Yet this man's voice from a mountain radio station was coming through with undeniable conviction. It thundered unshatterable in belief. In shock I muttered to myself, "They believe it! They really do!"

Those of us who have gravitated free of religion via science or genes, must respect the unyielding character of man's religious convictions. In the face of reason, by countless savants, from John Payne, Clarence Darrow, to the evolutionary jaws of Darwin, the religious defy change of belief. Their argumentation is amassment of contradiction. Yet they are not dismayed. Their ranks swell. They look upon heretics not as spawn of the devil but as unfortunate.

For religion to persist we may conclude instinctive belief is stronger than logical reason. Religious rituals originating millions of years ago at a period of underdeveloped thought-ability have continued to command priority in genetic chemistry — religion versus reason — unto the present.

Faith. Scholars have sought to find a common denominator for religions. They have come up with little better than belief in spiritual beings. Religion may be answering questions for which no one has plausible answer, and may involve the psyche when things arise such as anxiety, danger, uncertainty, crises of death, and adversity.

The true denominator of religion is gene implantation. In evolution of society religion provided selective value. A troop of baboon-like hominids shuffling across an African savanna on their way to a water hole, threatened by feline predators, holding aloof the skull of a dead hyena, may have been provided bravery, screams and sacrifices that ensure success and survival by religious fervor. It was in similar vain-glorious manner that troops of Russia carrying a holy icon marched reassuredly into crossfire of German machine-gunners at Tannenberg. In this latter case, the spiritual prop failed. But many more times it succeeds in cohesing and firing spirits of combatants. Constantine conquered by the sign of the cross. Pieces of colored cloth have always rallied soldiers to the standard. Thoughts of holy glory and heavenly protection provide solace and resolve. Religious genes win battles as certainly as do cannons — few successful generals have failed to mobilize them.

A healthy belief in the hereafter, a firm belief in invulnerability, and a fixed belief that some unseen being is looking after their interest, provides a society with untold advantages over one of non-believers.

Hypnosis has religious similarity. It is a mentally-produced condition in which the subject is highly susceptible to suggestion. Not all people can be hypnotized. One of the first tasks of the hypnotist it to weed out those that are resistant and poor subject material.

It is a part of dominance-submissive hierarchies by which societies are structured. It was important in an evolving society. Leaders could handle masses by built-in mechanisms for submissiveness, especially to a prestiged individual. One would expect greatest concentration of hypnotic subjects within the proletariat class. Within the upper bourgeois resistance can be found. Yet many hypnotists claim only the more intelligent can be hypnotized. These are not leaders, but upper echelon followers. Many leaders have exerted hypnotic power over their countrymen, Hitler being prime example.

Psychological manipulations by hypnotic formula are illustrated by religious techniques. As in hypnosis, there is a bright, shiny, startling, and prestiged focusing point. The hypnotist's watch, ring, oscillating disk or intense stare is replaced in religion by the cross, swinging incense urns, stained glass windows, Gothic spirals, flashy robes and hats, holy relics and, most of all, by mystical, supernatural reverence for old literature as the Bible, Torah or Koran.

Religious genes have a baby-talk all their own. Like mothers resorting to innate gooey speech mechanisms to communicate with offspring, so do ministers resort to slowed, drawled form of instinctive speech to relate to faithful flocks and unlock conversions in those pure-of-heart. "Gaah-ah-ah-dud Sa-ah-hay-ve Ah-us Ah-ah-alll." Speech delivered of prestiged person, elevated and standing before pulpit similar to a stage, is dreary, monotoned language which similates hypnotist's repetition to unlock the subconscious to heightened suggestibility.

A calming and tranquilizing effect is sought by the religious leader and the hypnotist. Bells and candles, choir and praise are all theatrical trappings. There is wide individual differences in susceptibility to such suggestion. Thus we find believers and non-believers genetically based. If religion was not a genetically-based trait, how could you account for an appalling number of people convinced in holy tenets that have no scientific basis? Thus, hypnotic techniques buttress religion.

Instinct. Catholic church has instinctive knowledge of cultural neurogenic imprintation. They insist on having their own private schools to inculcate the young into virtues of religion, morality, loyalty, and obedience. These early formative years of childhood is the period in which educational benefits to society become the most rewarding.

In 1871, Chadbourne, in *Instinct in Animals and Men,* outlined the component religious instincts: (1) Belief in some supernatural being. (2) Belief in accountability as for good or evil. (3) Belief in immortality. (4) Instinct of prayer as a means of establishing relations with the Being. (5) Instinct of worship, including veneration.

Today, instinct is a solid genetic science — an innate programmed DNA-coded behavior. It is surprising, back in 1871, to have tied into objectivity. Some of these beliefs may have originated in dreams. Dreams replay ideas. Through the dreamer new ideas help form society and consequent evolution-ary direction. Out of dreams comes not only religious basis but pioneering thoughts. Society with the best dreamers succeeds superiorly in the adapta-tional frontiers.

Sin. An important genetic emotion has been capitalized on by religion. This geneticism known as guilt roots solidly in the transition from ape to man. Its conscious manifestation is a category of behavior expressed as sin. In the Bible (Corinthians) we are told that Jesus Christ was sinless. While it is true that many within society are sinless, Christ was not one of them, because he did transgress against authority of his social order. There are vary-ing degrees of fault from individual to individual, depending upon their neurogenic inheritance; that is, their sensitivity to feel guilt.

As society evolved, selection was in favor of those that felt guilt, were guided by it, repented and mended their ways. For existence of society, it became imperative the individual would recognize rights and property of others. Thus, there was premium placed upon those that did not kill their brethren. Neither was anti-social acts acceptable without mental awareness of guilt. There had to be innate reminder to mankind what constituted social violation. In habitual criminals who murder, rape and plunder, aggressiveness is shown which demonstrates lack of social guilt neuroses. These throwbacks persist because on occasion crime did pay off.

The Christian church craftily perceived that since there was no way one could rid oneself of guilt, washing the blood off one's hands as Lady Mac-beth, there was necessity for psychological solace. Where better could it be found than in the supernatural? They wasted no time informing everyone they were sinners. And impressing upon their flocks that "the wages of sin is death." (Romans 6:23) In other words, the message went out "since you are a sinner, you are going to die."

The sales gimmick in this pitch is that Jesus is the only one who can for-give your sins. Therefore, you are to open your heart to him. Now that you are a proven sinner, what is the therapeutic agent which must be employed? It is nothing of this earth, but a spiritual contract wherein Christ wants to forgive your sins (I John 1:9). Your participation is to repent your sins. To do so you welcome Jesus Christ into your life as personal Savior and Lord. It is magnificent psychological wizardry. No tools or props are needed; it can be performed solitarily in a quiet place. Your pleading will transmit some-where and Jesus will hear you and grant your pardon. It is much better for the wayward and those that have failed in their efforts to meet the standard of life God has set for man (Romans 3:23), to entreaty with those earthly beings who purvey the goods of the Almighty to intercede in their behalf.

Never let it be said that these dedicated men who administer God's earthly affairs are charlatans. They are caught up in an unresolved genetic evolutionary process toward which selection was imperative. Truly I say unto you . . . human genetics is the heart of religion. Ye that have sinned shall be made pure by the recognition of this fact in the same manner that human evolution demanded awareness of proper societal conduct.

Charity Genes. It is perversity to bestow excessive amounts unto ethnic rivals. The real biological inversion comes when one deserts dictates of heretiable genetic pools to aid the enemy in forwarding their evolutionary march. They deprive their own kind of their rightful position in the future by reason of their successful economic adaptation and consequent higher living standard.

There is no reason why sugar-cane-producing countries should not continue to be likewise. No biological reason can be established to conclude that Negroes of Africa should not remain in their presently adjusted adaptabilities. It is sacrilegious for nations that have admirably succeeded to undertake equalization of their bountifulness. Nothing here suggests that such attitude defies man's love for man. It simply states a principle that for fifty million years Homo sapiens came into existence by survival of the fittest and elimination of the weakest. Such evolutionary pressures over the ages were tremendous tools in screening out the unfit. Any attempt to divert societies' evolutionary ascent of the capable and the best elements is to evoke a curse upon each subrace's code — the earth being the poorer for the effort. So, when Trotsky speaks of a bounteous economy integrated for the entire earth, he is not speaking as a scientist-biologist but as a religious zealot who does not appreciate the complications of economic equality on the destiny of the ape who walks upright.

Care for monsters as hydrocephalics are a prime illustration of charitable genes in misplaced functioning. These bulging, hideous-headed infants with short-lived futures, are committed to costly state institutions for humanitarian care. Unyielding religious tenets decree against violation of life because charitable genes are in idealistic flower. At odds is the fact that people are to be served. To terminate grotesque masses of miscoded DNA would, under human guidance, provide relief for the family and society so grief and resources could better be spent upon the living and not the unreasoning doomed.

Contributions overseas through charity of Americans is stupifying. It is doubtful it has aided the welfare of the United States. Usually it creates envy and hatred. This misdirected kindness of potential populous enemies occurs through underlying DNA prompting. Such epimeletic behavior, or giving of care and attention, is well developed in humans. Facets of it are so inconsistent with intelligent behavior that it can only be attributed to genetic coding.

Billions of dollars have been given by the U.S. to India. Oftentimes their cooperation in an organization such as the U.N. has been withheld. Further, we witness gullible individuals who contribute to faraway charities where 75% of the proceeds never reach the intended subjects but instead line the pocketbooks of promoters. The problem in society is too little for far too many. We should look to the church — to encourage only local charity —

biologically-gened spiritualism necessary for human advancement. For foreigners we would be wise to limit charity to population control.

Genetic Reformation. Pomp, pageantry, prestige, and power — as the heavenly mediator for the masses has characterized Christianity up until 1521 when Luther's Reformation became a popular movement. Curtailment of the Vatican's monopolistic role did not diminish its splendor, but permitted a rival beachhead of theological sovereignty. Take-off of Protestantism in its many forms was rapid and bitterly antagonistic.

Scholars speculate that the Reformation was necessary to correct the abuses of power by the papacy; to reinterpret the gospel; to give believers full access to God, directly and without intermediaries; and to stress the importance of the Scriptures alone. It became a marketing of a religious commodity tailored to the common man and written in the venacular that he could understand. It was a new sales pitch for an old product, and the public eagerly purchased it.

It is too trite to regard this powerful movement in terms of religious or political divergence. As was to be expressed four hundred years later by the Bolsheviks' usurpation of Russia into the arms of Godless communism, the Reformation was a similar genetic movement in serving the head of the Pope to the priestless masses. In both instances politicians were directing their attention toward the proletariat — the common people — in an effort to gain their minds and souls. In both instances the biologicity was genetically abnormal. Power was being moved from normal dominants into hands of lesser-ranking knaves capable of controlling the proletariat. It was a shuffling from dominant historic authorities to lower bourgeois.

History has given evidence of abberant mutations which have established themselves within genetic pools to rival the traditional dominants and wrest from them control of helpless, submissive masses. As Hans Hillerbran states in his excellent text, *The Protestant Reformation,* "The Protestant reformers made a determined effort to speak to the common people. In so doing, they broke with tradition." Later, Lenin and Trotsky would perform the same service under the aegis of Karl Marx.

Worlds apart, the Reformation and communism were identical evolutionary selective factors probing at the command of the masses by other than normal biological dominants. In fact, Karl Marx was anything but dominant. He wrote from bitterness of insecurity and despair. His protegé, Lenin, was to identify himself as a revolutionary assassin and not as a true dominant by collaborating with the arch-terrorists, Trotsky and Stalin.

Religious Origin. For a million years humans were developing neurogenes which selected religion as a survival mechanism, especially within the emerging social framework. It provided solace in depression and courage to be used in the face of death. It was not only a Marxist opiate for the masses, it was hope that shone eternally. It placed on firm foundation the loose fabric of dreams to serve as a biological weapon in easing boredom and enriching the lot of this animal, who became able to reason, who became able to interpret significance of death and cessation.

Death and dreams figured prominently in the formation of this compulsive cerebrating. It was an answer to "awareness" of death. Evolution and

reason provided a new insight — the "existence" of death. And it was therefore demanded that the same evolution cushion the shock by the mechanism
known as religion.

Thus, an orderly transition was insured. In the structure of animals there
was an unawareness of death. The organism moved within this framework.
One of evolution's forbidden secrets was unveiled with the dawn of man's
reasoning. Unthinking, genetically-automated behavior could no longer
advance the higher evolutionary form unless it was supported by an opposing
force. Religion was the flying buttress which supported the new plane of
reason.

With reason, religion may have been passed down by a phenomenon in
the brain in which "print now" transpires; events are startlingly remembered
in detail. It happens infrequently and alters certain groups of memory
neurons to clear pemanency recall. This chemical reaction can just as easily
alter neurogene coding within the developing germinal cells. In a heterozygote, a dominant can be blocked to produce the functional recessive. There
are delayed action genes within neurological portions of germinal cells. These
have open option and before fertilization can be set by actions of the parents
to produce alteration of the offspring. Thus, religious experience may be
forwarded to offspring.

Right To Life. The church is faced with conflicting philosophies —
humanitarianism versus birth control. When the church condones massive
birth control which will become mandatory; it violates a delicate segment of
ethics. It has now become Siva, agent of death, which does not sit well with
God, agent of eternal life. Few deny within species there resides a geneticism
that inhibits destruction of offspring. If this were not so, shortly the line
would become extinct. The greatest power is preservation of young by
maternal and paternal forces. It is unlearned, unconscious, but of first order
in design of nuclear coding. To religion falls this sacred charge, and those so
gened.

Unfortunately, man in his evolvement has reached circumstances that
outdate the code which specifies preservation of offspring. There are too
many humans for too few pieces of land, too few jobs, and too little food.
In folly we comfort the "life genes" — that force which prompts forward
movements of species, its obsession to procreate. Regard the French after
wars not permitting contraceptives to lowest-class whores in a valiant subracial attempt to recoup losses from battlefield dead. Or Mussolini's tax on
bachelors and rewards for large families. Or Russia's pre-second world war
prohibition of abortion. Or mid-century America's penitentiary sentence for
abortioners. They were all in the name of DNA — *patria uber alles.*

Arts and Architecture. Portions Related to Genes. Architectural design is
related to genetic coding. Art often serves as phenotypes revealing subconscious genotypes. Both are related to religion by their spiritual quality.

Early in the beginnings of art it was great copy to merely reproduce a
scene verbatum, much as early man viewed reflections in the water and
latterday man admired mirrored images from metal reflecting surfaces. But
there was only one form of art occurring during one epoch that achieved
supreme greatness, and this form was based upon underlying genetic upris-

ings — Renaissance art. It solidified the spiritual at a time when religion was foremost — at a despairing time, with humans enmeshed in plagues and bloody turmoils, seeking solutions to the unexplainable, when religion became solace, hope, a way of life, and a way of government.

In Renaissance art is revealed the majesty, subconsciousness yearnings, grandeur and hopes that are parts of the supernatural, supreme, and almighty. Its great masters were inspired. Not only did those awakening out of the Dark Ages appreciate the paintings, but also those to come; people are vividly conscious of underlying religious neurogenes. The color, form, texture, draftsmanship, sketching and composition are little more than canvas and surface. What lies beneath these great masters' works are the psychoanalytical portrayals of our religious encodings.

As we are awe-struck by the high spiraling Gothic cathedrals with their stained-glass portals stabbing the dark interior, we admire them not from a sense of architecture, but from a sense of serene relief. Long ago, our small, agile, pre-human ancestors, as they descended from trees and viewed dangerous predator-filled savannas, they looked for reassurance toward the towering forests where a safe retreat of branched foliage opened to daggered radiance of the hot African sun. Thus, cathedrals and stained glass were blue-printed in the human mind long before their construction.

Fire Ritual. Watson, in *Man and Nature,* states that it is possible that rituals constituted the first religious celebrations. Man utilized fire, imprinted its comfort (preparation of food, warmth, a weapon against predators) indelibly into neurogenes. It is not only that we get heat radiancy from the fireplace, we sense it in every way. We look at it burning, smoking, changing color and shape, listen to its crackling, and find it assailing our nostrils; we are reliving pleasantries at campfires of forebearers. The fire spectacle fits snugly into a scheme for delighting our sense receptors of ancient genes.

When we watch a building burning, many secretly hope it gets out of hand. We are stirred as long as flames appear, and then we walk dejectedly from the scene when the edifice has been blackened, soaked, and the flames deadened. It is not that we have pyromanical tendencies; in evolutionary laws of variance a radical fire-watcher and fire-starter is produced from rare combination of neurogenes. Movies such as "Towering Inferno," a forest fire or building fire will attract attention and pleasant admiration. This whole process is genetic. And from such small observations we can begin to realize what great percentage of daily activity is rooted not in learning, but is innately registered in our brains.

Crafts. In early Central Mexico there was enormous growth of temples and architectural complexes. They were crucial centers for skills as writing, keeping accounts, and innovative centers for metallurgy and stone sculpture. In Europe, crafts flourished under the aegis, serenity, and protection of the church. The church lent stability to society. As man evolved there was great survival selection toward societies which contained a strong priesthood, church, and spiritual element.

From a period before agriculture, back forty thousand years, there appeared a man who dominated the earth, known as Cro-Magnon. He portrayed hunter and gatherer lifestyle. He came on stage at the end of the great last Ice Age, when there were land bridges between larger land masses to enable worldwide radiation of culture. The Cro-Magnon was modern-looking with adequate brain capacity. He contrasted sharply with the more primitive, Neanderthal-type man, whose physical attributes were cruder. One of his outstanding accomplishments were his cave paintings. From excellently executed designs mainly of animals and rarely of himself, one can observe the artist had come into being. Artistic genes had now been selected toward and a few in each population, possibly one or two in five hundred, were capable of representing art forms that served encouragement, religious enhancement, and entertainment to others. Long before Cro-Magnon period we found forms of art in weaponry. Society advanced and those inherent talents were selected toward.

Today we know, regardless of training given to a child, that if talented genes are not present, a sculptor, painter or musician of quality cannot result. So we see that in cave paintings found throughout Europe there existed artists endowed with proper genes to render first compositional art. Had everyone been entrusted with similar ability, every flat surface in Europe could have been covered.

A second specific occupational individual was thrust into society — the tool-maker. Those capable of shaping beautiful flints into laurel-leaf blades were our first skilled technicians. They were proletariat, but with inherited skill. Of all divisions occupationally that were to become the genetic stew of modern man, none is so clearly called for than the tool-maker. Few men can fashion projectile points today, even with expert instruction. These manual geniuses that appeared from time to time within the tribes were the forerunners of sculptors such as Michaelangelo, Cellini, and da Vinci. Pre-historic society selected strongly in their favor, for in hunting and survival they depended upon well-fashioned armament.

Within this category of manual dexterity and art there developed sculptors who fashioned in clay and stone small, misshapen figures called Venuses which have been found throughout Europe. These represented pregnant women with their large breasts and abdomens. At this stage of mankind, with its low life span, children were extremely welcome to fill depleting ranks winnowed out by disease and trauma. Wall paintings were the artist's effort to recreate a desired effect, namely plentiful game. Within caves and burial sites, by locational composition, abstract markings, and hard-to-reach recesses, there is evidence of commencing religion — an engagement in magic, ritual, and appeals to a supernatural power.

Yet religion far antedated Cro-Magnon and possibly went back millions of years. In its early formation it was a potpourri concerning the unknown, the problematic and the unexplained. As the brain enlarged to question habits of animals and determine edible fruits and vegetables, it also had to inquire into the mysteries of the heavens — lightning, waters, climate, birth and death. To kill and consume an animal was an easy lesson for man. But when his companion, who days before had been swollen, red and heated, failed to rise for the morning hunt, there had to be more to the whole process than eating his flesh and digging out the brain in the fashion he had scavaged skulls left by predators on the savannas.

Theatre. Our minds are programmed to the smallest of unitization. Rarely can we correctly multiply many zeroes mentally, but resort to such schemes as combinations or synonymous for 2, 3, 6, 9 zeroes being 100, 1,000, 1,000,000, 1,000,000,000 respectively. This we carry into our appreciation of theatre. An author is on safe ground when there are few people involved in a plot. Viewers relish simplistic, one-, two- and three-presentations. When it comes to history and movements of great masses of nameless people, audiences become bored. It is why we see few historical presentations unless they are jazzed-up for light brains by putting in a love story. Most TV, radio, and newspaper audiences are proletariat and middle class. One will find the upper bourgeois class represented in theatre, symphony, opera, and literary media. This message is not unknown to TV sponsors, who mate their commercials and programs to the class they seek. Soft-drink vendors peddle non-nutritive junk to lower classes by giving them dramatic slop. Whereas, intellectuals are so few in number they are passed by in mass sales pitch.

Music. Music ability and appreciation are derived biologically. Sound in the primitive forest of apes was used as a weapon. It could be used to harrass enemies below, taunt them, and keep them awake. In choruses, it was used as a group offensive missile to proclaim territoriality, as a bombardment preliminary to forays, or as pronouncement of numerical strength via voice power. Charging into battle with horrendous screams was used as a fright mechanism. It is why voice amplitude increases when we are bluffing against a superior challenge.

Kettle drums in symphony denote thunder, cymbals denote lightning, flutes denote the calls of birds. What is less apparent is the primeval source of the stringed instruments. Ancient forests are filled with dead trees which had fallen into the crotch of another. The slightest movement of wind produced wailing sounds characteristic of the violin. It is not an unpleasant sound because we do not associate it with danger. It is not beyond thought that since man's liberation came with utilization of sticks, he became an early violinist by rubbing the stick across resinous vines or to beat out a rhythm.

Symphonies reach a crescendo which resembles a stampeding herd of animals — the primitive chase. When we hear the silence which follows such thunder, it represents the last pointed stick that bloodily dispatched the animal of the hunt. If we hear a few additional slight sounds, it is blood gurgling to the dried grass as we all stand gaping in admiration and exhaltation of the kill.

A majority of music, as well as literature, is written for the genetically disadvantaged. One has but to turn the radio dial to hear the manifestation of the proletariat. Country music appeals to laborers; classical music to the educated and intelligent. Drum beats find a ready market in lower I.Q.'s, "druggers," and uneducated. Every musical presentation has its optimal social class. It is intellectually selective.

Music is not harmonious sounds pleasantly receptive to human ears. It is a form of sounds or vocals that is appealing to innate genetic programming.

A non-transferable trait, the "dying calf" wailing of country-music singers, or the nitwitted drama of western films are one man's meat and another's poison. The purpose of music ranges from the soothing of idiots to mental calisthenics for intellectuals; from beat stimulus for primitives to cooing for lovers. Its input formulation is guided by receptiveness of class genes to whom it is directed.

Placing Benny Goodman, jazz clarinetist, in Carnegie Hall is analogous to asking a surgeon to share his operating room suite with the local butcher. Music is not universal. In fact, folk songs are just that — songs for common folks. Guitarists and hillbilly singers are just that — for hillbillies. And Bach, Beethoven or Brahms — guess for whom?

Symphonic music is subconsciously programmed. It may have been written supposedly without a goal or message in mind. Nevertheless, neuro-genes are there preferentially weeding out human inexperience and opting for scoring of sensational events of groups and individuals long dead which are archived within the species. One of the most recurring themes in symphony is man's conquest over predators and his triumphs or failures in battle or hunt. Love, birth, and death take large shares.

Jazz, rock and roll, modern rhythm, and noise reverberations of attempted music appeal to teenagers. They are the final limit of the child's egoistic concern with sheltering sounds. It is infantile din and chaos. Only a "note higher" is western hillbilly music and ballads. It derives from the time we spent in the trees and came out for a brief land sally.

Superb rhythm supremacy expressed by Negroes dates to their African experience. Whereas, whites, by virtue of cold climate, were more often separated. The Negro, by climatical blessing, held more frequent social groupings. Pounding out pleasant sound is a genetic inheritance. It is no great deal for Negroes to tap out rhythm. Leisure, socialization, and warm nights were the prodding ingredients.

Baseball games are normally opened with playing of the national anthem. It is received warmly. But if such were the case (outside of wartime), in legitimate theatre, symphony concert, or staff meetings, its reception would produce boredom. Higher intellectuals are resistant to repetitive phenomena or to devices testing patriotism; it is not so with lower classes. They have magnificently loyal genes dedicated to country and leaders.

This is what we expect. Biological hierarchy demands submissiveness and loyalty from lower echelons. Therefore, reiteration and pledging is natural and timely. Too, it is tragedy. With such devotion it was facile for Lenin and Mao to enslave the proletariat without slightest insight from them that they were being bilked. Even music is a pheno-typical window to the analysis of gene coding.

Architecture. When classical Greek and Roman were diluted by other races, their architectural genes were eliminated or became recessive. We find no such skills as theirs in ensuing centuries. Their creation of beauty was one of the rare moments evolution paused to view itself and bask in luxury.

Their architecture was suavely superb because it mirrored nature. Stately columns were magnificent trees. Their capitals were Corinthian leaf or Doric tree platforms. Steps leading to their temples were cliffs of bedded rock, notched for access. The setting was nature. And the most simple roofs were treetops man had huddled under for eons. It was not an art of function. Theirs was an art of forest reconstruction, appeasing neurogenic translators. In modern times, there are similar parallels: American football is "running the coconut," parades with girls swirling pom-poms are simulations of leafy branches in wind-evoked agitation, the goalposts being safety of forest trunks.

There is a notion that architecture and its development arises out of the mind of man from consideration of utility and practicality, with economy foremost. Then there are new and changing building supplies, exciting and more efficient materials coming into the marketplace. Lastly, there is the aesthetic value, and this is relegated to an artistic category which appeals to our sense of beauty and repose. It becomes an art form the same as poetry or music.

Once again we revert to considering composition and underlying codes of human neurogenes to understand the true success of architectural art. Why was the world startled at the beauty of the columns of the ancient Greek Parthenon? A column is a column, a support, be it prolifically inscribed with figures, as in Egyptian temples, or be nothing more than a Norwegian hewed beam. There are some designs that are basically appealing to visual sensation.

Pre-human man had no experience with architectural creations. They have only resulted since the widespread use of agriculture and the founding of cities. Within his gened apparatus there was imprinted forms of beauty that would serve as reference. What he did possess was an intimacy with the forests, land, elements, and changing scenery. What made him comfortable was his instincts as a herd of deer who stayed close to woods and avoided open patches. Every animal, by innate instruction, has environments in which they feel comfortable and ones in which there is a feeling of wariness or demands avoidance. What would make us comfortable architecturally and achieve art form is none other than appealing to environment we covet.

It is too short a time since the agricultural revolution for man to encode new architectural preferences. Yet, with the pre-human, millions of years shaped what was an environmentally acceptable art form. Consequently, the stateliness of the classical Greek columns — their appeal is measured not in hues, color, massiveness or regularities, but in their resemblance to trees — our primary abode.

Greek columns are like tree trunks — wider at the base than at the top. They are capped Ionic, Doric or Corinthian to resemble the branches and tops of trees, are fluted to achieve the resemblance of bark, and they tower majestically and firmly. They are spaced to brachiate like for our ancestors among pleasant fruited groves, high above terrestial predators. All is testament to comfort one enjoyed tens of millions of years ago.

It is no small wonder that great buildings of cities filling us with cold awe at the same time inspire in us a sense of rejection. People flee the cities because of crime, racial problems, and stress, but most flee them to reinhabit the domain of ancestors with open land, clean air, and low, plush dwellings.

At one time shutters served a function — to shut out elements and predators. Today they are ornamental, but a necessity in the rendition of beauty. This vestigal organ of quaint homes has no basis for preservation other than neurogenic set from long cave experience. At that time the shutters at the entrance were skins, boulders, tree branches, or even earth mounds, which constricted the opening to provide security. It is why the pleasant house with the pastel shutters becomes subsconsciously so appealing. And it isn't out of architectural necessity that we have one main entrance. Often there is only one entrance to a building for it recapitulates our long term spent in cave dwellings.

Homes and buildings which combine and utilize nature in design have particularly broad human appeal. It isn't that a genius as Frank Lloyd Wright incorporates a waterfall into a famous dwelling or that Florida contractors sell a disproportionately large number of kidney-shaped swimming pools. It is that we are reverting to the naturalness of a pool in nature that is never rectangular. We are capturing in the waterfall the plentifulness of a substance on which survival of our primate tree in drought hung by a thread. Our ears listen for patter of rain and splashing of streams.

Consequently, we can make a premise for architectural beauty. It is dependent upon encoded neurogenes which have been innately fixed over millions of years. What constitutes a safe and comfortable environment translates into art. As long as the architect remains within innate neurogenic preceptional guidelines, his creation shall be that of beauty. Beauty is not in the eyes of the beholder, it is in instinctive codes. They interpret our mutual history. Buildings that appeal will be those that most resemble nature.

Wonderment has always been expressed that royalty and dictatorship have accomplished more in the form of creative art, literature, architecture, even science, than democracies or communism. It may appear puzzling why such restraint upon independence or the individual was productive of great cathedrals, masterworks of sculpture, literature, and art, and for the size of the populations, the rapid advancement of inventions, such as the industrial revolution.

The answer is the natural forms of dominant governments were of intellectuals and the capable. They had freedom of execution. Peasant and the proletariat had little representation. Nor did political jackals exhort lower classes to their own advantage. There was no diminishment of natural social genetic stratified interaction.

Communism possesses this Achilles heel in concern for the masses. They designate expensive programs to the appeasement. Such direction, abhorrent to social evolutionary geneticism, stifles the expression of upper classes and bourgeois which are programmed to lead and create. The banality of communistic arts in comparison with previous achievements of tzarist government in historical retrospect is appalling.

There is similar excellence in bourgeois art treasures, cathedrals, wealth and spiritual splendor of the Vatican, prior to Martin Luther's commencement of the Reformation. Unfortunately, the papal system restrained literature and science. The break from Catholicism into Protestant factions opened these vistas. It performed an overdue genetic correction.

Superb arts, architecture, and music that originated in Europe subsequent to the Dark Ages were the products of the upper bourgeois. Royalty, being of high geneticism, had the wisdom to sponsor genius talents as they appeared. It was a fantastic relationship whereby wealth and power of princes and kings, even despots, were diverted into creative munificence by gifted upper class. It is why democracy that attempts social equalization of unequally-gened humans produces so little in creative arts. Too much energy is wasted upon the laboring class. Communism shares with democracy in the stifling of talent. Based on socialistic principles, it negates aristocracy of human DNA coding.

XIII Cure and Release of Criminals

CRIME IN SOCIETY

EMILE DURKHEIM contended that "crime is societally normal . . . a part of a healthy society." This was true in our past. Few crimes were punishable. Since property was communal, there was no theft. Because women were readily available to all, there was no rape. Homosexuals remaining in a non-competitive position were not considered lawbreakers. Even murder under challenge to leadership was approved as normal biological law. Drugs were growing free in fields.

Today, each society sets limits of what it considers criminal behavior. Obviously, the animal-man cannot successfully conform to legislated edicts which are contrary to his innate chemistry. A great deal of crime could be immediately eliminated if we would recognize what has been biologically permissible and what has been only recently restricted. Certainly prostitution, gambling, imbibing in drugs and alcohol are normal forms of ancient behavior. As society evolved, thievery had to be suppressed. This does make the problem difficult because it is a normalcy. In a modern society, murder cannot be condoned.

Crimes occur in low-income neighborhoods not because of deprivation, but because of lower-gened individuals. Poverty has never caused crimes. Rather, it is impoverished genes which cause them. Criminal lifestyle is indigenous to certain subraces, as witness varying criminal punishments among nations. One man can highjack an airplane and be executed, while another can be welcomed in the stolen craft as a hero and be released several years later.

Criminal Personality. Researchers Yochelson and Samenow, in a book, *The Criminal Personality,* concluded that "Criminal thinking patterns which cause criminals to think about committing every sort of crime almost constantly, cannot be dealt with by understanding, forgiveness or sympathy. They must be eliminated, coldly, with surgical precision, and replaced with other patterns of thought."

As reported in the *St. Petersburg Times,* "Criminal thinking patterns, they say, begin early in a person's life, have no relationship to the home or neighborhood in which the potential criminal is reared, and are not generated by childhood frustrations, mistreatment or neglect."

Although these authors skirt the genetic reasons for the makeup of criminal minds, they deserve due honor in bringing the concept to attention. Far too long have stupidities of environmentalists, educators, and behaviorists dominated thinking that crime is a matter of poverty, disrupted homes or lack of education and opportunity.

The Criminal Personality provides chilling evidence that criminals released from today's penal institutions will continue to prey upon society no matter what attempts are made to change them. Criminal thinking is a mental factor, a kind of mind-set that dominates the lives of some individuals the moment they begin to perceive the world around them. Criminals do not share the same values, attitudes or perceptions of society as the responsible person does. Criminals see themselves as superior and smarter. They are not mentally ill.

The authors go on to explain a correctional program emphasizing self-disgust and fear. From the evidence presented, criminals do know society's distinction of right from wrong, but believe only less clever people than they obey society's rules. What the criminal wants to do is his "right" and the only thing that is "wrong" is if he gets caught doing it.

This new insight into criminality fits the framework of *Genetic Basis of Society.* Criminality has been rewarded and heavily selected toward in the advancement of society. Unfortunately, man's innate neurogenes were laid down before definitive codes of laws were. Rape and theft were unchallenged or dealt with minor punishment. Drug usage was culturally approved. Even murder oftentimes carried no penalty. As thieving is widespread, there is coding. These genes cannot be exorcized or educated away.

Perhaps the only solution is to permit their expression under supervised conditions. That is how pinball machines are constructed — so the operator can cheat. Yet he only cheats himself.

Criminal Tendency of Races and Subraces. Some nations have higher quantities of thieving genes where their tolerance is great and punishment is small. For over a century, Italian Mafia have been inked on police blotters in ever-increasing numbers. Over centuries, it has continued to terrorize Sicily and Southern Italy. This sick organization of hoods, gangsters, rapists, white slave traders, extortionists, and murderers for hire, deriving funds from prostitution, gambling, and drug traffic, has succeeded in establishing a firm base in America and Italy through political graft.

When we look back at the fall of the Roman Empire, we expect these same genetic monstrosities were playing a part in its breakup. Criminal elements have always been with society. But, on occasion, particularly bad infestations are propagated out of proportion. Crime has selective value. It presents humanity with an evolutionary anomaly of frightening nature. Today, Italian people are tremendously incensed and embarrassed at connecting them with the scum of the Mafia.

If the majority of American gangsters have Italian names and still speak Italian, there must be something to genetic origin. Young German people are embarrassed with the memory of Hitler, as are decent republicans with the memory of Nixon and Watergate, so those of Italian extraction should not be over-sensitive to this bad seed that originated on their soil.

Today, with aid of clever lawyers, Mafia have moved into fields of respectability. Insurance business is old extortion hat for them. They have little difficulty cowering tradesmen in slum areas of New York, forcing them to pay extortion demands. These criminals have control of segments of the labor movement. A quick look at the docks in New York will convince you who is running the racket.

Consider crime in Puerto Rico, an island 110 miles long by 36 wide, supporting a population of three million. There were over 519 assassinations registered in 1975, the great number of them being work of the underground. On a clear day in January, 1976, a new victim was cut down before witnesses in front of a pharmacy by Mafia thugs. Criminal investigators stated it was difficult to get adequate leads on the killers. They complained further that in 77% of cases, even those in which they had the names of assassins, they could do nothing because witnesses would not step forth to testify against the underworld. When witnesses did testify against this mal-genetic slime, before the trial they suddenly disappeared or were found shot through the head. Immediately one asks why this type of drug-peddling criminal is permitted to exist, let alone create a powerful organization. Can it be that police, local government or even the Justice Department are in on the cut, or beneficiaries of vote and favors are indirectly given?

The accuser, under controlled circumstances, should with modern technology be able to give testimony without facing the accused or without the accusing knowing his accuser. Proper safeguards should be granted by, for example, a panel of judges set up specifically to handle these type cases.

Occasionally, Puerto Rican police take direct action. A narcotic mobster who ordered the killing by his two henchmen of an undercover police agent received a sentence of 104 years. The police ordered to bring in the two killers claimed they resisted arrest, and transported them directly to the morgue.

Why is crime rampant in Puerto Rico and the barrios of New York and Chicago? Puerto Rican blood is a blend of three races — native Indians, Taino or Carib, of Mongoloid origin; Caucasoid, of Spanish conquerors; and Negroid, from importation of slaves. Red, white, black, resulting in dark curly hair, dark eyes, and bronze skin. Their heritage gives them special emotional characteristics predisposing them to excessive crime.

It is similar with other races. The Negro is generous, kind, sociable, amiable, well-integrated, and at peace with God and nature. But when he is mixed with other races, there are changes which take place within his neurogenes. This is not only true of colored people, but is equally true of Mongoloids and Caucasoids. It even relates to divisions of race. Interbreeding does not bring out the best. It is a problem of genetic pool isolation. Once the three great races had been isolated over a period of hundreds of thousands of years, they went through a process of physical and social evolution in adapting to conditions of environments they had chosen. Out of this forge of competition and survival resulted major groups of people whose skills, dispositions, neurogenic reactions and emotions, as well as innate social programmings, fitted them magnificently to one another, their own kind, and to territories they had staked out. Within a single pregnancy, genetic wisdom of ages can be violated. Is there a tendency toward criminality in the mixed breed? We know organized killing is programmed superiorly in whites and individual killing is superior in blacks. If we put them together, do we get half and half? By no means!

The breed of men that went West and those that brought the South into fertile harvest were composed of highly geneticized dominants. They were ones that had nerve enough to pack bags and take off from Europe and the East coast into the heartlands of America. Once the fort had been secured and provisions appeared adequate, more timid would venture forth. It is from these later migrations of southern Europeans that the cheek is turned away from strong disciplinary action. Proletariat, who flooded shores of America after the Civil War, brought with them submissiveness, tolerance of crime, and fear of capital punishment, which is the by-word of the proletariat. With their votes and acquiescence of weak-kneed Supreme Court Justices, capital punishment was overturned to disgust of rightists, dominants, and bourgeois. Recently, repenting their obvious error, the death penalty has been limitedly reinstated. The court has belatedly realized capital punishment deters serious crime. What is paradoxical is that communist countries, who proclaim championship of the proletariat, never relinquished capital punishment or assassination without trial to those that threaten the state.

Bourgeois are Anti-Crime Leaders. It is not only racial composition that influences crime rate and types. Within subracial groups arises organized citizenry that develops strong attitudes against crime. These are the bourgeois. In the old West, people took law into their own hands by formation of vigilante groups. After the Civil War in the South, white rape was non-existent due to depredations of the Ku Klux Klan. When citizens were sick with poor law enforcement, many cities swept in reform candidates. But modern American jurisprudence has discouraged citizen action.

What is acting in these instances is bourgeois control of proletariat crime. Proletariats have never corrected their own crime problems. They are too close to anarchy and have a paucity of inhibition. Consequently, they are directed by dominants and court systems staffed by the higher educated and more intelligent. If the proletariat manned the judicial system — lower classes judging lower classes — jails would rapidly empty. But there would be less security for the establishment and wealthy. That the proletariat sit on juries to determine guilt is a small potato. It's a bone for a good puppy. Punishment and enforcement of bourgeois law resides with the judge, a select geneticism which usually cannot interpret proletariat behavior.

Locks as a Genetic Indication of Thievery. Number of keys possessed or access to them reveals personal wealth. Number of keys per person, nationally, indicates extent of thievery and insecurity. Utilage of keys, outside of poverty, signals thievery phenotypes among various ethnics.

In Puerto Rico it is not uncommon to see a man lock a three-foot gate to his front yard with a key. In some hotels in Germany one hangs the key outside the door. In Spain, the *serano* still stands guard overnight to apartment residences laced with attractive iron grillwork. As one travels from northern to tropical regions, there is a direct increase in thievery and its acceptance. By no means are northern lands free of thievery. But it is held in genetic restraint by citizen genotypes which developed in cooperation and sharing of ancient hunting behavior. Are Mediterranean peoples more theft-prone than Scandinavians?

Access to Justice — a "bemoanment" by Jimmy Carter, to a convention of lawyers, illustrated his lack of insight into underlying human biology. The uneducated and unintelligent poor shall never have equal justice when compared with the bourgeois rich. It is not a matter of money nor social deprivement. It is that the proletariat commit dumb crimes because they are dumb. Their stupidity does not easily lead to redemption so their justice cannot be on the same par as the more fortunate compatriots. Carter failed to realize class structure is biologic.

To the reformer justice appears to be maldistributed because he does not recognize that those charged with majority of crimes are not criminals because of lower standards of living, educational lack or slum factors, but rather, they are criminals because of lower intelligence, lower genetic class structure, and because they are programmed to theft, rape, and drug addiction. Poverty is genetically determined. It is not derived from a lack of opportunity, schooling or environment.

Crime Begins in Youth. The *San Juan Star*, January 4, 1976, "School Violence Gets More Vicious" — this headline was describing a small school district in House Springs, Missouri, where in recent years conflicts and aggressions became alarming. Teachers' cars were burned, windows smashed

and teachers shot at. Drug use was rampant. In a year ten students over-
dosed on school property. Beatings, ugly playground fights and knifings
occurred regularly. In two months, 146 windows were broken in one school
building. But this is peanuts when compared to the Senate Subcommittee
report on juvenile delinquency which assessed a cost of five hundred million
dollars a year for violence in the schools.

Between 1970 and 1973, assaults on students rose 85%, robberies 36%,
murder 18%, rape 40%, and the number of confiscated weapons increased by
54%. A teacher, Peggy T. Cockrand, who tried to do something about it, was
frustrated by the school board, and her cry was "We need help."

Honor systems in schools provide release of anti-social genes by permitting cheating in exams, where proctors and fellow students look the other
way. Businesses, as markets, rather than face distasteful prosecution, set
aside a percentage of loss to cover shoplifting and add costs to honest cus-
tomers' bills. Restaurateurs have long figured a modicum of acceptable
thievery among employees.

Anti-social behavior is parcel to the human animal, especially those
genetically programmed. Individuals fortunate enough to transport high
intelligence, carry superior inhibitory neurogenes. That and that alone makes
the difference between criminal and the law-abiding. Crime is located within
the central nervous system and the non-biologic attitudes of reformers.

Crimeless Crime. Crime — an act committed in violation of a law prohibiting it. Nations have manufactured crime contrary to biological normalcy.
They have created victimless crime and expanded minor crime to major
crime to satisfy: (1) religious puritanical fetish, (2) select opinionated crusaders, (3) tradition, (4) judicial systems, courts, police, and attorneys who
desire business perpetuation, and (5) gangsters who profit from unrealistic
laws.

Drugs — Right to Body Control. If the taking of drugs for pleasure or
relief is a crime, every physician, pharmaceutist and manufacturer of drugs
would be in jail. People poison their bodies with caffein, additive chemicals,
dairy products, bread and fats. If some poor devil decides to go to "pot" or
hard drugs, it is a tragedy. But it is not crime. It is up to relatives, friends,
and society to get them off drugs, if they voluntarily wish to do so. It is not
a function of government to punish those treating their own bodies the way
they desire. If one wishes to commit suicide, we should dignify the process.
If a rational mind cannot be talked out of it, we should honor the resolve.

The prerogative of the individual is to program his body as he chooses.
Right of control over one's physiology is the privilege of biological society.
That includes contraception and abortion.

Sexual Behavior. In our past there were no holds barred in sexual conduct. There was no punishment for adultery or sodomy. There was no
marriage contract and consequently no divorce. Youngsters were voluntarily brought into sexual acts with adults. Exhibitionism was a laugh, while
homosexuality was ignored. There was a taboo on incest, but if it occurred,
no one sweated the deed.

Rape was not the big deal femininists make of it today. Rather, it was an
event which was shrugged off. Women didn't become hysterical or go mad

because they got laid by a suitor not of her choice. Psychological trauma to rape in today's world is attributable to learned propaganda and not normal biologic response. There is no such thing as statutory rape between consenting adults, nor can a husband rape his wife. If the act must be forced, there is obviously no need for the marital bond.

The sexual behavioral neurogenes which we transport from millions of years of evolution are vastly different from legal codes mandated by modern society. Intelligent accommodation between gene disposition and law is long overdue. As a starter, prostitution, homosexuality, adultery, sodomy, and sex between consenting adults, must be recognized as normative behavior and removed from criminal statutes.

Rape is to be deplored. Yet the magnitude of sentences must be reduced to reason. With abortion safe and venereal disease controlled, the historic trauma of rape has been mitigated. If the act is carried out under threat of a lethal weapon or bodily injury, then mercy should not be tempered. In a bar in New Bedford, in March 1983, a 21-year-old girl was held down on a pool table and raped by four men. A dozen others looked on cheering. Now there is criminal suit against the rapers and $10,000,000 against the bar. Was the act violent? Hate? A brutal edge of our world? Because men witnessed the act it made women's skin crawl with terror. Some asked what the victim was doing in such a bar. "She knew the men. She wanted it. She asked for it." Was it torture? Was she held down and burnt with lighted cigarettes? Was she well-acquainted with sex? Was she a prostitute? This is a classic example of misunderstanding between biological and statutory law. Were it not for the fact that prostitutes exist and trick a greater number of men in an evening the act would be truly devastating. If the girl had said when the action terminated, "All right, guys, I want $100 apiece for the act and $10 each from the voyeurs witnessing the show," there would have been no issue.

Rape with restraint but non-violent is a traditional normalcy. We cannot alter genes, so law must be alerted to accommodate these tempests in a teapot. Women are certain to disapprove this. Biologically they are not voyeur gened. Unfortunately, it's the way the cookie crumbles.

On the lighter side of sexual conduct it is interesting how our leaders behave. John Kennedy captured the affection of the whole world. He came to power young, fresh, handsome, unspoiled, and dignified — a president of tremendous personal charm. His background and presidential actions showed him to be a leader of superb quality. There was no question he was a dominant. At the end of 1975, when the Senate Intelligence Committee, as part of its CIA probe was investigating the assassination attempt on Cuban Dictator Fidel Castro, there came to light the character of the ex-president which shocked the public.

Time, Dec. 29, 1975, headlined "JFK and the Mobsters' Moll." It stated that Judith Campbell visited Kennedy at the White House more than twenty times, usually for intimate lunches, and that she received countless phone calls from him. J. Edgar Hoover also learned, during an investigation of Giancana and Roselli, of a disconcerting friendship between Judith Campbell and these gangsters. She admitted that her relationship with Jack Kennedy was of a close personal nature. In the same magazine a further article, "Jack

Kennedy's Other Women," stated that after he entered the White House, the handsome, fun-loving Kennedy never stopped pursuing attractive women, nor they him. He never hid his fondness for attractive women. He confided that if he went too long without women he suffered severe headaches.

Actress Jayne Mansfield claimed to have carried on a three-year, intermittent romance with Kennedy. It was reported that Marilyn Monroe also had sexual relationships with the President. Sources familiar with the Kennedy White House contend that the President's liasons were mostly with relatively unknown young women — two worked on Kennedy's staff and were given code names by the Secret Service.

It was apparently not uncommon for Kennedy's male friends to send willing young women to the White House. More frequent visitors included a number of airline stewardesses. Jack would sometimes lounge naked around the White House swimming pool, when Jackie was away, women would arrive, undress, and join him.

In *El Mundo*, a photo showing Joan Hitchcock Lundberg titled *"Se Adjudica Amorios,"* said that in San Francisco she had been *"una de las amantes de John F. Kennedy durante tres anos."* Good and moral people were shocked. The foregoing excerpts indicate the President was a swinger with good taste. Here geneticism fits in. Politicians, for the most part, rarely have extensive association outside married life for fear it will reflect unfavorably with the electorate. There are too many proletariat, Bible-thumping voters on the pampas to allow them to inject into political lives promiscuity. Unfortunately, strong dominants, men who have excellent gened sexuality, cannot readily enter politics. Jack Kennedy was the exception and was able to get away with it.

If one remembers Kadu bulls and the stamping ground where one fights for the honor of mating most of the females — if one recalls the dominants in the non-human primate groups such as the chimpanzee, etc., where these have first privilege with females, there can be little doubt that good sexuality is a quality of good leadership and dominancy.

In 1964, the FBI anonymously sent to Martin Luther King's wife Coretta a tape of some bedroom conversations that had been secretly recorded while King was traveling. Such a tape was a prized possession of Hoover's and he once had it played for Lyndon Johnson, who in turn entertained reporters with his version of King's extramarital conquests. Here, as reported in *Time*, is evidence of the sexual prowess of another leader, Nobel Prize-winner, Martin Luther King, Jr. What is notable is that both Kennedy and King had charming and beautiful wives with high personality and intelligence. When the strong male leader is possessed of strong sexual genes, no woman, of whatever caliber, can keep him faithful to one bed. For the spouse there may be economic loyalty, respect, and love, yet his inherited DNA coding obsesses him to perform the obligated function which is normal to dominants.

When nations choose leaders they should sweep promiscuous sexuality under the rug and not consider it immoral and contrary to matrimony. The excellent genes of promiscuity and sexuality run counter to the usual mores and conflict with legalistics, but may be the keynote of a strong and vital society led by those that are programmed not only to dominate it but also to propagate it. Thus we come to the door of morality, not to open it, to advantage ourselves of powerful men who should be supplanting political weaklings.

Physical Violence. Mugging — attack from the rear or plain armed robbery. This book gives you sociological tools to work with. One is genetic behavioral profile reflecting dominancy or upper bourgeois inherited status.

In March, 1983, letters to a national magazine commented on an article concerning being kind to your mugger. The victim was robbed with a death threat. He complied but thought murderously. One writer noted the criminal puts little value on his life and is willing to risk punishment, whereas the victim treasures his life and is willing to part with money and pride in return for it. Another stated, "There was little or nothing that could be done," offering no solution. Another bemoaned a situation that if the victim had carried a gun he would be facing a trial for manslaughter for killing a couple of "irritating kids" over a $17 exchange. Violence does not solve the problem. Another proposed severe punishment by the courts.

Only one pointed a finger at bleeding-heart liberals, proposing, "If they suffered the humiliation and fear of the victim, they would stop feeling sorry for the 'disadvantaged.' " Out of the foregoing five, there isn't one dominant. Three could be classified bourgeois simply because the magazine is non-proletariat-oriented. None came up with the solution. It is why strong men in dictatorial roles solve these problems easily — because the proletariat can't lead, and only a very small percentage of upper bourgeois are fit to direct society.

How would a strong leader clean up mugging in New York City? Hundreds of armed decoys with hand-drug-guns. The answer is society, courts, and police do not want cure. Democracy is at work strangling itself with obsessions of equalitarianism and perverse compassion for the proletariat. Natural biological leaders are prevented from their appointed mission to society. This does not mean communistic tyranny. It means genetic society. It does not mean a lack of compassion of Christianity. It simply means that legitimate society is paramount.

Criminals who mug have taken an illegal license to kill. Isn't it time we gave strong licenses of control to police for the good of society? After all, for centuries we have been doing just that in armed forces.

Terrorism. Terrorism is increasing in Western democracies because governments are staffed by proletariat. Confronted with situations which demand bourgeois-dominant fascism, they respond mealy-mouthed from inferior peasant genes. Instead of hanging jailed terrorists one every hour without right of law, when they seek to release jailed members of their gang by bargaining for the life of a kidnapped victim such as the German industrialist Schleyer, or the Italian politician Moro, politicians confusedly negotiate like weak boys. Schleyer and Moro were killed.

Crime waves of terrorism never existed under Mussolini, Hitler or Stalin. In pursuit of political stability, they disposed of state enemies long before any groups could seek terrorists' release by kidnapping blackmail. Modern terrorism is a prime example of the deficiencies of the proletariat in attempting to govern. Castro, as a dominant bourgeois in Cuba, never had trouble extinguishing proletariat rebels, even though he was the No.1 boss communist.

Wordage, Incarceration, or Pain as Correctional Tools for Crime. Biology does not learn from threats or wordage. Exception is the death threat for major crimes which, by its very grossness, inserts strong consideration into decisioning of neurogenes — much more so if death penalties were to revert to centuries-past practices of public hangings. These spectacles are unpleasant to proletariat because they visually fill their minds with not-so-easily-erased imagery of what can transpire with violent wrong-doing. They are not necessarily an unpleasant sight to upper bourgeois, whose geneticism has been entrusted with stabilizing society and who, consequently, regard such proceedings as unfortunate but necessary.

In a two-hour period I watched a doctor try to discipline his young sons by shouting threats at them. They kept doing bad things and he kept shouting a variety of wordage that acted like water on a duck's back. What he needed to see was a Madrid woman discipline her child. You wince with its physical toughness. The children learn obedience and respect for parents and, oddly enough, love. It is possibly why the criminal rate was low in the capital of Franco.

Biologically, for child adolescents, the most effective means of insuring non-repetition of violation of codes is inflicting painful physical punishment and repeating it for reinforcement in the more severe cases. It is distasteful to think about physical punishment. An adolescent who has knifed a classmate should be publicly flogged under supervision of a physician. The rules should be that it is a painful and unforgettable experience. It appears inhumane, yet it is remedial. It is not a new idea but an effective method from our recent past.

There are many ways to inflict pain upon the human body. This should be detailed by a commission. With passive means of punishment, as detention and incarceration, inmates have no strong preventive mechanisms registered in their neurogenes and, consequently, no sooner leave the penitentiary until they are back at old crimes. With physical pain, especially if at the time, the cause of the pain is continuously made known, excellent learning can be instituted.

The easiest way to stop smoking is when the smoker picks up a cigarette and commences beating himself on thigh or upper arm until he is filled with painful bruises. In Pavlovian fashion this conditioned reflex very shortly eliminates any desire for smoking. The treatment takes a week and the nerve mechanism is reinforced whenever a cigarette is picked up, which is seldom. A cigarette is now associated with pain.

With strong and repeated painful applications to the criminal for his deed, there will be such an anathema that the specific crime will rarely be repeated. When he leaves the punishing institution, he will go forth with a definite neurologic check on specific behavioral patterns for which he has been convicted. Crime repetition will plummet in direct proportion to physical punishment received. An eye for an eye, tooth for a tooth — a wise biblical policy, based on social biology.

Alexis de Tocqueville made the observation that in the Middle Ages, it being difficult to reach offenders, judges inflicted frightful punishments on the few that were arrested, but this did not diminish crime. He concluded that when justice is more certain and more mild, it is more efficacious — lessening the penalty therefore facilitating conviction. He may be right that such procedure puts more criminals behind bars, but the substance of rational criminal law is that the offender pays for his act against society and, by so doing, deters others from performing similar violations and, too, is discouraged from repeating the offense. In absolute failure is the premise which prevents repeated criminal actions. It is because correctiveness by the law is based on incarceration, sermons and verbage, rather than upon neurological behaviorism.

Crimes arise within cerebral apparatus and are propelled under a variety of influences such as drugs, mental capacity, emotions, and training. Yet no matter how the cake is sliced, crime originates within the thought processes of the individual. Further, they arise because of underlying geneticism. As leaders are born so are criminals. A delightful movie taking advantage of this obvious trait is "Bad Seed," which depicts a very young girl as a clever murderess. Another movie, "Arsenic and Old Lace," makes millions laugh at two elderly spinsters who kindly invite vagrants to tea, dispatch them, and bury them in the cellar.

In development of society aggression was treated harshly by dominant leaders. On broad African savannas it took place as beatings, clawings, or biting attacks to those that challenged authority or acted unfavorably. With emergence of Homo sapiens, exquisite tortures ensued which were perfected by totalitarian police states such as Soviets, Nazis, Cubans, and religious medieval orders. Historically developed, corporal punishment is a well-remembered and effective method of biological control. It presaged the brilliant works of Pavlov, the Russian physiologist, and his discoveries of conditioned reflexes. Corporal punishment constitutes the strongest of forces which instruct the body. It is No. 1 stimulus by an immense network of sensitive afferent nerve fibers which guarded us through evolutionary survival.

One may remember Pavlov's experiments with Albert, a white rabbit, a loud gong, and food. Fundamentally, Albert was conditioned to fear the appearance of the white rabbit because he associated painful gonging sounds which accompanied its appearance. Later, he was deconditioned to like the furry mammal by being rewarded with food before the rabbit's appearance, each time moving him closer to the feared object.

For the criminal who experiences physical punishment, it is direct neural response. It is ancient and absolute. It represents the highest type of behavioral adaptation. Therefore, it is used widely in animal experiments in inflicting pain to promote the action-coding desired. Pleasurable rewards have effect in promoting desired behaviors, but not so much as pain.

Control of crime should be at crime deconditioning therapy laboratories in which criminals and addicts are treated according to biological principles. Whether the criminal be in attendance voluntarily would depend on how much he wanted his sentence reduced. Those unwilling to participate in physical deconditioning should not be left in society. The advantages would be overloading in penal institutions could be decreased and society would receive more amiable rehabilitated individuals.

The penal system, its efforts for rehabilitation and discouragement of repeat offenses, has been a failure. When one is dealing with a chronic criminal, lecturing, sermonizing, indoctrinating, criticizing sessions, or even psychotherapy, are all a waste of time. Criminals have lower intellect, defective neurological structure, strong obsessions, hatreds, excessive emotional imbalance, and insufficient moral inhibitory neurons. Treatment for this problem can only be effective by direct approach to the neurology which is socially faulty.

There are numerous ways in which decriminalization therapy laboratories can be set up. They should treat specifically each problem. Drug addiction is easy to cure under Pavlovian techniques, providing they are stringent enough. The criminal patient is given the drug and, at the same time, is given vomiting emetics, electric shock, anaphalactic reaction, or death-fear syndrome. Pain which is to be associated with the drug must be much more severe than pleasure of the drug itself. As refinements in pain science are developed, it may be possible to insert pain reaction syndrome below conscious levels, but effective in its control of neural behavior. Hospitals unwillingly dish out plenty of pain, discomfort, and terror. Physical therapy of a painful nature is to be regarded in the same light as a painful operation necessary to save the life of a patient.

The criminal patient should receive direct neurological therapy in the holding institution until he is deemed neurologically under positive inhibitional specific crime control. After his release (at the time he visits his probation officer), he would have to bring statements that he had received outpatient treatment at regularly prescribed intervals. This is of maximum importance in reinforcing the inhibitory features of conditioning, and it may be necessary to continue these throughout his lifetime in decreasing amounts, much like vaccination.

In the past a perfect biological remedy was employed that assured certain crimes would not be repeated — they cut off fingers or hands of robbers. Unless society learns more capable methods, refined measures may have to be employed such as welded iron locked gloves, screens in which the individual could function but which would not give him dexterity to commit crime.

Courts should decree conditioning of perpetrators of armed aggression to repulsion of picking up a knife, gun or weapon. When a gun is picked up, a jolting life-remembering shock is given to center in inhibitional areas of the brain. If this conditioning is reinforced many times, the patient will develop aversion and fear to the use of weapons. In fact, he will eat with fingers or spoons.

To non-domineering proletariat this may sound inhumane. It is not so when we consider unfortunate victims of these mentally miswired and misdisciplined criminals. Society must take the offensive against lawless infestation based upon physiology. At a later time refinements may come. When they do, they will be based solidly upon deconditioning by way of strong compelling neural inhibitions. Criminals may welcome these procedures as it could result in early release from prison. Any criminal institution contemplating this new approach to correction, the author would be willing to help set up and supervise the deconditioning laboratory.

XIV Education
The Genetic Rip-Off

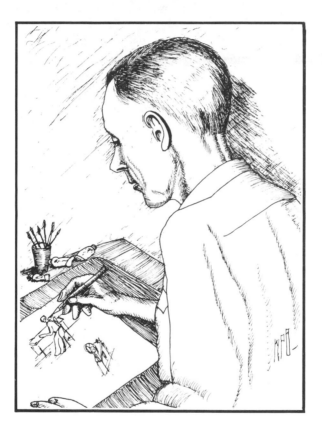

I N SOCIETY there is no greater fraud, legitimized thievery or conspiratorial monopoly than educational systems. Incredibly, without whimper taxpayers submit to outrages in hopes their none-too-bright offspring will blossom profitably or by some unknown mechanism the nation will be saved from unemployment, depression, and disastrous war.

In no realm of human endeavor is a con artist portrayed more angelically. Nowhere are to be found scoundrel wolves dressed in respectable sheep's clothing than in teaching professions. Without exception teachers pilfer more from gullible citizenry than criminals. They are confidence game artists *magna cum laude*.

Education is a scam of the public so successful that few dare to reveal its *modus operandi*. School propaganda is entrenched in respectability. Brotherly love, dedication, and neighborliness are emblazoned on its shields, while masses of teachers march under unassailable banners proclaiming quality education. Do we mean to say teachers are crooks? Are we implying these outstanding citizens of the community are pulling something slippery? Are we trying to tell you high-school and college teachers are ripping off tax-payers, or their associations are Mafia-styled lobbies and they consciously, without reflection, are out to defraud the public? Of course not. But they are devoid of insight into what modern education could be. Paychecks have blinded their compassion for taxpayers' pocketbooks.

George Gissing: "Education is a thing of which only a few are capable: teach as you will only a small percentage will profit by your most zealous energy."

Carl Linnaeus: "A professor can never better distinguish himself in his work than by encouraging a clever pupil. For the true discoverers are among them, as comets amongst stars."

What the teaching profession, their unions, administrators, and service industry personnel have pulled off is a super-sale of equality (egalitarian) education. Every child is equal, therefore every child gets the same brain dosage. Packaged with equality comes a pablum termed "quality education" — a lure for funding excessive salaries and spending. Quality is the rip-off that provides for "personalized teaching." This means secure, well-paying jobs, benefits, and pensions. No one is interested in cost efficiency by sub-stituting robots for teachers.

Almost three-quarters of school costs are reflected in its teachers, ad-ministrators, personnel services, salaries with their pensions and benefit costs. Here is an example of a Pennsylvania school district, twelve grades servicing only 6,150 pupils for 180-day periods, five hours per five-day week, 1982-83:

Administration	$ 482,045
Instruction	8,784,723
Pupil Personnel	332,279
Retirement	746,034
S.S. Tax	317,616
Health Ins.	724,040
Student Activity Salary	36,038
Payments to Intersystem	642,592
	$12,065,367
Less books & supplies	$ 445,924
Teaching Cost	$11,619,443
Pupil Transportation	1,784,739
Capital Outlay	562,194
Debt Service	359,000
	$ 3,828,349

For a class of 30 (6150 + 30), meaning 205 classes — ($11,619,443 + 205) = $56,680 yearly cost. This, divided by 900 hours' instruction, equals $63 per hour paid for one teacher, while the cost of his/her equivalently-trained person in industry or business, 1983, does not exceed $10.

Teachers as a group have much more intelligence than the average citizen. Coordinating their efforts, unionizing, and establishing a monopoly, they milk less astute compatriots. They have become progressively more militant with longer strikes as they hold children for ransom. There's nothing illegal in their action. It's American enterprise of getting one's own.

The educational racket is predicated upon a philosophical principle that men are created equal (equalitarianism) when biological law dictates otherwise. Yet schools are magnificent testament to inequality by grading, diplomas, and preferential scholar systems. They do recognize gifted brains and provide for them adequately. What they don't tell you is that these gifted and a very few lesser lights beneath are all that society needs. The dummies and relative dummies are 50-80% of the population. After learning fundamentals, they will fit nicely into factories, farms, soldiery, and service industries without an inordinate amount of wasted tutelage.

Genetic Educational Law:

1. Educate fully *only those who have the capacity* to utilize to advantage the proffered material. Recognize biological inequality, especially the elite.

2. Quality education is meaningless and wasted on the majority of pupils. *Quality is to be reserved for the chosen few,* by only the few quality teachers.

3. Stop gilding the lily for sake of retaining surplus teachers and paying high salaries. Use robots — teacher substitutes. One great teacher in a color TV documentary is worth 10,000 average teachers teaching from blackboard or text. Use computers, films, TV, tapes, etc. Over half the teachers in the U.S. can be supplanted by artificial means in one year to produce higher quality education.

4. Remove the notion that schools are to take kids' off the streets, relieve harried housewives, or kindergartens are to substitute for parental care. Forget athletics. *Schools are for one thing – to train brains.*

5. Eliminate monopoly of American education. Open schools to free marketplace. Institute competition, the entrepreneural system — capitalism. Give parents tax money to choose their own schools the same as health insurance gives the ability to choose physician or hospital. Then set up comprehensive state examinations for licensure — not only written but oral and laboratory. Set them up for achievement — not for those with proper diplomas.

6. Educational costs can be sliced 80% within a few years. Start laying off bad teachers, inefficient ones, and especially surplus teachers. In their place utilize audio-visual technicalities that are available. Shift from teachers to computers, from classroom to bedroom, car, factory, dining room or cabin. Let students learn where and when they want. Eliminate the expense of most colleges and schools. They are obsolete in a computer-, TV-, and movie-world. Concentrate on museums and libraries, especially of electronic ware. Go to national experts — public professors; let them teach millions

magnificently for pennies per pupil. Invest the savings in research. With good libraries, academic movie houses, language laboratories, computers, non-teaching, supervised laboratories, majority of teachers will no longer be necessary. Private lectures for the masses are absurd. Cinema classes taught by outstanding teachers can outrank in quality education hordes of standard teachers. It's appropriate to curtail traditional educational rip-off. Institute business practices in a field that has been a privileged monopoly.

* * * * *

Schools without teachers, professors or administrators shall light the future. A few factory workers and foremen shall run the majority of education, while a small elite, brilliant group will provide quality teaching programs for a hundred million students.

If you're truly worried about dummies not getting education, if you wish to dream of proletariat-bourgeois equalitarianism, then change to robot education. This way the disadvantaged, less intelligent, lazy, mesomorphic and non-strivers can have their fill of all the education they'll ever need, whenever they want it, and there will be no ceiling on accomplishments. Opportunity will be there. Education will not be forced or hurried. Students can attend whichever section of robot academia interests them. Brooding parents can go along. When students feel ready for passing a grade, they take the exam. It's as simple as that.

What's wrong with these ideas? A million teachers on the gravy train are not going to relinquish a good racket. How can society be superiorly adjusted for future prosperity? Vote schools three-quarters of present taxation. You don't have to eliminate the Department of Education, just modernize it and coordinate superior mechanical education by diverting 90% of the teaching profession to industry.

Please do not misinterpret this chapter and feel we do not respect members of the teaching profession. We do. But with modern science the entire concept of education must be revamped and its costs slashed by more than 80%. Teachers are too close to the problem, too involved in salaries, to have insight into the fact they are wasting the public's money. They are fine citizens. Yet, as the medical profession constantly strives to cure one disease after another for the benefit of mankind with a consequent reduction of income, so should teachers be willing to phase themselves out of business, seek new careers for benefit of society of which they are a part.

What Are the Educational Purposes?

1. To improve our society. That is why the state enters the act. Provide scientists, military leaders and administrators to outslick enemies. To perpetualize the state, its unique genetic and cultural format. To insure economic prosperity and ability to compete or excel other nations. To promote health and general welfare. In short, to conquer and advance one's own.

2. To enrich personal life — provide happiness, success, and security. This goal has wide divergence of followers. Churches and their schools regard moral values and a God-centered education as primary target. They concentrate more on basic skills due to limited funds. And while they encourage academic achievement, they require participation in religious instruction.

These people are anti-communistic rightists. On the left and less religious right we see materialism and financial success as the objective. Success is measured by wealth, prestige, and power — entrance into professions and upper business echelons. To achieve marketable skills for accumulation of worldly goods and lucrative jobs — the *dolce vita.*

3. To provide educational feeding troughs for the gifted and self-driven. True scholars need not be taught but led to archives of knowledge.

4. To provide the proletariat with fundamentals of literacy, reading, writing, arithmetic — if possible some algebra — physics, biology, and foreign languages, trades, vocations, and life-situational-problem studies. They are not genetically geared for much erudition. Give them sports, bread, beer, cigarettes, religion, wars, babies, and cry if you may at the cruelty of genetic coding, but do not derogate fortunate masters who lead us.

Is Educational Environment Important?

A simple straight answer is: It is valueless unless underlying biology is capable of accepting it. Nothing is accomplished by paternal and educational tutelage, except to bring out the best of what resides within the subjects' varigated genes. Phrases like "genius will out" and "you can't make a silk purse out of a sow's ear" are indeed folksy truisms.

"There is a fifty-fifty percentage that what we are depends half on educational environment and opportunity and the other half upon the heriditary components." This theory gives far too much weight to education in preserving employment of teachers, administrators, and supportive personnel. Education bilks the public outrageously for services which are unnecessary and feudal.

Parental and academic encounters account for little more than 10% of the students' achievement ability. Obviously, no student can enter a high profession without a great deal of education. But the ability to achieve that rank did not derive from formal education but rather from genetic capacity. Along the entire road of academia are strewn the bodies of flunk-outs, drop-outs, and those who changed direction to reflect lesser, more easily achievable goals.

Predetermination is not a dead concept. By the privileges genes convey to some, they provide wealth, power, reward, and direction — even longevity. Once conception takes place, lives are divinely directed — all that befalls them has been foreplanned. There is no doubt at the time of conception an individual's unique variability has been permanently set, with all attributes that pertain to ability, talent, drive (the opposite of them), and all the neurological facets that go to make success and/or failure. Thus, the role of the individual shall be to act out the status riveted in the genetic body shop. If the properly-oiled cogs and combinations are not there in the first place, no amount of indoctrination will forward a scholar to the top.

Billions of dollars are wasted to educate masses. The resulting social structure, however, is not very different from the structure we would enjoy if we selectively reduced education by 80%. Attempt to foist abstract learning upon improper receptors is promulgated because teachers solicit over-paying jobs and because a burgeoning population attempts to solve unem-

ployment by keeping prospective workers off the market. Clever subter-
fuges are employed. Most obvious is the cry for more education as if it
solves all or produces a Utopian mankind. Premise is based on contention
that mass education will produce a betterment of culture.

To achieve this self-perpetuating larceny by educators, a ruse of dia-
bolical dishonesty is employed. The working class, those of genetic structure
determined by heredity, who shall never rise above the mentality and
thought processes of workers, are given false status. Instead of recognizing
this genetic type immediately and placing them in the apprentice trades
where they could contribute to general welfare, they are kept in useless academic courses. This colossal fraud is paid for by taxpayers.

Educators breed more educators. To accommodate the working class it
is necessary to set up colleges of low rank. These are hideouts requiring minimum of effort for workers to be licensed as teachers. The blind leading the
blind! Such an educational system fails in its obligations to society. Selective
education is the future.

Why are Public Schools Flunking in spite of the Tremendous Funds Granted Them?

In 1983, the National Commission on Excellence in Education, com-
missioned by the Secretary of Education after eighteen months' study,
delivered a biased and shallow report on school problems, contending:
— Average achievement of high school students is lower than 25 years ago.
— Functional illiteracy is 13% in 17-year-olds and as high as 40% in
   minorities.
— Steady decline in science achievement.
— College Board Scholastic Aptitude Test (SAT) steadily declining since
   1963-80.
— College graduate achievement is lower.
— Students have migrated from vocational and college preparatory courses
   to general track courses as physical and health education, home manage-
   ment, training for adulthood, driving, remedial English, math, and de-
   velopment courses — all less intellectual or demanding.
— Homework has decreased.
— Half of the gifted students are not matching abilities.

The Commission criticized and recommended:
— Teachers are being drawn from the bottom quarter of the schools. They
   are then taught a preponderance of courses in educational methods
   rather than subjects they will be teaching.
— There is an overpopulation of teachers but a shortage of math, science,
   and foreign language instructors, which are emphasized in Japan, Russia,
   and West Germany.
— School year and hours are too short. In the U.S., 180 days average, 4-5
   hours per day. In East Germany, China, Japan, 240 days, 6-8 hours. U.S.
   schools should consider 7-hour days, 11-month years, and more English,
   math, science, homework, higher college admission requirements, better
   teachers at higher salaries, with less administrative and disciplinary duty.
   "Master" teachers should design school programs.

— More money for education.

The Commission did not mention genetic causes of school failure nor did they address the staggering waste of public funds in training the nation's scholars. Failure of the school system to shape up is genetically based in civil and minority rights' pressures and failure to recognize limitation of the proletariat. There is a reluctance to discard equalitarianism as biological fantasy.

In the attempt to equalize public education, turn out scholars as stamped nickels and dimes, in the hysteria of civil rights and lofty proclamations of democracy, the very fundamental of educational process is ignored — human divergency and differences. Loading the nation's schools with blacks, Puerto Ricans, and Mexicans is a colossal blunder. These marvelous but specially-gened individuals require separate schools not necessarily equal. They require schools suited to their racial dispositions and cultures. Busing minorities into white schools is evolutionary heresy. It does great disservice to all races.

Too, we may not be dealing with the purer breeds we once schooled. There has been considerable interracial mixing in America, not only racial but subracial. Breeding a German and Jew, English and Irish, French and Vietnamese, black and white — does this produce less I.Q., drive, a less integrated human with fewer positive goals?

Have we poisoned our youth in the last quarter century with tobacco? Has cigarette smoking in the pregnant mother put out dull, non-striving children? What about chemicals in food; has that influenced cerebral development of youth? Has fats in the fast food chains retarded the nation's youthful brains? All these factors influence mind and its drive. Do we need to be a less well-fed nation? Or possibly guarantee less promise of social security? Wouldn't that make students achieve if they knew the government does not owe them a living and will not care for them? If we scrapped social security, would we have better students?

Finally, America needs less money for education, 80% less teachers. It needs intelligent, new scientific educational techniques devised by skilled professors and taught by master teachers. It needs to de-emphasize the dumb, the proletariat, the unintended for much education, and open its arms to the gifted by God privileged. They will light and cushion the way for their more unfortunate brethren. Differentiate education according to genetic ability and drive will solve both taxpayers' and nation's problem. Did the type education the world has been fed make earth a better place in which to live during the 20th century? Count the wars, dead, and costs.

During the year 1982 to 1983 there was considerable controversy between taxpayers and school interests in a small Pennsylvania community. We include ads and letters to the editor to present this situation in microcosm which is occurring nationwide. The ad —

I. OUR WASTEFUL SCHOOLS — "Schools follow meaningless procedures to obtain meaningless answers to meaningless questions."

Clinton County schools take 71% of the real estate tax.

II. SCHOOLS ARE NO LONGER IMPORTANT. "There is little correlation between income and quality of schooling." "Equalizing opportunity will not guarantee equal results." "There's a lot of luck in economic success." — Christopher Jencks, 1972.

Pouring more money down the educational drain for a better student is a fallacy.

III. EDUCATION AIN'T A-GOIN' TO HELP. At reduction division-conception gene combinations-formulate DNA. When baby arrives its potential for academic advancement is permanently stamped. "Half of upper middle class children end up with upper middle class credentials, while half lower class children end up with lower class credentials." — Jencks.

One is born to intelligence quotient. When genetic endowment is low, schools waste tremendous sums attempting to train that which will not and cannot be trained. They burn money in teaching subjects of no value to the particular student. But "family background has more influence than I.Q. genotype on an individual's educational attainment." — Jencks. Your family and I.Q. are more important than schools. Practically every great man in history was born creative and self-educated.

"Schooling does almost nothing to equalize distribution of skills. The schools' output depends on the characteristics of the entering children — the schools' budgets, policies, and teachers are secondary or completely irrelevant. The dream of bringing culture to the masses by making higher education widely available has failed; mass higher education has only facilitated the spread of mass culture, impoverishing popular culture and higher culture alike. Higher education is for people . . . who plan to spend their lives in intellectual pursuits." — "Inequality and Education," — Christopher Lasch.

"Schools are places where children are coerced, controlled, sorted and categorized. Far from developing the potential of each child, schools make children stupid, they destroy the natural intelligence of the child." — "Limits of Schooling" — Chris, Hurn, 1978.

IV. SCHOOL COSTS CAN BE CUT BY 50%. "Education efficiency is dealt with by competitive forces — meaning costs of production. Teachers' salaries could be determined by schools bidding for personnel." — Econ. in Ed., O'Donoghue.

1. Slash non-teaching non-productive positions.

2. Cut school hours to the legal minimum.

3. Discourage formal schooling. Forget "drop-out" propaganda.

4. Decrease attendance. "Keeping people in school the same length of time, we see nothing to be said for it." — C. Jencks, educator. Increase homework for the capable and willing.

5. Cut curricular. "School reform and equalizing educational opportunity cannot bring about social change or make adults more equal." — Jencks.

You don't need Phys.Ed., athletics or gym. If they don't pay, let them go. Pupils can exercise at desks, walking to school or running upstairs. History can be taught by movies. Driver's Ed. by car companies for free. Languages in automated laboratories, and Latin by homework. Penn State Library blazons across its marbled facade: "A University is a Collection of Books."

6. Cut administration to the bone. Administration costs tax-burdens the whole system and creates a wasteful bureaucracy. Use business techniques and business training educators.

7. Decrease busing. Why are elementary and high school students picked up at same time and taken home separately?

8. Utilize radio, TV, movies, computers, technology to decrease labor costs. "The cost of education must increase in perpetuity in the absence of technological improvements." — Macroeconomics, Baumol.

9. "Demand for education can be lowered. Concentrate on those whom benefit most. But all must have the three R's to be literate. There's no need for dumbing down just to pass the students, and gleaning away from excellence." — R. Zahn.

10. "Eliminate counseling. They look for falibility in teachers. It's up to the teachers to counsel." — R. Zahn.

11. "Stop icing the cake. Music, art and dramatics are taught by educational TV." — B.I.

12. "Oppose minimum standards of education. They take from parents the primary responsibility to determine the education of their children. They take from the church responsibility." — Ohio's Trojan Horse, Grover.

13. Encourage private schools, free enterprise and competition. "Catholic schools are financed by parish and diocesan support, tuition, fees, contributed services by religious and lay school staff and fund-raising. Also federal financial support under Child Benefit Principle." — Catholic Ed. Notre Dame U.

Jewish Day Schools in America by Schiff — "Parents and church members contribute to tuition." "Christian schools growing by leaps, provide excellent education at fraction of public school costs." — Rev. Park.

14. "Kindergarten especially and early primary years are wasted money and talent. The mind is not mature enough for formal education." — F.W.

15. "Jointure can be responsible for heavy school costs. Maybe we should be rid of it?" — H.L.

16. "In declining enrollments shift grades to utilize expensive high school resources." — John Riew.

V. THESE VARIOUS OPINIONS BY GREAT EDUCATORS may not be a consensus of our group. They are presented that you can think and judge. We are not opposed to education, only to its unwarranted extravagances. . . .

Or maybe you have better ideas on how tax revenues other than real estate can be obtained. Is income tax more fair — being levied upon profit and ability to pay rather than real estate which may profit one not like a home or the clothes on one's back?

VI. ARE YOU TIRED OF FEEDING THE EDUCATIONAL SACRED COW? — OVEREDUCATION — THE GREAT TRAINING ROBBERY.

"More than 40% of workers in the U.S. reported having more education than is required by their jobs." — Econ. of Ed. Review, Greg Duncan, 1981.

"Surplus education has outpaced the skill requirements of jobs. Large pools of overeducated workers are widespread." — Inequality, Jencks.

Weir (1977) found the school curriculum in the non-academic pupil's final years at school irrelevant to the world of work which they were about to enter.

VII. SURPLUS EDUCATION CAN BE HARMFUL. "Incidence of overeducation increased between 1960 and 1976 because (1) the skill requirements of the jobs changed little in this period, and (2) the educational attainments of the working population increased dramatically. Overeducation could have potentially disruptive and adverse effects in the workplace." — Econ. of Ed. Review, Rumberger, 1981.

VIII. WHO PROFITS FROM FAT-BUDGETED SCHOOLS? "Not students! But administrators, their bureaucracy and non-teaching personnel." — T. Z. Litt states: "The major beneficiaries of affirmative action policies have been federal bureaucracies and professionals."

"It is estimated over 50% of wages in the school system go to non-teaching hang-abouts. This surplus manpower not only gluttonizes itself but is responsible for propagandizing taxpayers for their necessity and costly education." — T.Z.

"Administrations create problems to perpetuate their own existence." — B. Temple.

"Education, along with other activities which use scarce resources, must be placed in the perspective of a community's limited resources." — Econ. Dimensions in Ed., O'Donoghue.

IX. SET EDUCATIONAL GOALS. "Equalizing knowledge is not a sensible objective." — Jencks.

Stop shoving good mechanics, technicians, farmers, workers, through worthless curricular subjects. We don't only want the cost per student, but the output of each teacher. Administration costs don't teach your children. "Increase in educational output does not match increase in [financial] inputs. Increase in educational spending . . . has been wasteful." — Econ. of Ed., Sheehans.

Admiral Rickover urged federal examinations of all school children so taxpayer could judge his school's performance. Evaluate what the school is tooled up to do.

X. FINANCING. "Most citizens feel school funds should come from state tax money, not local property tax. One school superintendent said, 'We must get away from the property tax. It's ruining people.'" — Meltsner.

XI. THE PUBLIC SCHOOL MONOPOLY EVERHART, 1982. Public Policy Research relates, "Diminishing faith in public education. In many schools 30% absent on a given day. Schooling is a ritual more than an opportunity. Today's schools are no better than the schools of their parents."

"Can education be best produced by monopoly or competition? Education is a marketable commodity subject to laws . . . of economy as are corn or cotton." — Ecl. Review.

"Authorize educational tax credits to widen diversity of school offerings and improve quality. A fraction payment of the per-pupil cost in public schools would encourage a shift from public to private schools and be a great relief to taxpayers. Tax credits would cause public expenditures to drop several times as much as revenues."

XII. TEACHERS. "There is no evidence relating performance to *teachers' educational achievements*. As teachers move up the educational ladder they are less likely to stay in teaching. Deterioration of urban education has been unaffected by rising credentials of teachers." — Edu. and Jobs, Ivan Berg.

"Stop paying salaries for teachers' achievements. Teachers' salaries should be based on *productivity*. If a teacher can teach 200 students as effectively as some teach 20, he should be teaching 200. Workloads can be overlapped. A good teacher should be able to teach the majority of subjects the school offers. Give teachers greater autonomy from administration." — F.W.

Responses to Ad:

September 3, 1982 —

1. "Dear Fellow Taxpayer: You asked for ways to save money in the school district — Freeze the present salary schedule for all school employees including administrators. Submit to no negotiations by the teachers for a new contract calling for the $1000.00 and up increases they have been getting yearly. (Each employee at the present is working under a contract that gives them an automatic increase yearly until he or she reaches the maximum.)

"Since getting a Master's or Doctor's degree does not necessarily make one a *better* teacher, make the acquiring of a higher degree a 'one shot' deal and award a lump sum at that time. Don't tack it on the salary year after year. At the same time try to eliminate the 'equivalency' award law. This is an insult to the holder of a real degree.

"If you feel any pity for the employees, don't forget the little goodies added to salaries such as Blue Cross-Blue Shield, dental care, sick pay, personal days, reimbursement for education credits, legal holidays, hunting days, in-service days, extra pay for extra-curricular activities, and a three-month vacation.

"Eliminate *compulsory* education!! Offer only eight grades of public education and then let the ambitious ones decide if they want more. More education could be partially subsidized with the student paying a fair share.

"Change the vacation period from June, July and August to December, January and February. You'll get some howling, but not as much as you might think. Individual vacation problems could be solved. Parents could take children on their vacations, but the passing or failing of the children would be the parents' responsibility. Early starts and shortened sessions could be put into effect on extremely hot days of the summer months. Summer vacation is a holdover from the days of the farmer who needed his kids for help. Then again, think of the cost of energy saved. Think, too, of all the school holidays that fall in the three winter months.

"If we can be crucified with professional sports for month after month, high school sports could adapt too. High school baseball, track, soccer, swimming and wrestling would get a better deal, using cool months for football and basketball.

"Concentrate on the basics and let the number of people desiring (sincerely) art, music or language determine the size of the teaching corps.

"Discourage the creation of new positions and/or titles of any description. This will eliminate the possibility of an increase in salary commensurate with the 'title' later on. I've seen it happen."

2. (Edited) "Gentlemen:

"My purpose in writing is to suggest to your group that they might be interested in looking into state taxes and the amount of money spent on college faculty incomes and benefits. It would be of help if you could get a copy of the Union booklet distributed to college faculty showing their rights, etc. You would be amazed. They are . . . the taxpayers blind and most people aren't aware of this. . . . They can fight dismissal and get paid full salary benefits at the same time, plus the possibility of being reinstated at their job.

"It is almost impossible to fire a faculty member at one of the state colleges. Also, if their hours were checked, you would find that the actual teaching time they put in is almost nil. They don't keep their office hours, sometimes don't teach if they can get out of it (and this is often the case) as they have personal things to tend to. They also get personal days now, even with all of the break periods they have during the school year. They get their salary, plus overload, if they teach over the required number of hours. Their benefits exceed those of industries and private employers.

"These people have people lobbying in Harrisburg and have gotten out of hand as far as commitment and responsibility to their profession. Check with students and non-professional staff at the colleges. They will tell you what is going on.

"These people use college equipment for private use, those who are involved in politics spend more time on their involvement in politics than they do on their classwork. They also use college supplies and equipment for their political work. They have free rein as there is no checking on them.

"A few years ago, when they were organized, they elected to have department chairmen who are over a particular area with a dean covering several departments. These people do not do their job in making their peers accountable because they will have these other people as their chairmen in time. Each chairman serves two years. No matter how poorly an instructor does his/her job, they support each other.

"The above needs your attention.   — Anonymous."

XIII. THE RECENT POOR ACHIEVEMENT SCORES OF SCHOLARS is definitely the result of increased minority groups transporting lower I.Q.'s to classrooms and dysgenics — mixing subraces to intellectual detriment of pure lineage. "Dumbing Down of America" is price extracted from our Statue of Liberty and Bill of Rights. Prolific immigration of lower-talented minorities, surging populations of proletariat, mesomorphs, minorities, and lower classes, has flooded school systems with geneticism which does not and cannot aspire to the same goals as northern European, Soviet, and Japanese students. Eugenics is the beacon to the future — a road which, if America does not follow, will destroy her. Selective human breeding and discouragement of excessive populations of lesser-intelligenced within any society will outrank in survival value all armaments and soldiery guarding its ramparts.

WARNING NOTE:

From personal observations, I am convinced one problem of sagging SAT scores — poor performance of America's school children in past decades, is not due so much to poor educational techniques, disrupted or undisciplined homelife, but genetic alteration and depression caused by tobacco usage. Smoking not only during pregnancy but before and by the husband alters neurogenic codes. Dull, less intelligent children will result. There is no question that cigarette usage decreases mental ability and permanently impairs cerebration. On the other hand, alcohol, because it is a normal constituent of the bloodstream resulting from intestinal fermentation, has no known effect in moderation usage. That caffein, sister to nicotine, both xanthine derivatives, can cause permanent damage to genetic structure, is anyone's guess.

XV War

"And ye shall hear of wars and rumors of wars: . . .
for all these things must come to pass . . ." — Matt. 24:6

SOME PEOPLE have fun in war — enjoy war, delight in war. Or why would so many wars come to pass? What doth it profit my brethren?

1. War profits from *armament manufacture* are colossal, not its spoils, for they are outdated. Production of radar, guns, missiles, nuclear weapons, ships, tanks, planes, ammunition, space electronics, bombs, clothing, trucks, gear, etc., etc., are the world's largest and busiest industry. Earth's pre-occupation is merchandizing death. Factory owners and stockholders acquire continuous fortunes.

2. Not only capital investiture gains but *workers* at all echelons of

supply, manufacture, sale, distribution, and maintenance rake in good to exorbitant wages, commissions, kickbacks, bonuses, pensions, and benefits. It has become standard economic theory that cure for unemployment is a good war. America never came out of the early '30s' depression until Roosevelt commenced maneuvering and finally entered the United States into World War II. It is not above the charitable nature of world statesmen to engage someone into war to divert attention from problems at home and be able, under war control, to eliminate native dissidents.

3. For *those that thrust nations into war,* rewards can be staggering — or nullifying. They may end up national heroes or historic bums slaughtered by their own people. Fortunately for civilization, in the last great war the vanquished, instead of having to turn in their sword and retreat to plush retirement, were executed, hanged or forced to commit suicide. Unfortunately, leaders of conquerors were not treated likewise. Yet, for statesmen, this precedent may be a personal concern before committing one's minions to cause that could fail.

Politicians are not bright people. They are consensus-oriented, usually lying, deceiving, devious. To enter their nation into war assures them of: (a) a preferential place in history; (b) orgasms from personal power; (c) ecstasy of playing God with other men's lives; (d) exhileration of playing a real war game; (e) rhapsodic obsession with fulfilling one's destiny or furthering one's cause; (f) recipient of flattering tribute and egoistic expansion, at least in the beginning; (g) enthrallment with their role. Excitement, dedication to the cause and sacrifice — of possibly sweets and occasional interruptions of sleep. A feeling of majesty with lofty oral pronouncements slurping with honey, indignation, righteousness, and outrage, "Great delivery chief. Take another applause. The champagne and caviar are awaiting." (h) Lastly, self-assessment. "I'm doing great, boy! Look at me. My a - - is dumping all over you dumb clowns. Salute, stand up, bow, kneel when you're in my divine presence. Love to work, work — make decisions — I am the master. It's my moment of history, fame, greatness. I am infallible. I am God am I not? Now is the time to get even with those dirty bastards that oppose me, in MY nation."

If wars come out favorably, there follows, in addition, prestige, wealth, and honor. So, in every politician's craw, no matter how reverently he proclaims peace, is *the innate desire to lead his nation into war.* Both world wars were the result of egostic, selfish, stupid, greedy, power-seeking politicians on both sides of the conflictional line. Half a hundred men held supreme power to sensibly negotiate differences. Instead they chose to murder and maim one hundred million men, women, and children.

4. *Killers. KK.* The game couldn't be played with politicians, armament manufacturers and workers. Executive branch of the art has been supplied by evolution. Sadly it is our *raison d'etre.* For killers and killing has been rungs to climb species' ladder. We're great killers. It's what we are all about. It is our noblest achievement. With a few nuclear wars wiping out a billion citizens, we'll have something to brag about.

If you believe for one second that in armies of earth there are not men who enjoy killing, enjoy war, relish fighting, then you have not comprehended genetic inheritance. Military academies in every nation are flooded with applicants. Their scholastic aspirations are to learn to kill humans. Politicians learn diplomacy. Lawyers the law. Physicians medicine. Priests the gospel. Do these fine, clean, loyal youths enter citadels of destruction in the name of national defense? Hardly. Within the U.S. there has never been a defensive war of significance. Then how can you account for huge military establishments dotting the globe?

Killer genes exist as certainly as religious or pigmentational genes. Killers are born. Killing is their dish. They are genetically programmed to do so. Five percent of the male population? More? Many more under propaganda-activating, open-ended, aggressive genes. What is paradoxical is that in peacetime, KK genes lay dormant — preparing for the next bloodbath — quiescence before quietus.

They say proof of the pudding is in the tasting. The record is there — continuous savagry — constant wars — greater and more lethal conflicts. Man is a killer by historic record and present manifestation. Wars and killers can be none other than genetically directed. Man kills with the same consistency he eats or sleeps. Rarely is he repentive. Decades after he has ravished a foe, they kiss and trade automobiles. War and killing is human sport, and only God can help us — or one day the genetic engineering of non-aggressivity.

War may be the price of freedom. But it is evolutionary struggle that sets cost amount. For wars' profits derive not only from war itself, preparation for war, maintenance of fighting men, but genetic pool enhancement (killing off stupid males), niche enrichment (territory and substance), and elimination of biological rivals. Any one of the last three is sufficient to demand natural selection imprint killer genes in Homo sapiens.

Three famous veterans were interviewed Memorial Day, 1982, on the TV program, "Good Morning America." A retired commander asked about World War II, said he deplored the attitude of today, "Hell no, we won't go" and other immature attitudes. "We elected representatives and if they said to go fight, we have to do it."

A photographer stated we had to go into World War II or the Nazi would have been over here. And a renowned cartoonist said our army was modeled after the Prussian model due to formative efforts of Von Steuben, a drill master. He explained his cartoons as an attempt to reform the American army.

Three famous veterans, many years after the war has passed, are genetically incorrect. Elected representatives do not fight wars. They send innocent and uninformed young men, most of whom have never voted, into battle or face severe punishment. Democracy and representative government are not at work unless wars are fought by volunteers. Genetics involved is wars originate with privileged dominants who have reached supreme posts by political chicanery or biological innateness.

That Nazi Germany could have invaded the U.S. was absurd propaganda. The war transferred Nazi non-threat to Soviet Union definite threat of nuclear invasion with holocaustic casualty. From historic view, it was a tragic mistake for America. Flare-up of age-old European struggles for subracial expansion and domination was the genetic underpinning.

Lastly, the cartoonist who would reform army discipline was not aware of dominance hierarchy role, biologically based.

Hamlet. There has been a great deal written concerning territorial defense in animals. Ordinarily, it is the function of the males, like in the stickleback. In song birds the females enter in. From sea elephants to red deer, there is systematic aggression to defend one's turf. These animal characteristics were never weeded out from man and are a consequence of inane wars to defend a spot of land. As the Captain in *Hamlet* stated, Act IV, Scene IV, "Truly to speak, and with no addition, we go to gain a little patch of ground that hath in it no profit but the name. To pay five ducats, five, I would not farm it, nor will it yield to Norway or the Pole a ranker rate, should it be sold in fee."

Hamlet: "Why, then the Polock never will defend it."

Captain: "Yes, it is already garrisoned."

Hamlet: "Two thousand souls and twenty thousand ducats will not debate the question of this straw. This is th'impostume of much wealth and peace, that inward breaks, and shows no cause without, why the man dies. I humbly thank you, sir."

Shakespeare summed it up most eloquently when he had Hamlet ask the Captain why the troops marched forth. Man has been trying to answer that question long before the Garden of Eden. The absolute inane compulsion of grouped humans with irrational characteristics to purloin a worthless piece of territory or to prevent another nation from obtaining a remote piece of non-important defense area, is one of the majesties of human idiocy. To hear British or American propagandists tell it to gullible proletariat, one would have thought the invasion of Belgium in World War I and the invasion of Poland in World War II were earthquaking Neptunes in which continents would split and seas drain to earth's interior. It was nothing more than one of the hundreds of aggressions repeated periodically for thousands of years over prized fertile fields, fish-filled streams, and minerals of Europe. No propaganda to incite a people toward either aggression or defense is so basically genetically constituted as recitation of land violation.

The tragedy of these consistently bigger and better bloodbaths over a piece of national real estate, is the fact that within a generation the entire wicked mess is forgotten. Hardly have rifle barrels cooled, the last victim's muscles twitched, than the conquerors deluge vanquished with alimentary supplies and funds to rebuild their war-torn economies — by the holy rites of the humanitarian genes.

No matter how one edits the pages of history, the entrance of America into World Wars I and II was based on skillful British propaganda and fifth-column interests in America in the munition industries, profiteers, ethnically benefitting groups, and pathological haters high in government. Most useful, as it has always been, is propaganda based upon ravishment of established territories. In final analysis, America emerged in the last of these wars to the first precarious position she has ever known.

America challenged in equal nuclear capability is due to the rashness of past actions. Recent wars opened the world to miseries, horrors, and enslavement of communism, especially in eastern Europe, and to subversion of peaceful nations to the theory and practice of revolutionary dogma originated in the devil's workshop.

We reiterate Nazi persecution of Jewish people is the most horrendous event of history. It is doubtful German people will live it down, unless other people commit greater atrocities. If Hitler had been permitted to conquer Russia to destroy the communistic base, one may have been able to see a renaissance of Europe of the highest magnitude. What actually passed, by aiding and abetting the evil forces of communism in Russia and China, one set upon the earth an avalanche of venomous, serpentine, false philosophy with revolution its bloody vanguarded banner, and ragged proletariat its excited killers, to enslave the free of the earth. The evil of Hitler was tragic, as was the evil of communism, leaving little choice whom to aid. There is tremendous variation in instinctible disposition toward land possession. Peasants who for centuries farmed the same plots, retain an immense amount of traditional attitude toward land. It is here, where large haciendas have consolidated land and peasants have been made virtual slaves unto it, that rebellion bears its sweetest fruits — as was seen in Mexico and Russia.

In America we have squatters' rights and adverse possession. In adverse possession, if one declares himself the possessor of land contrary to the owner of that land, the owner usually an absent one, and if he farms, fences the land and lives on it twenty-one years, he may possess good title to it. This legal procedure arose out of man's biology. Carried a step further, any nation who owns land or proclaims defiantly its possession, possesses similar good title.

One can see how small tribes radiating over Europe paused by a good cave or set up hide windbreakers in a favorable feed area, proclaimed the land as their own. Such a principle carried into common law pacified the most rudimentary territorial genes.

As Western civilization advanced from the Dark Ages there were errors made toward disposition of real estate equal to the error of the present day communists, who are blind to biological right of possession of land.

Colonialism was indeed a fracas. The mightily-armed nations of Europe in the 20th century pulled their tails beneath them and fled for home. They were defeated by hordes of ill-educated, poorly-organized, rabble-rousing peasants. Leaders of the Western nations were soft and poorly-gened in territorial drive. The battle they lost was not of such splendrous heroics as The Charge of the Light Brigade or the taking of San Juan Hill. Their failure was in the mother country who refused to repopulate the new lands with her own genotypes.

The United States had no illusions of how to create a viable nation. They killed and starved out the Mongoloid inhabitants of America. Then they re-seeded the land with geneticism to their own liking — Anglo-Saxon, northern European. Restrictive immigration was a genetically conceived program to amalgamate the blood and secure the territory. What escaped without notice because they entered the back door of economic advantage, was the colored infiltration. Injected as laboring slaves, it was felt they would possess no challenge to white man's welfare nor to the land. The programming genie, which subconsciously in masses of similarly related peoples, their political representatives and dominants, who determine the composition and future composition of the state, never dreamed that one day blacks would be set free, regarded as equals, and be given full equalitarian rights.

Such a mass genetic genie as the blueprinted DNA consistency of North Americans was caught in an unperceived program. Suddenly the mass is confronted with over 15% of its population of a different race, namely black. This can never be resolved with calmness. All the genetic sequences which relate to race, pride consistency and tolerance, hatreds and tenacious biological inclination toward certain racial selection will pose problems for a long, long time.

Besides this, thinking in terms of colonialism, Americans performed it correctly by removing the natives and substituting their own. On the other hand, if the English with land they controlled had not been so interested in exploiting the people but instead had eliminated the natives in American fashion and propagated their own biology, the sun still would never be setting on an empire truly their own. Where colonialism succeeded is where native populations were displaced by new controlling biology. And it is in this context, and this context only, that nations develop, strengthen, and progress.

Rome, that great civilization of a thousand years, that majestic first world empire with its great laws, writings, armies, and justice — with its Caesars, Pliney, Cicero, Horace, Virgil, household names today — didn't fall because of amorality, failures of leadership, Christianity, or hard times. It fell because the strong geneticism of its tremendous core people was not expanded. They permitted blood dilution with barbarian invaders, slaves, the vanquished and imported laborers. It wasn't Rome and its culture that lost the battle. The battle was lost in the bedrooms, from Sicily to Milan. Where there should have been hybridization of these magnificent people, there was a heterozygeous dilution, with inferiorly-advanced genetic peoples.

Quite the opposite was claimed with the fall of the Roman Empire in that society was too class-oriented and citizenship applied to too few people. Yet any breeder knows that good stock which is dominantly, evolutionarily progressing, can be harmed by crossing it with those of inferior traits. This is not to say that revitalization with those of more remote characteristics is not on occasion valuable providing the remote traits possess desirable attributes. We see the colonialism failure had nothing to do with exploitation of people. It failed because it did not exploit its own biology at the expense of the native biologies. Classic example of a success is the United States and Australia. Land has never been the domain of polyglot races. It is why nations from Russia to Spain try as rapidly as they can to unify their people as one nation biologically. Western civilizations' land error was permitting dominants to acquire huge estates of the best lands and pay little taxes. This was feudal privilege carried into the new world. Morally and humanitarily it appears unjust. Yet it had the biological logic that went with feudalism.

For the dominant who anthropologically controlled land, he masterminded its greatest utility for the benefit of his own group. It was an evolutionary necessity. The peasants of China and Russia controlled much land, but did not develop it well. Soviets and Chinese communists seized it, grouped it into great communal efforts, because they thought they could do a better and more efficient job. Under many circumstances in the capitalistic world, this same logic is forthcoming. Large land holdings by dominants, if properly processed, results in superior benefits to the workers.

It is an enigma that we see great communist nations practicing the very thing they rallied against — private ownership. They took the land from the peasants in the name of land reform to place its ownership into a giant monopolistic corporation known as the Communist Party. On the other hand, capitalistic societies have permitted over-centralization of ownership residing within a few privileged. It was soon corrected, permitting each man his own plot for small sums. They taxed the large owners to an extent that some land went begging.

In modern capitalistic society land ownership has reached a zenith in which biological territoriality is satisfied, be it a small home purchased through long-term, low-down payment or a hunting camp in the forests. It is within everyone's means that they can satisfy this biologic compulsion. The impropriety of large holdings in some South American countries will disappear as nations realize the importance of catering to rooted geneticism of territoriality, even though the subdivisions may be less efficient. If you give to men a piece of land which they can work and profit from, you have made a capitalist and a true enemy of communism. Communism and Russian communism will only achieve permanency when they give people individual ownership of land which is biologically theirs.

We think of culture as non-biologically transmitted information. How we speak, by what method we clothe ourselves, avoid incest, thieve, even pray, are to be regarded as cultural accumulations passed on to us by learning. Animals, birds, and insects have complex forms of behavior which are innate, such as the waggle-dance of bees telling others where to obtain nectar and pollen, a robin knowing how to construct a nest, a trout in its feeding habits, and turtles determining how to navigate oceans. Were it not for innate behavior patterns, we would consider them cultural. Since they have been proven otherwise in experimentation, we cannot go on blithely believing that the majority of things humans perform are passed down only in learning from father to son. With so much built into the animal world locked within genes, it is utter folly to think that man does not have the similarly locked-in culture that he propagates as certainly as he instructs his son how to shoot a gun. Learning how to shoot a gun is obviously at this date cultural. But the fact that he shoots the gun at all, either for human killing purposes in war or animal killing purposes in sports, is innately behaviorally programmed.

To verify this observe men marching off to foreign wars, the unfortunate enemy being no threat to them, to their families or their nation, but merely a fetish of a sap-headed politician; or watch red-coated hunters on a designated day in hunting season take to the woods. In Pennsylvania hunters shoot at practically any moving target and, occasionally, succeed in bagging a human. Therefore, one can never doubt that within male breasts there suffuses ancient fires of hunting and killing art.

There is a statue in Hamburg, Germany, that shows soldiers abreast marching around a column in non-ending fashion. It represents man's killer genes that upon the least pretext, through pages of history, continue in vicious non-ending conflict. If culture had anything to do with teaching or learning, most assuredly, from lessons of horrendous wars man has experienced, we would find cessation of these malignant outrages.

Man would learn for the comfort of himself, his own family or his country, to say "*fini*" to unnecessary brutality. But he has not learned this because he cannot learn. In the midst of peace his greatest industry and joy is in the manufacture and pompous display of death armaments. Killer genes permit man no respite. Possibly, some day, by eugenic breeding, aggressive genes will be phased out. There is a remote chance that microgenetic surgery operating upon DNA coding could remove this monstrous compulsion. But, once again, why should the strong submit to the weak?

E. Ibel Eibesfelt observed that strong differences between species support the idea that horns were developed for intraspecies fighting rather than predator defense. We find genes within nuclear families selfishly directed — outsiders are potential enemies, there is a built-in compulsive competitive aggressiveness to survive over other members of the same species. One notices this in the Spanish family: it is closely-knit and directed inwardly in interests and progeny. Evolutionarily, genetic survival compulsion is the important factor in adaptation and personal furtherance. The genetic programming for personal family survival — husband, wife, and children — outvotes all other drives. Yet each carries within their genes the rebelliousness to challenge and evolve his own specific line. The enemy is always at the door. Family comes first, group second.

It seems wasteful for inner societal feuding while the important issue is perpetuation and advancement of the species. Species' advancement is a by-product to the continuously-emerging variances that are demanding their DNA coding be forwarded. Species is only a conveniently grouped vehicle that prevents adversity, a population ploy that widens the biological niche with variance to assure forward momentum. Most people carry within their genes the ultimate drive of life, which is to continue the chemical sequence whose origin dates back billions of years.

Aggressiveness against one's own is illustrated by the introduction of a strange rat into a group. It may be inspected for hours, but will finally be attacked and killed. There is little social inhibition. Rhesus monkeys demonstrate fierce intergroup fighting. Baboon troops attack other troops, and modern nations wage bitter civil wars.

From lion prides and baboons to sheep, several males join force to create central authority, much in the manner military juntas take over nations to stabilize their social systems. There is no way that man can remove himself from the hierarchial dictates of his biology.

John Pfeiffer, in *The Emergence of Man*, states, "Cultural evolution has come to dominate genetic evolution." We would prefer the reverse. Culture is limited and defined by genetic structures that support it. Wars exist to satisfy bellicose genes. Churches flourish by hallucinations of religious genes. Social order is derived from grooming genes. There is tradition in sports; a continuum of millions of years past. Families are bonded in sex chromosomes X and Y, and if at times we wonder that education may be a product of modern culture, we have but to watch the antics of any socially-grouped animals.

It was with the origin of K (killer) genes that modern man came into being. Three million years ago we scrounged for fruit and roots, lizards and insects, turtles and birds, young or dying animals, small and available, with the minimum of rational thought. When we moved to big-game hunting, utilized tools and tactics, our brain needed remodeling, and we exploded evolutionarily into the man being — a rational killer.

Killing was our meat, our delight, our reward. The bellicose genes give saisfaction to soldiers and hunters alike. K genes are our greatest accomplishment — our *raison d'etre*. It will be many millions of years before we eliminate them.

Social class arose from the miracle of our hands. Man was a slight animal. His teeth, adapted for vegetables, couldn't kill a young gazelle. He had no claws. He was defenseless — save for fingers which grasped his first weapons: the stick, stone, bone, and whip. He was not programmed to hunt for big game. It was thrust upon him when he watched brothers wield a thigh bone.

Within this first industrial revolution class distinction was demanded. Only a few leaders can command a successful campaign. There were needed brush-beaters, flankers, and "ammo" bearers. Most fearless and fleetest were the killers. Bringing up the rear were the skinners, marrow-breakers, and porters. Firemen stoked festive fires. A hunt was an organized affair, requiring political strategy and a hierarchy of workers and warriors. From these beginnings human society gelled, and all the Karl Marxes and Lenins that may issue forth shall never split it asunder.

We have difficulty explaining royalty and kingly rule if we rely on the "divine right" theory. We are on substantial ground when we realize our early sojourn as man was under dominating members of the tribe. Social groupings require leadership. We were too early for the complicated machinery of democracy. Dominate ape males favored, sired, and retained the females of the group. Since they were with females at the most favorable time of mating, it was consequential they beget the future leaders. Royalty begets royalty. Jungle divine rights go back millions of years to our first killers.

Our genes have blessed us with many forms of biological struggle. Class stuggle, which is due to the innate hierarchy, we fail to tribute fully. Saddest are the two subracial wars. When these hideous bits of fluff are over, cemeteries are still apart — left out of the final peace settlements.

Why shouldn't the victor and vanquished share honored space for their heroes? Why should the conqueror bury his dead in one location and the defeated another? Has the war not ended? Or does the genetic battle still engage the dead, dedicated eternally to precepts of their long forgotten conflict, to causes blown as grains of sand? The dead become property of the living — the conqueror — the custodian of their genes. The vanquished, extinct, lie by the wayside in evolution's march. Cemeteries well-kept or abandoned become testament to genetic progress.

A formula is seen in war genes, WW. How else could you coerce millions of men to engage in hideous trench warfare as the French and Germans in World War I? They were willingly fed into slaughter machines with only the mildest of protest toward the end. Assuredly not under the aegis of patriotism, homeland, conquest, economics or loyalty, but because self-destruction is an anomaly in evolutionary advancement. The answer to these periodic war-madnesses is that within the human lies the more recent WW genes (war) and the more ancient KK genes (killer), which to many bring joy and satisfaction, as one can witness in hunting. This harshness visited upon humanity, criminality of huge defense budgets and preparation for war instead of peace, is aided, abetted, and sponsored by genetic remnants of our savage, immoral past.

Coon puts it even more succinctly when he states, "In many structurally simple societies the trouble-maker is killed one dark night by his fellows, or driven away, and so the genes which may have contributed to his anti-social behavior are thus, in a sense, fished out of the pool. Social adaptation, which is the capacity for living together in groups, has been influential in human evolution, if not more so than environmental adaptation, through technology."

However, trouble-makers are still with us. Anti-social behavior is a component in criminality. The quote by Coon supports our contention that society is an evolutionary factor which is strongly selected toward. There is much more. Capital punishment and compulsory sterilization of criminals convicted of violent crimes is imperative to future society. To allow people with unstable genetic mechanisms to propagate is absurdity. A cleansing mechanism of the gene pool is long overdue. Humanity has been too obsessed with religious and false humanitarian concepts to prune the culls. It has avoided its responsibility to the future welfare of mankind. This is no Hitlerian Nazi doctrine. Had such a principle been in effect ages before, insensitive and immoral aggressiveness such as that in Hitler may never have come to be. Weeding human seed is our best hope for the future. It is time to impose mandatory sterilization upon all convicted of premeditated violent crimes.

In an extremely useful book, *Primate Social Behavior*, by Charles H. Southwick, there is stated, "One may generalize by saying that among monkey and ape societies, intraspecies competition and group antagonisms are much stronger than between groups of different species genera."

Nations become their own worst enemies. Our Civil War was the bloodiest and cruelest of all our wars, as was the Spanish Civil War. Evolutionary struggle is severest where the DNA is the most similar, because here there is the greatest threat to one's share of the ecological niche.

Prescription for genocidal genes begins with the DNA chromosomes coded to self-perpetuation. In every aspect of that which we term life is the chemical compulsion to continue. This is the *sine quo non* that separates us from undirected chemicals, that divider of air and water from algae and men. Life is an essentially selfish, covetous, monopolistic and egocentric process which has but one sole overriding and obsessive purpose — to procreate its own kind at the expense of every living form, be it close relatives, a neigh-

boring tribe or distant nation. Once it is on stage, it is compulsed to take
that which is needed to forward its own code. It is as if every living individual possesses his own god which demands perpetuation and almightiness.
Without this "My code is best and it is the one that shall inherit the earth,"
life and evolution could not exist. There would be no struggle for domination or change, no incentive to continue. It is this rivalry, this innate drive,
that lays the basis for war — for political domination — for crime.

During the Vietnam War, an author in *Life* magazine presented a study
of an army general. What makes the article's content fascinating is that the
general is the purest of soldiers and the author is an excellent perceptionist
of human psychology. If the article appears slanted, one must recall that the
majority of American people were disenchanted with the first war they were
not winning and with the rationale of fighting a Mongolian conflict on
Asiatic soil on the other side of the earth. Assuming that the genotype code
in the genes composes a good warrior in the same fashion as genotypes endow the talents for music, art or mathematics, then we should expect to see
their revelation in phenotypes.

Commencing the case study with a full-page portrait, one discerns the
narrow depressed tight lips one would expect of the northern Caucasoid.
From the hundreds of thousands of years as northern hunting bands, it is
small wonder that the Caucasoid and the Mongoloid were selected for large
cooperative, destructive war-styles rather than the Negroes. Too, physiognomy may be utilized as a tool because it expresses phenotype to detect
underlying genotypes. Old psychological studies held that appearances were
deceiving. And, for example, if individuals were dressed alike, one could not
tell criminal from reputable business types. Unfortunately, flat black and
white photos were used in the studies, which were inaccurate. TV shows,
"What's My Line?" and "Guess Who's the Real One" capitalize on this same
thesis by using cleverly-simulated ruses to make genotypic discovery by way
of phenotypic traits difficult or impossible.

Man's face is indication to intelligence and underlying personality. Let us
return to the colored photo of the general. Thinness in the face and neck
illustrates not only muscular effort but dietary discipline. Slit-like eyes, even
though the sun was a factor in the photo, reveals a peripheral crows-feet
pattern of personality intensity rather than the broad, deep crows-feet
pattern which one finds in completely content, non-driving people. The
pointed, extended ear is anyone's guess, but certainly would have value in
better hearing ability. Such a forceful face is rarely seen inside the proletariat. It is to be expected because bourgeois and upper class are interested
in achievement.

How a man rises to rank of general is the author's thesis. Older generals
had suggested the specific general, expressing him as the ideal American
soldier — what the profession would like to believe itself to be. It is because
of this context that the article in *Life* is important. Without equivocation
not only is intelligence and drive innate, but leaders are born, not made. If
genetic material of specific type is not present, there is no rise of that individual in any profession, let alone the military.

Described as a brave and selfless man, the general had exposed himself so often to enemy fire that he had "no right to survive." Chalk one for patriotism and bravery. The author was struck by his military bearing and self-confidence, which he came to recognize as a necessary characteristic of the warrior-hero. He could imagine him back at Thermopylae.

The author, note well, is speaking of acquired characteristics. But are they acquired or is there a formula which can be utilized in the diagnosis of most types of human behavior? Bravery, selflessness, self-confidence, military bearing are not acquired traits, they are genetic blessings. The author notes, too, the aggressive forward slant of the jaw, a face that would lend itself to carving in stone. "He stands so erect that he bends slightly backward and sets an example of high standard."

A poignant observation by the author is the contradiction between the general's devout Christian faith and the killing necessary to his profession. There have been marvelous philosophical debates over the centuries relating to good and evil in man. No amount of brain power could have resolved the quandry. Lacking knowledge of genetics and evolution, philosophers had to content themselves with lofty wordy theories which did not probe chemical facts of the organism.

In the simplest of evolutionary terms, religion provided solace and benevolent code behavior. The killing art provided food and elimination of competition for survival of the specific pool. Both genetic complexes were extremely important to subracial furtherance, for each intraspecies pool had its own battle flag which was to be defended and furthered at the expense of others.

An interesting dilemma in the general's life was that he was afraid if he went to the academy he might not have graduated in time for the war. But his father explained that in the history of West Point, no class ever failed to take part in at least one war. He sought out war the same as a surgeon seeks out bodies to heal.

Most nations graciously provide every generation an opportunity to exercise war genes and rid themselves of nagging instinctive aggressions. No matter how much at peace and love, in the ashes and embers of the last war opposing sides are "divied" up and seeds for new wars spawned. It makes little difference that the victors have been allies. It would be horrendous if there was no nation to fight or an enemy lurking on some distant boundary. So immediately, subconsciously, genetically-inspired opponents are chosen in relatively equivalent strength.

In the last world war, no sooner were Nazis, Japanese and Italians crushed than the world split into two viciously antagonistic camps. No one proposed the Americans and Russians saying to one another, "Together we shall control the world in ten thousand years of peace." Such a suggestion would have appalled the military and restrained healthful war genes. There was no reason at all why the conquered Japanese and Nazis shouldn't have remained conquered and the allies rule supreme. This is the skeleton joker with wars. There is always the hue and cry that the world is out of balance, that the opponent is seeking world domination.

Beneath this seeming irrationality is strong genetic prompting. As long as there are racial and subracial variations with their unique pools, there must be intraspecies competition and rivalry. Moreover, for the very direction of evolution, because the world is small, these isolated geographic pools must express themselves to advance lest they face extinction common to the past.

Within our instinctive genes are not only reflex actions, gross behavioral patterns, but underlying attitudes, unlearned, which affect our reactions toward a situation. The general spoke about exhileration of attack, command being the most satisfying job, and of the camaraderie and spirit of closeness among men who fight together. War can be likened to a fox hunt, football or baseball game, or even cowboys and Indians. One of the best places to study human nature is on the battlefield. There is contentment to carry out orders of the commander-in-chief. "During the entire fight, with people on either side of me being killed, I never once feared death."

The foregoing are strong attitudes which would be difficult to initiate through education or training. In tribute to a remarkable soldier in his beliefs, one can see that there is underlying genetic talent and resolve which is not programmed in ordinary mortals.

A last insight in the article was revelation that the Vietnam War was a great boon because the Russians were envious of Americans' opportunity for on-the-job training. Twenty-five thousand officers rotated every year in Vietnam. Most of humanity not possessed with KK genes are not particularly happy with wars planned for the sake of training soldiers, testing new and modern weapons, and stimulating the armament industry. Like philosophers of old, the dilemma is not easily resolved. With gratitude we must continue to respect and honor those who possess these most horrid of talented genes — KK — which daily valiantly guard our evolutionary biological pools.

Seten Indian, by William MacLeod, points out in English history considerations for annihilation of enemies and subjects. It is another example from the American conquest of the West, to Hitler, to Atilla. There is a tendency to feel that national wars are only for defense, conquest, or settling minor disputes. There is rarely a consideration that within gened pools annihilation of the opponent is not only good genetic practice, but is subconsciously programmed.

A few excerpts are in order:

"James, speaking from his London throne, through his privy council in Scotland, was very clear on these points. He insisted that it be agreed in writing that if the Marquais left any natives alive on the Islands [Hebrides] after a year had passed, the land should revert to the crown and the Marquais get nothing for his expense."

"Queen Elizabeth's nobles who received lands and governing powers in Ireland, provided they could conquer the natives in the territories assigned, generally decided that it would be necessary to exterminate the Irish — 1594."

And, "For although in 1654 the hand-picked Parliament denied it officially, it was evident that the object of Cromwell and the hope of Parliament was the extermination of the million natives of wild Ireland . . . a unique reservation scheme was devised which was planned to result in the death of hundreds of thousands."

So we see through the history of mankind there is operating instinctive neurogenic genes programmed toward eliminating competitive gene pools and for expansional purposes of the mother pool.

This fits nicely with observations of most forms of mammalian life concerning warfare and intraspecies competition. It is far from Christian charity and mercy. Within leaders, and to lesser extent blind followers, is the adaptational mechanism of annihilation of rival group humans.

War's final scenarios should eliminate proletariat participation. With super long-range missiles and keener awareness of sociobiology, targets of conflict should be reserved for upper bourgeois — the higher echelons of command, political, economic, and military. Pawns of war have been the masses in horrendous numbers. A keener sense of biology will limit aggression to specifically wiping out the central nervous system directing war effort.

For hundreds of years wars have been based upon the philosophy of equalitarianism — leaders arising from the ranks to supplant the fallen. Not so for future generals. First-strikes and continuing strikes will be full houses of Congress, parliaments, and meetings of the supreme Soviet by offshore submarines. Military objectives will not be territory but elimination of leadership.

Stranger than fiction, super-powers are poised for a doomsday nuclear holocaust. It is no lark. It is within the genes and, providing one of the great subracial pools can get away with it, the inner DNA codes will trigger blood-drenched oceans.

Under present theories it is impossible to explain the universality and persistence of war. War genes possessed by the more aggressive members of society and supportively subsidized by the majority of its members under emotional and territorial neurogenes are a furtherance to rapid evolution of a specific gene pool. War genes and warrior nations, when successful, do eliminate intraspecies competition. Not only does the individual leap forward because of his surviving progeny, but there is a great step forward of entire genetic pools. The Americans eliminated the Mongoloids in territorial United States, the Nazis liquidated its Jewish population, and the Spanish drove the Moors back across the Straits of Gibraltar.

Survival of the fittest individuals as an evolutionary procedure must be correlated with survival of the socially fittest. Unfortunately, great warrior nations whose national banners represent human genetic pools rather than individuals, conquer and populate at the expense of the weak. "Verily I say unto you, the meek shall inherit the earth." That is, a hole in the ground.

Impediments to our vision is employment of psychosociologic or philosophic political rationalization to group conflict. Let us begin with the base that war is biologically waged. It is the action of a living species, man. Species behave in predictable, programmed, and instinctive patterns. Smallest of wars is the intrafamily struggle, Cain and Abel. Next comes inter-family war characterized romantically, e.g., mountain hillbillies such as the Hatfields and McCoys. When a few families band toward allegiance, we have tribal rivalries such as the Hudson and Iroquois.

Murderous conflict in the smallest unit is frequent. Support for ingrained hostility derives from animal studies which demonstrate assertions for territory, mates, and feeding areas, to exclusion of their own kind so their specific seed traits may propagate.

Social behavior does not arrive from the impulse of "Come on, fellows, let's all cooperate." It arises only out of rewards ensuing from such cooperation. Beneath are laws of self-preservation linked closely with family preservation and laws of instinct in which the animal blindly obeys gene print, be it mating death in the spider web or honey bee castration. In the organism challenged by being deprived of food or mating (unless desexed purposefully as the worker bee), conflict ensues because prearranged biology has been alerted.

One day I watched a robin and bluejay fight over a nest in a spruce tree. It was a magnificent sight as they fought vertically ten feet above the ground. One can find red ants and black ants in community warfare, and hornets defending their garret against rivals, even bumble bees slugging it out. I have witnessed hounds chasing deer, raccoons swiping trout, aerial dogfights by many different bird species. A quiet mountain is not a retreat of peace but rather a veritable battleground of intraspecies and species conflicts.

Our earth is one seething sea of conflict. It is parcel and inseparable from life. How is man to be different? Man does not fight by reason. Wars are genetically formed and maintained. They exist and continue because his instinctive structure prompts their action. It is so true — "Only the dead have seen the end of war." It's not that the strong love war, it is that man must wage war to advance his special genetic code.

Desmond Morris, in *The Naked Ape*, observes, "Wolves or lions — they have of necessity developed powerful inhibitions about using their weapons on other members of their own species. These inhibitions appear to have a *specific genetic basis:* they do not have to be learned. Special submissive postures have evolved which appease a dominant animal."

We too inherit submissive traits. Where we differ from animals is in the rapidity with which we achieved social order. And it is this unpruned order that provided warriors for security, which was evolutionarily heavily selected toward, that we outbalance civilized conduct. A premium for advancement was given those tribes most successful in eliminating their competing neighbors.

King (1954), in testing cocker spaniel females found that they exhibited most aggression against strangers most like themselves rather than other animals. It is here that the intraspecies' hostility is evident and why civil wars are so common and violent. It appears *the closer in biological relationship, the more vicious the competition,* which is true to the precept of natural selection. Intraspecies competition reaches its highest manifestation in man and his wars. One can compare this premise in Schjelderup-Ebb's studies, which are confined largely to the competitive aspect of individual recognition in birds.

We refer to the behavior of Galapagos finches. Males will defend their territories against males of their own species, but will usually tolerate males of other species. Paradoxically, warriors of the white Western world are guilty of the same short-sightedness. Nations lock in protracted murderous and debilitating wars, sowing good seed of their youth in windrows of death to protect some insignificant piece of territory or deny competitive economic challenge.

The only reason poison gas became outlawed was because the dominants of society became as susceptible to injury as the proletariat they commanded. It is truly to be regretted that special nuclear shelters are provided for those higher governmental echelons, as this only increases the chances of nuclear contest. The army's generals are ordinarily more liberal with risking other men's bodies than their own.

That diverging races or species create violent antagonisms when competing within the same ecological niche is time honored. That they actively seek the extinction of one another is evident evolutionarily. This was the true "Jewish problem." Isolated (ghettoed) human genetic banks competing within the same territory economically. This warfare was one-sided. It was the most subtle form. Within the crucible of a state, Jews were persecuted by pogroms, massacres, assassinations, and premeditated mass murder. It resembled the systematic destruction of the American Mongoloid Indians by the Europeans.

These mass genetic destructions of Jews and Indians were in a sense not war. There were not huge armies charging, trumpets blaring, generals in the rear, sword-waving their stalwarts into the cataclysm. Rather, they were sinisterly designed aggressions against a foreign genetic nidus, with consensus of population, to achieve elimination by economic, sociological, and traumatic methods. Once the pattern was set, fixed in accord with survival-supremacy DNA code of the aggressor, there needed only time to accomplish security. Wars are conflicts of evolutionarily coded chemicals. Thus we see persecution of Jews and Indians, a subracial war between Caucasoids and an interracial war between whites and Mongoloids.

Intraspecies' antagano-genes do not work in a vacuum. They coordinate, relate, assist, and inhibit sister genes in other locations. Antagonisms and aggressions are programmed to recognize diverging banks within the same species, much as one species recognizes its own by signals, colors, and movements. A white dove does not seek out a blue bird. Recognition that mating is impossible is immediate. A white woman does not normally seek a black male, even though mating is possible, contrary to anti-racists who believe culture is responsible for the attitude. If this were so, we would have to discredit a prime force of evolution sexual selection.

Intraspecies' antagano-genes are forces that recognize enemies, competitors, threats to its particular evolutionary strain. Add to these synergistic war genes, those residual of our past that prompt us to look for wars, to enjoy weaponry, to seek killing, to be thrilled and appalled by it. Fortunately, not everyone has war genes or we never would have survived.

In genetic determination of occupations, a percentage are chosen in Mendelian ratio as soldiers, knights, murderers, or warriors. These are born to kill — to either enjoy killing or to execute its direction. It is our warrior legacy which protected us and permitted us conquest of rhinoceros, cave bear and mammoth when we were retreating before European glaciers. We commenced killing millions of years ago. In such a period we selected for survival, our noblest of achievements. Killing was not a cultural acquisition. It was a biological necessity for advancement. It provided us sustenance and leisure. We selected killers to prosper. We have rank because some individuals have instinct to preserve related genetic code with greater intensity than others.

War is meant to be an intraspecies affair. The massive horns on the stag are not designed for his defense or the defense of the herd. They are an offensive weapon to slay his sexual rivals and to exert his dominance. The horns are shed in January, leaving him and his charges wide open to the winter attacks of carnivorous predators. These are unimportant. The enemy is his stag brothers — the compulsion is the advancement of his solitary code.

War's reasons lie in fur-covered ancestors — in the ancient hunting and killing codes. The least of stimuli is necessary to alert purines and pyramadines. Some purines are actively seeking out the exhileration of the kill. For all the lofty oratory of war leaders, one has but to look to sugars and phosphates — the code — their pitiful words and illogic are launched from a very real helixed chemical of primitive intent.

It has been pointed out that culture, conquest, and civilization progress from east to west. Explanations are meager — China to India to Egypt — to Russia — Greece — Rome — a French-Spanish-English-German session — and then America. The torch that is civlization — prowess at arms, law, literature, the sciences — is passed to the next-door neighbor; the past holders having become debauched, careless, quarrelsome or weary of the burden.

The warrior is the creator and custodian of civlized progress. Ruthless as his charge may be, he provides security for the arts to emerge and flourish. He provides stability for poet, painter, priest. He guards and extorts wealth unto his homeland.

That war and brute strength are the pinnacle of man's efforts becomes an unpleasant reflection. If we pause to examine the military budget of any great nation — be it Roman legions, Spanish galleons, British Navy or an American Armored Division —   civilization trails in its wake. Military excellence alone is too thin a line to provoke this upheaval — sifting bastions of culture. Soldier societies are population-supported. They need farmers to provide vitals, women to birth fodder, politicians to inflame passions, armsmakers to turn a profit, priests to oath benedictions. With every soldier marches dozens of weaponless compatriots. This collusive mass, frontstaged every century or so, the torch-bearer of civilization, represented by armed might, is a gigantic conspiracy to protect, defend, and forever obey the particular geneticism they have chosen to honor.

When we say civlization moves West, it does. Not because land is vacant, not because home people are bawdy, quarrelsome or decadent, not because far-off fields are greener, not because there's more iron, gunpowder, and gold — but because the genetic spark traveled Westward.

Genetic pools bred with poor performing genes were incapable of competing with new DNA codes traveling West. The more inquisitive daring and pioneering mixed their bloods with sturdy warrior stocks, multiplying in isolation until they were ready to explode into their role in history.

Genes moving Westward improved their DNA codes. Genes remaining at home unchallenged and not challenging bred with stock of non-warrior, non-missionary. Evolution's crucible on the homefront cooled. Others probed unknown worlds for unknown gene combinations. Selective factors provided the march of civilization.

There are many examples of intraracial hatreds in history. Pizzaro, with only 200 men and 27 horses, was able to overturn the Peruvian Empire torn by civil war. Cortez, with similar forces, achieved the conquest of Mexico. In both cases it was not so much the hatred of the invader as it was the hatred of those that were struggling within the nation. A nation locked in civil war is prime candidate for outside conquest because innate hatreds against one's own are fierce. The West was simply too late with too little in the civil war that occurred after the Russian defeats in 1917.

Recognition of enemy is easy when we have stereotypes prepared for us by culture and genetic direction. Yet, when we get down to individual cases, it becomes more difficult. How often does one hear, "I simply don't trust him — I don't know why"? Here our subconscious geneticism is doing the prompting. Our geneticism gives us few guides what to look for. We select up the evolutionary scale. Headhunters of Borneo, with their large noses and small eyes, are distrusted; but a blond, thin Swede gives one reason to explore approachment.

We recognize friends genetically. This is nuclear acid chemistry. By education we are alerted where we should expect to find friendship. The third is personal experience. Experience can be as simple as Pavlovian conditioned reflex. It explains the old Indian proverb, "An enemy who eats at one's campfire is no longer an enemy."

Association can, therefore, defuse enemy sets we have received genetically and culturally. Such genetic and cultural conjointure in the American Army's success is accounted for by experience association. It is not of sufficient force when it comes to blending races. In the '60s and early '70s there were many reports of racial riots within American troops. There existed individual friendships, but command and legislation were not sufficient to blend underlying racial animosities.

Recitations of animal loyalties to their own group are legend. Marais, the South African naturalist, half a century ago, recorded the self-sacrifice of two male baboons. Hurtling at dusk from a twelve-foot-high cliff to the back of a stalking leopard, they permitted the escape of their troop. The leopard disemboweled one baboon instantly, and jawed the other, resulting in his demise. Animals have been reared in isolation so they could not learn aggression. When introduced to other isolated animals, they attacked one another, showing normal threat and fighting patterns. This is instinctive behavior. With man, when provocations are not met with aggressive discharge, thus reducing tensions, repressed forces can culminate in a severe explosive state more vicious than the original instinctive base.

After drum-beating, newspaper sabre-rattling and jazzing the populace with non-truths about atrocities, nations often go to war, as did the United States in 1917, when neither existence, land, nor competitive markets are threatened. This could be a reason for periodic war every generation. We seek wars to relieve innate dammed-up tensions which have been propagandized. In the past we were at war daily with the elements, animals, and other men. In today's serenity, the same inner pressures still exist. Therefore, newspaper and television news are based on irritating news rather than niceties of culture.

A demand for "Lebensraum" has repeatedly been made as a cause for aggressive war. This is predicted upon population density or environmental sustenance scarcity. It was most certainly not a factor in the politics of the United States in two bloody world wars, or even to the English or French — all victors who did not increase their territory significantly at the conclusion of those wars.

To conquer land is only incidental to compulsive seeding of germinal plasma. As frontiers open and permit exchange of goods, culture, husbands and wives, the necessity for war as a genetically unitized pool will cease.

"Death to Israel and its Inhabitants" was a slogan of the Islamic Confederation. Yet, with the enemy in their midst, do we see concerted effort to eradicate the foe? Instead we witness intra-Arabic conflict. Due credit for Arabic splintering must go to the Israelis and their allies' efforts in formenting disruption. This is part of the picture. Success was achieved because of a fundamental genetic law — "In the proposition of conflict, *the primary enemy shall be the closest related nucleic beings* — those whose gene chains are most similar and, consequently, the most competitive for future specie determination, excluding the minimum national or tribal unit." So Arabs fight Arabs instead of Israelis.

Briefly, the real enemy (dictated in genetic-coded chemistry) are individuals which are closest in structure and culture. For the closer one comes — with exclusion of a basic group — to others, the greater is kinship rivalry. Indians greeted Cortez when he invaded Mexico and made possible his overthrow of Montezuma. They were not so concerned with their own welfare and perpetuation of Indian culture as they were with defeat of their "blood brothers."

A forest may tolerate white oak, scotch pine, hemlock, spruce, and hundreds of other trees within its borders, but, as with robins or yellow-bellied flycatchers, the enemy is not the unrelated in the great geneticism that surrounds them; it is their kin competitors.

Some species survive in large social groups. Within these units exists a continuous rivalry for mates and food. Even here the primary enemy is close at hand. There may not be five kings or thirty leaders. Chemistry of genetics in its wisdom designed that single groups shall be forthgoing. It is not a chemistry of the whole of a species, but an ever-changing chemistry selfishly bent on perpetuation of the fittest and most aggressive. For example, baboons engage in frequent and violent aggressive behaviors, especially in areas of high population density — DeVore and Hall, 1965.

As we project similar behavior forward in the highest primate, we understand why people living in cities are callous and indifferent. One needs to have lived in the country and go to the city to observe the deterioration of human relationships. With the development of society, the thought in mind was small units ranging to a maximum of 500 people. As larger cities developed, there was created a high degree of aggressive people.

As in Darwin's "survival of the fittest," competition within the group is fiercest. One needs but to go to religious meetings, be they Catholic, Protestant or Jewish, to witness the inanity of intragroup conflict. When they have the precepts of love, order and harmony as the basis of their togetherness, it is trageo-comedic to witness their intense hatreds and rivalries. Proof positive are the split-offs that occurred in religious denominations. Civil war aggression' combatants are by blood-and-culture-related. They are doing their "thing" to eliminate competition of brothers, the oldest form of social behavior, a "survival of the fittest."

In the 19th century, under Lincoln's leadership, America fussed out of proportion over the issue of slavery. This led to a horribly bloody four-year war, even though slaves had become unprofitable and were being phased out. Yet, in the 20th century, the more ruthless slavery of the masses by Soviet hierarchy went unheeded and was abetted by agencies of the allies.

Whereas, indignant rage over the ownership of humans transpired in the Civil War, communist enslavement seized Eastern Europe with but the mildest protest from the West. The divergency was not a question of justice. It was that the rulers of the West were selling out in an appeasement to minorities in their population which had been ravished and atrocitized by the Nazi. There was no humanitarianism in the Roosevelt "love Russia" era. There was only hatred of things German, which blocked any effort to save the Soviet masses and, as Solzhenitsyn has explained, the peculiarly bad behavior of the American leaders toward aiding Russian freedom.

The genes involved were aggressive, intraspecies war genes on the part of the Western nations. Once they had locked into their deadly targets, they could not be switched off. It was the Soviets that took advantage of the intramural Western conflict, U.S., England, France vs. Germany. Like Pizzaro and Cortez, the Russian position was to high advantage, one of conquest and enslavement. It will be left for the future Western generations, unfortunately, to free the Russian people.

In *War*, Morton Fried makes some powerful points, as follows: "Aggressive behavior appears most frequently and is most intense between or among animals of the same species." Intraspecies' antagonisms of non-human primate is not accounted for by the ecological niche theory. For example, siamangs and gibbons eat the same food in the same tree areas, yet their aggressive conflicts are rare.

"War satisfies the drive and urge to attack people and the urge to sacrifice oneself for one's self or one's fellow citizens."

Civil wars are magnificent examples of evolution at work, closely related intraspecies conflict for perpetuation of their specific gene types — by way of survival of the fittest.

"We have learned that good people can do impersonal evil and that war does not require hate. You do not need to train people to hate, to fight a war, simply to obey." It's why anarchists upset us — they don't cooperate. On the other hand, a volunteer army is a good army because those with high killer genes respond.

"Lethal weapons are reserved for men. The female fights only for food or the defense of her young rather than fight to kill."

Warfare is used to repel attack, add territory, establish freedom, establish dictatorship, provide an external target for internal troubles, to provide food, materials, employment and profits. We do not employ women in warfare, in order that the species can be perpetuated. Man is expendable, much as the deer hunter kills primarily bucks. All is based on group loyalty and group advancement. Loyalty is the bond developed as social hunters.

Charles Darwin, one of the world's greatest scientists, observed in the *Descent of Man*, "At some future period not very distant, as measured by centuries, the civilized races of man will almost certainly exterminate, and replace the savage races throughout the world." Having low regard for uncultured humans, he noted the inevitability of wars and selection toward the fittest.

Charles Tilley stated, "We do not need a stifled universal instinctive aggression to account for violent conflicts in our past or in our present, nor need we go to the opposite extreme and search for pathological moments and sick men in order to explain collective acts of protest and destruction. Historically, collective violence has flowed regularly. . . ." This leaves an out for the likes of Hitler, Mussolini, Roosevelt, Stalin, Churchill, and shifts the seat for our violent recurrent behavior to society rather than a few killer leaders.

Man is a predatory killer in that he enjoys the hunt, engages in it, yet does not understand why. He is happy to fire off guns and missiles to destroy something or other. He is elated at bloodshed and murder, which are the most pervasive elements in his theatre. Beneath the violent behavior is the genetically-coded war genes. We recognize that they are better entrenched within dominants who evolutionarily were entrusted with forwarding society. We cannot blame brave mesomorphic people who fight wars. Their dominants jazz them into aggressive hysteria and they innocently sally forth in ancient ritual as if they were on the hunting trail of an extinct woolly mammoth. Our northern bloody past, our savagry in the hunt, and our imbuement of the "big kill" as a way of life takes precedence over the southern nations where the diet was more vegetarian and their way of life less gory.

The institution of war is brilliantly rationalized by combatants who justify the conflict. Each side is saving their women from ravishment, protecting a free world for their children — and all actions, no matter how remote from home base, are taken in the spirit of national defense. Every nation prepares for war. It is a most lucrative business.

No one taught my beagle to attack the strange black bear seeking food outside my door at our mountain camp. Now, when I purposely solicit the intruder's visitation by a dish of sugar mixed with honey, I hold the beagle in my lap, while we peer out the cabin window at the bear ten feet away. One witnesses innate aggressiveness displayed with finest flourish. The beagle's muscles tense, hair is erect, and a most murderous, threatening growl utters from his throat. Although the bear is over twenty times the dog's size, he'll take after that bear with wild leaps and ferociousness. This behavior came to the dog not only by man's selection as his long-time hunting partner, but it dribbled down in acquisition of acquired traits throughout the bear-hunt culture period.

The bear does not fear the dog, will often turn on him, or simply ignore him in feeding. Yet add the presence of the man to that of the dog and there is a perceptional set which triggers escape genes to send the huge beast thundering back into the forest.

Thus it is with man and war-waging. It is not only instinctively ingrained within neuron tissue, it appears that each generation must have its gory sampling of conflict. Far the greatest problem is that political knaves and lesser intellects are in control and, by false dominance, charge their nations headlong into the maelstrom to compensate for their inferiorities. Were true biological dominants in command, there would be a greatly reduced incidence of mass destruction because, in their genetic structure, they possess balancing, restrictive genes.

Whereas, the politician is an out-of-place fop in command, a true leader asserts his coded role, which is properly tempered. In modern society, true leaders heading government are hard to come by because their road to success is by ability rather than political trickery, deceit, and enchantment of the masses.

One of the wonders of the male behavioral world is to watch from the elderly to young, from a square in Madrid to a smoky meeting room in rural Pennsylvania, males engaged in the science of philately, who devote hobby-lives and dreams to the collection of stamps. It is an underlying genetic compulsion deriving from man's pursuit and defense of territory.

A poor man can a king be, as he shuffles his small bits of paper from envelope to booklet or exchanges with another small representations of nations in the form of postage stamps. As the possessor of a stamp he owns a small part of a far-off land in the same fashion as sovereigns past. There can be a profit motive, and he can be fortunate enough to obtain a rare stamp. Yet this is not the motivation. Underneath is demonstrated how genetic codes become translated within society. Who would have dreamed philately was genetic until the animal scientist performed his studies on territoriality? We have known about territoriality for thousands of years as a game of monarchs, the rich and fortunate. Little did we suspect programming in those of lesser wealth would surface past the mind's censor in substitutional behavior. This drive is also behind land reform and why nations who do not adopt proper land distribution are subject to rebelliousness. By far the greatest curtain raised of all time — "Drama Never Surpassed," as Winston Churchill was to call it — was the unfolding of World War I in 1914.

Ready to be implemented by Germany was the Schlieffen Plan as formulated in 1905, which proposed violation of Belgium neutrality and, thence, to sweep rapidly to Paris and victory by delivering a devastating weight of army against the French left. Schlieffen retired in 1906, and although he did not think much of the plan and felt it would not work, his successors kept it up to date without detailing an alternative.

France had her plan, Russia hers, Austria hers — they all had plans, contingencies, open agreements, secret agreements. Across length and breadth of Europe, bristling with shining new armament, with millions of well-fed and well-disciplined soldiers alert and ready for action, their commanders headily wined with prospects of quick victory and glory, the cue came on time, in a small Balkan city on the 28th of June, 1914.

Arch-Duke Ferdinand and his wife were assassinated by a Serb of Austrian nationality. Princip, at Sarajevo, had lit the fuse which, within the next 31 years, was to send almost 100,000,000 people to their deaths and cost nations of earth more wealth than had ever been accumulated or spent in the entire history of mankind.

Sent marching on the dusty roads of Europe in that fateful early August were seven German armies, under Kluck, Bulow, Housen, Albrecht, Crown-Prince, Rupprecht, and Herringen. Driving west, they were to contact seven French armies under Du Bail, Castlenu, Ruffey, Langle, Lanrezac, Maunoury and Pau, plus the British expeditionary force under French. Similar drives by Russians, Germans and Austrians were in progress in the eastern frontiers.

Schlieffen had somehow felt that his plan of violating the neutrality of Belgium was justified due to Germany's strong encirclement, under the law of self-preservation. The Kaiser had spoken about *liebesraum*, or living space, and the British were babbling about honoring their treaty to the Belgiums. They were more concerned about Germany's challenge on the high seas and the specter of a strong German state. Russia and Austria must have had some good reason. But over time, as one looks back, there was no adequate explanation. Wars were waged periodically over lands of Europe, and once they were terminated, the same ethnic groups within the same ethnic boundaries settled down to life as usual. That millions of men would mobilize and meet their deaths over such an inconsequential event as the assassination at Sarajevo is opera. It was an excuse to go into action.

Yet what sent huge masses of Russian infantry into the line of march? What prompted German Uhlan cavalry to deploy toward concentration area? French infantry to go forward, a spectacle of spectacles? The flower of the northern Caucasoid race was on the march. Its subracial groupings, its ethnic divisions assimilated, integrated, and lined up like so many lead soldiers in loyal obedience to upper bourgeois masters. They were to be sent unquestioningly into the jaws of human sausage machines.

What was the recurring miracle of miracles within this violent century was that only under vilest and inhumane conditions did soldiers counteract their leaders' desires. What had the God of man placed in their neurogenes to send them unrevoltingly and with cheers from smiling lips to certain self-destruction? Was it love of country? Does a rag stained with indio and saffron serve to incite the beastly bull charge that lurks within man? Or perhaps it was the eagle standard of the Romans? Or the baton of the marshall? Was it the hypnotist's wand?

What resides within the DNA coding in reference to facility with which the male of the species can permit himself to be uniformly clothed, disciplined in war and stacked in columns, like so many sheep driven down the gangway of a slaughterhouse, is not a pretty picture, nor does it argue well for the future. We may be quite certain that these explosions of aggressive geneticism do not derive from such clichés as "Saving the world for democracy," "For Fatherland and for country," or, more comically, a reminder as

King George V's August 12th message to the troops of the British Expeditionary Force, "You are leaving home to fight for the safety and honor *of my empire.* Belgium, whose country we are pledged to defend, has been under attack."

Often nothing is needed more than an attack to precipitate war. Such was the case after Pearl Harbor. Roosevelt had successfully maneuvered America into the war, so there was no point coming out with any soul-stirring slogans. Nothing could have pleased him more. He had worked for it and looked for it. He had chosen sides long before, personally and without the process of democracy. The American people had nothing more to do than fight and die because of his sick whim.

Yet the foregoing is too placid an explanation for war. Man has always moved easily across frontiers in immigration and emigration, to settle and commence a new life under a new flag and a new nation. Nationality is not that strong a force, or America could have never put together races that entered her ports over centuries. There is only one force that can explain this incomprehensible self-destructive hysteria — it is that it lies within DNA coding.

Greater power than that of either 420mm Krupp seige howitzers or 305mm Skoda howitzers was being moved into seige positions before Liege. What was transpiring was fully-alerted genetic codings attacking competitive racial-pooled chemistries. Instead of firing armor-piercing projectiles, they were prepared to discharge trillions of bullet-shaped nuclears propelled by fish-like tails.

For the first time, ethnic divisions of the white-raced north were prepared to enter into massive combat. Each Cuirassier, Zouave, and Colonial infantryman, each German Jagers, each Uhlan, Scotch Girard and French Dragoon, each Cossask, besides carrying the rifle of issue, carried a more determinate issue — the issue of progeny — a half-million coded projectiles, representing the intimacy of their stock, carried within but one cc. of semen.

This was the real war, the underlying war. It was so historically and evolutionarily. This mightily DNA force lodged between their groins was what had brought them out of the trees past the feline predators and competitively radiated them to the corners of the earth.

This was the inexplicable drive, the confessions of loyalty and honor that cemented them resolutely into an effort of irrational but biologically normal insanity. Like lemmings on their march to the sea and death, either to control their population or from some genetic infestation, these men marched forward to their own destruction in concerted obedience to an underlying instinct.

Many sides kindled the war. Yet none of them, seemingly, wanted war. Especially Germany, which was faced without sufficient war plans, and by two strong adversaries on either side of her. Only the British desired the war, fearing Germany's power on the sea and their land acquisitions. So they quickly entered. Politicians were bumbling and falling all over each other. Though they were suspicious of who was going to mobilize first, the show was being put on the road with nothing to stop it. The British artfully propagandized Americans as to the nature of the struggle, and succeeded in tardily duping them into action.

That which the fumbling politicians and diplomats did not understand was the biology of their subjects. It was no emotional freak that, upon hearing the news of mobilization, Parisians took to the streets shouting and waving their hats jubilantly or that their adversaries were doing the same *Unter Den Linden* in Berlin. There was sufficient opportunity between news reports which issued from the assassination at Sarajevo on June 28, 1914, and mobilizations in the first days of August, to prepare the neurogenes for critical roles, namely, preparation for the death struggle. Insidiously, citizenry of Europe were being imbued with rumors and exciting news. So when the time of decision was to take over from non-decision, disbelief, and indignation, the primate code of highest order was prepared and ready for action. Mobilization was an afterthought. Biological and military alert are synonymous. Visualize the TV news commentators announcing nuclear missiles have been launched. The United States has retaliated. The citizenry has 25 minutes to take to shelter. Obviously, people are not going running into the streets to wave hats and shout "hurrah." Human biology requires time to respond to long-range aggressiveness if it is to act in concert with inherent ritualized instincts.

When the curtain rose on that bloody August of 1914, ushering in the century of violence, the forces at work were not guns, steel or cavalry, but were instinctive expressions of underlying biology of distinctive subracial genetic pools. By agricultural and industrial revolutions people had been forced into over-populated adjacent territories. This was a new environmental challenge for Homo sapiens. He met it head on, obsessively compelled to defend the honor of his emperors, leaders and, especially, his country. This was the upper five percent of the iceberg. What he was fighting for was not the protection of the state, or by battle commands, but for perpetuation of the genetic codes he carried within his trousers.

To align men in splendrous formations, magnificently brave and loyal to commanders, to be sent forth to death, is a fact that requires more than slogans, urgings, and propaganda. It requires an underlying, unreasoning biological coding which, in the past, sufficed to evolve the original race. It made races and subraces into distinctive units by the process of natural selection. Unfortunately, that process which was minor in a world sparsely settled, continues in geometric increase. Population pressures have expanded, resulting in charge of the brigades — brave, ignorant fools obeying outdated codes of primitive genetic biology.

Finally, to you readers who have struggled with concepts of this book, I hereby declare you are upper bourgeois. You have no trace of proletariat. You receive three credits in philosophical tolerance. You are hereby granted the degree "M.B." — Master Bourgeois — with all rights pertaining thereunto.

DEFINITION OF TERMS

POLITICAL

BOURGEOIS — Capitalists, middle and upper class, or owners of property. Individuals with an I.Q. above 110. Synonym — capitalists, upper and middle class, or owners of property.

PROLETARIAT — The laboring class. Those with I.Q.'s below 110. Historically without property. Synonym — communistic masses.

COMMUNISM — An atheistic form of government by privileged, totalitarian minority, known as the Party, which controls the people — the proletariat masses. Private property, as well as democratic representation, initiative, free press, right to unionize and strike forbidden. Synonym — police state.

CAPITALISM — A form of government or economic system in which freedom from governmental regulation is minimized, private property and initiative are encouraged, and which operates within democratic principles, which recognizes and rewards human biological divergencies. Synonym — conservative.

SOCIALISM — A form of government which fails to recognize genetic variability. Under the theory of equalitarianism, attempts to legislate equitable sharing. A mothering of the masses. Tyranny by the majority. Synonym — welfarers, free-loaders, agitators, radicals, communists, liberals.

THE RIGHT AND CONSERVATIVES — Individuals following precepts of capitalism and biological democracy. Those of status, rank, elevated position, private property, higher intelligence, and initiative. Highly patriotic, colonially expansive, territorially protective. Represent bourgeois and upper echelon genes. Former primate dominants. Non-equalitarian and religious. Synonym — entrepreneurs, capitalists, middle and upper classes, bourgeois, intellectuals.

THE LEFT AND LIBERALS — Toward socialism, atheism and communism. Obsessed with lower and working classes, usually demogogic self-seeking politicans in search of votes. If wealthy, often traitorous to their own genetic dispositions. Highly equalitarian. Formerly primate bachelors and challengers to established authority. Represents proletariat and criminal elements. Opposed to capital punishment, but open to political terrorism and revolution.

EQUALITARIANISM — A false biological precept of government, which assumes that since humans are equal before law, they must be treated as equals biologically. Originally a thesis of the Age of Enlightenment. It succumbed to the 20th-century knowledge of genetics and evolution, demonstrating the substantially wide differences between individuals and races.

FASCISM — A dictatorial form of government. Synonym — Mussolini, Stalin, Hitler; Churchill and Roosevelt during wartime.

GENETIC DEMOCRACY — A form of biologically natural government controlled by bourgeois and intellectual dominants with non-voting proletariat as submissive strata. Synonym — akin to a benign monarchy with nobility, clergy, academicians, and armed forces in upper echelon positions. Government by enlightenment.

GENETIC AND EVOLUTIONARY

NATURAL SELECTION — "Survival of the fittest." Survival of life forms best adjusted to the environment and extinction of poorly adapted forms. An important factor in evolution.

ASSIMILATION — An interaction process in which differences between groups are gradually minimized.

CULTURE — Systems of learned behavior among a society that are communicated from one generation to the next. In this text, culture is veneer to the underlying instinctive genetic behavior.

SOCIETY — Living forms with an interdependent way of life — cooperative behavior.

INSTITUTION — A functioning division of society, such as the family, government, religion, education, business.

GENETICS — The study of heredity.

EVOLUTION — Development of new forms of life from pre-existing forms.

GENES — Hereditary coded chemicals which reside within chromosomes of the cell's nucleus which are capable of producing other chemicals, such as enzymes and proteins, to structure and function the organism. They are observable and some of their locations have been mapped. Numbering in thousands, they provide blood type, eye color, hemoglobin, etc.

NEUROGENES — Genes found in the human brain that control instincts and the majority of human behavior. Neurogenes determine the architecture, communicative science and programming of the central nervous tissue. They work in conjunction with thousands of other inter-relating genes. The task of physically identifying neurogenes is almost insurmountable, except that of overt evidence in displays of innate behavior and instincts. Their genotype does not produce a phenotype. Rather, they function to direct the individual within the environment, their programming having been determined by millions of years of evolution.
Chagnon and Irons have stated that most sociobiologists adhere to the idea that genes provide a tendency to certain behavior, which can then be modified by environmental factors.

INTELLIGENCE — I.Q. Intelligence Quotient. Idiot, 0-20; Imbecile, 20-50; Feeble-minded, 50-70; Normal, 70-120; Superior, 120-170. Possibly gene locations go into intelligence inheritance.

MESOMORPH — Muscular people. A body built with a preponderance of muscle, bone, and connective tissue. Heavy, hard physique, laboring class.

ECTOMORPH — Brain people. A body built with preponderance of linearity, fragility, and thin muscles. Intellectuals. Bourgeois.

ENDOMORPH — Fat people. Soft roundness throughout the body with large vicera and accumulation of fat. Lower classes. Proletariat.

SHORT PRIMER ON GENETICS

1. Living organisms are composed mainly of proteins.
2. Proteins are chemicals which consist of strings of amino acids.
3. Amino acids are manufactured within cells in small granules called ribosomes.
4. A crystalline structure of transfer (t RNA) is a molecule that brings amino acids to the ribosome for assembly into protein.
5. In each cell there are 46 chromosomes, 23 from the father, and 23 from the mother. Two are sex chromosomes, XX female and XY male. Liver and kidney may have multiple of chromosomes. Chromosomal rod-shaped bodies appear in the cell nucleus at the time of cell division.
6. These chromosomes in cell division split lengthwise into identical halves to form a new cell. The cells multiply into ten trillion cells in the human adult.
7. Chromosomes carry the hereditary material, genes, in thin threads packed in the nucleus. These are a double chain of sugar molecules, bound by phosphate groups and fitted with organic bases.
8. A giant nucleic acid molecule with these chain links forming codes by the sequence of bases and short sections of these operating as the genes.
   The gene location in the chromosome is called the locus, each gene has a specific function. Each pair of chromosomes, one from the father and one from the mother, has a similar gene locus. Thus, the gene is represented twice in a pair of chromosomes.
9. Genes of these identical locations, one on each of the pair of chromosomes, are called alleles if they are different in function.
10. Each gene is assumed to produce only one type of chemical compound which influences the action of the cell.
    A gene is a segment, on the long chained molecule of deoxyribonucleic acid (DNA) which composes the chromosome. It contains a code for the manufacture of usually one type of chemical which is responsible for a certain type of body building and maintenance. A gene occupies an identical position to its brother gene on the mate chromosome.
11. A pair of chromosomes are homologous to each other, meaning they are related according to their content of genes.
12. When the gene at each location of each paired father and mother chromosome is identical, they are termed homozygous. They may be identically dominants or identically recessives. But when they are one of each, they are termed heterozygous or allelic. So you have three possibilities — in homos, DD or dd, and in heteros, Dd.
13. Recessive genes only manifest themselves when they are homozygous. That is, when they are the only ones in the pair of the father and mother chromosomes.

14. The dominant gene is so powerful that it shuts out the recessive gene when it is paired with one to produce its own effect.

15. We speak of phenotype or a trait when we can see and judge its manifestation. It is caused by the underlying genotype or codes of the genes. The phenotype is merely the manifestation of the genotype. Example:

Phenotype	Genotype
Rhesus + positive	DD homozygous
Rhesus + positive	Dd heterozygous
Rhesus — negative	dd homozygous (absent in China in 20% of whites)

16. A gene may have more than one allele as in blood types where, for example, there may be combinations of A, B, or O.

17. Allele — a contrasting or different gene in one location of the father-mother chromosome pair. Alleles occupy the same loci on homologous chromosomes, being heterozygotes.

18. Mutations — Permanent alterations in the gene structure, by influences as radiation poisonings, error, and environment.

A THROW OF THE DICE

Few question genetics as the basis of evolution. Through variety of offspring, mechanisms such as natural selection, "survival of the fittest," sexual selection, gene pool geographical isolation, and chance mutation; adaptation to altering environments and competition, is achieved.

Human inequalities and variances are the pieces which must pass through the adaptional sieves. Those which succeed go on to modify the species, or form new species in the process known as evolution.

Root of inequalities lie within the germinal cell coders, the chemical DNA chains of amino acids, the hereditary material that provides that no two humans shall be alike.

By the creation of unequals, a species may probe its future and alter its course to conform with the problems of ever-changing environment. For those which cannot adapt and procreate, extinction is the rule.

One man alone, with a single orgasm, could theoretically produce almost half a billion differing human beings. Key to evolution is variability. All life has priced its future security upon the ability to meet new challenges with new forms.

There is no problem whatsoever to relate genetic variance to the process of evolution. But is this same genetic variance the creative and basic factor in the formulation of man's society?

BIBLIOGRAPHY

Over a decade perusing thousands of texts and articles, it has been impossible to list them all. Only the more outstanding are mentioned. For further reference, I suggest a university library and years of study in various disciplines.

Altman, Joseph, *Organic Foundations of Animal Behavior*, Holt, Rinehart and Winston, Inc., Sept. 1966.

Ardrey, Robt., *The Social Contract*, Dell Publishing Co., c.1970.

Berdyaev, Nicholas, *The Origin of Russian Communism*, The University of Michigan Press - Fifth Printing, 1969.

Billingsley, Andrew, *Black Families in America*, Englewood Cliffs, N.J., Prentice-Hall, 1968.

Birney and Tievan, *Instinct*, D. van Nostrand Company, c. 1961.

Bleibtreu, Hermann K., *Evolution Anthropology*, Allyn and Bacon, Inc., August 1969.

Boas, Franz, *The Central Eskimo*, Seattle: Shorey Book Store, 1970.

Bohannon and Plog, eds., *Beyond the Frontier*, The Natural History Press, c.1967.

Boughey, Arthur, *Ecology of Populations*, The Macmillan Co., c.1968.

Brace, C. Loring, *The Stages of Human Evolution*, Prentice-Hall, Inc., c.1967.

Broderick, Alan, *Man and His Ancestry*, Fawcell Publications, Inc., Sept. 1964.

Chagnon, Napoleon, *Yanomamo, The Fierce People*, Holt, Rinehart and Winston, c.1968.

Christman, Henry M., ed., *Essential Works of Lenin*, Bantam Matrix editions, Nov. 1971.

Cohen, Yehudi A., ed., *Man in Adaptation — The Cultural Present*, Aldine Publishing Co., c.1968.

Coon, Carlton S., *The Living Races of Man*, N.Y., Knopf, 1965.

Coon, Calrton S., *The Origin of Races*, N.Y., Knopf, 1966, c.1962.

Dentler, Robt. A., *Major Social Problems*, 2nd Edition, Rand McNally and Co., c.1967.

Deutscher, Isaac, *The Age of Permanent Revolution: A Trotsky Anthology*, Dell Publishing Co., c.1964.

Dunn, L. C., *Heredity and Evolution in Human Populations*, Antheneum, c.1959.

Ellis, Havelock, *Man and Woman*, Boston and New York, Houghton Mifflin Co., 1929.

Engel, Leonard, *The New Genetics*, Avon Books, c.1967.

Etkin, William, *Social Behavior and Organization Among Vertebrates*, The University of Chicago Press, c.1964.

Etzioni, Amitai, *Genetic Fix*, Harper and Row, c.1973.

Frazer, Thomas M., Jr., *Fisherman of South Thailand*, Holt, Rinehart and Winston, Inc., c.1966.

Fried, Morton, *The Evolution of Political Society*, Random House, c.1967.

Gardner, Martin, ed., *Great Essays in Science*, Washington Square Press, c.1957.

Gibbon, Edward, *The Decline and Fall of the Roman Empire*, Dell Publishing Co., c.1963.

Hardin, Garrett, *Nature and Man's Fate*, The New American Library, c.1959.

Heilbroner, Robt. L., *The Future As History*, Harper and Row, c.1959.

Hoebel, E. Adamson, *The Law of Primitive Man*, Antheneum, 1968.

Honegger-Lavater and Burla, *Genetics, Heredity, Environment and Personality*, Dell Publishing Co., c.1962.

Jacobs and Baerwald, eds., *Chinese Communism*, Harper and Row, c.1963.

Johnston, Francis E., *Micro-Evolution of Human Population*, Prentice-Hall, Inc., c.1973.

Kaplan and Manners, *Culture Theory*, Prentice-Hall, Inc., c.1972.

Keegan, John, *Opening Moves; August 1914*, Ballantine Books, c.1971.

Keesing and Keesing, *New Perspectives in Cultural Anthropology*, Holt, Rinehart and Winston, Inc., c.1971.

Kirchner, Walther, *Western Civilization to 1500*, Barnes and Noble, Inc., c.1960.

LeBarre, Weston, *The Human Animal*, The University of Chicago Press, c.1954.

Lerner, I. Michael, *Heredity, Evolution and Society*, San Francisco, W. H. Freeman, 1968.

Lessa, William A., *Ulithi, A Micronesian Design For Living*, Holt, Rinehart and Winston, c.1966.

Linton, Ralph, *The Cultural Background of Personality*, Appelton-Century-Crofts, Inc., c.1945.

Marx and Engels, *The Communist Manifesto*, Washington Square Press, July 1964.

McC. Adams, Robt., *The Evolution of Urban Society*, Aldine Publishing Co., c.1966.

Montagu, Ashley, *The Human Revolution,*Bantam Books, c.1965.
Pritchard, John Reichstag, *Fire Ashes of Democracy*, Ballentine Books, Inc., February, 1972.
Rand, Ayn, *Capitalism: The Unknown Ideal*, New American Library, c.1946.
Rapport and Wright, *Anthropology*, Washington Square Press, February 1968.
Romer, A. S., *Man and the Vertebrates*, Penguin Books, c.1933.
Sadler, William, *Living A Sane Sex Life*, Chicago, New York, Wilcox & Follett, 1946, c.1944.
Salthe, Stanley N., *Evolutionary Biology*, Holt, Rinehart and Winston, Inc., c.1972.
Sanger, Margaret, *Women and the New Race*, N.Y. Truth Publishing Co., 1920.
Sauer, Carl O., *Agricultural Origins and Dispersals*, M.I.T. Press, c.1952.
Savage, Jay M., *Evolution*, Holt, Rinehart and Winston, Inc., c.1963.
Schumpter, Joseph, *Imperialism Social Classes*, New American Library, c.1951.
Service, Elman R., *Profiles in Ethiology*, Harper and Row, c.1958.
Shatz, Marshall S., ed., *The Essential Works of Anarchism*, Bantam Books, Dec., 1971.
Shaver, Berlak, *Democracy, Pluralism and the Social Studies*, Houghton Mifflin Co., c.1968.
Sinclair, Andrew, *The Better Half: Emancipation of the*American Woman, New York, Harper & Row, 1965.
Smith, John Maynard, *The Theory of Evolution*, Penguin Books, Ltd., c.1958.
Southwick, Charles, *Primate Social Behavior*, D. van Nostrand Co., Inc., c.1963.
Swinson, Arthur, *The Raiders: Desert Strike Force*, Ballantine Books, Inc., c.1968.
Tinbergen, N., *Social Behavior in Animals*, Chapman and Hall, Ltd., Reprinted 1972.
Titier, Mischa, *The Science of Man*, Holt, Rinehart and Winston, Inc., c.1954.
Uchendu, Victor, *The Igbo of Southeast Nigeria*, Holt, Rinehart and Winston, Inc., c.1965.
Wallace, Robert A., *The Ecology and Evolution of Animal Behavior*, Goodyear Publishing Co., Inc., c.1973.
Wallace and SRB, *Adaptation*, Prentice-Hall, Inc., c.1961.
Watson and Watson, *Man and Nature*, Harcourt, Brace & World, Inc., c.1969.
Whittaker, Robt. H., *Communities and Ecosystems*, The Macmillan Co., c.1970.
Wirth, Arthur G., *John Dewey as Educator*, John Wiley and Sons, Inc., c.1966.
Wolf, Eric R., *Peasants*, Prentice-Hall, Inc., c.1966.
Ziemke, Earl F., *Battle for Berlin: End of the Third Reich*, Ballantine Books, Inc., c.1968.

BIBLIOGRAPHY FOR CHAPTER VII — THE JEWS

Agus, Irving, *The Heroic Age of Franco-German Jewry — 10th & 11th Centuries*, N.Y. Yeshiva University Press, distributed by Bloch Pub. Co., 1969.
Adler, Dr. H. G., *The Jews in Germany*, University of Notre Dame Press, 1969.
Ausubel, Nathan, *Pictorial History of the Jewish People*, N.Y., Crown Publishers, 1967, c.1953.
Byrnes, Robert, *Antisemitism in Modern France*, New Brunswick, N.J., Rutgers Univ. Press, 1950.
Cohn, Norman, *Warrant For Genocide*, N.Y., Harper & Row, 1967.
Dawidowicz, Lucy S., *The Golden Tradition*, N.Y., Holt, Rinehart and Winston, c.1975.
Dickinson, John K., *German and Jew*, Chicago, Quadrangle Books, 1967.
Friedlander, Albert H., *Out of the Whirlwind*, Doubleday and Company, Inc., c.1968.
Glicksman, William, *In the Mirror of Literature*, N.Y., Living Books, 1966.
Greenberg, Hayim, *Anthology*, selected with an Introduction by Marie Syrkin, Detroit, Wayne State University Press, 1968.
Hausner, Gideon, *Justice in Jerusalem*, N.Y., Schocken Books, 1968.
Hitler, Adolph, *Mein Kampf*, translated by Ralph Manheim, Boston, Houghton Mifflin Company, c.1943.
Isaacs, Harold Robert, *American Jews in Israel*, N.Y., John Day Co., 1967.
Kahler, Erich, *The Jews Among the Nations*, N.Y., F. Ungar Publishing Co., 1967.
Katcher, Leo, *Post-Mortem, The Jews in Germany Today*, London, Hamilton, 1968.
Landyn, Stephanie, *A World Problem*, American Catalogue Printing Co., 1920.
Laurence, Gunther, *Three Million More*, Doubleday & Company, Inc., c.1970.
Lazare, Bernard, *Antisemitism (Its History and Causes)*, Britons Publishing Co., 1967.
Levenberg, Selig, *European Jewry Today*, Leeds, England, Leeds University Press, 1967.

Marcus, Jacob R., *The Jew in the Medieval World*, N.Y., Meridian Books, 1961.
Memmir, Albert, *Liberation of the Jews*, N.Y., Orion Press, 1966.
Reitlinger, Gerald, *The Final Solution*, South Brunswick, N.J., T. Yoseloff, 1968, c.1961.
Roth, Cecil, *The Jewish Book of Days*, N.Y., Herman Press, 1966.
Runes, Dagobert D., *The War Against the Jews*, Philosophical Library, c.1968.
Schleunes, Karl A., *The Twisted Road to Auschwitz*, Urbana, University of Illinois Press, 1970.
Seiden, Morton, *Paradox of Hate*, Thomas Yoseloff Publisher, c.1967, by A. S. Barnes & Co., Inc.
Selznick, Gertrude J., *The Tenacity of Prejudice*, N.Y., Harper & Row, 1969.
Singer, Howard, *Bring Forth the Mighty Men*, Funk & Wagnalls, c.1969.
Stember, Charles Herbert, *Jews in the Mind of America*, N.Y., Basic Books, 1966.
Tacitus, Publius Cornelius, *The Histories, II*, translated by W. Hamilton Fyfe, Oxford, The Clarendon Press, 1912.
Vogel, Rolf, *The German Paths to Israel*, Dufour Editions, 1969.
Zhitlowski, Chaim, *The Jewish Factor in My Socialism*, Leiden, E.J. Brill, 1968.
Zink, Harold, *American Military in Germany*, N.Y., The Macmillan Company, 1947.